CALCULUS in the first three dimensions

CALCULUS in the
first three dimensions

SHERMAN K. STEIN
Professor of Mathematics
University of California, Davis

New York
San Francisco
St. Louis
London
Toronto
Sydney   **McGRAW-HILL BOOK COMPANY**

CALCULUS in the first three dimensions

Library of Congress
catalog card number: 65-28827

1234567890 ST 72106987
61000

Preface

Nowadays a beginning calculus class contains a variety of students: engineers, social and physical scientists, mathematicians, and a host of others, as well as the uncommitted. This variety prevents the teacher from treating all his students as candidates for a Ph.D. in mathematics. On the other hand, the students, whatever their eventual specialty, will need not only skill in using the calculus, but also some understanding. I believe that as long as we restrict the duration of the introductory calculus course to at most one year, we can meet the demand of the nonmathematician, and yet not delay the education of the mathematician. In a sense the challenge itself suggests a solution. After all, those who will apply the calculus should have some understanding of the definite integral, the derivative, and the relation between them, while the mathematics major should be aware of some of the applications of mathematics to other sciences.

This means that a first calculus course should have mathematical substance without encroaching on real analysis; it should have ample motivation and yet cleanly distinguish theory from application. The somewhat novel organization of this book is a response to this challenge. In Part I (Chapters 1 to 9) the student concentrates on three basic ideas: the definite integral, the derivative, and the fundamental theorem of calculus. (The definite integral is placed in Chapter 1 in order to have many pages between it and the antiderivative, with which it is too easily confused, and to alert students who may already have had a smattering of calculus.) After Chapter 6

v

the student may be directed along any one of several routes, perhaps into Part II or Part III. In Part II he meets such topics as the maximum and minimum of a function, Taylor's series, partial derivatives, differentiation of vectors, and Green's theorem in the plane. Part III, containing no new mathematical development, applies the techniques developed earlier (mainly those of Part I) to significant problems in the natural, social, and physical sciences.

The introductions to many concepts, such as the definite integral, the derivative, and the limit of a sequence, begin with numerical examples and exercises (whose answers are usually rounded off to three decimal places). This is done not only to make the abstract concrete, but also to compensate for a lack of down-to-earth mathematical experience in high school. In particular, both the definite integral and the derivative are preceded by four of their applications.

Such analytic geometry as is needed is developed in the text (slope of a line is defined when we examine the tangent to a curve, and the equation of a plane is obtained as an application of dot products). For convenience, an appendix on the rudiments of analytic geometry is included. Two of the other appendixes are devoted to the real numbers and functions.

Although the ε,δ terminology is introduced, and formal definitions of limits and the definite integral are presented in Chapter 3, the proofs of the basic properties of limits are left to an appendix. I do not think that there is time in a first-year calculus to develop skill with ε,δ. Rather than try to rush a heterogeneous group of students through this form of "rigor," I have chosen to include many counterexamples, and to devote more attention to the fundamental theorem of calculus.

The logarithm is considered as the inverse of a given exponential function. This approach makes more sense to most students than does the integral approach. However, the integral approach is included later (optionally) as an illustration of the fundamental theorem of calculus.

The exercises in each section are broken into two groups by the symbol ☐ ☐ ☐ The second group in each section explores fine points, extends the material, or presents more difficulties than the first group, which, it should be emphasized, contains more than enough routine problems to give the students an opportunity to develop both skill and understanding. Answers accompany many exercises in the first group; the Teacher's Manual contains, in addition to answers to exercises in the first group, solutions to exercises in the second group.

It seems to me that a student of the calculus should become familiar with a handbook of mathematical tables, which includes such useful items as the decimal expansion of $1/n$ and a review of trigonometry. Hence the text contains only the briefest tables—enough to point out the behavior of the principal functions met in the calculus.

The Teacher's Manual discusses the use of the text in greater detail, as well as its relation to CUPM recommendations.

The criticisms of two mathematicians, Raymond A. Barnett of Oakland City College and George N. Raney of the University of Connecticut, led to most of the differences between the first and final drafts of this book. Edwin H. Spanier of the University of California at Berkeley and William Simons of Oregon State University influenced the exposition in several chapters. My colleagues in the mathematics department and several other departments on my campus advised me on many problems that arose during the writing.

Furthermore I wish to thank the *American Mathematical Monthly*, published by the Mathematical Association of America, for permission to quote from its pages. The many reviews of calculus texts and pedagogical articles published there in the past forty years—surprisingly consistent in their disappointments and suggestions—helped shape this book.

These acknowledgements would be incomplete without my expression of appreciation to my wife and children, who sustained my morale during the many months of writing and rewriting.

Sherman K. Stein

To my parents

Harry Stein and Fannie Kopald Stein

Contents

PART II: TOPICS IN THE CALCULUS

CALCULUS in the first three dimensions

PART I

The core
of the calculus

If an object moves at a constant speed, then we can find the distance it travels by simply multiplying its speed by the duration of its journey. But if the speed varies from instant to instant, how can we then compute the length of its journey? Four questions of this type lead us in Chapter 1 to the definite integral, *one of the two basic concepts of the calculus.*

The question can be turned around: If we happen to know how far an object, moving with a varying speed, travels during any interval of time (for instance, a rock drops $16t^2$ feet in the first t seconds of a free fall), then how can we find its speed at any instant? Such questions, posed in Chapter 2, introduce the derivative, *the other basic concept of the calculus.*

In Chapters 3 through 6 we develop tools for answering both questions. Chapters 7 through 9 offer an opportunity to develop skill in applying these tools in a variety of situations.

1

1

The definite integral

THIS chapter introduces one of the most important concepts of the calculus, the definite integral. The approach, which will be gradual and concrete, utilizes for the sake of simplicity geometric and physical illustrations, but a few exercises show that the definite integral has far more varied applications. Later chapters will exploit it in such diverse fields as economics, traffic, and psychology. The definition of definite integrals given in this chapter will be made more precise in Chap. 3.

1. Estimates in four problems. We pose four problems which at first glance might seem unrelated. As we make estimates for their answers, however, we shall find a theme that underlies all of them.

PROBLEM 1. *Find the area of the region bounded by the curve* $y = x^2$, *the x axis, and the vertical line* $x = 3$.

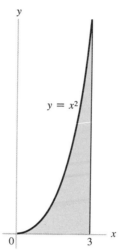

$y = x^2$

PROBLEM 2. *A thin nonuniform string 3 feet long is made of a material that is very light near one end and very heavy near the other end. In fact, at a distance of x feet from the left end it has a density of $5x^2$ ounces per foot. Find the mass of the string.*

Nonuniform string

Light end   0   3   Heavy end

The notion of "density at a point" will be made precise in Chap. 2.

PROBLEM 3. *An engineer drives a car whose clock and speedometer work, but whose odometer (mileage recorder) is broken. On a 3-hour trip out of a congested city into the countryside he begins at a snail's pace, and as the traffic thins, he gradually speeds up. Indeed, he notices that after traveling t hours his speed is $8t^2$ miles per hour. Thus after the first half hour he is crawling along at 2 miles per hour, but after 3 hours he is traveling at 72 miles per hour. How far does the engineer travel in 3 hours?*

PROBLEM 4. *Find the volume of a tent with a square floor of side 3 feet, whose pole, 3 feet long, rises above a corner of the floor.*

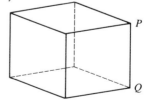

The tent can be thought of as related to the cube shown, or as the surface obtained when this piece of paper is folded along the dotted lines and the free edges taped in such a way that A, B, C, and D come together (to become P).

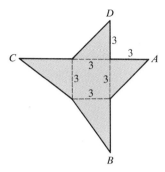

We shall now estimate the answers to each of the four problems, showing as we do so that they all offer the same mathematical challenge.

ESTIMATE FOR PROBLEM 1 (AREA UNDER $y = x^2$). We estimate the area by use of a "staircase" of six rectangles:

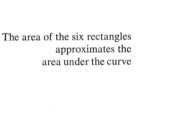

The area of the six rectangles approximates the area under the curve

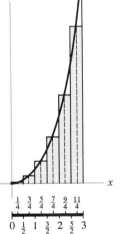

First we break the interval from 0 to 3 into six smaller intervals, each of length ½. Then above each small interval we draw the rectangle whose height is that of the curve $y = x^2$ above the midpoint of that interval. The total area of the six rectangles is easily computed. This is equal to

$$(\tfrac{1}{4})^2(\tfrac{1}{2}) + (\tfrac{3}{4})^2(\tfrac{1}{2}) + (\tfrac{5}{4})^2(\tfrac{1}{2}) + (\tfrac{7}{4})^2(\tfrac{1}{2}) + (\tfrac{9}{4})^2(\tfrac{1}{2}) + (\tfrac{11}{4})^2(\tfrac{1}{2})$$

which reduces to $\tfrac{286}{32}$, or decimally, to 8.9375.

We have *not* computed the area. All we have is a single estimate.

ESTIMATE FOR PROBLEM 2 (THE NONUNIFORM STRING). Let us cut the string into six sections of equal length:

Nonuniform string

$$0 \qquad \tfrac{1}{2} \qquad 1 \qquad \tfrac{3}{2} \qquad 2 \qquad \tfrac{5}{2} \qquad 3$$

The density of the string in each piece varies less than it does over the whole length of the string. To obtain an estimate of the mass of each of the six sections, let us multiply the density at the midpoint of the section by the length of the section.

The left section has a density of $5\,(\tfrac{1}{4})^2$ ounces per foot at its midpoint, $\tfrac{1}{4}$, and thus has a mass of about $5\,(\tfrac{1}{4})^2(\tfrac{1}{2})$ ounces. The next section, from $\tfrac{1}{2}$ to 1, has a density of $5\,(\tfrac{3}{4})^2$ at its midpoint, and thus has a mass of about $5\,(\tfrac{3}{4})^2(\tfrac{1}{2})$ ounces. An estimate of the mass of each of the four other sections can be made similarly. An estimate of the mass of the nonuniform string is then the sum

$$5\,(\tfrac{1}{4})^2(\tfrac{1}{2}) + 5\,(\tfrac{3}{4})^2(\tfrac{1}{2}) + 5\,(\tfrac{5}{4})^2(\tfrac{1}{2}) + 5\,(\tfrac{7}{4})^2(\tfrac{1}{2}) + 5\,(\tfrac{9}{4})^2(\tfrac{1}{2}) + 5\,(\tfrac{11}{4})^2(\tfrac{1}{2})$$

This sum is equal to $5\,(8.9375)$, a little less than 45 ounces. More important is the similarity in form between this sum and the sum we used in the first problem.

ESTIMATE FOR PROBLEM 3 (THE BROKEN ODOMETER). The speed during the 3-hour trip varies from 0 to 72 miles per hour. If we consider shorter time intervals, we will not meet such a wide fluctuation.

Just as in the first two problems, let us cut the 3 hours of the trip into six equal intervals, each $\tfrac{1}{2}$ hour long. Then we will estimate the distance covered during each of these smaller periods of time. We represent time by this line segment, cut into six parts of equal length.

$$0 \qquad \tfrac{1}{2} \qquad 1 \qquad \tfrac{3}{2} \qquad 2 \qquad \tfrac{5}{2} \qquad 3 \qquad \text{Hours}$$

To estimate the distance the engineer travels in the first $\tfrac{1}{2}$ hour, let us multiply his speed at 15 minutes by the first interval of time, $\tfrac{1}{2}$ hour. Since his speed at time t is $8t^2$, his speed after $\tfrac{1}{4}$ hour is $8\,(\tfrac{1}{4})^2$ miles per hour. Thus during the first half hour the engineer travels about $8\,(\tfrac{1}{4})^2(\tfrac{1}{2})$ miles. During the second half hour he travels about $8\,(\tfrac{3}{4})^2(\tfrac{1}{2})$ miles.

Making similar estimates for each of the other $\tfrac{1}{2}$-hour periods, we obtain this estimate for the length of the trip:

$$8\,(\tfrac{1}{4})^2(\tfrac{1}{2}) + 8\,(\tfrac{3}{4})^2(\tfrac{1}{2}) + 8\,(\tfrac{5}{4})^2(\tfrac{1}{2}) + 8\,(\tfrac{7}{4})^2(\tfrac{1}{2}) + 8\,(\tfrac{9}{4})^2(\tfrac{1}{2}) + 8\,(\tfrac{11}{4})^2(\tfrac{1}{2})$$

or

$$8\,(\tfrac{1}{4})^2(\tfrac{1}{2})\,(1^2 + 3^2 + 5^2 + 7^2 + 9^2 + 11^2)$$

which is

$$(8)(8.9375) = 71.5 \text{ miles}$$

It must be kept in mind that this is only an *estimate* of the length of the trip.

ESTIMATE FOR PROBLEM 4 (THE TENT). Observe that the cross section of the tent made by any plane parallel to the base is a square:

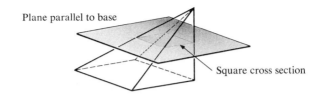

Plane parallel to base

Square cross section

This time we cut a vertical line, representing the pole, into six sections of equal length.

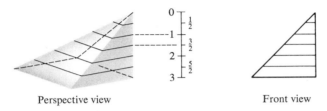

Perspective view   Front view

Then we approximate the volume of each slab by a flat rectangular box, ½ foot high. The cross section of the smallest box coincides with the cross section of the tent made by a horizontal plane through the midpoint of the highest of the six sections. The remaining five boxes are determined in a similar manner, as shown here:

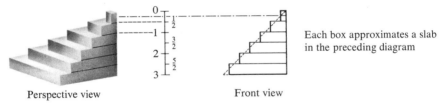

Each box approximates a slab in the preceding diagram

Perspective view   Front view

As the front view of the six boxes shows, the square cross section of the top box has a side equal to ¼ foot, the box below it a side equal to ¾ foot, and so on until we reach the bottom box, whose side is 1¼ feet.

Since the volume of a box is just the area of its base times its height, it is not difficult to see that the total volume of the six boxes is

$$(\tfrac{1}{4})^2(\tfrac{1}{2}) + (\tfrac{3}{4})^2(\tfrac{1}{2}) + (\tfrac{5}{4})^2(\tfrac{1}{2}) + (\tfrac{7}{4})^2(\tfrac{1}{2}) + (\tfrac{9}{4})^2(\tfrac{1}{2}) + (\tfrac{11}{4})^2(\tfrac{1}{2}) \text{ cubic feet}$$

This is the same expression we met in estimating the area under the curve $y = x^2$. Thus the volume of the tent is estimated as 8.9375 cubic feet.

We have solved none of the four problems. We emphasize that in each case we have made only a single estimate. In Sec. 2 we will find the precise answers.

EXERCISES

1. To show the similarity of the four problems, we have cut the interval from 0 to 3 into six sections each time, and used the midpoint of each section to sample the cross section, density, or speed. We are, of course, free to cut the interval into more or fewer sections and to use a point other than the midpoint in each section. Furthermore we need not restrict ourselves to sections of equal length.

   (*a*) Estimate the area in Problem 1 by using three sections of length 1 and the midpoint each time.

   (*b*) Estimate the same area by using the same three sections, but now use the ordinate above the right end of each section to determine the rectangle.

   (*c*) Draw the three rectangles used in (*b*). Is their total area more or less than the area under the curve?

   (*d*) Proceed as in (*b*), but use the ordinate above the left end point of each section.

   [Answer: (*a*) 8.75; (*b*) 13; (*d*) 5]

2. Using your answer to Exercise 1, complete this sentence: The area in Problem 1 is certainly less than ————— but larger than —————.

3. Cutting the interval from 0 to 3 into five sections of equal length, estimate the area in Problem 1 by finding the sum of the areas of five rectangles whose heights are determined by (*a*) midpoints; (*b*) right end points; (*c*) left end points.

   [Answer: (*a*) 8.91; (*b*) 11.88; (*c*) 6.48]

4. Cutting the interval of three hours into five periods of $\frac{3}{5}$ hour each, estimate the length of the engineer's trip in Problem 3. For the approximate velocity in each period use the speedometer reading at (*a*) the middle of the period; (*b*) the end of the period; (*c*) the beginning of the period.

   [Answer: (*a*) 71.28 miles; (*b*) 95.04 miles; (*c*) 51.84 miles. Incidentally, note that 71.28 = (8)(8.91) and compare with Exercise 3.]

5. Estimate the mass of the string in Problem 2 by cutting it into five sections of equal length. For an estimate of the mass of each of these sections use the density at (*a*) the midpoint of each section; (*b*) the right end point; (*c*) the left end point.

   [Answer: (*a*) 44.55 ounces; (*b*) 59.40 ounces; (*c*) 32.40 ounces]

6. Make an estimate for each of the four problems, using in each case the following partition into four sections.

   As the points where the cross section, density, or velocity is computed, use $\frac{1}{2}$, $\frac{3}{2}$, 2, and $1\frac{4}{5}$ (one in each of the four sections).

   [Answer: $\frac{3277}{300}$, 5 ($\frac{3277}{300}$), 8 ($\frac{3277}{300}$), $\frac{3277}{300}$]

7. Using a partition into nine sections of your choice, estimate the area in Problem 1.

8. A right circular cone has a height of 3 feet and a radius of 3 feet. Estimate its volume by the sum of the volumes of six cylinders, just as we estimated the volume of the tent with the aid of six rectangular slabs. In particular, (*a*) show with the aid of a diagram how the same partition and midpoints we used determine six cylinders, and (*b*) compute their total volume.

   [Answer: (*b*) 8.9375 π]

9. Carry out the analog of Exercise 3 for the cone of Exercise 8.

   [Answer: (*a*) 8.91 π; (*b*) 11.88 π; (*c*) 6.48 π]

10. A business which now shows no profit is to increase its profit flow gradually in the next 3 years until it reaches a rate of 9 million dollars per year. At the end of the first half year the rate is to be ¼ million dollars per year; at the end of 2 years, 4 million dollars per year. In general, at the end of t years, where t is any number between 0 and 3, the rate of profit is to be t^2 million dollars per year. Estimate the total profit during the next three years if the plan is successful.

□ □ □

11. Show that if you knew the volume of the cone in Exercise 8, you would be able to calculate the total profit in Exercise 10.
12. Estimate the area under $y = x^2$ and directly above the interval from $x = 1$ to $x = 5$ with the aid of a partition into (a) four sections of equal length; (b) eight sections of equal length.
13. Estimate the area between the curve $y = x^3$, the x axis, and the vertical line $x = 6$, using a partition into (a) three sections of equal length and midpoints; (b) six sections of equal length and midpoints; (c) six sections of equal length and left end points; (d) same as (c) but right end points.
    [Answer: (a) 306; (b) $^{2556}\!/_8 = 319½$; (c) 225; (d) 441]
14. Draw an accurate graph of $y = x^2$ and the six rectangles, with heights equal to the ordinate of the midpoints, that we used to estimate the area. Does each of these rectangles underestimate or overestimate the area under $y = x^2$ and above the base of the rectangle? (Form your opinion on the basis of your drawing.)
15. The kinetic energy of an object, for example, a bullet or car, of mass m and velocity v is defined as $mv^2/2$ ergs. (Here mass is measured in grams and velocity in centimeters per second.) In a certain machine a uniform rod, 3 centimeters long and weighing 32 grams, rotates once per second around one of its ends. Estimate the kinetic energy of this rod by cutting it into six sections, each ½ centimeter long, and taking as the "velocity of a section," the velocity of its midpoint.
    [Answer: $(^{16}\!/_3)\pi^2(8.9375)$ ergs]
16. Carry out the analogs of Exercise 3 for the kinetic energy in Exercise 15.

2. Precise answers to the four problems. We shall see that if we can solve any one of our four problems, we can easily solve the other three. And we will solve one of these problems by a geometric observation.

To minimize the arithmetic, we considered partitions into only a few sections, but partitions into a hundred, a thousand, or even more pieces should provide better estimates. Let us describe how these estimates are made in general.

For convenience, if a and b are numbers such that a is less than b, we shall denote the set of numbers from a through b as $[a,b]$ and call it the *closed interval from a to b*. The *open interval*, which we shall use only a few times, consists of all numbers from a through b except a and b; it is denoted as (a,b). We will usually abbreviate *closed interval* to *interval*. Frequently we will refer to the intervals in a partition as *sections*. For instance, in Sec. 1 the partition of $[0,3]$ has six sections.

First we cut [0,3] into many, say n, sections. These we describe by their end points

The partition:

$x_0 = 0$ x_1 x_2 $\ldots$ x_{n-2} x_{n-1} $x_n = 3$

No matter what our choice of n, we require a partition such that $x_0 = 0$ and $x_n = 3$. In the partition used in Sec. 1, we have

$$x_0 = 0 \qquad x_1 = \tfrac{1}{2} \qquad x_2 = 1 \qquad x_3 = \tfrac{3}{2} \qquad x_4 = 2 \qquad x_5 = \tfrac{5}{2} \qquad x_6 = 3$$

The first section has end points x_0 and x_1; the next has end points x_1 and x_2; the third has end points x_2 and x_3; and so on until we reach the nth section, which has end points x_{n-1} and x_n. The typical section has end points x_{i-1} and x_i where i is 1, or 2, or 3, . . . , or n.

Next we pick a point in each of the n sections—it may be the midpoint, or it may be some other point. The point we pick in the first section we shall call X_1; the point in the second section X_2, and so on. In general, the point we pick in the ith section, $[x_{i-1}, x_i]$, we shall call X_i. Pictorially we have

X_1 X_2 $\ldots$ X_i $\ldots$ X_{n-1} X_n

$x_0 = 0$ x_1 x_2 x_{i-1} x_i x_{n-2} x_{n-1} $x_n = 3$

Typical section
in partition

Each choice of x's and X's enables us to make an estimate for each of the four problems. For example, the typical estimating rectangle for the area in Problem 1 is shown in this diagram:

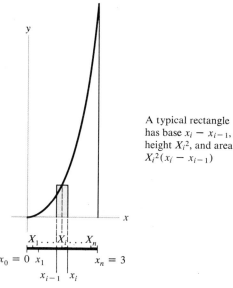

A typical rectangle has base $x_i - x_{i-1}$, height X_i^2, and area $X_i^2(x_i - x_{i-1})$

The sum of the areas of these typical rectangles,

$$X_1{}^2(x_1 - x_0) + X_2{}^2(x_2 - x_1) + \cdots + X_n{}^2(x_n - x_{n-1})$$

is an estimate of the area in Problem 1. Using the summation notation of Appendix D, we may write this lengthy expression as $\sum\limits_{i=1}^{n} X_i{}^2(x_i - x_{i-1})$.

The same general partition by the x's and choice of the X's provides a means of estimating the mass of the string.

X_1 $\cdots$ X_i $\cdots$ X_n

$x_0 = 0$ x_1 x_{i-1} x_i x_{n-1} $x_n = 3$

Typical section
in partition

Mass in typical section is roughly
$5X_i{}^2(x_i - x_{i-1})$ ounces

Density   Length of
at X_i section

Similarly, we can estimate the length of the trip in Problem 3. Since we have subdivided time, let us use t's and T's instead of x's and X's.

T_1 $\cdots$ T_i $\cdots$ T_n

$t_0 = 0$ t_1 t_{i-1} t_i t_{n-1} $t_n = 3$

Typical interval
of time

The distance the engineer travels during
a typical interval of time is roughly

$$8T_i{}^2(t_i - t_{i-1})$$

Speedometer reading   Duration of ith
at time T_i time interval

Lastly, the same x's and X's (or t's and T's) provide an estimate of the volume in the tent.

A typical box has
thickness $x_i - x_{i-1}$,
square cross section
of side X_i and volume
$X_i{}^2(x_i - x_{i-1})$

$0 = x_0$

x_{i-1} We partition this
X_i vertical axis
x_i

$3 = x_n$

A brief list on the next page summarizes these results:

Problem 1. $\sum_{i=1}^{n} X_i^2(x_i - x_{i-1})$ is an estimate of the area under $y = x^2$ and above $[0,3]$.

Problem 2. $\sum_{i=1}^{n} 5X_i^2(x_i - x_{i-1})$ is an estimate of the mass of the string.

Problem 3. $\sum_{i=1}^{n} 8T_i^2(t_i - t_{i-1})$ is an estimate of the distance the engineer traveled.

Problem 4. $\sum_{i=1}^{n} X_i^2(x_i - x_{i-1})$ is an estimate of the volume of the tent.

As we consider finer partitions and choose larger values for n, the sums in question should become more accurate estimates of the quantities we are seeking.

From this we see that if the volume of the tent is c (cubic feet), then the area under $y = x^2$ is also c (square inches), the string has a mass of $5c$ (ounces), and the engineer travels $8c$ (miles).

If we could find the volume of the tent (or solve any one of the other three problems), we would know the answers to all four. In the next few chapters we will develop rapid ways of solving these and similar problems. But rather than leaving all four problems unsolved, we will exploit a property of the cube to find c, the volume of the tent.

If you make three tents out of paper with the pattern given in Sec. 1, you will be able to fit them together easily to form a cube. If you have more geometric intuition than time, you might prefer to see that this is so by examining the following diagram.

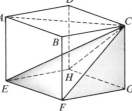

The three tents have
vertex C and base *GFEH*,
vertex C and base *ABFE*,
vertex C and base *DHEA*

Since the volume of the cube is 27 cubic feet, the tent has a volume of 9 cubic feet. With this information the remaining problems are quickly solved. For instance, the engineer traveled 72 miles.

EXERCISES

1. (*a*) Give the numerical value of each x_i in the estimates we made in Sec. 1. For instance, $x_0 = 0$, $x_1 = \frac{1}{2}$.
   (*b*) What is n for the partition used in Sec. 1?
   (*c*) Give the numerical value of each X_i in the estimates we made in Sec. 1.

2. (*a*) Draw the partition of [0,3] determined by $x_0 = 0$, $x_1 = 1$, $x_2 = 2$, $x_3 = 3$.

   (*b*) Select X_i to be the midpoint of each of the intervals in (*a*) and compute

$$\sum_{i=1}^{3} X_i^2 (x_i - x_{i-1})$$

   (*c*) Select X_i to be the right-hand end point of each interval in (*a*) and compute

$$\sum_{i=1}^{3} X_i^2 (x_i - x_{i-1})$$

   (*d*) Select X_i to be two-thirds of the way from x_{i-1} to x_i, and compute

$$\sum_{i=1}^{3} X_i^2 (x_i - x_{i-1})$$

[Answer: (*b*) 8¾; (*c*) 14; (*d*) 10⅓]

3. (*a*) Make the three paper tents and assemble them to form a cube.

   (*b*) What simple fact in plane geometry does "three tents fill a cube" generalize?

4. Compute $\sum_{i=1}^{5} 8T_i^2(t_i - t_{i-1})$ if $t_i = 3i/5$; $i = 1, 2, 3, 4, 5$; and (*a*) $T_i = 3i/5$;

   (*b*) $T_i = 3(i-1)/5$; (*c*) $T_i = 3(2i-1)/10$.

[Answer: (*a*) ²³⁷⁶⁄₂₅ = 95.04; (*b*) ¹²⁹⁶⁄₂₅ = 51.84; (*c*) ¹⁷⁸²⁄₂₅ = 71.28]

5. Compute $\sum_{i=1}^{6} 5X_i^2(x_i - x_{i-1})$ if $x_0 = 0$, $x_1 = 3$, $x_2 = 5$, $x_3 = 11½$, $x_4 = 17⅓$, $x_5 = 23¾$,

   $x_6 = 3$, and X_i is the left end point of the ith interval.

6. (*a*) If a tent shaped like the one we considered has a 7-foot pole and a square base of side 7 feet, what is its volume?

   (*b*) From (*a*) deduce the area under the curve $y = x^2$ and above [0,7].

7. (*a*) If a tent shaped like the one we considered has a pole b feet long and a square base of side b feet, what is its volume?

   (*b*) From (*a*) find the area under the curve $y = x^2$ and above [0,b], where b is some positive number.

8. Using Exercise 7(*b*), show that the area below the curve $y = x^2$ and above [a,b] is $b^3/3 - a^3/3$.

9. Making use of the volume of the tent, find the volume of the cone in Exercise 8, page 8.

10. Making use of the volume of the tent, find the total profit in Exercise 10, page 9.

□ □ □

11. Using Exercise 8, obtain the volume of the basket shown in this figure:

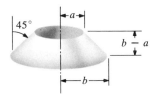

12. (*a*) Show that the sums of Problem 4, $\sum_{i=1}^{n} X_i^2 (x_i - x_{i-1})$, approximate the volume of this standard tent whose pole is over the center.

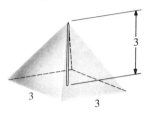

(*b*) From (*a*) deduce that this tent has the same volume as the one we studied.

13. The tent sketched in Exercise 12 is made of rubber stretched over the top of a pole and beneath the square frame of the floor. If the pole is moved about in such a way that it always rests on the floor and remains vertical, will air be taken in or expelled?

14. Our knowledge of the behavior of $\sum_{i=1}^{n} X_i^2 (x_i - x_{i-1})$ when the $(x_i - x_{i-1})$'s are small can be used to find the volume of a hemisphere of radius b (hence of the whole sphere). We outline an approach. Locate the hemisphere this way:

Equator

0   b

(*a*) Show that the cross section of the hemisphere made by a plane parallel to the equator but X units from it is $\pi(b^2 - X^2)$.

(*b*) Show that if $x_0, x_1, x_2, \ldots, x_n$ is a partition of $[0,b]$, and X_i is in the *i*th interval, then $\sum_{i=1}^{n} \pi(b^2 - X_i^2)(x_i - x_{i-1})$ approximates the volume of the hemisphere.

(*c*) Show that $\pi b^3 - \sum_{i=1}^{n} \pi X_i^2(x_i - x_{i-1})$ approximates the volume of the hemisphere.

(*d*) Combining (*c*) with Exercise 7, show that the volume of the hemisphere is $2\pi b^3/3$. What is the volume of the sphere?

15. Show, with the aid of a picture, that for any partition $x_0, x_1, x_2, \ldots, x_n$ of $[0,3]$ it is possible to choose an X_i in the *i*th interval, $i = 1, 2, \ldots, n$, in such a way that $\sum_{i=1}^{n} X_i^2(x_i - x_{i-1})$ is equal to the area under $y = x^2$ and above $[0,3]$.

3. The definite integral over an interval. The four problems have posed basically the same question: *What happens to certain sums of products as partitions become very fine?* Luckily, three lopsided tents fill a cube; and with that information we have solved all the problems. In any case it is evident that the procedure of cutting up an interval, forming certain sums, and trying to determine what happens to those sums when the partitions are indefinitely refined is important. To emphasize this, we present some general situations in which this procedure is followed; each is already illustrated in our four problems. Our presentation will be intuitive. A rigorous development of Examples 1 and 4 below depends on theorems in measure theory. (See Appendix E for an introduction to this topic.) A rigorous development of Examples 2 and 3 below depends on the precise definition of density and velocity, terms we shall discuss in Chap. 2.

Example 1. We wish to compute the area of some region S in the plane, and we happen to know the lengths of all the cross sections of S in some direction. We begin by drawing some line L perpendicular to the direction of the cross sections and furnishing it with a coordinate system.

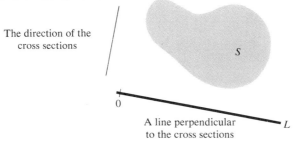

The direction of the cross sections

S

0

A line perpendicular to the cross sections L

The set of lines that are perpendicular to L and meet S intersect L in an interval, the end points of this interval have the x coordinates, let us say, a and b. The length of the cross section for each x we call $c(x)$:

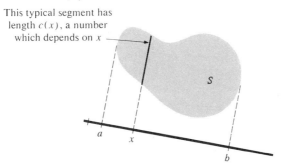

This typical segment has length $c(x)$, a number which depends on x

S

a x

b

In Problem 1 we had $c(x) = x^2$, $a = 0$, and $b = 3$.

To estimate the area of S, we proceed just as we did for the region under $y = x^2$. We first cut $[a,b]$ into n sections by means of the numbers

$$x_0 = a < x_1 < x_2 < x_3 < \cdots < x_{n-1} < x_n = b$$

$x_0 = a$ x_1 x_2 $\cdots$ x_{i-1} x_i $\cdots$ x_{n-1} $x_n = b$

Typical section
$[x_{i-1}, x_i]$

In each of these sections we select a number at random. In the section $[x_0, x_1]$ we select X_1, in $[x_1, x_2]$ we select X_2, and so on. Simply stated, in the ith interval, $[x_{i-1}, x_i]$, we choose X_i.

With this choice of x's and X's, we form a set of rectangles, whose typical member we show in this diagram:

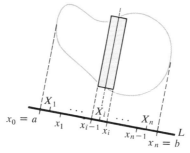

A typical rectangle has base $x_i - x_{i-1}$, height $c(X_i)$ and area $c(X_i)(x_i - x_{i-1})$

Thus $\sum_{i=1}^{n} c(X_i)(x_i - x_{i-1})$ is an estimate of the area of S. As we choose finer partitions we would expect that for the sets S which one usually meets these sums tend toward the area of S.

In order to speak more precisely about "fine partitions" we make the following definition.

DEFINITION: *Mesh.* The *mesh* of a partition is the length of the largest section (or sections) in the partition.

For instance, the partition used in Sec. 1 has mesh equal to ½. We may summarize Example 1 in this plausible assertion: *as the mesh of the partition approaches 0, the sum* $\sum_{i=1}^{n} c(X_i)(x_i - x_{i-1})$ *approaches the area of S.*

Example 2. A string is made of a material whose density may vary from point to point. (Such a string is called nonuniform or nonhomogeneous.) How would we compute its total mass if we knew its density at each point?

We place the string somewhere on the x axis and denote by $h(x)$ its density at x (h stands for heaviness).

Nonuniform string

Let us cut the string into small sections by a partition of $[a,b]$.

In a very small section the density is "almost" constant. So the mass of the ith section is approximately

$$h(X_i)(x_i - x_{i-1})$$

where X_i is some point in $[x_{i-1}, x_i]$. Thus $\sum_{i=1}^{n} h(X_i)(x_i - x_{i-1})$ is an estimate of the mass of the string. And, what is more important, it seems plausible that, *as the mesh of the partition approaches 0, the sum $\sum_{i=1}^{n} h(X_i)(x_i - x_{i-1})$ approaches the mass of the string.*

Example 3. An engineer takes a trip that begins at time a and ends at time b. Imagine that at any time t during the trip his speed is $v(t)$, depending on the time t. How far does he travel? (We have already met the case in which $a = 0$, $b = 3$, $v(t) = 8t^2$.)

We cut the time interval $[a,b]$ into smaller intervals by a partition and estimate the trip's length by summing the estimates of the distance the engineer travels during each of the time intervals.

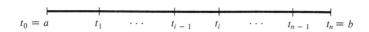

During a small interval of time, the velocity changes little. We may thus expect to obtain a reasonable estimate of the distance covered during the ith time interval $[t_{i-1}, t_i]$ by observing the speedometer reading at some instant T_i in that interval, say it is $v(T_i)$, and computing $v(T_i)(t_i - t_{i-1})$. Thus $\sum_{i=1}^{n} v(T_i)(t_i - t_{i-1})$ is an estimate of the length of the trip. Moreover, we suspect that *as the mesh of the partitions approaches zero, the sum $\sum_{i=1}^{n} v(T_i)(t_i - t_{i-1})$ approaches the length of the trip.*

Example 4. Suppose that we wish to compute the volume of a solid S, and we happen to know the area $A(x)$ of each cross section made by a plane in a fixed direction. We can estimate the volume of S if we know the area $A(x)$ of the typical cross section, shown in this diagram.

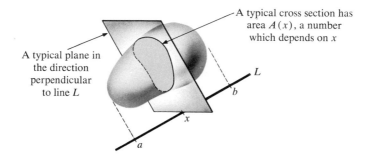

A typical cross section has area $A(x)$, a number which depends on x

A typical plane in the direction perpendicular to line L

L

b

x

a

[In the case of the tent, $a = 0$, $b = 3$, and $A(x) = x^2$.]

Every time we partition $[a,b]$ and select the X's we obtain, as an estimate of the volume of S, the sum of the volumes of slabs. A typical slab is shown in this figure:

A typical slab is an
irregular cylinder of
cross sectional area
$A(X_i)$ and thickness
$x_i - x_{i-1}$

Thus $\sum\limits_{i=1}^{n} A(x_i)(x_i - x_{i-1})$ is an estimate of the volume of the solid S. As we shrink the mesh of the partition, the slabs become thin and their total volume presumably becomes an increasingly accurate estimate of the volume of S. We expect that *as the mesh of the partition approaches* 0, *the sum* $\sum\limits_{i=1}^{n} A(X_i)(x_i - x_{i-1})$ *approaches the volume of S.*

A table will show the similarities of these examples. To emphasize these similarities we will denote the various function values $c(x)$, $h(x)$, $v(t)$, and $A(x)$ uniformly by $f(x)$. Also, if the sums $\sum\limits_{i=1}^{n} f(X_i)(x_i - x_{i-1})$ approach a number as the mesh approaches zero, we will denote that number by

$$\lim_{\text{mesh}\to 0} \sum_{i=1}^{n} f(X_i)(x_i - x_{i-1})$$

read as *the limit of the sum* $\sum\limits_{i=1}^{n} f(X_i)(x_i - x_{i-1})$ *as the mesh approaches* 0.

$f(x)$	$\sum\limits_{i=1}^{n} f(X_i)(x_i - x_{i-1})$	$\lim\limits_{\text{mesh}\to 0} \sum\limits_{i=1}^{n} f(X_i)(x_i - x_{i-1})$
Variable length of cross section of set in plane	Approximation to area of the set in the plane	The area of the set in the plane
Variable density of string	Approximation to mass of the string	The mass of the string
Variable velocity	Approximation to the distance traveled	The distance traveled
Variable area of cross section of a solid	Approximation to the volume of the solid	The volume of the solid

The table suggests that *we should free ourselves from undue attachment to* "area," "total mass," "distance traveled," and "volume." All we need to form the sums in question is an interval $[a,b]$ and some function f defined for every point in $[a,b]$. (The notion of *function* is discussed in Appendix C.) This leads us to an important definition, which we phrase informally and intuitively, using such expressions as "approach" and "shrinks toward 0." It is stated more formally and precisely in Chap. 3 (page 86).

DEFINITION: *The definite integral of a function f over an interval [a,b]*. If f is a function defined on [a,b] and the sums $\sum_{i=1}^{n} f(X_i)(x_i - x_{i-1})$ "approach" a certain number as the mesh of the partition of [a,b] "shrinks" toward 0 (no matter how X_i is chosen in $[x_{i-1},x_i]$), that certain number is called the *definite integral* of f over [a,b].

The word "approach" in the preceding definition is short for "get (and remain) as close as we please to."

The definite integral is also called *the definite integral of f from a to b* and *the integral of f from a to b*. The symbol for this number is $\int_a^b f(x)\,dx$. The "$\int$" comes from the "S" of Sum; the dx traditionally suggests *a small section of the x axis* and will be more meaningful and useful later. It is important to realize that area, mass, distance traveled, and volume are merely applications of the definite integral. It is a mistake to link the definite integral too closely with one of its applications, just as it narrows our understanding of the number 2 to link it always with the idea of two fingers.

We now have these terse expressions for the answers to the four problems of Sec. 1.

Problem 1. The area under the curve $y = x^2$ and above [0,3] equals $\int_0^3 x^2\,dx$

Problem 2. The mass of the string equals $\int_0^3 5x^2\,dx$

Problem 3. The distance that the engineer traveled equals $\int_0^3 8t^2\,dt$ (the t reminding us of time)

Problem 4. The volume of the tent equals $\int_0^3 x^2\,dx$

We showed by a geometric observation that $\int_0^3 x^2\,dx = 9$. With that information all four definite integrals were computed.

As another illustration of the concept of the definite integral, let us consider $\int_1^5 (1/x)\,dx$, which we will usually write as $\int_1^5 1/x\,dx$.

The function f is given by $f(x) = 1/x$, and the interval is [1,5]. As a convenient partition we cut [1,5] into four sections of equal length, and for the X's we use midpoints.

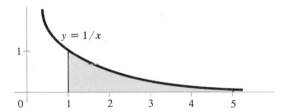

$X_1 = \frac{3}{2}, X_2 = \frac{5}{2},$
$X_3 = \frac{7}{2}, X_4 = \frac{9}{2}$

For this choice of x's and X's, the sum $\sum\limits_{i=1}^{n} f(X_i)(x_i - x_{i-1})$ is just

$$\frac{1}{\frac{3}{2}}(2-1) + \frac{1}{\frac{5}{2}}(3-2) + \frac{1}{\frac{7}{2}}(4-3) + \frac{1}{\frac{9}{2}}(5-4)$$

A little arithmetic changes this expression to

$$\tfrac{2}{3} + \tfrac{2}{5} + \tfrac{2}{7} + \tfrac{2}{9}$$

which is $\frac{496}{315}$, or 1.575.

Thus 1.575 is an estimate of the definite integral of $1/x$ from 1 to 5. This information is a bit of "pure" mathematics; if we place the function $1/x$ in a geometric or physical context, we can apply this information. For instance, the area of the shaded set is about 1.575. (Of course, we don't know yet how large the error is.)

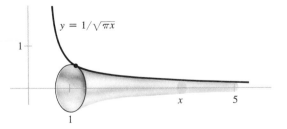

We also have obtained estimates for the following quantities.

1. The total mass of a string 4 feet long if its density is $1/x$ pounds per foot at x, when the string lies on the x axis thus:

Nonuniform string

The mass is about 1.575 pounds.

2. The distance a tiring turtle travels from 1 P.M. to 5 P.M. if its speedometer reads $1/t$ miles per hour at time t: It travels about 1.575 miles.

3. The volume of the solid obtained by rotating the curve $y = 1/\sqrt{\pi x}$ (from $x = 1$ to $x = 5$) around the x axis. The volume is about 1.575.

$y = 1/\sqrt{\pi x}$

The cross section at typical x is a circle of radius $1/\sqrt{\pi x}$; its area $A(x)$ is thus $\pi(1/\sqrt{\pi x})^2 = 1/x$.

If instead of making a mere estimate, we could compute $\int_1^5 1/x\, dx$ precisely, we would have the exact area under $y = 1/x$, the mass of the string, the distance the turtle travels, and the volume bounded by the rotated curve $y = 1/\sqrt{\pi x}$. The powerful machinery we develop in Chaps. 2 through 6 for computing definite integrals will easily give us, as a simple application of a general technique,

$$\int_1^5 \frac{1}{x}\, dx = 1.60944 \qquad \text{(to five-figure accuracy)}$$

EXERCISES

1. In our estimate of $\int_1^5 1/x\, dx$ we used the midpoints of the four sections for the X's.

   Use the same partition into four sections and estimate $\int_1^5 1/x\, dx$ using as the X's

   (a) the right end point in each section; (b) the left end point in each section.
   [Answer: (a) $^{77}\!/_{60} = 1.283$; (b) $^{25}\!/_{12} = 2.083$]

2. Estimate $\int_1^5 1/x\, dx$, using the irregular partition $x_0 = 1$, $x_1 = \frac{3}{2}$, $x_2 = 2$, $x_3 = 4$,

   $x_4 = 5$ and for the X's (a) midpoints; (b) right end points; (c) left end points.
   [Answer: (a) $^{496}\!/_{315} = 1.575$; (b) $^{25}\!/_{12} = 2.083$]

3. Recalling Exercise 1 and interpreting $\int_1^5 1/x\, dx$ as an area, show why

   $$1.283 < \int_1^5 \frac{1}{x}\, dx < 2.083$$

4. Using Exercise 2 and interpreting $\int_1^5 1/x\, dx$ as an area, give two numbers m and n such that

   $$m < \int_1^5 \frac{1}{x}\, dx < n$$

5. Preferably using a handbook of mathematical tables, estimate $\int_1^5 1/x\, dx$ to two

   decimal places, using a partition into eight sections of equal length, and for the X's (a) midpoints; (b) right end points; (c) left end points.

6. There are tables for square roots. (a) Estimate $\int_1^9 \sqrt{t}\, dt$; (b) Estimate $\int_1^9 5\sqrt{x}\, dx$.

7. (a) Draw a triangle whose area would be given by $\int_0^3 5x\, dx$.

   (b) Using the formula for the area of a triangle, evaluate $\int_0^3 5x\, dx$.

8. (*a*) (See Exercise 7.) Show that

$$\int_a^b x \, dx = \frac{b^2}{2} - \frac{a^2}{2}$$

(*b*) Recalling our work in Sec. 1, show that

$$\int_a^b x^2 \, dx = \frac{b^3}{3} - \frac{a^3}{3}$$

9. Let f be a constant function, $f(x) = c$, where c is a fixed number.

(*a*) Show that every approximating sum $\sum_{i=1}^{n} f(X_i)(x_i - x_{i-1})$ has the value $c(b - a)$.

(*b*) With the aid of (*a*), evaluate $\int_a^b c \, dx$.

10. Using a table of $\cos \theta$ (where angle is measured in radians) or recalling the cosines of familiar angles, estimate $\int_0^{\pi/2} \cos \theta \, d\theta$, using this partition of the θ axis.

As θ_1, θ_2, θ_3 (playing the roles of X_1, X_2, X_3, respectively), (*a*) use 0, $\pi/6$, $\pi/3$, respectively; (*b*) use $\pi/6$, $\pi/3$, $\pi/2$, respectively; (*c*) use $\pi/6$, $\pi/4$, $\pi/3$, respectively.

[Answer: (*a*) 1.24; (*b*) 0.72; (*c*) 1.09]

11. (*a*) Draw a region in the plane whose area is $\int_0^{\pi/2} \cos \theta \, d\theta$.

(*b*) Draw a solid whose volume is $\int_0^{\pi/2} \cos \theta \, d\theta$.

(*c*) What do the answers to Exercise 10 tell about the area in (*a*) and the volume in (*b*)?

12. Estimate $\int_1^3 10^x \, dx$, using the partition $x_0 = 1$, $x_1 = 2$, $x_2 = 3$ and (*a*) $X_1 = 1$, $X_2 = 2$; (*b*) $X_1 = 2$, $X_2 = 2$; (*c*) $X_1 = 2$, $X_2 = 3$.

[Answer: (*a*) 110; (*b*) 200; (*c*) 1100]

13. Using a table of $\log_{10}$, estimate (*a*) $\int_1^2 \log_{10} x \, dx$; (*b*) $\int_2^3 \log_{10} x \, dx$.

14. Cut [1,3] into eight sections of equal length and show that

$$1.020 = \tfrac{1}{5} + \tfrac{1}{6} + \cdots + \tfrac{1}{12} < \int_1^3 \frac{1}{x} \, dx < \tfrac{1}{4} + \tfrac{1}{5} + \cdots + \tfrac{1}{11} = 1.187$$

15. Show that the following three quantities equal $\int_0^5 32x \, dx$: (*a*) The area of a tri-

angle of base 5 and altitude 160; (b) the distance a falling particle travels from $t = 0$ to $t = 5$, if its speed at time t is $32t$; (c) the volume of this headlight:

The cross section above x is a circle of radius $\sqrt{32x/\pi}$

16. (a) What definite integral represents the volume of the cone in Exercise 8, page 8?
    (b) What is the numerical value of the definite integral in (a)?
17. (a) What definite integral represents the total profit of the business in Exercise 10, page 9?
    (b) What is the numerical value of the definite integral in (a)?
18. We used vertical cross sections to show that $\int_0^3 x^2\,dx$ equals the area of the region below the curve $y = x^2$ and above [0,3]. Using horizontal cross sections, obtain another definite integral for the same area. Be sure to (a) draw a neat diagram, (b) show the interval you partition, (c) show the typical rectangle and how you found its area.
19. What definite integral represents the mass of (a) the right half of the string on page 4? (b) the left half?
20. As n becomes large, $\sum_{i=1}^{n} (i/n)^3 (1/n)$ approaches a number that can be expressed as $\int_a^b f(x)\,dx$ for suitable a, b, and f. What are a, b, and f? Explain in detail.
21. Set up a definite integral $\int_a^b f(x)\,dx$ that equals the area of a disk of radius 5. (A disk is a plane set whose border is a circle.) Sketch the interval you partition and the typical rectangle, and show how you obtained a, b, and f. Do not evaluate the definite integral.
22. What definite integral represents the total profit in the last two years of the three-year plan proposed by the business in Exercise 10, page 9?

□ □ □

23. The area of a disk of radius a is πa^2. Using the fact that the shadow of a circle is an ellipse, show that the area of this ellipse is πab.

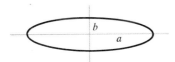

24. (*a*) By inspection of this picture, show that $\int_0^a \sqrt{y}\,dy + \int_0^{\sqrt{a}} x^2\,dx = a\sqrt{a}.$

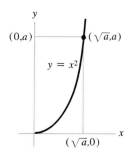

(*b*) From our knowledge of the definite integral of x^2 over any interval, deduce that

$$\int_0^a \sqrt{y}\,dy = \tfrac{2}{3}\,a\sqrt{a}\,(= \tfrac{2}{3}\,a^{3/2})$$

25. Show that the area of the region under $y = 1/x$ and above [1,2] equals the area of the region under $y = 1/x$ and above [3,6]. (Hint: Note that if $x_0, x_1, \ldots, x_n$ is a partition of [1,2], then $3x_0, 3x_1, \ldots, 3x_n$ is a partition of [3,6].)

26. Let $A(t)$ be the area of the region below $y = 1/x$ and above [1,*t*] for $t > 1$.
    (*a*) Using Exercise 25, show that $A(6) = A(2) + A(3)$.
    (*b*) Show that $A(uv) = A(u) + A(v)$ for any $u > 1$ and $v > 1$.
    (*c*) Does the property of the function A remind you of a specific function studied in algebra?

27. A man whose car has a vertical windshield drives a mile through a vertical rain consisting of drops that are uniformly distributed and falling at a constant rate. Should he go slow or fast in order to minimize the amount of rain that strikes the windshield?

28. (*a*) Show why a disk of radius r has an area equal to $\int_0^r 2\pi x\,dx.$ "Disk" is defined in Exercise 21. (Hint: Cut the disk into concentric rings and estimate the area of each ring by "straightening it out" and comparing it to a rectangle.) (*b*) Using Exercise 8, show that the disk in (*a*) has area πr^2.

29. Assuming that $\int_0^1 x^5\,dx = 1/6$, find $\int_0^2 x^5\,dx.$ (Hint: If $x_0, x_1, \ldots, x_n$ is a partition of [0,1], then $2x_0, 2x_1, \ldots, 2x_n$ is a partition of [0,2].)

4. The average of a function over an interval. The average of n numbers is simply their sum divided by n. Thus the average of 2, 3, and 7 is $(2 + 3 + 7)/3$, or 4. How can we define the average of the function x^2, for x in the interval [0,3]? It makes no sense to find the sum of all the squares of all the numbers from 0 to 3 and then divide by the number of those quantities, since the interval [0,3] contains an infinite set of numbers.

To define the average of a function f over an interval $[a,b]$ we can proceed as follows. Pick an integer n and then n equally spaced points in the interval $[a,b]$. If we call these points $x_1, x_2, \ldots, x_n$

For each i, $x_i - x_{i-1} = (b-a)/n$

then

$$(1) \qquad \frac{f(x_1) + f(x_2) + \cdots + f(x_n)}{n}$$

would be a reasonable *estimate* of the average value of f over $[a,b]$. And, as n increases, we would expect our estimate to be more accurate.

The sum (1) resembles the approximating sum for a definite integral. With a little algebra we can relate it to such a sum as follows: First of all,

$$(2) \qquad \frac{f(x_1) + f(x_2) + \cdots + f(x_n)}{n} = \frac{1}{b-a}\left[f(x_1)\frac{b-a}{n} + f(x_2)\frac{b-a}{n} \right.$$
$$\left. + \cdots + f(x_n)\frac{b-a}{n} \right]$$

To make the relation between (1) or (2) and $\int_a^b f(x)\,dx$ more evident, let us note that for each $i = 1, 2, \ldots, n$, we have $x_i - x_{i-1} = (b-a)/n$. Hence we may rewrite the right side of (2) as

$$(3) \qquad \frac{1}{b-a}[f(x_1)(x_1 - x_0) + f(x_2)(x_2 - x_1) + \cdots + f(x_n)(x_n - x_{n-1})]$$

The bracketed expression in (3) is an approximation to $\int_a^b f(x)\,dx$. This observation leads us to define the average of f over $[a,b]$ directly in terms of the definite integral.

DEFINITION: *Average value of a function over an interval.* The *average value* of f over $[a,b]$ is

$$\frac{\int_a^b f(x)\,dx}{b-a}$$

Example 1. Knowing that $\int_0^3 x^2\,dx = 9$, we can easily compute the average value of x^2 over $[0,3]$. We have

$$\frac{\int_0^3 x^2\,dx}{3-0} = \frac{9}{3} = 3$$

If $f(x)$ is positive for x in $[a,b]$, then there is a simple geometric interpretation of the average of the function over the interval. If we call the average A, then

$$A = \frac{\int_a^b f(x)\,dx}{b-a} \qquad \text{or} \qquad A(b-a) = \int_a^b f(x)\,dx$$

Now, as we saw in Sec. 3, we can, if we wish, interpret $\int_a^b f(x)\,dx$ as the area of the region below the graph of f and above the interval $[a,b]$. The equation

$$A(b-a) = \int_a^b f(x)\,dx$$

then asserts that A, the average value of the function, is the height of a rectangle whose base is $(b-a)$ and whose area is equal to the area of the region under the graph of f:

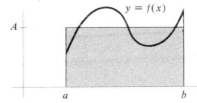

The height of this rectangle is the average value A of f over $[a,b]$, and the area is the same as the area of the region below the curve $y = f(x)$ and above $[a,b]$

One might think that every function has an average or, equivalently, that every function has a definite integral. Functions that are applied in the natural and social sciences usually do have a definite integral. But the function in the next example does *not* have a definite integral over any interval.

Example 2. We construct a function f that fails to have a definite integral over $[0,2]$. This construction makes use of the distinction between the rational and irrational numbers. A number is *rational* if it can be expressed as the quotient of two integers. For instance, ⅔ and -7 (which equals $-\frac{7}{1}$), are rational. A real number that is not rational is called *irrational*. For instance, $\sqrt{2}$ and ⅗ $\sqrt{3}$ are irrational. We shall make use of the fact that between any two numbers there are at least one rational number and at least one irrational number.

We define f by this rule:

$$f(x) = \begin{cases} 0 & \text{if } x \text{ is rational} \\ 3 & \text{if } x \text{ is irrational} \end{cases}$$

Thus $f(\tfrac{1}{2}) = 0$, $f(1) = 0$, $f(1.4) = 0$, $f(1.41) = 0$, $f(1.414) = 0$, $f(\sqrt{2}) = 3$, $f\left(\dfrac{\sqrt{2}}{100}\right) = 3$.

We cannot graph this function since it fluctuates too much. We now show that $\int_0^2 f(x)\,dx$ does not exist.

Let $x_0 = 0, x_1, \ldots, x_n = 2$ be any partition of $[0,2]$. No matter how small its mesh may be, we can choose the X's in such a way that

$$\sum_{i=1}^{n} f(X_i)(x_i - x_{i-1}) = 0$$

We simply choose X_i to be one of the rational numbers in the ith interval $[x_{i-1}, x_i]$.

On the other hand, if we choose each X_i to be irrational, then $f(X_i) = 3$ for each X_i. Then

$$\sum_{i=1}^{n} f(X_i)(x_i - x_{i-1}) = \sum_{i=1}^{n} 3(x_i - x_{i-1})$$

which is 3 times the sum of the lengths of the sections in the partition, that is, 3 times 2, or 6.

Therefore the sums in question do not tend toward a specific number as we make the mesh small. Indeed we can force them to take on the value 0, or 6, or values between, even though the mesh is small. Because of this the function does not have a definite integral; more tersely, $\int_0^2 f(x)\, dx$ does not exist.

EXERCISES

1. Find the average value of $f(x) = x^2$ over $[0,1]$.   (Answer: $\frac{1}{3}$)
2. Find the average value of $f(x) = x^2$ over $[1,3]$.   (Answer: $\frac{13}{3}$)
3. Find the average value of $f(x) = x$ over $[1,5]$.   (Answer: 3)
4. (a) Estimate the average value of $f(x) = 1/x$ over $[1,4]$ (by making an estimate of

$$\int_1^4 1/x\, dx).$$

   (b) Use the answers to Exercise 2, page 21, to estimate the average of $1/x$ over $[1,5]$.

5. (a) Partition $[2,5]$ into three sections of equal length, and select as X's their mid-points. Compute $\sum_{i=1}^{3} f(X_i)(x_i - x_{i-1})$, where $f(x) = x^3$.

   (b) Using (a), estimate the average value of x^3 over $[2,5]$.

                    [Answer: (a) $119\frac{7}{8}$; (b) $119\frac{7}{24}$]

6. Let $f(x) = 0$ for all x other than 2, and let $f(2) = 5$. (A graph of this function shows a jump at $x = 2$.) Does this function have a definite integral over $[0,4]$? If not, why not? If so, what is the numerical value of $\int_0^4 f(x)\, dx$? To answer these questions it is necessary to consider what happens to approximating sums when the mesh is small.

7. (a) What is the average vertical cross section of the region in Problem 1, page 4?
   (b) What is the average horizontal cross section of the same region?

8. What is the average velocity of the car with the broken odometer that we discussed on page 4?

9. A certain function f defined on $[1,5]$ has a definite integral over $[1,5]$. Also, we know that for each x in $[1,5]$ we have $3 \leqslant f(x) \leqslant 7$.

   (a) Between what two numbers must any approximating sum $\sum_{i=1}^{n} f(X_i)(x_i - x_{i-1})$ lie?

(b) What does (a) imply about $\int_1^5 f(x)\,dx$?

(c) What can be said about the average value of $f(x)$ over $[1,5]$?

10. A function f is defined by $f(x) = 3$ if $x < 4$ and $f(x) = 5$ if $x \geqslant 4$.

(a) Compute $\int_2^7 f(x)\,dx$.

(b) What is the average value of f over $[2,7]$?

11. A function is given by $f(x) = 10$ if $x \leqslant 2$ and $f(x) = 7$ if $x > 2$.

(a) What is the average value of f over $[0,1]$?

(b) What is the average value of f over $[0,3]$?

(c) What is the average value of f over $[0,19]$?

12. Show that the distance traveled by the car with the broken odometer in Sec. 1 is equal to (duration of trip) times (average velocity during trip).

13. A certain function f is defined throughout $[0,2]$, but only limited data concerning it are available from experiments. It is known that $f(0) = 3$, $f(\frac{1}{4}) = \frac{7}{2}$, $f(\frac{1}{2}) = 4$, $f(1) = 6$, $f(2) = 8$. What is a sensible estimate of the average value of f over $[0,2]$?

14. (a) Recall the function f that has the value 0 at rational x and the value 3 at irrational x. Devise a partition of $[0,2]$ into five sections and a choice of X's such that

$$\sum_{i=1}^{5} f(X_i)(x_i - x_{i-1}) - 2$$

(b) Can very fine partitions be found and approximate sums be formed such that

$$\sum_{i=1}^{n} f(X_i)(x_i - x_{i-1}) = 2$$

15. Recall Exercise 23, page 23, and compute the average value of the length of cross section $c(x)$ of the ellipse shown in this figure:

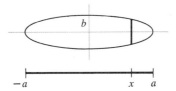

The cross section has length $c(x)$

(Answer: $\pi b/2$, about $1.57b$)

16. Show that the volume in this conical solid with an irregular flat base is $hA/3$. (Hint: Find the area of the cross section of this solid made by a plane that is parallel to the base and at a distance x from the vertex.)

The height of this point above the base is h

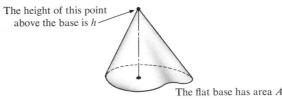

The flat base has area A

5. *The definite integral of a function over a set in the plane.* So far the problems we have met have led us to form approximating sums by partitioning an interval. We now present two problems that will lead us to form approximating sums
by partitioning a subset of the plane.

By a *set or region in the plane* we shall usually mean a set of points in the plane
enclosed by a curve or polygon. When such a set is partitioned into subsets, these
subsets will also be bounded by curves or polygons.

PROBLEM 1.   *Estimate the volume of the solid S which we now describe.*
Above each point P in the rectangle R we erect a line segment whose length,
in inches, is the square of the distance from P to the corner A.

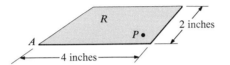

The rectangle *R*, shown in
perspective, is horizontal

These segments form a solid S which looks like this:

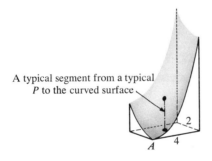

A typical segment from a typical
P to the curved surface

For instance, S reaches its highest point above the corner of R opposite A;
there it has a height $4^2 + 2^2 = 20$ *inches.*

The volume of *S* is certainly less than $4 \cdot 2 \cdot 20 = 160$ cubic inches, since *S* can be
put in a box whose base has area $4 \cdot 2$ square inches and whose height is 20 inches.

In order to make more accurate estimates we cut the rectangular base into smaller
pieces. For convenience, we cut it into four congruent rectangles, R_1, R_2, R_3, R_4.

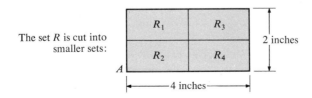

The set *R* is cut into
smaller sets:

We can estimate the volume of S by estimating the volume of that portion of S above each of the rectangles R_1, R_2, R_3, and R_4, and adding them together. To do this we select a point in each of the four rectangles, say the center of each,

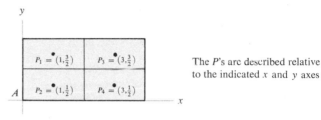

The P's are described relative to the indicated x and y axes

and form a box above each of the rectangles whose height is the height of S above the center of the corresponding rectangle:

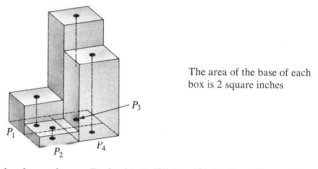

The area of the base of each box is 2 square inches

For instance, the height of the box above R_1 is $1^2 + (\tfrac{3}{2})^2 = \tfrac{13}{4}$ inches. Summing the volumes of the four boxes, we obtain this estimate of the volume of S:

$$\tfrac{13}{4} \cdot 2 + \tfrac{5}{4} \cdot 2 + \tfrac{45}{4} \cdot 2 + \tfrac{37}{4} \cdot 2 = 50 \text{ cubic inches}$$

This is only one estimate. With the same partition of R we could make other estimates by choosing other P's to determine the heights of approximating boxes. In fact, a general technique for estimating the volume of S is this: partition R into smaller subsets $R_1, R_2, \ldots, R_n$, and select a point P_1 in R_1, P_2 in R_2, $\ldots, P_n$ in R_n.

A typical partition of R:

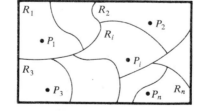

If we denote the height of S above a typical point P in R by $c(P)$, and the area of R_i by A_i, then

$$c(P_1) A_1 + c(P_2) A_2 + \cdots + c(P_n) A_n$$

is an estimate of the volume of S by a sum of the volumes of n solids, a typical one of which looks like this:

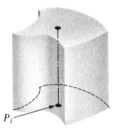

The cylinder has base R_i with area A_i and height $c(P_i)$

PROBLEM 2.   *Estimate the mass of the rectangular sheet R that we now describe. Its dimensions are 4 inches by 2 inches:*

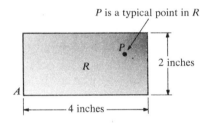

P is a typical point in R

The material is sparse near A and dense far from A. Indeed, let us assume that the density in the vicinity of any point P is equal numerically to the square of the distance from P to A (ounces per square inch). For instance, it is densest at the corner opposite A, where its density is $4^2 + 2^2 = 20$ ounces per square inch.

The total mass is certainly less than $4 \cdot 2 \cdot 20 = 160$ ounces, since the area of R is $4 \cdot 2$ square inches and the maximum density is 20 ounces per square inch.

In order to make more accurate estimates we cut the rectangle into smaller pieces, for instance, into these four congruent rectangles:

The set R is cut into smaller sets:

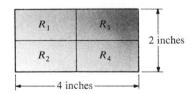

We estimate the total mass by estimating the mass in each of the rectangles, R_1, R_2,

R_3, and R_4. To do this, we select a point—say the center—in each of the four rectangles, and compute the density at each of these four points:

<table>
<tr><td rowspan="2" style="vertical-align:middle">A point is chosen in each
set of the partition:</td><td>$P_1 = \left(1,\frac{3}{2}\right)$</td><td>$P_3 = \left(3,\frac{3}{2}\right)$</td></tr>
<tr><td>$P_2 = \left(1,\frac{1}{2}\right)$</td><td>$P_4 = \left(3,\frac{1}{2}\right)$</td></tr>
</table>

For instance, the density at P_1 is $1^2 + (\tfrac{3}{2})^2 = \tfrac{13}{4}$ ounces per square inch. As an estimate of the mass in R_1, we have $\tfrac{13}{4} \cdot 2$ ounces, since the area of R_1 is 2 square inches. The sum of the estimates for each of the four rectangles,

$$\tfrac{13}{4} \cdot 2 + \tfrac{5}{4} \cdot 2 + \tfrac{45}{4} \cdot 2 + \tfrac{37}{4} \cdot 2 = 50 \text{ ounces}$$

is an estimate of the total mass in R.

This is only one estimate. Just as for the volume in Problem 1, we can obtain many estimates in the same way. We merely partition R into small subsets, $R_1, R_2, \ldots, R_n$, and select a point P_1 in R_1, P_2 in R_2, $\ldots, P_n$ in R_n. If we denote the density at P by $f(P)$ and the area of R_i by A_i, then

$$f(P_1) A_1 + f(P_2) A_2 + \cdots + f(P_n)A_n$$

is an estimate of the total mass.

Even though we have found neither the volume in Problem 1 nor the mass in Problem 2, it is clear that if we know the answer to one, we have the answer to the other: the arithmetic of any estimate for the volume is the same as the arithmetic for an estimate of the mass.

The similarity of the sums we have just formed to the sums we met in Sec. 3 suggest that we ought to generalize the idea of the definite integral from intervals $[a,b]$ to sets in the plane. First, in order to speak of fine partitions on the plane, we make two definitions.

DEFINITION: *Diameter of a set.* Let S be a set in the plane bounded by a curve or polygon. The *diameter* of S is the largest distance between two points of S.

For instance, the diameter of a square of side s is $s\sqrt{2}$, and the diameter of a circle whose radius is r is $2r$.

DEFINITION: *Mesh of a partition in the plane.* Let $R_1, R_2, \ldots, R_n$ be a partition of a set R in the plane into subsets. The *mesh* of this partition is the largest of the diameters of the sets $R_1, R_2, \ldots, R_n$.

For instance, the mesh of the partition used in this section is $\sqrt{5}$. Now we can define the definite integral over a plane set.

DEFINITION: *Definite integral of a function f over a set R in the plane.* Let f be a function that assigns to each point P in a set R in the plane a number $f(P)$. Consider the typical sum

$$f(P_1) A_1 + f(P_2) A_2 + \cdots + f(P_n) A_n$$

formed from partitions of R, where A_i is the area of R_i, and P_i is in R_i. If these sums "approach" a certain number as the mesh of the partition "shrinks toward 0" (no matter how P_i is chosen in R_i), that certain number is called the *definite integral* of f over the set R.

It is illuminating to compare this definition to the definition of the definite integral over an interval. Both are numbers that are approached by certain sums of products. The sums are formed in a similar manner, as this table shows:

Given	for each subset in a partition one computes	and selects in each of the subsets	and forms the sum
An interval and a function defined there	Its length $x_i - x_{i-1}$	A point (described by its coordinate X_i)	$\sum_{i=1}^{n} f(X_i)(x_i - x_{i-1})$
A set in the plane and a function defined there	Its area A_i	A point P_i	$\sum_{i=1}^{n} f(P_i) A_i$

The definite integral is not defined as a sum formed in this table, but rather as the number approached by these sums when the mesh approaches 0. The definite integral of f over R is sometimes called *the integral of f over R* or *the integral of f(P) over R*. The symbol for this number is

$$\int_R f(P)\, dA$$

For example, the volume in Problem 1 and the mass in Problem 2 are both given by

$$\int_R (x^2 + y^2)\, dA$$

where R is the rectangle that has vertices $(0,0)$, $(4,0)$, $(0,2)$, $(4,2)$.

Estimating $\int_R f(P)\, dA$ is much more tedious than estimating $\int_a^b f(x)\, dx$. In Chap. 9 we develop rapid means for computing definite integrals over plane sets and present more illustrations of their use.

At this point, to emphasize further the similarity between integrals over plane sets and integrals over intervals, we define the average of a function over a plane set.

DEFINITION: *Average value.* The average value of f over the set R is

$$\frac{\displaystyle\int_R f(P)\,dA}{\text{area of } R}$$

EXERCISES

1. In our estimates we used for the P_i's the centers of the "subrectangles." Make an estimate for the volume in Problem 1 by using the same partition but taking as the P_i's (*a*) the lower left corner of each R_i; (*b*) the upper right corner of each R_i. (*c*) What do (*a*) and (*b*) tell us about the volume of the solid?
[Answer: (*a*) 20 cubic inches; (*b*) 100 cubic inches]

2. Estimate the mass for Problem 1, using a partition of R into eight congruent squares and taking as the P_i's (*a*) centers; (*b*) upper right corners; (*c*) lower left corners.
[Answer: (*a*) 52 ounces; (*b*) 80 ounces; (*c*) 32 ounces]

3. A solid is formed in this manner. Above each point (x,y) in this rectangle R a line segment is placed, perpendicular to R, and of length xy.

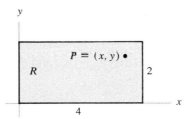

(*a*) Make a model of the solid formed. (Use toothpicks, clay, or soap. Another way is to make its floor R and two walls out of cardboard and indicate its top surface by yarn or string appropriately strung.)

This solid has a rectangular base, two triangular faces, and one curved face

(*b*) Estimate the volume of your model.

4. Estimate the volume of the solid described in Exercise 3. Use the partition of R that we used in Problem 1 and choose as the P_i's (*a*) centers; (*b*) lower left points; (*c*) upper right points.   [Answer: (*a*) 16; (*b*) 4; (*c*) 36]

5. Estimate the volume of the solid in Exercise 3. Use the partition and P_i's given in Exercise 2.

6. Let R be a set in the plane whose area is A. Let f be the function such that $f(P) = 5$ for every point P in R.

(a) What can be said about any approximating sum $\sum\limits_{i=1}^{n} f(P_i)A_i$ formed for this R and this f?

(b) What is the numerical value of $\int_R f(P)\, dA$?

7. (a) Prove that if the diameter of a set in the plane is d, then its area is less than d^2.
(b) Which has the largest area: a circle of diameter d, a square of diameter d, or an equilateral triangle of diameter d?
(c) How large an area do you think a set of diameter d can have?
(d) Can a circle of diameter d always be drawn to contain a given set of diameter d?

8. (a) Let f and R be as in Problem 1 or 2. Use our estimate of $\int_R f(P)\, dA$ to estimate the average of f over R.
(b) Using the information from Exercise 2, show that the average is between 4 and 10.

[Answer: (a) 5⅝%]

9. Let f be defined by $f(x,y) = x + y$. Find numbers m and M such that

$$m \leqslant \int_R f(P)\, dA \leqslant M$$

if (a) R is the rectangle that has vertices $(1,1)$, $(3,1)$, $(1,2)$, $(3,2)$; or (b) R is the circle that has center $(4,4)$ and radius 3.

10. A solid potato occupies a set S of points in space. Consider a line L in space and a plane perpendicular to L. Let R be the shadow (projection) of S on the plane by rays of light parallel to L. For each point P in R, the line through P and parallel to L intersects S in an interval of length $c(P)$, which we assume as known.

(a) With clear diagrams show that $\int_R c(P)\, dA$ equals the volume of S.

(b) Show that the product of the area of R and the average of the function c is the volume of S.

11. Which of these statements about partitions implies the other: Their mesh approaches 0; the number of sets in the partitions gets arbitrarily large? Explain.

12. Estimate the volume of the solid in Problem 1 above this right triangle T:

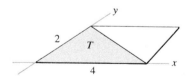

Cut T into four congruent triangles, and use P_1, P_2, P_3, and P_4 of your choice.

13. Let R be the square whose vertices are $(1,1)$, $(3,1)$, $(1,3)$, $(3,3)$, and let $f(P) = f(x,y) = 1/(2x + y)$.

   (a) Show that $\int_R f(P)\,dA$ is between $\frac{4}{9}$ and $\frac{4}{3}$.

   (b) Estimate $\int_R f(P)\,dA$.

   (c) Sketch in perspective a solid whose volume equals $\int_R f(P)\,dA$.

14. The kinetic energy of a particle of mass m slugs and velocity v (feet per second) is defined to be $\frac{1}{2}mv^2$ foot pounds. A 4- by 2-foot sheet of steel of mass 2 slugs rotates once per second around an axis perpendicular to its plane at the corner A.

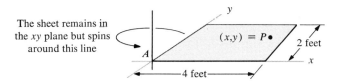

The sheet remains in the xy plane but spins around this line

$(x,y) = P\bullet$

2 feet

4 feet

   (a) What is the velocity of the point P with coordinates (x,y)?
   (b) What definite integral equals the kinetic energy of the rotating steel rectangle?
                    [Answer: (a) $2\pi\sqrt{x^2 + y^2}$ feet per second]

15. A forest-service firefighting helicopter that travels 1 mile per minute is stationed at A in a flat rectangular forest:

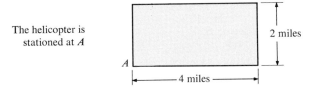

The helicopter is stationed at A

2 miles

A

4 miles

The damage caused by a forest fire is proportional to the area burned, and hence to the square of the duration of the fire. It is thus of some importance to be able to compute the average of the *square* of the time it takes the helicopter to travel to a typical point P in the forest.

   (a) Estimate the average.

   (b) Show that we would know the average precisely if we knew the answer to Problem 1 or Problem 2.

16. Let R be a circle and $f(P) = 0$ everywhere except on one diameter of R; for each point on that diameter $f(P) = 3$. Does $\int_R f(P)\,dA$ exist? If so, what is its numerical value? (Hint: Look closely at the approximating sums $\sum_{i=1}^{n} f(P_i)A_i$.)

17. Let R be the square

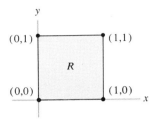

Let $f(x,y) = 1$ if x is rational, and $f(x,y) = 0$ if x is irrational. Does $\int_R f\,dA$ exist? Explain.

18. Exploiting the fact that cross sections of the solid described in Exercise 3 that are made by planes perpendicular to the x axis are triangles, express its volume in the form $\int_a^b f(x)\,dx$, and compute this definite integral.

6. The definite integral of a function over a set in three-dimensional space.

The notion of a definite integral over an interval in the line, or over a plane set, generalizes easily to integrals over solids located in space. (We shall consider these solids and their subsets to be bounded by smooth surfaces or planes.) Before we give the definition, let us illustrate the idea with a problem.

PROBLEM. *A cube of side 4 inches is made of a material of varying density. Near one corner, A, it is very light; at the opposite corner it is very dense. In fact, the density, f(P), at any point P in the cube is the square of the distance from A to P (ounces per cubic inch). How do we estimate the mass of the cube?*

We can proceed as we did for the string and the rectangle. First, partition the cube into subsets $R_1, R_2, \ldots, R_n$; then compute the density at a selected point P_i in each of the subsets R_i, and form the sum

$$f(P_1)\,V_1 + f(P_2)\,V_2 + \cdots + f(P_n)\,V_n$$

where V_i is the volume of R_i. As the R_i's become smaller we obtain more reliable estimates of the total mass of the cube.

Before we define the definite integral of a function f that assigns a number $f(P)$ to each point P in some set in space, we make two other definitions.

DEFINITION: *Diameter of a set in space.* Let S be a set of points in space bounded by some surface or polyhedron. The *diameter* of S is the largest distance between two points of S.

For instance, the diameter of a cube of side s is $s\sqrt{3}$, the length of its longest diagonal.

DEFINITION: *Mesh of a partition in space.* Let $R_1, R_2, \ldots, R_n$ be a partition of a set R in space. The *mesh* of this partition is the largest of the diameters of the sets $R_1, R_2, \ldots, R_n$.

DEFINITION: *The definite integral of a function f over a set R in space.* Let f be the function that assigns to each point of P of a set R in space a number, $f(P)$. Consider sums

$$f(P_1) V_1 + f(P_2) V_2 + \cdots + f(P_n) V_n$$

formed from partitions of R, where V_i is the volume of R_i, and P_i is in R_i. If these sums "approach" a certain number as the mesh of the partition "shrinks toward 0" (no matter how P_i is chosen in R_i), we call that certain number the *definite integral* of f over the set R.

The simplest way to think of this definite integral is to pretend that $f(P)$ denotes the density at P of some solid matter. Then the definite integral can be interpreted as the total mass of the solid.

Example. If $f(P) = 1$ for each P in R, then each approximating sum, $\sum\limits_{i=1}^{n} f(P_i)V_i$, is equal to $\sum\limits_{i=1}^{n} V_i$, the volume of R. Hence $\int_R 1 \, dV$ is equal to the volume of R. This fact will be used in Chap. 9.

The *average value* of a function f defined on a set R in space is

$$\frac{\displaystyle\int_R f(P) \, dV}{\text{volume of } R}$$

The *average value* and the *mass* are important applications of the definite integral over a solid, as they were for definite integrals for lower dimensions. We shall meet other applications when we compute the total gravitational attraction of the sun on the earth or of the earth on a satellite, and when we determine the centers of gravity of physical bodies. In Chap. 9 we will develop techniques for computing these definite integrals.

EXERCISES

1. What number is certainly larger than the mass of the cube in the problem?
2. Estimate the mass of the cube described in the problem by cutting it into eight congruent cubes and using their centers as the P_i's.   (Answer: 960 ounces)

3. If R is a sphere of radius r and $f(P) = 5$ for each point in R, compute $\int_R f(P)\,dV$

   by examining approximating sums. Assume that the sphere has volume $\frac{4}{3}\pi r^3$.
4. How would you define the average distance from points of a certain set in space to a fixed point F?
5. Using the same partition as in Exercise 2, estimate the mass of the cube, but now select as the P_i's (a) the point in R_i farthest from A; (b) the point in R_i closest to A. (Here $R_1, R_2, \ldots, R_8$ are the eight cubes in the partition.)
                                                                [Answer: (a) 1120; (b) 384]
6. From Exercise 5 what can you conclude about the mass of the cube?
7. If R is a three-dimensional set, and $f(P)$ is never more than 8 for all P in R,

   (a) What can we say about the maximum possible value of $\int_R f(P)\,dV$? (Hint: Consider approximating sums.)

   (b) What can we say about the average of f over R?
8. We can think of the average value of $f(x)$ for x in $[a,b]$ as the height of a certain rectangle.

   (a) Show that we may think of the average value of $f(P)$ for P in a plane set R as the height of a certain cylinder whose base is R.

   (b) If $f(P)$ is the density at P of a certain potato occupying the set R in space, how may we think of the average of $f(P)$ over R?

9. What can we say about the volume of a solid if we know that its diameter is 10?
10. The work done in lifting a weight of w pounds a vertical distance of x feet is wx foot-pounds. Let us imagine that through geological activity a mountain is formed consisting of material originally at sea level. Let the density of the material near point P in the mountain be $g(P)$ pounds per cubic foot and the height of P be $h(P)$. What definite integral represents the total work expended in forming the mountain?

7. Summary. This chapter introduced the definite integral of a function over a set, a number which depends both on a function f and on a set R. It is defined in terms of the behavior of certain sums of products. Any one of these sums is just an *estimate* of the definite integral. The goal of the next few chapters is to develop a general technique for computing many definite integrals exactly and quickly.

This table summarizes some of the applications of the definite integral discussed in the chapter.

Set	Function	Typical approximating sum	Definite integral	Physical interpretation of the definite integral
An interval	Density	$\sum_{i=1}^{n} f(X_i)(x_i - x_{i-1})$	$\int_a^b f(x)\,dx$	Mass
An interval	Length of cross section of a plane by a line	$\sum_{i=1}^{n} f(X_i)(x_i - x_{i-1})$	$\int_a^b f(x)\,dx$	Area
An interval	Area of cross section of a solid by a plane	$\sum_{i=1}^{n} f(X_i)(x_i - x_{i-1})$	$\int_a^b f(x)\,dx$	Volume
An interval	Speed	$\sum_{i=1}^{n} f(T_i)(t_i - t_{i-1})$	$\int_a^b f(t)\,dt$	Distance
A set in the plane	Density	$\sum_{i=1}^{n} f(P_i)A_i$	$\int_R f(P)\,dA$	Mass
A set in the plane	Length of cross section of a solid by line	$\sum_{i=1}^{n} f(P_i)A_i$	$\int_R f(P)\,dA$	Volume
A set in space	Density	$\sum_{i=1}^{n} f(P_i)V_i$	$\int_R f(p)\,dV$	Mass

Note that when density has constant value 1, mass is just area (if R is a plane set) or volume (if R is a set in space).

2

The derivative

WE leave the definite integral in order to introduce the second fundamental concept of the calculus, the derivative, which—as we will show in Chap. 6—is the main tool for the swift computation of definite integrals. In this chapter we will also give precise meaning to the terms "tangent," "density," and "velocity."

1. Estimates in four problems. Again we begin with several problems that will turn out to be one basic problem in various disguises.

PROBLEM 1.   *Estimate the slope of the "tangent" line to the curve $y = x^2$ at the point $P = (3,9)$, as shown in this figure:*

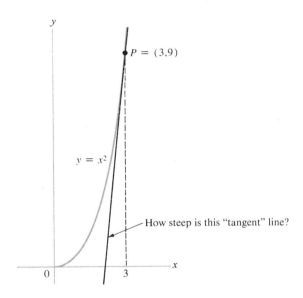

PROBLEM 2.   *The fuel in a certain rocket burns for 180 seconds. In the first t seconds the rocket reaches a height of $80t^2$ feet above the earth (for any t from 0 to 180). Estimate the "velocity" of the rocket 3 seconds after launching.*

PROBLEM 3.   *A light, two lines (a slide and a screen), and a complicated lens are placed as in this diagram:*

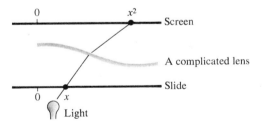

This arrangement projects the point in the bottom line whose coordinate is x to the point in the top line whose coordinate is x^2. For example, 3 is projected onto 9, and 4 onto 16. The projection of the interval [3,4] is [9,16], seven times as long. For large x the lens magnifies a great deal; for x near 0 the lens shrinks a great deal. Estimate the "magnification" at $x = 3$. The concept of magnification at a point will become clear by computations we make in this section and the next.

PROBLEM 4.   *The mass of the left-hand s inches of a nonhomogeneous string 10 inches long is s² ounces:*

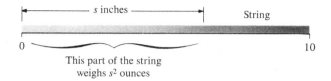

For instance, the left half has a mass of 25 ounces, while the whole string has a mass of 100 ounces. Clearly the right half is denser than the left half. Estimate the "density"—in ounces per inch—of the material in the vicinity of s = 3.

Now let us make some estimates for each of the problems. We will deal intuitively with the concepts *"tangent line," "velocity," "density,"* and *"magnification."* Later in the chapter we will define them precisely.

Before we begin Problem 1 we define the slope of a line, a numerical measure of steepness.

DEFINITION: *Slope of a line.* The *slope* of a (nonvertical) line that passes through the distinct points $P_1 = (x_1, y_1)$ and $P_2 = (x_2, y_2)$ is the quotient $(y_2 - y_1)/(x_2 - x_1)$, which is simply the ratio between the vertical and the horizontal changes along the line, as this diagram shows:

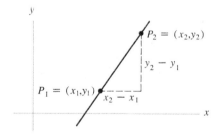

The slope of a line depends only on the line and not on the two points P_1 and P_2 that we might choose on it.

ESTIMATES FOR THE SLOPE IN PROBLEM 1.   One approach consists of carefully drawing the curve $y = x^2$ and trying to draw the line tangent to the curve at (3,9). Though this is a reasonable method, its precision is limited (as some of the exercises will show). In our problem in particular, where the line is so nearly vertical, a slight error in guessing the angle that the tangent line makes with the x axis can precipitate a large error in the slope.

We will choose a different approach, one whose accuracy is not limited. We will compute the slope of a line that approximates the tangent line at $P = (3,9)$. To do this, let us take a point Q on the curve $y = x^2$, near P, say the point $Q = (3.1, (3.1)^2)$ and compute the slope of the line passing through P and Q:

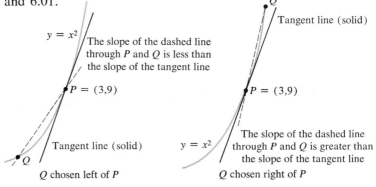

The slope of the line through P and Q is $[(3.1)^2 - 9]/(3.1 - 3)$, which is

$$\frac{9.61 - 9}{0.1} = \frac{0.61}{0.1} = 6.1$$

Thus our first *estimate* of the slope of the tangent line is 6.1. Note that in making this estimate we had no need to draw the curve.

For a more accurate estimate of the slope of the tangent line at $P = (3,9)$ we consider the line through P and a point in the curve even closer to P than our first choice. This time let us find the slope of the line through $(3,9)$ and $(3.01, (3.01)^2)$. This new line has slope $[(3.01)^2 - 9]/(3.01 - 3)$. A little arithmetic changes this to

$$\frac{9.0601 - 9}{3.01 - 3} = \frac{0.0601}{0.01} = 6.01$$

For a third estimate let us choose a point to the left of $P = (3,9)$ on the curve $y = x^2$. For instance, let us compute the slope of the line through $(3,9)$ and $(2.99, (2.99)^2)$. This slope is $[(2.99)^2 - 9]/(2.99 - 3)$, which is $(8.9401 - 9)/(2.99 - 3)$. A little arithmetic changes this to

$$\frac{-0.0599}{-0.01} = \frac{0.0599}{0.01} = 5.99$$

As the next two diagrams suggest, the slope of the tangent line at $(3,9)$ is probably between 5.99 and 6.01.

Before we go on to find the precise value of the slope of the tangent line, we attack the remaining three problems and then solve all of them simultaneously.

ESTIMATES FOR THE VELOCITY IN PROBLEM 2.   Three seconds after launching, the rocket is $80(3)^2$ feet above the earth. But this does not tell us how fast the rocket is moving at time $t = 3$. In order to estimate its velocity, let us examine how far the rocket travels in the small interval of time from $t = 3$ to $t = 3.1$.

During the first 3.1 seconds it travels $80(3.1)^2$ feet; in the first 3 seconds it travels $80(3)^2$ feet. Thus, during the interval of time we are considering, it travels $80(3.1)^2 - 80(3)^2$ feet, and it travels this distance in $3.1 - 3 = 0.1$ second.

A reasonable estimate of the velocity of the rocket 3 seconds after launching is

$$\frac{80(3.1)^2 - 80(3)^2}{0.1}\text{ feet per second}$$

which simplifies to $\dfrac{80[(3.1)^2 - 3^2]}{0.1}$ feet per second

A little arithmetic, very similar to that used in Problem 1, gives us

$$80\frac{9.61 - 9}{0.1} = 80(6.1) = 488 \text{ feet per second}$$

Presumably we would obtain a more accurate estimate by using a smaller interval of time, say from $t = 3$ to $t = 3.01$. This leads to the estimate

$$\frac{80(3.01)^2 - 80(3)^2}{0.01}\text{ feet per second}$$

which simplifies to $80\,\dfrac{(3.01)^2 - 3^2}{0.01}$ feet per second

Exploiting the arithmetic we used in Problem 1, we find that our new estimate is

$$80(6.01) = 480.8 \text{ feet per second}$$

The similarity of these computations to those we made for Problem 1 suggests that we examine a time interval preceding $t = 3$, say from $t = 2.99$ to $t = 3$. During this interval of 0.01 second the rocket travels $80(3)^2 - 80(2.99)^2$ feet. Our third estimate of the velocity at $t = 3$ is

$$\frac{80(3)^2 - 80(2.99)^2}{0.01}\text{ feet per second}$$

which reduces to $80(5.99) = 479.2$ feet per second

The similarity between the two problems shows in the arithmetic; an estimate for the slope of the tangent in Problem 1, when multiplied by 80, provides an estimate for the velocity of the rocket in Problem 2.

The lens projects the point having the coordinate 3 onto the point having the coordinate 3^2. More concisely, we say that the image of 3 is $3^2 = 9$; the image of 4 is $4^2 = 16$; the image of 5 is $5^2 = 25$; and so on. Let us join some sample points to their images by straight lines:

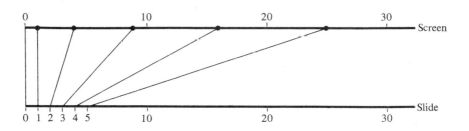

This shows that the interval [2,3] on the slide is magnified to become [4,9] on the screen—a fivefold magnification; [3,4] on the slide has as its image on the screen [9,16], a sevenfold magnification. Observe that the magnifying power of the projection increases from left to right.

To estimate the magnification at 3 on the slide we must examine the projection of a small interval in the vicinity of 3. Out of habit, let us see what the image of [3,3.1] is on the screen. Since the image of 3 is 3^2 and the image of 3.1 is $(3.1)^2$, the image of the interval [3,3.1] of length 0.1 is the interval $[3^2, (3.1)^2]$ of length $(3.1)^2 - 3^2 = 0.61$. The magnifying factor over the interval [3,3.1] is

$$\frac{0.61}{0.1} = 6.1$$

This is our first estimate.

The reader has probably guessed that we will next compute the magnification of the smaller interval [3,3.01]. That interval on the slide is projected onto the interval $[3^2, (3.01)^2]$, of length $(3.1)^2 - 3^2 = 0.0601$, on the screen. Hence the magnification of the interval [3,3.01] is

$$\frac{0.0601}{0.01} = 6.01$$

a number we met in each of the preceding problems. Our second estimate of the magnification at 3 is 6.01.

To obtain our third estimate, let us find out how the interval [2.99, 3], of length 0.01, is magnified. The image is the interval $[(2.99)^2, 3^2]$, of length $3^2 - (2.99)^2 = 0.0599$. Thus the interval [2.99, 3] enjoys a magnification of

$$\frac{0.0599}{0.01} = 5.99$$

Our three estimates for the magnification, 6.1, 6.01, and 5.99, are the same as for the slope of the tangent in Problem 1. And 80(6.1), 80(6.01), and 80(5.99) are our three estimates for the velocity of the rocket.

ESTIMATES FOR THE DENSITY IN PROBLEM 4.   To estimate the "density" of the string 3 inches from its left end, we examine the mass of the material in the interval [3,3.1]:

The material in the interval [3,3.1] has a mass of $(3.1)^2 - 3^2$ ounce. Thus the interval [3,3.1] of length 0.1 inch has a mass of

$$9.61 - 9 = 0.61 \text{ ounce}$$

Our first estimate of the "density" at 3 is the mass in this interval divided by the length of this interval, that is,

$$\frac{0.61}{0.1} = 6.1 \text{ ounces per inch}$$

If we use the smaller interval [3,3.01], a little arithmetic will provide the estimate 6.01 ounces per inch. If we use the interval [2.99, 3], our estimate will be 5.99 ounces per inch.

From a mathematical point of view, the problems of finding the slope of the tangent line, the velocity of the rocket, the magnification of the projection, and the density of the material are identical. Each leads us to examine quotients of a special type. The mathematics common to all four problems tells us that if we could answer one of them we could answer all. (In the next section we will solve these problems.)

EXERCISES

1. This exercise is intended to emphasize the limitation of graphs in finding the slope of a tangent line.
   (a) Draw the curve $y = x^2$ as carefully as you can.
   (b) Draw as carefully as you can the tangent lines at (3,9), (2,4), (0,0), (−3,9), and (4,16).
   (c) Using a ruler or the scale on your graph, estimate the slope of each line you drew in (a).
2. What estimate do you obtain for (a) the slope of the tangent in Problem 1 when you use, as the second point on the curve, the point $(3.001, (3.001)^2)$; (b) the velocity of the rocket in Problem 2 when you use the time interval from 3 to 3.001 seconds; (c) the magnification in Problem 3 when you compute the magnification of the

interval [3,3.001]; (d) the density in Problem 4 when you compute the mass of material in the interval [3,3001] and divide by the length of that interval?

[Answer: (a) 6.001; (b) 80(6.001) feet per second; (c) 6.001; (d) 6.001 ounces per inch]

3. Repeat Exercise 2, but use the interval from 2.999 to 3 instead.

4. (a) Making use of points near (2,4), obtain three estimates for the slope of the "tangent line" to the curve $y = x^2$ at (2,4).
   (b) Draw as well as you can the "tangent line" to the curve $y = x^2$ at (2,4) and estimate its slope.
   (c) How do your estimates in (a) and (b) compare?

5. (a) Using small time intervals, make three estimates for the "velocity" of the rocket of Problem 2, page 42, at 2 seconds after launching.
   (b) Compare the arithmetic in (a) with that in Exercise 4.

6. Make five estimates for the slope of the "tangent line" to $y = x^2$ at (1,1) and five for the "velocity" of the rocket 1 second after launching.

7. (a) Make two estimates of the magnification in Problem 3 at point $x = 0.5$ on the slide by examining the magnification of the intervals [0.5,0.51] and [0.49,0.5].
   (b) If the magnification at 0.5 is a well-known number, what is it?

[Answer: (a) 1.01, 0.99]

8. (a) Make two estimates for the slope of the "tangent line" to $y = x^2$ at ($\frac{1}{2}$, ($\frac{1}{2}$)^2) by computing the slope of the line through ($\frac{1}{2}$, ($\frac{1}{2}$)^2) and (0.51, (0.51)^2) and the slope of the line through ($\frac{1}{2}$, ($\frac{1}{2}$)^2) and (0.49, (0.49)^2).
   (b) If the slope of the "tangent line" in (a) is a well-known number, what is it?
   (c) If your guess in (b) is correct, what angle does the "tangent line" in (a) make with the x axis?

[Answer: (a) 1.01, 0.99]

9. (a) Estimate the "density" of the material in Problem 4 at points 1 inch, 2 inches, 3 inches, and 3½ inches from the left end. In each case, use an interval of length 0.001 inch.
   (b) What do you think is the "density" of the material at a point s inches from the left end?

10. (a) Estimate the "velocity" of the rocket of Problem 3 at 1, 2, 3, and 3½ seconds after launching.
    (b) What do you think the "velocity" of the rocket is at t seconds after launching?

11. (a) Estimate the slope of the "tangent line" in Problem 1 at (1,1^2), (2,2^2), (3,3^2), (3½, (3½)^2). (In each case use a second point, Q, near the given point.)
    (b) What do you think is the slope of the line tangent to the curve $y = x^2$ at the typical point (x,x^2)?

□ □ □

12. Compute the slopes of the lines passing through (a) (2.9, (2.9)^2) and (3.1, (3.1)^2); (b) (2.99, (2.99)^2) and (3.01, (3.01)^2); (c) $(3 - h, (3 - h)^2)$ and $(3 + h, (3 + h)^2)$ where h is not 0. (d) What do you conclude about the slope of the "tangent line" at (3,9)?

13. (a) Draw the curve $y = x^3$.
    (b) Draw a line "tangent" to it at (2,8), and estimate its slope.

(c) Using Q's near (2,8), make three estimates of the slope of the "tangent" to $y = x^3$ at (2,8).

(d) Can you find the slope of the "tangent line" in (c)?

14. (See Exercise 13.)

(a) Compute the slope of the line through (2,8) and $(2 + h, (2 + h)^3)$, where h is not 0.

(b) How does the slope in (a) behave when h shrinks toward 0?

15. (a) Compute the slope of the line through $(2 - h, (2 - h)^3)$ and $(2 + h, (2 + h)^3)$, where h is not 0.

(b) What number does the slope in (a) approach as h shrinks toward 0?

16. Points $P_1 = (x_1, y_1)$, $P_2 = (x_2, y_2)$, $P_1' = (x_1', y_1')$, $P_2' = (x_2', y_2')$ are all on one line. Using similar triangles, show that $(y_2 - y_1)/(x_2 - x_1) = (y_2' - y_1')/(x_2' - x_1')$. Why is this important?

2. The derivative.

To make a typical estimate in each of the preceding problems, we began by moving from the number 3 to a nearby number,

$$3 + \Delta x \qquad \Delta x \neq 0$$

(The symbol Δx is read "delta x" and traditionally signifies a small change in x.) The change Δx may be positive or negative. Then we computed the quotient

$$\frac{(3 + \Delta x)^2 - 3^2}{\Delta x}$$

for $\Delta x = 0.1$, $\Delta x = 0.01$, and $\Delta x = -0.01$.

If we interpret these steps in terms of the curve $y = x^2$ of Problem 1 of Sec. 1, we obtain this figure:

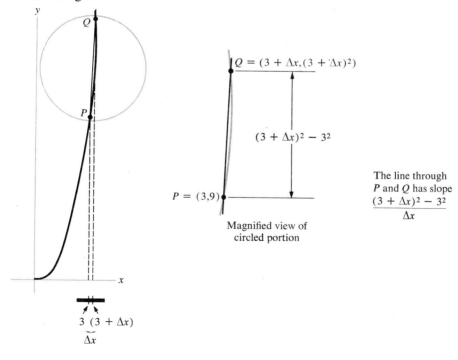

$Q = (3 + \Delta x, (3 + \Delta x)^2)$

$(3 + \Delta x)^2 - 3^2$

$P = (3,9)$

Magnified view of circled portion

The line through P and Q has slope

$$\frac{(3 + \Delta x)^2 - 3^2}{\Delta x}$$

$3 \quad (3 + \Delta x)$

Δx

Now, the quotient

$$\frac{(3 + \Delta x)^2 - 3^2}{\Delta x} \qquad \Delta x \neq 0$$

can be simplified as follows:

$$\frac{(3 + \Delta x)^2 - 3^2}{\Delta x} = \frac{9 + 6\Delta x + (\Delta x)^2 - 9}{\Delta x} = \frac{6\Delta x + (\Delta x)^2}{\Delta x} = 6 + \Delta x$$

As Δx approaches 0, that is, as our second point Q comes closer to P, the quotient, which equals $6 + \Delta x$, approaches 6. Thus the slope of the tangent at the point (3,9) is 6; the "velocity" of the rocket in Problem 2 is $(80)(6)$ feet per second; the "magnification" in Problem 3 is sixfold, and the "density" in Problem 4 is 6 ounces per inch.

We need not restrict ourselves to 3. We can consider similar problems at 2, for instance. We form the estimating quotient

$$\frac{(2 + \Delta x)^2 - 2^2}{\Delta x} \qquad \Delta x \neq 0$$

which reduces to

$$\frac{4 + 4\Delta x + (\Delta x)^2 - 4}{\Delta x} = \frac{4\Delta x + (\Delta x)^2}{\Delta x} = 4 + \Delta x$$

In this case the quotient approaches 4 as Δx approaches 0. The reader may, using Sec. 1, interpret this fact in terms of a line tangent to $y = x^2$ at (2,4), the "velocity" of the rocket 2 seconds after launching, the "magnification" at 2 on the slide, or the "density" of the material 2 inches from the left end.

It is just as easy to form the same type of quotient for general x, and not restrict ourselves to the special cases $x = 2$ or $x = 3$. We then have

$$\frac{(x + \Delta x)^2 - x^2}{\Delta x} \qquad \Delta x \neq 0$$

which we simplify to

$$\frac{x^2 + 2x(\Delta x) + (\Delta x)^2 - x^2}{\Delta x} = \frac{2x(\Delta x) + (\Delta x)^2}{\Delta x} = 2x + \Delta x$$

As Δx approaches 0, note that the quotient approaches $2x$, in agreement with the cases $x = 2$ and $x = 3$.

All four problems in Sec. 1 involved the "squaring" function (or, in the case of the rocket, 80 times that function). However, we can form the quotients and let Δx approach 0 for any function—not just the function whose value at x is x^2.

This brings us to the derivative, the basic concept of the differential calculus. Here we define the derivative informally; in Chap. 3 we will give a more precise definition, including a mathematical equivalent of the word "approaches."

DEFINITION: *The derivative of a function.* Let f be a function. If, as Δx approaches 0, the quotient

$$\frac{f(x + \Delta x) - f(x)}{\Delta x} \qquad \Delta x \neq 0$$

approaches a certain number, that number is called the *derivative* at x of the function f. (For each x considered, the derivative at x of f is a number.)

The derivative of f is thus a function. For example, if we begin with the function that assigns to each x the number x^2, the derivative (a function) assigns to each x the number $2x$, just as the function x^2 assigns a number to each x. The preceding rather involved sentence is usually replaced by the cryptic, perhaps misleading abbreviation, *the derivative of x^2 is $2x$*. This mathematical shorthand is consistent with our replacing the cumbersome *the function that assigns to each x the value x^2* by the brief *the function x^2*, and finally the laconic x^2.

Now that we have the concept of the derivative, we are in a position to define "tangent line," "velocity," "magnification," and "density," terms we have used loosely up to now. These definitions are suggested by the similarity of the computations we made in the four problems.

DEFINITION: *Tangent line to a curve.* The *line tangent* to the graph of $y = f(x)$ at the point $P = (x_0, y_0)$ is the line through P that has a slope equal to the derivative of f at x_0.

DEFINITION: *Velocity of a particle moving on a line.* The *velocity* at time t_0 of an object whose location on a line at time t is $f(t)$ is the derivative of f at time t_0.

DEFINITION: *Magnification of a linear projector.* The *magnification* at x_0 of a lens that projects the point x of one line onto the point $f(x)$ of another line is the derivative of f at x_0.

DEFINITION: *Density of material.* The *density* at x_0 of material distributed along a line in such a way that $f(x)$ ounces are in the left-hand x inches is equal to the derivative of f at x_0.

Let us see now what kinds of problems arise when we try to find the derivatives of some well-known functions.

Example 1. As we have seen, the derivative of the "squaring" function at 3 is 6; at 2 it is 4; at x it is $2x$. This offers no difficulty.

Example 2. We find the derivative of the cubing function, $f(x) = x^3$, at x. Here we form the quotient

$$\frac{(x + \Delta x)^3 - x^3}{\Delta x} \qquad \Delta x \neq 0$$

and simplify as follows. Using first the binomial theorem, we rewrite the quotient as

$$\frac{x^3 + 3x^2\,\Delta x + 3x(\Delta x)^2 + (\Delta x)^3 - x^3}{\Delta x} = \frac{3x^2\,\Delta x + 3x(\Delta x)^2 + (\Delta x)^3}{\Delta x}$$

$$= 3x^2 + 3x\,\Delta x + (\Delta x)^2$$

As Δx approaches 0, the quotient approaches $3x^2$. Thus the derivative of the cubing function is three times the squaring function. Or, briefly, *the derivative of x^3 is $3x^2$*.

Example 3.   Consider the exponential function,

$$f(x) = 10^x$$

For example, $f(0) = 10^0 = 1$, $f(1) = 10^1 = 10$, $f(2) = 100$, $f(-1) = \frac{1}{10}$. Let us examine the corresponding quotient,

$$\frac{10^{x+\Delta x} - 10^x}{\Delta x}$$

Using the law of exponents, $10^{a+b} = 10^a \cdot 10^b$, we may rewrite the quotient as

$$\frac{(10^x)(10^{\Delta x}) - 10^x}{\Delta x}$$

or

$$\frac{10^x(10^{\Delta x} - 1)}{\Delta x}$$

Now, 10^x is fixed; the challenge comes from the quotient $(10^{\Delta x} - 1)/\Delta x$. We must examine the behavior of

$$\frac{10^{\text{small number}} - 1}{\text{same small number}}$$

This is harder than Example 2 and will be solved in a roundabout manner in Chap. 4.

Example 4.   We consider the square root function, $f(x) = \sqrt{x}$, and examine the quotient

$$\frac{\sqrt{x + \Delta x} - \sqrt{x}}{\Delta x}$$

for small $\Delta x \neq 0$.

A little algebra changes this problem into a simpler one:

$$\frac{\sqrt{x + \Delta x} - \sqrt{x}}{\Delta x} = \frac{(\sqrt{x + \Delta x} - \sqrt{x})(\sqrt{x + \Delta x} + \sqrt{x})}{\Delta x(\sqrt{x + \Delta x} + \sqrt{x})} = \frac{x + \Delta x - x}{\Delta x(\sqrt{x + \Delta x} + \sqrt{x})}$$

$$= \frac{\Delta x}{\Delta x(\sqrt{x + \Delta x} + \sqrt{x})} = \frac{1}{\sqrt{x + \Delta x} + \sqrt{x}}$$

As Δx approaches 0, the last expression,

$$\frac{1}{\sqrt{x + \Delta x} + \sqrt{x}}$$

approaches $\dfrac{1}{\sqrt{x} + \sqrt{x}} = \dfrac{1}{2\sqrt{x}}$ (x positive)

Thus the derivative of $\sqrt{x}$ is $1/(2\sqrt{x})$ for all positive x. The derivative does not exist at $x = 0$.

Example 5. The common logarithm function, $f(x) = \log_{10} x$, leads us to consider the quotient

$$\frac{\log_{10}(x + \Delta x) - \log_{10}(x)}{\Delta x} \qquad \Delta x \neq 0$$

Now, $\log_{10} A - \log_{10} B = \log_{10}(A/B)$, so the quotient becomes

$$\frac{\log_{10}[(x + \Delta x)/x]}{\Delta x} = \frac{\log_{10}[1 + (\Delta x/x)]}{\Delta x}$$

whose behavior for small Δx is not immediately clear. We will scrutinize it in Chap. 4.

Example 6. Let $f(x) = x$ if $x \geqslant 0$ and $f(x) = -x$ if $x \leqslant 0$. This function is called the *absolute-value* function. We might think of $f(x)$ as the "size of x." Usually $f(x)$ is written $|x|$. The graph of f is

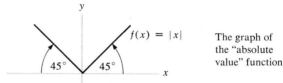

The graph of the "absolute value" function

It is not difficult to show that f has a derivative equal to 1 at points to the right of the y axis and equal to -1 at points to the left of the y axis. Does f have a derivative at 0? We must examine the quotient

$$\frac{f(x + \Delta x) - f(x)}{\Delta x} \qquad x = 0, \Delta x \neq 0$$

that is,

$$\frac{f(0 + \Delta x) - f(0)}{\Delta x} \qquad \Delta x \neq 0$$

This quotient reduces to $|\Delta x|/\Delta x$. If $\Delta x > 0$, then $|\Delta x|/\Delta x = 1$; if $\Delta x < 0$, $|\Delta x|/\Delta x = -1$.

Thus the quotients do *not* approach a single number as Δx approaches 0. This function has no derivative at 0.

Example 7. Consider the sine function, $f(x) = \sin x$. For instance,

$$f(0) = 0 \qquad f\left(\frac{\pi}{4}\right) = \frac{\sqrt{2}}{2} \qquad f\left(\frac{\pi}{2}\right) = 1 \qquad f(\pi) = 0$$

The graph of the sine function is

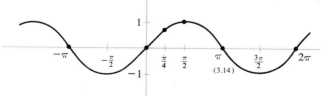

Let us examine the quotient

$$\frac{\sin(x + \Delta x) - \sin x}{\Delta x} \qquad \Delta x \neq 0$$

Recalling that $\sin(A + B) = \sin A \cos B + \cos A \sin B$, we can rewrite the quotient as

$$\frac{\sin x \cos \Delta x + \cos x \sin \Delta x - \sin x}{\Delta x}$$

and then as

$$\sin x \frac{\cos(\Delta x) - 1}{\Delta x} + \cos x \frac{\sin \Delta x}{\Delta x}$$

But it isn't clear what happens to

$$\frac{\cos(\Delta x) - 1}{\Delta x} \qquad \text{and} \qquad \frac{\sin \Delta x}{\Delta x}$$

as Δx approaches 0. In Chap. 4 we will learn how these two quotients behave for small values of Δx.

The point of these examples is that we can form the quotient

$$\frac{f(x + \Delta x) - f(x)}{\Delta x}$$

for functions other than the squaring function, and can study its behavior for small values of Δx. For most of the familiar functions, this quotient approaches a certain number, depending on x, as Δx shrinks toward 0. That certain number, which we call the *derivative of f at x*, has many interpretations, as the accompanying table shows.

If we interpret x as	and f(x) as	then $\frac{f(x + \Delta x) - f(x)}{\Delta x}$ is	and, as Δx approaches 0, the quotient approaches
The abscissa of a point in the plane	The ordinate of that point	The slope of a certain line	The slope of a tangent line
Time	The location of a particle moving on a line	An average velocity over a small time interval	The velocity at time x
A point on a linear slide	Its projection on a linear screen	An average magnification	The magnification at x
A location on a non-uniform string	The mass from 0 to x	An average density	The density at x
Just a number	Just a number	Just a quotient	The derivative at x (just a number)

This table is an important one. In the fifth row we take the detached viewpoint of the mathematician, who is curious about the behavior of certain quotients that he can form for *any* function. In this context, free from the bias of practical applications, we say that the quotient approaches the derivative. However, if we think "practically" as in the first four rows, we speak of the "slope of the tangent line," and so on. Clearly the underlying concept is the derivative—and each of the first four rows in the table is simply an application of the derivative.

The derivative is a measure of how fast one quantity changes as a result of changes in a second quantity. For instance, the rate at which the ordinate of a curve changes as we increase its abscissa is measured by the slope of the tangent line; the rate at which the height of a rocket changes as time increases is given by the velocity; the rate at which the mass of a string increases as we consider longer sections of the string is given by the density.

Most functions encountered in applications of mathematics have derivatives for all x where they are defined; such functions are called *differentiable*. We have already seen that x^3 and x^2 are differentiable functions. In Chap. 4 we will obtain the derivatives of most of the commonly used functions. In Chap. 6 we will discuss the relation between the derivative and the definite integral.

EXERCISES

1. An engineer's car has a broken speedometer but a working clock and odometer.
   (a) Find his speed at time t if he travels t^3 miles in t hours.
   (b) What is his speed if he travels $f(t)$ miles in t hours?
2. An irregular diamond is placed on a tray and lowered slowly into water. It is observed that the lowest x inches of the diamond displace x^3 cubic inches of water. What is the area of the cross section of the diamond made by the plane of the water surface when the diamond is submerged to a depth of (a) one inch; (b) 2 inches? (c) The diamond cutter wants to cut the diamond in such a way that the slice has an area of three-quarters of an inch. Where should he cut it?
3. An engineer's car has a broken clock but a working speedometer and odometer. He notices that after x miles his speed is $f(x)$ miles per hour, where f is given by a complicated formula. To find how long his journey takes, should he use the definite integral or the derivative? Explain in detail what he should do.
4. (a) Draw the curve $f(x) = 1/x$ carefully.
   (b) As well as you can, draw the tangent line at $(2,\frac{1}{2})$.
   (c) Choosing two convenient points on the line that you drew in (b), estimate its slope.
   (d) Compute the slope of the line passing through $(2,\frac{1}{2})$ and $(2.1, 1/2.1)$.
   (e) Express as simply as possible the slope of the line passing through $(2,\frac{1}{2})$ and $(2 + \Delta x, 1/(2 + \Delta x))$, with $\Delta x \neq 0$.
   (f) What is the derivative of the function $1/x$ at $x = 2$? What is the slope of the tangent line at $(2,\frac{1}{2})$?

   [Answer: (d) -0.238; (f) -0.250]

5. (See Exercise 4.)
   (a) Find the derivative of the function $1/x$ at $x = 3$.
   (b) Find the derivative of the same function at any x other than 0.
6. Use a $\log_{10} x$ (common logarithm) table to carry out the following calculations.
   (a) Draw the graph of $f(x) = \log_{10} x$ from $x = 1$ to $x = 10$.

    (*b*) Draw as well as you can the tangent at the point $(2, \log_{10} 2)$.

    (*c*) Estimate the slope of the line you drew in (*b*).

    (*d*) Compute the slope of the line through $(2, \log_{10} 2)$, and $(2.1, \log_{10} 2.1)$.

    (*e*) Compute the slope of the line through $(2, \log_{10} 2)$ and $(2.01, \log_{10} 2.01)$.

                         [Answer: (*d*) 0.21; (*e*) 0.22]

  7. (See Exercise 6.)

    (*a*) Draw as well as you can the lines tangent to $y = \log_{10} x$ at $(1,0)$ and at $(4, \log_{10} 4)$.

    (*b*) What is the slope of each line you drew in (*a*)?

    (*c*) Compute the slope of the line through $(1,0)$ and $(1.1, \log_{10} 1.1)$.

    (*d*) Compute the slope of the line through $(4, \log_{10} 4)$ and $(4.1, \log_{10} 4.1)$.

    (*e*) Review the data in (*b*), (*c*), and (*d*), and suggest a general formula for the derivative of the function, $f(x) = \log_{10} x$, at any x.

  8. (*a*) Draw the curve $y = x^3$.

    (*b*) Draw the tangent lines at $(0,0)$, $(-2,-8)$, $(1,1)$, $(2,8)$.

    (*c*) Estimate the slopes of the lines you drew in (*b*).

    (*d*) We showed that the derivative of x^3 is $3x^2$. Compute $3x^2$ for $x = 0, -2, 1, 2$ and compare with the results in (*c*).

  9. (*a*) Draw the curve $y = x^4$.

    (*b*) Find the derivative of x^4 at any x.

    (*c*) Using (*b*), draw the tangent line to the graph in (*a*) at $(1,1)$, $(-1,1)$, and $(2,16)$.

                         [Answer: (*b*) $4x^3$]

10. To carry out the necessary computations in this exercise, use a table of the natural trigonometric functions (the angle is measured in radians).

    (*a*) Compute $(\sin \Delta x)/\Delta x$ for $\Delta x = 0.5, 0.1$, and -0.1.

    (*b*) On the basis of (*a*), what do you think happens to $(\sin \Delta x)/\Delta x$ as Δx approaches 0?

    (*c*) Compute $(1 - \cos \Delta x)/\Delta x$ for $\Delta x = 0.5, 0.1, -0.1$.

    (*d*) On the basis of (*c*), what do you think happens to $(1 - \cos \Delta x)/\Delta x$ as Δx approaches 0?

    (*e*) On the basis of (*b*) and (*d*), find the derivative of $f(x) = \sin x$ at arbitrary x.

        [Answer: (*a*) 0.958, 0.998, 0.998; (*c*) 0.245, 0.005, -0.005; (*e*) $\cos x$]

11. The numerical data in Exercise 10 suggest that the derivative of the sine function is the cosine function. In particular, it would imply that the derivative at 0 is $\cos 0 = 1$, that at $\pi/3$ it is $\cos(\pi/3) = 0.5$, and that at $\pi/2$ it is $\cos(\pi/2) = 0$. Draw the sine curve and tangent lines at the three points having abscissas 0, $\pi/3$, and $\pi/2$. Do their slopes agree within experimental limits with the alleged derivatives?

12. Here is the graph of a certain function f.

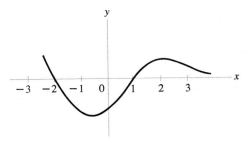

    (*a*) For which x is $f(x)$ positive? Negative? Zero?

    (*b*) For which x is the derivative of f positive? Negative? Zero?

13. Consider the function $f(x) = 5x + 3$.
    (a) Find the slope of the line through $(x, f(x))$ and $(x + \Delta x, f(x + \Delta x))$.
    (b) In view of (a), what is the derivative of f at any x?
    (c) Graph the function $f(x) = 5x + 3$. What is the tangent line to the graph at any point?
14. For this exercise, use a table for the function $f(x) = 10^x$ (or a common logarithm table read backwards).
    (a) Graph the function.
    (b) Draw tangent lines at $(0,1)$, $(-1, \frac{1}{10})$, $(1, 10)$.
    (c) What are the slopes of the lines you drew in (b)?
    (d) Compute the slopes of the lines through $(0,1)$, and $(0.1, 10^{0.1})$; $(-1, \frac{1}{10})$ and $(-0.9, 10^{-0.9})$; $(1, 10)$ and $(1.1, 10^{1.1})$.
    (e) Are the answers in (d) close to your answers in (c)?
15. (a) Find the derivative of the function $y = 128x - 16x^2$.
    (b) When is the derivative equal to 0?
    (c) A ball has height $128t - 16t^2$ feet t seconds after being thrown straight up. This formula is valid until the ball reaches the ground. At what time will its velocity be 0 feet per second?
    (d) What points on the curve $y = 128x - 16x^2$ have a horizontal tangent?
                                                          [Answer: (a) $128 - 32x$]

16. Using a table of common logarithms, $\log_{10} x$, or a table of 10^x, make estimates of the type in Exercise 14(d) for the derivative of 10^x at $x = 0$; at $x = 1$; at $x = 2$.
17. (a) Using the definition of the derivative as the number certain quotients approach, find the derivative of $2x^3 - 9x^2 + 12x + 1$ at any x.
    (b) Where would the graph of $y = 2x^3 - 9x^2 + 12x + 1$ have horizontal tangents?
                           [Answer: (a) $6x^2 - 18x + 12$; (b) when $x = 1$ or 2]
18. (a) Using the definition of derivative, find the derivative of $3x^2 - 6x + 8$ at any x.
    (b) Where does the graph of $y = 3x^2 - 6x + 8$ have horizontal tangents?
19. Show that if you knew the derivative of 10^x at 0, you would know it at any x.
20. Show with the aid of Exercise 10 that the derivative of the cosine function is the negative of the sine function. Or more tersely, the derivative at x of the function $\cos x$ is $-\sin x$.
21. (a) Show that the derivative of πr^2 is $2\pi r$.
    (b) Is it a coincidence that the rate of change of the area of a disk with respect to its radius is its circumference? Explain.
22. (a) Show that the derivative of $(\frac{4}{3}) \pi r^3$ is $4\pi r^2$.
    (b) Is it a coincidence that the derivative of the volume of the sphere with respect to its radius is its surface area? Explain.
23. Let f be defined for all positive x. Assume that for any positive x and y,

$$f(x/y) = f(x) - f(y)$$

Also, assume that f has a derivative equal to 1 at $x = 1$. Prove (a) that $f(1) = 0$; (b) that $f(1/x) = -f(x)$; (c) that $f(xy) = f(x) + f(y)$; (d) that f has a derivative for any positive x and it is equal to $1/x$. (e) What familiar function f satisfies the equation $f(x/y) = f(x) - f(y)$?

3. Standard notations related to the derivative; the differential. There are other notations for the important quotient,

$$\frac{f(x + \Delta x) - f(x)}{\Delta x} \qquad \Delta x \neq 0$$

and many notations for the derivative.

For example, $f(x + \Delta x) - f(x)$, the "change in the value of the function," is frequently denoted Δf. If we use the notation $y = f(x)$, then we sometimes write Δy instead of Δf. Similarly, if we let s denote the height of the rocket (of Sec. 1) at time t, where $s = 80t^2$, then we denote the change in s by Δs. Thus

$$\Delta s = 80(t + \Delta t)^2 - 80t^2$$

In the graph of a typical function, x, Δx, y, and Δy appear as in this figure:

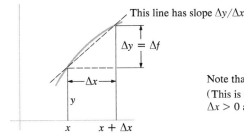

This line has slope $\Delta y/\Delta x$

$\Delta y = \Delta f$

$-\Delta x-$

y

$x \qquad x + \Delta x$

Note that $f(x + \Delta x) = f(x) + \Delta f$
(This is the diagram for
$\Delta x > 0$ and $\Delta y > 0$.)

Sometimes, instead of Δx one uses the symbol h for the (horizontal) change. Then the quotient

$$\frac{f(x + \Delta x) - f(x)}{\Delta x}$$

takes the form

$$\frac{f(x + h) - f(x)}{h}$$

Another approach is to denote the point (x, y) as (x_1, y_1), and to call the nearby point (x_2, y_2). Here

$$y_1 = f(x_1) \qquad y_2 = f(x_2) \qquad x_1 \neq x_2$$

Then the quotient

$$\frac{f(x + \Delta x) - f(x)}{\Delta x}$$

takes the form

$$\frac{y_2 - y_1}{x_2 - x_1}$$

Example 1. We form the quotient $(y_2 - y_1)/(x_2 - x_1)$ for the function x^2 and examine its behavior as x_2 approaches x_1. We have

$$y_1 = x_1^2 \qquad \text{and} \qquad y_2 = x_2^2$$

where x_2 is different from x_1. Thus the quotient $(y_2 - y_1)/(x_2 - x_1)$ is

$$\frac{x_2^2 - x_1^2}{x_2 - x_1}$$

Since $x_2{}^2 - x_1{}^2 = (x_2 - x_1)(x_2 + x_1)$, the quotient is equal to $x_2 + x_1$. As x_2 approaches x_1, the number $x_2 + x_1$ approaches $x_1 + x_1 = 2x_1$. Thus the derivative of x^2 at x_1 is $2x_1$, in agreement with our computation in Sec. 2. Notice that the algebra is somewhat simpler than that involved in the study of

$$\frac{(x + \Delta x)^2 - x^2}{\Delta x}$$

though both quotients carry the same message.

There are many *notations for the derivative*. If f is a function and we write $y = f(x)$, then the derivative is denoted $Dy, dy/dx, df/dx, y'$, or f' and is called *the derivative of y (or f) with respect to x*. Sometimes we pronounce the symbol dy/dx as "d-y-d-x" and y' as "y prime," and so on. Frequently the symbol f in df/dx is replaced by the formula for $f(x)$.

If $y = f(t)$, where t represents time, then the derivative of y with respect to t is frequently denoted $\dot{y}$ (read as "y dot").

Example 2. Let $y = f(x) = x^2$. We saw in Sec. 3 that this function has the derivative $2x$. We may therefore write

$$\frac{d(x^2)}{dx} = 2x \quad \text{or} \quad D(x^2) = 2x \quad \text{or} \quad \frac{dy}{dx} = 2x \quad \text{and so on}$$

Example 3. If $y = f(t) = \sqrt{t}$, then (by Sec. 3) the derivative of y with respect to t is $1/(2\sqrt{t})$. We may write

$$\frac{df}{dt} = \frac{1}{2\sqrt{t}} \quad \text{or} \quad \frac{d(\sqrt{t})}{dt} = \frac{1}{2\sqrt{t}} \quad \text{or} \quad \dot{\sqrt{t}} = \frac{1}{2\sqrt{t}} \quad \text{and so on}$$

Observe that the notation

$$\frac{d(x^2)}{dx} = 2x \quad \text{or} \quad \frac{d(\sqrt{t})}{dt} = \frac{1}{2\sqrt{t}}$$

has the advantage that it contains a description of the function. But typographical, pedagogical, or historical considerations sometimes argue in favor of the other notations.

The symbol $\dfrac{dy}{dx}$, so similar to $\dfrac{\Delta y}{\Delta x}$, might tempt us to the *erroneous* belief that we have defined the derivative as the quotient of two numbers. Such a distortion of the facts must be avoided. At this point we should no more interpret the symbol $\dfrac{dy}{dx}$ as a quotient than the symbol 8 as two zeros. However, we can give meaning to the individual symbols dy and dx in such a way that their quotient, dy divided by dx, will equal the derivative.

To accomplish this, consider the tangent line at $P = (x, f(x))$. Let dx denote the horizontal change, and let dy denote the rise (or fall) from P as we move from P *along the tangent line* to a second point, Q, on that line.

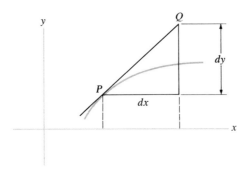

The slope of the tangent line, which equals the derivative at x, is also equal to the quotient, dy divided by dx. In other words, the ordinary quotient dy/dx coincides with the derivative of f at x. This geometrically worded definition of dy is equivalent to the following definition, which requires no diagram.

DEFINITION: *Differential*. If f is a function such that $y = f(x)$, and if dx and x are numbers, then the *differential* of y is the product $D(y)\,dx$. It is denoted dy.

Thus dy is the change as we move along a tangent line, while Δy is the change as we move along the graph of the function in question, as this diagram shows:

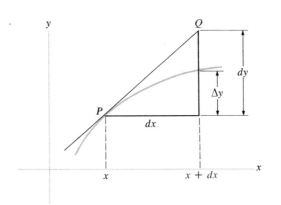

$$dy = D(y)\,dx;$$
$$\Delta y = f(x + dx) - f(x)$$

Example 4. The diagram suggests that when dx is small, dy might be a good approximation of Δy. For instance, consider the function $y = x^3$, whose derivative is $3x^2$ and whose differential is therefore $3x^2\,dx$. If $x = 5$ and $dx = 0.1$, we have

$$dy = 3(5)^2(0.1) = 7.5 \qquad \text{and} \qquad \Delta y = (5.1)^3 - 5^3 = 7.651$$

This tells us that if a particle travels x^3 feet in x seconds, it travels 7.651 feet during the time interval [5,5.1]. This is well approximated by multiplying its speed when $x = 5$ by the duration of the time interval; that is, $(75)(0.1)$.

It is illuminating to compare dy and Δy for a fixed x but shrinking dx. We do this for the function x^3 and compute dy and Δy for $x = 5$ and the dx's indicated in the following table.

dx	dy	Δy
3	225	387
2	150	218
1	75	91
0.1	7.5	7.651
0.01	0.75	0.751501
0	0	0
-1	-75	-61

$$dy = 75\,dx$$
$$\Delta y = (5 + dx)^3 - 5^3$$

When dx is small, so are dy and Δy. But the diagram preceding Example 4 suggests, as does the table, that dy is a good approximation to Δy in the sense that the quotient, $\Delta y/dy$, approaches 1 as dx approaches 0. We will show that this is so, assuming that the derivative is not 0.

Using the definition of dy, namely $D(y)\,dx$, we can then write

$$\frac{\Delta y}{dy} = \frac{\Delta y}{D(y)\,dx}$$

Now, dx is just another name for Δx, a change in x. Thus

$$\frac{\Delta y}{dy} = \frac{\Delta y}{D(y)\,dx} = \frac{\Delta y}{D(y)\,\Delta x}$$

The last expression can be written as

$$\frac{1}{D(y)}\frac{\Delta y}{\Delta x}$$

But as Δx approaches 0, $\Delta y/\Delta x$ approaches $D(y)$. Thus

$$\frac{1}{D(y)}\frac{\Delta y}{\Delta x}$$

approaches

$$\frac{1}{D(y)}\,D(y) = 1$$

as Δx approaches 0. This shows why $\Delta y/dy$ approaches 1.

Example 5. We exploit the differential to estimate the volume of a cube of side 5.1 inches. Our first estimate would be $5^3 = 125$ inches. To obtain the precise volume we would add $(5.1)^3 - 5^3$ to 125. But to obtain this difference, which is Δy, we would have to cube 5.1. Instead, we compute dy for the function x^3 at $x = 5$ and $dx = 0.1$.

This has been done in the above table; $dy = 7.5$ Our estimate would be $125 + 7.5 = 132.5$ cubic inches. The correct answer is $125 + 7.651 = 132.651$ cubic inches, as the table shows. Clearly the differential dy provides a rapid estimate that is better than the crude one obtained by merely computing the volume of a cube of side 5 inches.

If we had denoted x^3 in Example 5 by V (V for volume), then instead of dy we would use the symbol dV for the differential.

EXERCISES

1. (a) Check that the entries in each of the seven rows of the table on page 61 for dy and Δy are correct.
   (b) Interpret the fourth row in the case in which the function x^3 records the mass of the left-hand x inches of a string.
2. Make a table like the one in the text for the same function x^3 and the same dx's, but at $x = 1$ instead of at $x = 5$.
3. (a) Use the differential to estimate the volume of a cube whose side is 4.9 inches.
   (b) What is the exact volume of the cube in (a)?
   (c) Compute ΔV, the difference between the volumes of the cubes of side 5 inches and 4.9 inches. Is $\Delta V / dV$ close to 1?
                    [Answer: (a) 117.5 cubic inches; (b) 117.649 cubic inches;
                              (c) -7.351 cubic inches; yes, $\Delta V / dV = 0.980$]
4. Assume that $d(1/x)/dx = -1/x^2$. (a) Graph the curve $y = 1/x$ and the tangent at $(1,1)$.
   (b) Fill in the following table, where $x = 1$. That is, fill in $dy = -dx$ and $\Delta y = (1/(1 + dx)) - 1/1$:

dx	dy	Δy
1	-1	$-\frac{1}{2}$
0.5		
0.1		

   (c) On the graph in (a) show where the dy's and Δy's of the table in (b) appear.
5. Using differentials for the function $1/x$, show that (a) $1/0.98$ is approximately 1.02; (b) $1/1.04$ is approximately 0.96.
6. Complete the following table, where $f(x) = x^2$ and $x = 2$.

dx	dy	Δy	$\Delta y / dy$
1	4		
-1		-3	
0.1			
-0.1	-0.4		
0	0		Meaningless

7. Recall that $d(\sqrt{x})/dx = 1/(2\sqrt{x})$. Use this fact to estimate (a) $\sqrt{9.1}$; (b) $\sqrt{8.9}$; (c) $\sqrt{9.2}$; (d) $\sqrt{8.8}$; (e) $\sqrt{17}$; (f) $\sqrt{15}$.

[Answer: (a) $3\frac{1}{60}$; (b) $2\frac{59}{60}$; (c) $3\frac{1}{30}$; (d) $2\frac{29}{30}$; (e) $4\frac{1}{8}$; (f) $3\frac{7}{8}$.

For (a), (b), (c), and (d) we used $x = 9$; in (e) and (f), $x = 16$.]

8. Using differentials, show that a good estimate (a) of $\sqrt{25 + dx}$ is $5 + dx/10$; (b) of $\sqrt{a^2 + dx}$ is $a + dx/2a$, with $a > 0$. (c) Use the formula in (b) to estimate $\sqrt{65.6}$.

9. (a) For the function x^3, show that the slope

$$\frac{y_2 - y_1}{x_2 - x_1} \qquad x_2 \neq x_1$$

for (x_1, y_1), (x_2, y_2) on the graph reduces to $x_2^2 + x_2 x_1 + x_1^2$.

(b) What happens to $x_2^2 + x_2 x_1 + x_1^2$ as x_2 approaches x_1?

(c) What does (b) say about $D(x^3)$?

10. (a) For the function $1/x$ show that the quotient

$$\frac{y_2 - y_1}{x_2 - x_1} \qquad x_1 \neq x_2 \qquad x_1 \neq 0 \qquad x_2 \neq 0$$

when $y_2 = 1/x_2$ and $y_1 = 1/x_1$, reduces to $-1/x_1 x_2$.

(b) What happens to the quotient in (a) as x_2 approaches x_1?

(c) According to (b) what is

$$\frac{d(1/x)}{dx}$$

[Answer: (c) $-1/x^2$]

11. Complete this table:

Function $y = f(x)$	$D(y)$ (its derivative)	dy (its differential)	$\Delta y = f(x + dx) - f(x)$ (its change)
x^2	$2x$	$2x\,dx$	$2x\,dx + (dx)^2$
x^3	$3x^2$		$3x^2\,dx + 3x\,(dx)^2 + (dx)^3$
$1/x$			
$\sqrt{x}$			

□ □ □

12. Interpret dy and Δy and describe them in good English or a clear diagram (a) if $f(x)$ is the mass in the left-hand x inches of a nonhomogeneous string; (b) if $f(x)$ is the location on a line at time x of some moving particle; (c) if $f(x)$ is the shadow on the linear screen of x on the linear slide; (d) if $f(x)$ is the total profit of some business up to time x.

13. A certain function f has the property that $dy = \Delta y$ for a specific x and all dx. What must the graph of f be? What is the formula for $f(x)$? Will $dy = \Delta y$ for all x and all dx?

14. If $y = f(x)$ and if $f'(x) = 0$ at a certain x, then $dy = 0$ for that x and any dx. The quotient $\Delta y / dy$ is then meaningless, for the denominator is 0. Prove the following assertion, which says in another way that dy is a good approximation to Δy: The difference between Δy and dy is small, even when compared to dx. That is, show that as dx approaches 0,

$$\frac{\Delta y - dy}{dx} \qquad dx \neq 0$$

approaches 0. Observe that this assertion is meaningful even when $f'(x) = 0$.

4. A generalization of the derivative.

In Chap. 1 we referred to the "density" of mass along a string, in the plane, or in a solid. In this chapter we have defined density in a string as the derivative of mass with respect to distance along the string (see Sec. 2). We now sketch briefly the way in which density of matter distributed in the plane may be defined. The case of a solid is almost identical and will be left to the reader.

Imagine a flat object (lamina) of total mass M occupying a plane region R. If the material is homogeneous, its density is simply $M/(\text{area of } R)$ at any point in R. If the material varies from point to point, however, we face the same type of difficulty we met at the beginning of this chapter, and we resolve it in a similar way.

Let P be a point in R. Consider a small set S in R and containing P.

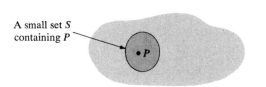

A small set S containing P

A plane region furnished with a distribution of matter

Call the area of the small set ΔA and the mass in it ΔM. If the quotient $\Delta M / \Delta A$ approaches a certain number as the diameter of S shrinks toward 0, we call that number the *density* at P.

Fluid pressure can be defined similarly. To define the pressure at a point P on the surface of a submerged dam, consider a small set S on the dam around P. Let its area be ΔA and the force of the fluid against it ΔF. We shall define as the *pressure* at P the number approached by $\Delta F / \Delta A$ as the diameter of S shrinks toward 0.

It is a theorem of advanced mathematics that if the distribution of matter or of fluid satisfies certain conditions, then the definite integral of density is total mass and the definite integral of pressure is force.

EXERCISES

1. Using the definition of density given in this section, give an intuitive argument that shows why the definite integral of density over a plane set R yields the total mass in the set.

2. (a) Define density for a distribution of matter in space.
   (b) Using the definition given in (a), indicate why the definite integral of density over a solid R should yield the total mass in R.

3. (a) Review the definition of the average of a function defined on a plane set (page 34).
   (b) Show that the total mass in a plane set equals the product of the area of the set and the average density.

4. On page 51 we defined the density of mass at a point x in the string as the number approached by $[f(x + \Delta x) - f(x)]/\Delta x$ as Δx shrinks toward 0. Show that this definition can be rephrased as follows: Let a small interval with x as one of its end points have length ΔL and contain mass ΔM. Then the density at $P = x$ is the number that $\Delta M/\Delta L$ approaches as ΔL shrinks toward 0.

$$\square \quad \square \quad \square$$

5. The definition in Exercise 4 is different in spirit from the definitions we have given for density in a plane or solid set; in Exercise 4 we considered only intervals of which P is an end point. Show that if the quotients of the special type formed in Exercise 4 approach a certain number, then the quotients $\Delta M/\Delta L$ formed for intervals of which P is the midpoint approach the same number (as ΔL shrinks toward 0).

6. Extend Exercise 5 to intervals containing $P = x$ of which P need not be the midpoint.

5. Summary. We have defined the derivative of a function; the derivative measures the rate of change of the function, and has many applications and interpretations, including slope, velocity, density, and magnification. Most of the familiar functions are differentiable wherever they are defined, as we shall see in Chap. 4. The differential, a function of x and dx, is useful in estimating small changes. In later chapters we will study both concepts in greater detail and present many more of their applications.

3

Limits and continuous functions

IN our discussions of the definite integral and of the derivative, we have used such statements as "The sums $\sum_{i=1}^{n} f(X_i)(x_i - x_{i-1})$ approach a certain number as the mesh shrinks toward 0" and "As Δx approaches 0, the quotient $[f(x + \Delta x) - f(x)]/\Delta x$ approaches a certain number." Underlying both of these assertions is the fundamental notion of *limit*, which we now examine through a variety of examples, and in a more general setting than the context of the definite integral and the derivative. Finally, we give precise definitions of the various types of limits.

1. The limit of a sequence. A sequence is a function f that assigns a number $f(n)$ to each positive integer n. Usually $f(n)$ is written f_n, or a_n, or b_n, or in some similar form, and the sequence is written $a_1, a_2, \ldots, a_n, \ldots$. Even more briefly, we may say *the sequence a_n*. We shall examine the behavior of a_n for several sequences.

Example 1 (The sum of many small numbers remaining bounded). Suppose the government spends an extra billion dollars without raising an extra billion in taxes. What is the total increase in spending in the U.S.A. due to this action? We assume each business or individual spends 80 percent of any income or revenue, and invests or saves the remaining 20 percent.

The initial billion dollars leads directly to the spending of another 0.8 billion. In turn, 80 percent of this 0.8 billion is spent; that is, another $(0.8)^2$ billion is spent. Thus, at the end of three transactions, $1 + 0.8 + (0.8)^2$ billion dollars are spent.

The total amount in billions of dollars spent at the end of n transactions is

$$a_n = 1 + 0.8 + (0.8)^2 + \cdots + (0.8)^{n-1}$$

To determine the long-range impact of the government's expenditure, we must see what happens to a_n as n increases. Using the formula for the sum of a geometric progression (developed in Exercise 2), we obtain

$$a_n = \frac{1 - (0.8)^n}{1 - 0.8} = \frac{1 - (0.8)^n}{0.2} = 5\,[1 - (0.8)^n]$$

As n increases without bound, $(0.8)^n$ approaches 0; hence the sequence $a_1, a_2, \ldots,$ $a_n, \ldots$ approaches 5. The total spending is five times as large as the initial amount. (The "multiplier" is said to be 5.)

Example 2 (The sum of many small numbers becoming large). In Example 1, as we added more and more terms of the sequence, the sums did not grow arbitrarily large; in fact they approached 5. We now show that even though the terms of a sequence become very small, their sum can become arbitrarily large.

Let

$$a_n = \frac{1}{\sqrt{1}} + \frac{1}{\sqrt{2}} + \frac{1}{\sqrt{3}} + \cdots + \frac{1}{\sqrt{n}}$$

As n increases, a_n increases. Just as in Example 1, there are two influences operating: (1) the number of terms in a_n increases, and there is thus a chance that a_n increases without bound, eventually passing 100, then 1000, and so on; (2) the additional terms shrink as n increases, and there is thus a chance that a_n does not grow arbitrarily large, but instead approaches some number. In Example 1 the second influence was the more powerful of the two.

In the present example, the first influence dominates; that is, a_n increases without bound as n increases. To see why, note that if $n > 1$, then

$$a_n = \frac{1}{\sqrt{1}} + \frac{1}{\sqrt{2}} + \cdots + \frac{1}{\sqrt{n}} > \frac{1}{\sqrt{n}} + \frac{1}{\sqrt{n}} + \cdots + \frac{1}{\sqrt{n}} = n\left(\frac{1}{\sqrt{n}}\right) = \sqrt{n}$$

Since $\sqrt{n}$ grows arbitrarily large as n increases, so must a_n.

Example 3 (The product of many positive numbers less than 1 not being near 0). The following sequence arises in probability theory (see Exercise 18, page 167).

Let

$$a_n = \left(1 - \frac{1}{2^2}\right)\left(1 - \frac{1}{4^2}\right)\left(1 - \frac{1}{6^2}\right) \cdots \left(1 - \frac{1}{(2n)^2}\right)$$

For instance,

$$a_1 = 1 - \frac{1}{2^2} = 0.750$$

$$a_2 = \left(1 - \frac{1}{2^2}\right)\left(1 - \frac{1}{4^2}\right) = \text{⁴⁵}\!/\!_{64} = 0.703$$

$$a_3 = \left(1 - \frac{1}{2^2}\right)\left(1 - \frac{1}{4^2}\right)\left(1 - \frac{1}{6^2}\right) = \text{¹⁷⁵}\!/\!_{256} = 0.684$$

Clearly $a_1 > a_2 > a_3 > \cdots > a_n > \cdots$. The question now is whether a_n approaches 0 or a number larger than 0. Again there are two influences: Since the factors are all less than 1, there is a chance that the products may approach 0; but as the factors come closer to 1, there is also a chance that a_n will behave like a product of 1's, and not drop far below 1. It turns out that a_n approaches $2/\pi = 0.637$, as is shown in Exercise 10, pages 165–166, and Exercise 16, page 166, with the aid of the definite integral.

Example 4 (A sequence given recursively). Sometimes a sequence is described by a rule that expresses each member of the sequence in terms of earlier members of the sequence. Such a sequence is given *recursively*. We examine a sequence used by the Babylonians 4,000 years ago and now used by electronic computers for computing square roots. If s is the square root of 3, then $3/s = s$. If s is less than $\sqrt{3}$, then $3/s$ is larger than $\sqrt{3}$. This suggests that if s is an estimate of $\sqrt{3}$, then a better estimate of $\sqrt{3}$ might be provided by the average of s and $3/s$, that is, by $(s + 3/s)/2$. Let us explore this idea when we make the initial guess, 2, for $\sqrt{3}$, and obtain a sequence $a_1 = 2, a_2, a_3, \ldots$, of successive estimates of $\sqrt{3}$ Then

$$a_2 = \frac{a_1 + 3/a_1}{2}, a_3 = \frac{a_2 + 3/a_2}{2}, \ldots, a_n = \frac{a_{n-1} + 3/a_{n-1}}{2}, \ldots$$

Thus

$$a_2 = \frac{2 + 3/2}{2} = \text{⁷}\!/\!_4 = 1.750$$

$$a_3 = \frac{\text{⁷}\!/\!_4 + 3/(\text{⁷}\!/\!_4)}{2} = \text{⁹⁷}\!/\!_{56} = 1.732$$

Now, 1.732 is a well-known approximation of $\sqrt{3}$. In Chap. 12 we will prove that the sequence $a_1, a_2, \ldots$ approaches $\sqrt{3}$, but here we will show that *if $a_1, a_2, \ldots$ approaches some number, A, then A must be $\sqrt{3}$.*

If a_n approaches A as n increases, so does a_{n-1}. Now,

$$a_n = \frac{a_{n-1} + 3/a_{n-1}}{2}$$

As n increases, the left side, a_n, approaches A, and the right side approaches

$$\frac{A + 3/A}{2}$$

Thus we have

$$A = \frac{A + 3/A}{2}$$

an equation for A. Rewriting it as $2A = A + 3/A$, then as $A = 3/A$, and finally as $A^2 = 3$, we see that $A = \sqrt{3}$ (since A is positive).

Example 5. Let a_n be the approximation of $\displaystyle\int_0^1 x^2\,dx$ obtained by partitioning $[0,1]$ into n sections of equal length and using as X_i the right end point of the ith interval. Since there are n sections, each of length $1/n$, we have $x_i = i/n = X_i$ and $x_i - x_{i-1} = 1/n$.

Since $f(x) = x^2$, the sum

$$\sum_{i=1}^{n} f(X_i)\,(x_i - x_{i-1})$$

takes the form

$$\left(\frac{1}{n}\right)^2\left(\frac{1}{n}\right) + \left(\frac{2}{n}\right)^2\left(\frac{1}{n}\right) + \cdots + \left(\frac{i}{n}\right)^2\left(\frac{1}{n}\right) + \cdots + \left(\frac{n}{n}\right)^2\left(\frac{1}{n}\right)$$

and thus

$$a_n = \frac{1^2 + 2^2 + \cdots + n^2}{n^3}$$

For example,

$$a_1 = \frac{1^2}{1^3} = 1 = 1.000$$

$$a_2 = \frac{1^2 + 2^2}{2^3} = \tfrac{5}{8} = 0.625$$

$$a_3 = \frac{1^2 + 2^2 + 3^2}{3^3} = \tfrac{14}{27} = 0.519$$

Since the numerator of a_n grows without bound, there is reason to suspect that a_n might also grow without bound; on the other hand, the denominator also grows without bound, and thus there is an influence or force pushing a_n toward 0. As a matter of fact, we know that a_n approaches $\tfrac{1}{3}$ as n increases, for $\displaystyle\int_0^b x^2\,dx = b^3/3$, since $\displaystyle\int_0^b x^2\,dx$ can be thought of as the volume of a tent, three duplicates of which fill the cube of side b, as we learned in Chap. 1.

Example 6. A bank pays 100 percent interest per year. Thus 1 dollar left in the bank for 1 year becomes $1 + 1 = 2$ dollars at the end of the year. If the bank compounds interest twice a year, then at the end of half a year the dollar has become $(1 + \tfrac{1}{2})(1 + \tfrac{1}{2})$ dollars, that is, $(1 + \tfrac{1}{2})^2 = 2.25$ dollars. A competing bank offers to compound the interest quarterly; at the end of a year, a dollar becomes $(1 + \tfrac{1}{4})^4 = 2.441$ dollars. Another bank compounds monthly, and thus a dollar becomes $(1 + \tfrac{1}{12})^{12}$ dollars at the end of a year. Some banks even compound daily; since a bank year has 360 days, a dollar becomes $(1 + \tfrac{1}{360})^{360}$ dollars at the end of the year. What happens to a dollar in one year if interest is compounded every hour? Every minute? Every second?

We wish, in short, to examine the sequence

$$a_n = \left(1 + \frac{1}{n}\right)^n$$

for large n. The above considerations suggest that $a_1 < a_2 < a_3 < \cdots < a_n < \cdots$.

Two influences operate on a_n. Since $1 + 1/n$ approaches 1 as n increases, a_n is like a product of 1's, and so might not grow arbitrarily large. On the other hand, $(1 + 1/n)$ is multiplied many times to obtain a_n; for this reason, a_n might grow arbitrarily large. In Exercise 28, and in Chap. 6, Sec. 4, it is shown that a_n approaches a specific number, whose decimal expansion begins as 2.718 . . . . This number, of great importance in the calculus, will be denoted e.

With these examples as background we are ready to define the limit of a sequence. A more formal definition is given later in the chapter on page 87.

DEFINITION: *Limit of a convergent sequence.* Let a_n be the nth term of a sequence. If, as n grows arbitrarily large, a_n approaches some specific number A, then A is the *limit* of the sequence. The sequence is *convergent*, and *converges* to A. In this case we write

$$\lim_{n \to \infty} a_n = A$$

(This is read as "the limit of a sub n as n approaches infinity is A" or "the limit of a sub n as n gets arbitrarily large is A.")

The preceding examples are summarized in the following expressions.

Example 1 $\lim_{n \to \infty} [1 + 0.8 + \cdots + (0.8)^{n-1}] = 5$

Example 2 $\lim_{n \to \infty} \left(\frac{1}{\sqrt{1}} + \frac{1}{\sqrt{2}} + \cdots + \frac{1}{\sqrt{n}}\right)$ does not exist

Example 3 $\lim_{n \to \infty} \left[\left(1 - \frac{1}{2^2}\right)\left(1 - \frac{1}{4^2}\right) \cdots \left(1 - \frac{1}{(2n)^2}\right)\right] = \frac{2}{\pi}$

Example 4 $\lim_{n \to \infty} a_n = \sqrt{3}$ $a_1 = 2$ $a_n = \dfrac{a_{n-1} + 3/a_{n-1}}{2}$

Example 5 $\lim_{n \to \infty} \dfrac{1^2 + 2^2 + \cdots + n^2}{n^3} = \dfrac{1}{3}$

Example 6 $\lim_{n \to \infty} \left(1 + \dfrac{1}{n}\right)^n = 2.718$ . . . , known as e

EXERCISES

1. If consumers were persuaded to spend 90 percent of their income instead of the 80 percent assumed in Example 1, what would be the value of the multiplier?
2. Let r be a number not equal to 1 and let $a_n = 1 + r + r^2 + \cdots + r^{n-1}$.
   (a) Show that $a_n - ra_n = 1 - r^n$.

(b) From (a) deduce the formula for the sum of a geometric progression consisting of n terms, whose first term is 1 and whose ratio is r: $a_n = (1 - r^n)/(1 - r)$.

3. A rubber ball rebounds 70 percent of the height from which it is dropped. If it is dropped from a height of 6 feet, how far does it travel? (Assume that it bounces infinitely often.) (Answer: 34 feet)

4. Assume that when light strikes a pane of glass, half the light passes through, a quarter is absorbed, and a quarter is reflected.
(a) What fraction of the light passes through two parallel panes of glass?
(b) What fraction is absorbed? [Answer: (a) $^{10}/_{60}$; (b) $^{25}/_{60}$]

5. With the aid of Example 2 show that the area of the region below the curve $y = 1/\sqrt{x}$ and above the positive x axis is not finite.

6. A man who is walking to his home one mile away walks first a quarter of the distance, then a 16th of the remaining distance, then a 36th of the remaining distance, and so on. At the nth stage he walks $(1/2n)^2$ of the remaining distance. Will he get arbitrarily close to his home? If not, how close will he get? (Hint: Compute the distance remaining at the end of the nth stage and recall Example 3.)

7. (a) Draw the curve $y = x^2$.

(b) Shade the region whose area is equal to $\int_0^1 x^2 \, dx$.

(c) On your diagram show the rectangles whose total area is a_5, defined in Example 5.

8. (a) Compute a_n for $n = 1, 2, 3, 4, 5, 6$, if $a_n = (-1)^n + 1$.
(b) What happens to a_n as n becomes arbitrarily large?
(c) Is the sequence $a_1, a_2, \ldots$ convergent?

9. (a) Compute a_n for $n = 1, 2, 3, 4, 5$, if $a_1 = 1$ and

$$a_n = \frac{a_{n-1} + 3/a_{n-1}}{2}$$

(b) Proceed as in (a), but with $a_1 = 3$.
(c) Proceed as in (a), but with $a_1 = \sqrt{3}$.
(d) What happens to a_n in (a)? in (b)? in (c)?

10. Let $a_n = 1/1 \cdot 2 + 1/2 \cdot 3 + 1/3 \cdot 4 + \cdots + 1/n(n + 1)$.
(a) Compute a_n for $n = 1, 2, 3, 4$.
(b) What simple fractions are a_1, a_2, a_3, a_4? [Hint: See (a).]
(c) Devise a simple formula for a_n.

$$\left(\text{Hint: } \frac{1}{1 \cdot 2} = \frac{1}{1} - \frac{1}{2}, \frac{1}{2 \cdot 3} = \frac{1}{2} - \frac{1}{3}, \cdots \right)$$

(d) With the aid of (c), prove that $\lim_{n \to \infty} a_n = 1$.

[Answer: (a) 0.500, 0.667, 0.750, 0.800]

11. (See Exercise 10.) Let $a_n = 1/2^2 + \cdots + 1/(n + 1)^2$.
(a) Compute a_n for $n = 1, 2, 3, 4$.
(b) With the aid of Exercise 10, prove that $a_n < 1$.
(c) With the aid of (b), show that the present sequence is convergent. What property of the real numbers do you use in your reasoning? With the aid of the derivative and the definite integral, it will be shown in Exercise 55, pages 178–179, that

$$\lim_{n \to \infty} \frac{1}{2^2} + \frac{1}{3^2} + \cdots + \frac{1}{n^2} = \frac{\pi^2}{6} - 1$$

12. Four thousand years ago the Babylonians estimated $\sqrt{2}$ by means of this sequence:

$$a_1 = 1, a_n = \frac{a_{n-1} + 2/a_{n-1}}{2} \qquad n > 1$$

   (a) Compute a_n for $n = 2, 3, 4$.
   (b) Show that if the sequence converges, then $\lim_{n \to \infty} a_n = \sqrt{2}$.

   [Answer: (a) 1.500, 1.417, 1.414]

13. Let $a_n = (1 - 1/2^2)(1 - 1/3^2)(1 - 1/4^2) \cdots (1 - 1/n^2)$ for $n \geq 2$.
   (a) Compute a_2, a_3, a_4, a_5 to three decimals.
   (b) Show that $a_n = (n + 1)/2n$. [Hint: $1 - 1/n^2 = (n - 1)(n + 1)/n^2$]
   (c) Does the sequence a_n converge? Explain.

   [Answer: (a) 0.750, 0.667, 0.625, 0.600; (c) yes]

14. Compute $(1 + 1/n)^n$ to three decimals for $n = 1, 2, 3, 4, 5, 6$.

15. The Fibonacci sequence $F_1, F_2, F_3, \ldots$ is defined by $F_1 = 1$, $F_2 = 1$, and $F_n = F_{n-1} + F_{n-2}$ for $n > 2$. Thus $F_3 = 2$, $F_4 = 3$, $F_5 = 5$, $F_6 = 8$. Let $a_n = F_{n+1}/F_n$. For instance, $a_1 = 1$, $a_2 = 2$, $a_3 = 1.5$.
   (a) Compute a_n for $n = 4, 5, 6, 7$.
   (b) Assuming that the sequence a_n converges, prove that its limit is $(1 + \sqrt{5})/2$.

   [Answer: (a) 1.667, 1.600, 1.625, 1.615]

16. Let a sequence be defined by $a_1 = 1$, $a_2 = 1$, and $a_n = (1 + a_{n-1})/a_{n-2}$ for $n > 2$.
   (a) Compute a_n for $n = 3, 4, 5, 6, 7, 8, 9, 10, 11, 12$, leaving the answer as a fraction.
   (b) What happens to a_n as n increases?
   (c) Prove that if the sequence converges, then its limit is $(1 + \sqrt{5})/2$.
   (d) Is the sequence convergent?

17. Proceed as in Exercise 16, but with $a_1 = 2$ and $a_2 = 1$.

18. (a) Compute $a_n = \frac{1}{1} + \frac{1}{2} + \frac{1}{3} + \cdots + 1/n$ for $n = 1, 2, 3, 4, 5$.
   (b) Note that $1 + \frac{1}{2} + \frac{1}{3} + \frac{1}{4} + \frac{1}{5} + \frac{1}{6} + \frac{1}{7} + \frac{1}{8} > 1 + \frac{1}{2} + \frac{2}{4} + \frac{4}{8} = 1 + \frac{3}{2}$, and show similarly that $a_{2^m} > 1 + (m/2)$.
   (c) Is the sequence convergent?

19. (a) Proceeding as in Example 5, obtain a sequence whose nth term, a_n, is an estimate of $\int_0^1 x^4 \, dx$.
   (b) Compute $a_1, a_2,$ and a_3.

20. In elementary school we met the equation $\frac{1}{3} = 0.3333 \ldots$
   (a) What sequence $a_1, a_2, \ldots$ is involved in that equation?
   (b) Show that $\lim_{n \to \infty} a_n = \frac{1}{3}$, using the formula for a sum of a geometric progression, as we did in Example 1.

21. Sketch a graph of a_n as a function of n for (a) Example 1; (b) Example 2; (c) Example 4.

22. Define a sequence by $a_1 = 3$, and $a_n = 1/(1 - a_{n-1})$ if $n > 1$. Compute a_2, a_3, a_4, a_5, a_6. Does $\lim_{n \to \infty} a_n$ exist?

23. Define a sequence by $a_1 = 1/2$ and $a_n = 1/(2 - a_{n-1})$ if $n \geq 2$.
   (a) Compute a_2, a_3, a_4, a_5, a_6, and express as reduced fractions.
   (b) If $\lim_{n \to \infty} a_n$ exists, what must it be?
   (c) Does it exist?

24. On a large piece of paper draw several parallel lines whose distance apart is the same as the length of a needle or toothpick you might have (or if you have a wood floor, find a needle-like object whose length is the width of the boards). Toss the needle up at random and observe, when it comes to rest, whether it crosses one of the lines. In the first n experiments let a_n = (number of times needle crosses a line)/n. Clearly $0 \leqslant a_n \leqslant 1$.

(a) Toss the needle 50 times, recording the results and the order in which they occur.

(b) Compute to two decimals a_1, a_2, a_5, a_{10}, a_{20}, a_{30}, a_{40}, and a_{50}.

(c) What happens to a_n as you increase n?

25. Toss a penny 50 times. Record the results and the order in which they occur. Let a_n = (number of heads in first n throws)/n. Clearly $0 \leqslant a_n \leqslant 1$. Carry out the analogs of Exercise 24.

26. Let $a_n = n/2^n$.

(a) Compute a_1, a_2, a_5, a_{10} to three decimals.

(b) What happens to a_n as n increases?

27. Let

$$a_n = \frac{1}{n} + \frac{1}{n+1} + \cdots + \frac{1}{2n}$$

(a) Compute a_n to three decimals for $n = 1, 2, 3, 4, 5$.

(b) What two influences operate on a_n for large n?

(c) What happens to a_n for very large n?

28. The symbol $n!$, where n is a positive integer, denotes the product, $(n)(n-1) \cdots (1)$. For instance, $4! = 4 \cdot 3 \cdot 2 \cdot 1 = 24$. It is customary to let $1! = 0! = 1$.

(a) Use the binomial theorem to prove that

$$\left(1 + \frac{1}{n}\right)^n = 1^n + n\frac{1}{n} + \frac{1}{2!}\frac{(n)(n-1)}{(n)(n)} + \frac{1}{3!}\frac{(n)(n-1)(n-2)}{(n)(n)(n)} + \cdots$$

$$+ \frac{1}{n!}\frac{(n)(n-1) \cdots (2)(1)}{(n)(n) \cdots (n)(n)}$$

(b) From (a) deduce that

$$\left(1 + \frac{1}{n}\right)^n < 1 + 1 + \frac{1}{2!} + \frac{1}{3!} + \cdots + \frac{1}{n!} \qquad \text{if } n > 1$$

(c) Noting that

$$\frac{1}{3!} + \frac{1}{4!} + \cdots + \frac{1}{n!} < \frac{1}{2^2} + \frac{1}{2^3} + \cdots + \frac{1}{2^{n-1}}$$

prove that

$$\left(1 + \frac{1}{n}\right) < 3$$

(d) Using the same method as in (c), obtain a smaller bound on $(1 + 1/n)^n$.

(e) Using (a), show that $(1 + 1/n)^n$ increases as n increases and approaches a number less than 3.

29. (See Exercise 28a.) Let

$$b_n = \frac{1}{0!} + \frac{1}{1!} + \frac{1}{2!} + \cdots + \frac{1}{n!} \qquad n \geqslant 1$$

(Recall that $0! = 1! = 1$.) Explain why

$$\lim_{n \to \infty} \left(1 + \frac{1}{n}\right)^n = \lim_{n \to \infty} b_n$$

30. (See Exercise 29.) (a) Prove that $(1 + 1/n)^n < 1/0! + 1/1! + \cdots + 1/n!$ if $n > 1$.
    (b) Show that $(1 + 1/1)^1 = 1/0! + 1/1!$.
    (c) Prove that the only pair of integers r and s for which $(1 + 1/r)^r$ is equal to $1/0! + 1/1! + 1/2! + \cdots + 1/s!$ is the pair $r = 1$, $s = 1$.

31. (a) Show why $a_n = \dfrac{1}{n+1} + \dfrac{1}{n+2} + \cdots + \dfrac{1}{2n}$ is an approximation to $\displaystyle\int_1^2 \frac{1}{x}\, dx$.
    (b) Prove that $a_n < 1$ for every n.
    (c) Prove that $a_1 < a_2 < a_3 < \cdots < a_n < \cdots$.

32. (a) Toss a penny until the total number of heads differs from the total number of tails by 2. Do this whole experiment 10 times, each time recording the score of the "winner" (whether it is tails or heads is irrelevant). Average the winning score.
    (b) Let $a_n = 2(\frac{1}{2}) + 3(\frac{1}{2})^2 + \cdots + (n + 1)(\frac{1}{2})^n$. Show that as you performed more and more experiments in (a), the average winning score would probably approach $\lim_{n \to \infty} a_n$. (Hint: What fractions of the time would you expect the winning score to be 2, 3, and so on?)
    (c) Compare a_{15} to the experimental result in (a).

33. There are interesting sequences about which little is known. Consider the endless sequence of primes and the gaps between them:
    Primes: 2 3 5 7 11 13 17 19 23 29 31 37 41 43 47 53 59 61 67 71 73 79 83 89 97 . . .
    Gaps: 1 2 2 4 2 4 2 4 6 2 6 4 2 4 6 6 2 6 4 2 6 4 6 8 . . .
    It is known that in an irregular way the gaps increase. For example, we meet a gap of 8 for the first time between 89 and 97. It is not known whether the gap 2 occurs infinitely often.

    Now, place a "U" between two gaps if the right gap is more than the left, an "E" if the right gap is equal to the left gap, a "D" if the right gap is less than the left gap ("U" stands for "up," "D" for "down," and "E" for "equal"). We have

    1 2 2 4 2 4 2 4 6 2 6 4 2 4 6 6 2 6 4 2 6 4 6 8
     U E U D U D U U D U D D U U E D U D D U D U U

    It is not known whether the set of E's is infinite.

    Now let $a_n =$ (number of D's among first n U's and D's)$/n$. Thus $a_1 = \%_1$, $a_2 = \%_2$, $a_3 = \frac{1}{3}$, $a_4 = \frac{1}{4}$, $a_5 = \frac{2}{5}$. What do you think happens to a_n for large n? (The answer is not known.)

2. The limit of a function of a real variable.

In Sec. 1 we considered sequences —functions defined on the positive integers. Now we examine the behavior of functions defined on part or all of the x axis. As a simple instance, we might ask: How does $f(x) = x^2 + 1$ behave as x approaches 2? This offers no difficulty. When x is near 2, then x^2 is near 4, and thus $x^2 + 1$ is near 5. Thus, as x approaches 2, we see that $x^2 + 1$ approaches 5.

Our first challenging example, which will be devoted to an important trigonometric limit, employs the radian measure of angles. To measure an angle in radians, we place its vertex at the center of a circle. If the circle has radius r and the angle cuts off an arc s on this circle, we say that the angle is s/r radians. For instance, a straight angle is $\pi r/r = \pi$ radians, and a right angle is $\pi/2$ radians.

Example 1. Let $f(x) = (\sin x)/x$ for $x \neq 0$. When x becomes very large, $f(x)$ becomes very small, since $-1 \leqslant \sin x \leqslant 1$. We say, as with sequences, that *as x becomes very large, $f(x)$ approaches* 0. But there is another question that tempts us: How does $f(x)$ behave when x is very small—close to 0? This is a harder question, for now there are two influences, whose relative strength is not immediately clear. As x approaches 0, the numerator, $\sin x$, also approaches 0; thus there is a force that might drive $(\sin x)/x$ toward 0. On the other hand, the denominator, x, approaching 0, provides a force that might make $(\sin x)/x$ huge. We shall now see how these two influences balance.
     Observe that

$$f(-x) = \frac{\sin(-x)}{-x} = \frac{-\sin x}{-x} = \frac{\sin x}{x} = f(x)$$

Thus the behavior of $f(x)$ for positive x determines the behavior of $f(x)$ for negative x. We can therefore restrict our attention to positive x, and, for convenience, to $x < \pi/2$.
     Consider this figure:

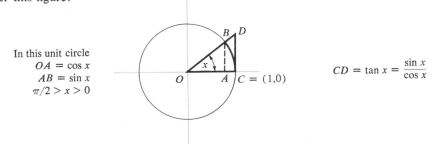

In this unit circle
$OA = \cos x$
$AB = \sin x$
$\pi/2 > x > 0$

$CD = \tan x = \dfrac{\sin x}{\cos x}$

Clearly
           Area of triangle OAB < area of sector OCB < area of triangle OCD

We rewrite the above inequalities in terms of x:

$$\tfrac{1}{2}\cos x \sin x < \frac{x}{2} < \tfrac{1}{2} \cdot 1 \cdot \tan x$$

thus
$$\cos x \sin x < x < \frac{\sin x}{\cos x}$$

Taking reciprocals, we obtain

$$\frac{1}{\cos x \sin x} > \frac{1}{x} > \frac{\cos x}{\sin x}$$

(Note the reversal of the inequality signs. If $a < b$ then $1/a > 1/b$; for instance, $3 < 4$ and $\tfrac{1}{3} > \tfrac{1}{4}$.)
     Next we multiply these inequalities by the (positive) number, $\sin x$, to obtain

$$\frac{1}{\cos x} > \frac{\sin x}{x} > \cos x$$

Now we are in a position to see how $(\sin x)/x$ behaves as x decreases toward 0. Inspection of the diagram shows that $\cos x$ approaches 1 as x approaches 0; hence $1/\cos x$ also approaches 1. *Thus* $(\sin x)/x$, *squeezed between two functions that approach* 1, *must itself approach* 1 *as* x *approaches* 0.

Example 2. We examine the behavior of $(1 - \cos x)/x$ for small x. Again note that there are two contrary influences, for both numerator and denominator tend toward 0 as x approaches 0.

To decide what happens, we will express this problem in terms of $\sin x$, and exploit Example 1. We have

$$\frac{1 - \cos x}{x} = \frac{1 - \cos x}{x} \frac{1 + \cos x}{1 + \cos x} = \frac{1 - (\cos x)^2}{x(1 + \cos x)} = \frac{(\sin x)^2}{x(1 + \cos x)} = \frac{\sin x}{x} \frac{\sin x}{1 + \cos x}$$

As x approaches 0, the quotient $(\sin x)/x$ approaches 1, by Example 1, and the quotient $(\sin x)/(1 + \cos x)$ approaches $0/(1 + 1) = 0$.

Thus $\dfrac{\sin x}{x} \dfrac{\sin x}{1 + \cos x}$ approaches $1 \cdot 0 = 0$, as x approaches 0. We conclude that

$$\frac{1 - \cos x}{x} \text{ approaches } 0 \text{ as } x \text{ approaches } 0$$

This implies that the numerator approaches 0 much more rapidly than the denominator.

Example 3. We examine the behavior of $(1 + x)^{1/x}$ as x approaches 0. Again there are two influences. When x is small and positive, $1 + x$ is close to 1. Thus one influence pushes $(1 + x)^{1/x}$ toward 1. At the same time, however, the arbitrarily increasing size of the exponent $1/x$ might influence $(1 + x)^{1/x}$ to be very large. This is similar to Example 6 in Sec. 1, where we examined the sequence $(1 + 1/n)^n$. Indeed, if we consider only those x that are reciprocals of integers, $x = 1/n$, then

$$(1 + x)^{1/x} = \left(1 + \frac{1}{n}\right)^{1/(1/n)} = \left(1 + \frac{1}{n}\right)^n$$

As remarked in that example, $(1 + 1/n)^n$ approaches the important number $e = 2.718 \cdots$. As we now show, this implies that $(1 + x)^{1/x}$ approaches e as x approaches 0. We consider only $x > 0$; Exercise 13 treats $x < 0$.

Since we are interested only in small positive x, we assume that $x \leqslant 1$; there is therefore a (unique) positive integer n, depending on x, such that

$$\frac{1}{n + 1} < x \leqslant \frac{1}{n} \qquad \text{or equivalently} \qquad n + 1 > \frac{1}{x} \geqslant n$$

(Note that as x approaches 0, the integer n becomes increasingly large.) From these inequalities it follows that $(1 + x)^{1/x}$ is larger than $[1 + 1/(n + 1)]^{n+1}/[1 + 1/(n + 1)]$ and is smaller than $(1 + 1/n)^n(1 + 1/n)$; specifically, we have

$$(1 + x)^{1/x} > \left(1 + \frac{1}{n + 1}\right)^{1/x} \geqslant \left(1 + \frac{1}{n + 1}\right)^n = \frac{[1 + 1/(n + 1)]^{n+1}}{1 + 1/(n + 1)}$$

and

$$(1 + x)^{1/x} \leqslant \left(1 + \frac{1}{n}\right)^{1/x} < \left(1 + \frac{1}{n}\right)^{n+1} = \left(1 + \frac{1}{n}\right)^n \left(1 + \frac{1}{n}\right)$$

Since $\lim\limits_{n \to \infty} [1 + 1/(n + 1)]^{n+1} = e = \lim\limits_{n \to \infty} (1 + 1/n)^n$ and $\lim\limits_{n \to \infty} 1 + 1/(n + 1) = 1 = \lim\limits_{n \to \infty} 1 + 1/n$, it follows that $(1 + x)^{1/x}$, being between two expressions that approach e, itself approaches e as x approaches 0.

Example 4. We examine the behavior of $\dfrac{x^5 - 2^5}{x - 2}$ for x near 2. In this case the numerator tends toward $2^5 - 2^5 = 0$ and the denominator toward $2 - 2 = 0$. Again we meet the problem of determining the strength of contrary influences; the solution of this problem is one of the aims of the calculus.

This time we recall the algebraic identity

$$a^5 - b^5 = (a - b)(a^4 + ba^3 + b^2a^2 + b^3a + b^4)$$

which can easily be verified by expanding the right side. As a special instance of the identity we have

$$x^5 - 2^5 = (x - 2)(x^4 + 2x^3 + 4x^2 + 8x + 16)$$

We deduce that if x is different from 2, then

$$\frac{x^5 - 2^5}{x - 2} = x^4 + 2x^3 + 4x^2 + 8x + 16$$

Though the behavior of $(x^5 - 2^5)/(x - 2)$ for x near 2 is not easy to guess, the behavior of $x^4 + 2x^3 + 4x^2 + 8x + 16$ is evident. When x approaches 2, this polynomial approaches $2^4 + 2(2^3) + 4(2^2) + 8(2) + 16$, that is, $5(2^4) = 80$.

The reader should note that in this example we have just shown that the function x^5 has the derivative 80 at $x = 2$.

With these examples in mind we give an informal definition for the limit of a function of a real variable. (A formal definition is presented on page 86.)

DEFINITION: *Limit of a function of a real variable.* Let f be a function and a some fixed number. If as x approaches a, $f(x)$ approaches some specific number A, then we call A the *limit* of $f(x)$ as x approaches a. We write

$$\lim_{x \to a} f(x) = A$$

If as x becomes arbitrarily large through positive values, $f(x)$ approaches some specific number A, then we say *the limit of $f(x)$ as x approaches ∞ is A*, and write

$$\lim_{x \to \infty} f(x) = A$$

In a similar manner, considering only negative x, we define

$$\lim_{x \to -\infty} f(x) = A$$

Our conclusions concerning the first four examples in this section are succinctly stated as

Example 1 $\lim\limits_{x \to 0} \dfrac{\sin x}{x} = 1$

Example 2 $\lim\limits_{x \to 0} \dfrac{1 - \cos x}{x} = 0$

Example 3 $\lim\limits_{x \to 0} (1 + x)^{1/x} = 2.718 \ldots = e$

Example 4 $\lim\limits_{x \to 2} \dfrac{x^5 - 2^5}{x - 2} = 80$

Example 5.   Let $f(x) = \sin(1/x)$. As x becomes very large, $1/x$ tends toward 0, and therefore $\sin(1/x)$ also tends toward 0. In short,

$$\lim_{x \to \infty} \sin \frac{1}{x} = 0$$

If x tends toward $2/\pi$, then $1/x$ tends toward $\pi/2$ and hence $\sin(1/x)$ approaches $\sin(\pi/2) = 1$; that is,

$$\lim_{x \to 2/\pi} \sin \frac{1}{x} = 1$$

Now consider x near 0. Then $1/x$ is large. If we choose x of the form $(1/\pi n)$, where $n = 1, 2, 3, \ldots$, then $\sin 1/x = \sin[1/(1/\pi n)] = \sin(\pi n) = 0$.

On the other hand, if we choose our small x to be of the form

$$\frac{1}{(2n + \tfrac{1}{2})\pi}$$

then $\sin \dfrac{1}{x} = \sin \dfrac{1}{1/[(2n + \tfrac{1}{2})\pi]} = \sin[(2n + \tfrac{1}{2})\pi] = \sin \dfrac{\pi}{2} = 1$

Also, if we choose $x = 1/(2n - \tfrac{1}{2})\pi$, then

$$\sin \frac{1}{x} = \sin \frac{1}{1/[(2n - \tfrac{1}{2})\pi]} = \sin[(2n - \tfrac{1}{2})\pi] = \sin \left(-\frac{\pi}{2}\right) = -1$$

Thus in any interval around 0 the function $\sin(1/x)$ fluctuates wildly, taking on infinitely often each of the values $0, 1, -1$ (and in fact any value between 1 and -1). The graph of $\sin(1/x)$ looks like this:

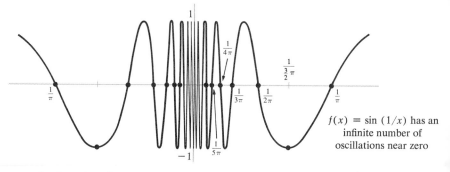

$f(x) = \sin(1/x)$ has an infinite number of oscillations near zero

In this case the function fluctuates so much near 0 that $\lim\limits_{x \to 0} \sin(1/x)$ does not exist; that is, there is no fixed number that $\sin(1/x)$ tends toward (and stays close to) as x approaches 0.

The derivative, a special case of limit, may be written as

$$\lim_{\Delta x \to 0} \frac{f(x + \Delta x) - f(x)}{\Delta x} \quad \text{or as} \quad \lim_{x_2 \to x_1} \frac{f(x_2) - f(x_1)}{x_2 - x_1}$$

or as $\lim_{\Delta x \to 0} \Delta y / \Delta x$. Thus to say that the number dy/dx is the derivative is to say that $\lim_{\Delta x \to 0} (\Delta y / \Delta x - dy/dx) = 0$. For use later we will rephrase this. Let ε denote the difference $\Delta y / \Delta x - dy/dx$. We have $\lim_{\Delta x \to 0} \varepsilon = 0$. Hence

$$\frac{\Delta y}{\Delta x} = \frac{dy}{dx} + \varepsilon$$

where ε approaches 0 as Δx approaches 0. In other words, $\Delta y = \dfrac{dy}{dx} \Delta x + \varepsilon \Delta x$, where ε approaches 0 as Δx approaches 0. We shall set $\varepsilon = 0$ when $\Delta x = 0$.

EXERCISES

1. (a) Using the definition of the derivative, show that the derivative of $\sin x$ at 0 is $\lim_{x \to 0} \sin x / x$.

   (b) In view of (a) and Example 1, what angle does the tangent line to the curve $y = \sin x$ at (0,0) make with the x axis?

   (c) Make a graph of $y = \sin x$, and draw the tangent line at (0,0). Does it seem to make an angle of $\pi/4$ with the x axis?   [Answer: (b) $\pi/4$]

2. (a) Recalling the definition of the derivative, show that the derivative of $\cos x$ at $x = 0$ is

$$\lim_{x \to 0} \frac{(\cos x) - 1}{x}$$

   (b) In view of Example 2, show that the derivative of $\cos x$ at $x = 0$ is 0.

   (c) Draw the curve $y = \cos x$ and a line tangent to it at (0,1). Does it seem to have slope 0?

3. (a) Prove that $\lim_{x \to 0} (1 - \cos x)/x^2 = \frac{1}{2}$. [Hint: Use the method we used in computing $\lim_{x \to 0} (1 - \cos x)/x$.]

   (b) In view of (a), why would $1 - x^2/2$ be a good estimate of $\cos x$ when x is near 0?

   (c) Compare $1 - x^2/2$ and $\cos x$ for $x = 1, 0.1, 0.01, 0$. (Use a table of $\cos x$, where angle is measured in radians.)

4. (a) Compute to three decimals $(1 + x)^{1/x}$ for $x = -\frac{1}{2}, -\frac{1}{3}, -\frac{1}{4}, -\frac{1}{5}, -\frac{1}{6}$.

   (b) In view of (a), does it seem reasonable that $(1 + x)^{1/x}$ is near a certain number for all x sufficiently close to 0, whether x be positive or negative?

5. Fill in this table. (Use tables, arithmetic, and intuition.)

x	$-\frac{7}{8}$	$-\frac{1}{2}$	$-\frac{1}{5}$	$\frac{1}{3}$	1	2	3	4	1,000
$(1 + x)^{1/x}$									

(a) In view of the table, how does $(1 + x)^{1/x}$ behave when x is to the right of -1, but near -1? When x is near 0? When x is very large?

(b) Graph $y = (1 + x)^{1/x}$ for $x > -1$.

(c) Examine $(1 + x)^{1/x}$ for $x = -2$ and $x = -3$.

6. (a) In view of Example 4, what is $\lim_{\Delta x \to 0} [(2 + \Delta x)^5 - 2^5]/\Delta x$?

(b) Compute $\lim_{\Delta x \to 0} [(2 + \Delta x)^5 - 2^5]/\Delta x$ directly by making use of the binomial theorem, which asserts that

$$(a + b)^5 = a^5 + 5a^4b + 10a^3b^2 + 10a^2b^3 + 5ab^4 + b^5$$

7. (a) Determine $\lim_{x \to 0} (x^5 - 1)/(x - 1)$.

(b) Using the technique in Example 4, compute $\lim_{x \to 1} (x^5 - 1)/(x - 1)$.

[Answer: (a) 1; (b) 5]

8. (a) Using the technique in Example 4, compute $\lim_{x \to 3} (x^5 - 3^5)/(x - 3)$.

(b) Using the technique in (a), compute $\lim_{x \to a} (x^5 - a^5)/(x - a)$, where a is a fixed number.

(c) What does (b) tell us about $d(x^5)/dx$?

[Answer: (b) $5a^4$]

9. Using the technique of Example 4, find $d(x^6)/dx$ at $x = 1$; at $x = -1$; at $x = \frac{1}{2}$.

(Answer: 6; -6; $\frac{6}{32}$)

10. (See Exercise 9.) Find $d(x^6)/dx$ in general, not just at 1, -1, $\frac{1}{2}$.

(Answer: $6x^5$ at the argument x)

□ □ □

11. (Recall Example 5.) Graph the curve $y = x \sin(1/x)$. Note that the function $x \sin(1/x)$ is not defined at $x = 0$. Devote special attention to very large and very small x.

12. Let $f(x) = 1/(1 + 10^{1/x})$. Note that f is not defined at 0. (a) Fill in this table.

For x =	$-\frac{1}{10}$	$\frac{1}{10}$	1	-1	2	-2	' Positive very large	Negative very large
$10^{1/x} =$								
$1 + 10^{1/x} =$								
$\dfrac{1}{1 + 10^{1/x}} =$								

(a) Does $\lim_{x \to 0} f(x)$ exist?   (c) Does $\lim_{x \to -\infty} f(x)$ exist?

(b) Does $\lim_{x \to \infty} f(x)$ exist?   (d) Graph $y = 1/(1 + 10^{1/x})$ for $x > -1$.

13. (a) Show that

$$\left(1 - \frac{1}{n}\right)^{-n} = \left(1 + \frac{1}{n-1}\right)^{n-1} \left(\frac{n}{n-1}\right).$$

(b) Show that, in view of (a), if one of the two sequences,

$$\left(1 - \frac{1}{n}\right)^{-n} \quad \text{and} \quad \left(1 + \frac{1}{n}\right)^{n}$$

converges, then so does the other, and that they have the same limit.
(c) What does (b) suggest concerning

$$\lim_{x \to 0} (1 + x)^{1/x} ?$$

14. What happens to $(x^5 - 2^5)/(x^2 - 2^2)$ as x approaches 2? ·

3. Continuous functions. In examining the behavior of $f(x)$ for x near a, and $\lim_{x \to a} f(x)$, if the limit exists, we are not concerned with the value of f at a, that is, with $f(a)$. In Example 1 of Sec. 2, where $f(x) = (1 + x)^{1/x}$, we see that f is not defined at 0. In Example 4, where $f(x) = (x^5 - 2^5)/(x - 2)$, we see that f is not defined at 2. *In determining whether $\lim_{x \to a} f(x)$ exists, we examine $f(x)$ for x near a, but we are not concerned with the value of f at a, even if it is defined.* Some further examples will illustrate this and lead us to the idea of a *continuous function.*

Example 1. Let $f(x) = (\sin x)/x$ if $x \neq 0$ and, whimsically, $f(0) = 17$. Then $\lim_{x \to 0} f(x) = 1$, just as in Sec. 2. The value of $f(0)$ does not influence our conclusion concerning $\lim_{x \to 0} (\sin x)/x$.

Example 2. Let $f(x) = (\sin x)/x$ if $x \neq 0$ and $f(0) = 1$. Then $\lim_{x \to 0} f(x) = 1$, just as in Example 1. This time, note that $\lim_{x \to 0} f(x) = f(0)$.

Example 3. Let $f(x) = (x^5 - 2^5)/(x - 2)$ if $x \neq 2$ and $f(2) = 1967$. Then, as we saw in Sec. 2, $\lim_{x \to 2} f(x) = 80$. Thus $\lim_{x \to 2} f(x)$ exists but does not equal $f(2)$.

Example 4. Let $f(x)$ be defined for x in $[0,1]$ in this manner:

$$f(x) = \lim_{n \to \infty} x^n$$

For example,

$$f(1) = \lim_{n \to \infty} 1^n = 1 \qquad f(\tfrac{1}{2}) = \lim_{n \to \infty} (\tfrac{1}{2})^n = 0$$

In fact, $$f(x) = 0 \qquad \text{if } 0 \leqslant x < 1 \text{ and } f(1) = 1$$

The graph of f is easy to draw:

The graph of f consists of a horizontal segment that lacks its right end point, together with the point $(1,1)$

Note that f jumps at 1: We have $\lim_{x \to 1} f(x) = 0$ and $f(1) = 1$.

With these examples in mind we introduce a concept of great importance, the *continuous function*.

DEFINITION: *Continuous function*. A function f is *continuous* at a if these conditions hold:

(i) $f(a)$ is defined.

(ii) $\lim_{x \to a} f(x)$ exists.

(iii) $\lim_{x \to a} f(x) = f(a)$.

A function f is *continuous throughout a set* if it is continuous at each number a in the set.

The function in Example 1 is continuous everywhere except at 0. The function in Example 2 is continuous everywhere. The function in Example 3 is continuous everywhere except at 2. The function in Example 4 is continuous at all x for which it is defined, except at 1. But most functions we meet in concrete situations are continuous; for example, any polynomial is continuous; so are $\sin x$ and $\cos x$.

We can think of a continuous function as one that doesn't fluctuate wildly, one whose graph has no jumps. We can draw its graph without lifting the pencil from the paper. Outdoor temperature T, considered as a function of time t, is continuous: a sufficiently small change in t induces a small change in T. But the number of cars parked in a certain parking lot, considered as a function of time, is not continuous. It jumps when a car enters or leaves the parking lot.

If f is continuous at a, then

$$\lim_{\Delta x \to 0} f(a + \Delta x) - f(a) = 0$$

Now, $f(a + \Delta x) - f(a)$ is the numerator of the quotient we would use in defining the derivative of f at a. This is the basis of the proof of the following theorem.

THEOREM. *If f has a derivative at a, then f is continuous at a.*

PROOF. We assume that

$$\lim_{\Delta x \to 0} \frac{f(a + \Delta x) - f(a)}{\Delta x}$$

exists, and we give the limit the name $f'(a)$. Then

$$\frac{f(a + \Delta x) - f(a)}{\Delta x} - f'(a)$$

approaches 0 as Δx approaches 0.

We can write

(1) $$\frac{f(a + \Delta x) - f(a)}{\Delta x} = f'(a) + g(\Delta x)$$

where g is a function of Δx such that $g(0) = 0$ and

$$\lim_{\Delta x \to 0} g(\Delta x) = 0$$

Multiplying both sides of (1) by Δx, we obtain

$$f(a + \Delta x) - f(a) = f'(a)\,\Delta x + \Delta x\, g(\Delta x)$$

Then

$$\lim_{\Delta x \to 0} [f(a + \Delta x) - f(a)] = \lim_{\Delta x \to 0} f'(a)\,\Delta x + \lim_{\Delta x \to 0} \Delta x\, g(\Delta x)$$

$$= f'(a) \cdot 0 + 0 \cdot 0 = 0$$

The theorem is proved.

The converse of the above theorem is not necessarily true: A continuous function need not have a derivative, as the function $f(x) = |x|$ shows. It lacks a derivative at $x = 0$, but it is continuous there.

Indeed, in 1834 Bolzano discovered a function that is continuous everywhere and has a derivative nowhere. (An example of such a function is included in Appendix F.) Nevertheless, we may think of the continuous function as "well behaved." For example, when in Chap. 1 we said "During a small interval of time, the velocity changes very little," or "In a very small section of the string the density is 'almost' constant," we were assuming that *velocity is a continuous function of time,* and *density is a continuous function of position.*

We will later use several important properties of continuous functions. The proof of these theorems, while not difficult, would delay us too long. We are more interested in applying the derivative and the definite integral.

THE INTERMEDIATE VALUE THEOREM. *Let f be continuous throughout $[a,b]$. Let m be any number between $f(a)$ and $f(b)$. [That is, $f(a) \leqslant m \leqslant f(b)$ if $f(a) \leqslant f(b)$, or $f(a) \geqslant m \geqslant f(b)$ if $f(a) \geqslant f(b)$.] Then there is at least one number X in $[a,b]$ such that $f(X) = m$.*

In ordinary English, the intermediate value theorem reads thus: *A continuous function defined on $[a,b]$ takes on all values between $f(a)$ and $f(b)$.* Pictorially, it asserts that a horizontal line of height m must meet the graph of f at least once if m is between $f(a)$ and $f(b)$:

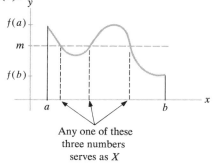

Any one of these
three numbers
serves as X

THE MAXIMUM VALUE THEOREM. *Let f be continuous throughout* [a,b]. *Then there is at least one number X in* [a,b] *for which f takes on a maximum value. That is,*

$$f(X) \geqslant f(x) \qquad \text{for all } x \text{ in } [a,b]$$

The maximum value theorem tells us two things. It tells us first that if f is continuous, then $f(x)$ cannot become arbitrarily large if x is in $[a,b]$. Second, it tells us that there is a point X at which f takes on a maximum value. An analogous minimum value theorem is also valid.

These theorems need not be true if we weaken their assumptions, as is shown in the exercises.

EXERCISES

1. Let $f(x) = (1 - \cos x)/x$ if $x \neq 0$. Is it possible to define $f(0)$ in such a way that f is continuous everywhere? If so, do we have any choice in assigning this value $f(0)$?
2. Let $f(x) = (\sin x)/x$ if $x \neq 0$ and $f(0) = 1$.
   (a) For which x is $f(x) = 0$?
   (b) Graph the curve $y = f(x)$.
   [Answer: (a) $n\pi, n = \pm 1, \pm 2, \ldots$]
3. Which of the following functions are continuous? Explain. (a) The population of the world as a function of time. (b) The speed of a car as a function of time. (c) The weight of a person as a function of time.
4. Let $f(x) = 1$ if x is an integer, and $f(x) = 0$ otherwise. (a) Graph $y = f(x)$. (b) Where is f continuous? (c) For which a does $\lim_{x \to a} f(x)$ exist?
5. Let $f(x)$ equal the greatest integer not larger than x. For example, $f(2.1) = 2$, $f(2.9) = 2$, $f(3) = 3$, $f(\sqrt{2}) = 1$, $f(-1.3) = -2$.
   (a) Graph $y = f(x)$.
   (b) Where is f continuous?
6. Let $f(x) = \sin(1/x), x \neq 0$.
   (a) Graph $y = \sin(1/x)$.
   (b) Is it possible to define $f(0)$ in such a way that the resulting function is continuous at 0? Explain.
7. Let $f(x) = x^2$, $a = -1$, $b = 2$. Show that the intermediate value theorem is valid in this case. Find for each m such that $f(a) \leqslant m \leqslant f(b)$, all corresponding X's.
8. Let $f(x) = \sin x$, $a = 0$, $b = 5\pi/2$.
   (a) Draw the graph of f from $x = 0$ to $x = 5\pi/2$.
   (b) For $m = 0$, find all the X's guaranteed by the intermediate value theorem.
   (c) How many X's are there for various choices of m, $f(a) \leqslant m \leqslant f(b)$?
9. Let $f(x) = 1/x$, $a = -1$, $b = 1$, $m = 0$. Note that $f(a) \leqslant m \leqslant f(b)$. Is there at least one X in $[a,b]$ such that $f(x) = m$? If so, find X; if not, does this imply that the intermediate value theorem is sometimes false?
10. The symbol $(0,1)$ denotes the "open interval," which consists of all numbers in $[0,1]$ except 0 and 1. Let $f(x) = 1/(x - x^2)$ for all x in $(0,1)$. Does f have a maximum value for x in $(0,1)$? How does your answer compare with the maximum value theorem?

11. Let $f(x) = 2x^3 - 5x^2 - x + 1$. Compute $f(0)$ and $f(1)$. What theorem guarantees that f has a root between 0 and 1?

12. What functions that are defined for all x satisfy this condition for all a:
$$\lim_{x \to a} f(x) = f(\lim_{x \to a} x)$$

13. If $\lim_{n \to \infty} x^n/(1 + x^{2n})$ exists, call it $f(x)$.

(a) Compute $f(0)$; $f(\frac{1}{2})$; $f(-2)$; $f(1)$.
(b) For which x is $f(x)$ defined? Graph $y = f(x)$.
(c) For which x is f continuous?

[Answer: (a) $0, 0, 0, \frac{1}{2}$; (b) $x \neq -1$]

14. If $\lim_{x \to \infty} x^{2n}/(1 + x^{2n})$ exists, call it $f(x)$.

(a) Compute $f(\frac{1}{2})$, $f(2)$, $f(1)$.
(b) For which x is $f(x)$ defined? Graph $y = f(x)$.
(c) Where is f continuous?

[Answer: (a) $0, 1, \frac{1}{2}$]

15. Let $f(x) = x$ when x is rational, and $f(x) = 1$ when x is irrational. Where is f continuous?

16. (a) Study the example of a continuous function f that has derivative nowhere (pages 594–596).
(b) Compute $f(i/10)$ for $i = 0, 1, \ldots, 10$.

17. Using the maximum value theorem, prove the minimum value theorem: If f is continuous throughout $[a,b]$, then there is at least one number in $[a,b]$ for which f takes on a minimum value.

18. (a) Let f be a continuous function such that $f(x)$ is in $[0,1]$ when x is in $[0,1]$. Prove that there is at least one X such that $f(X) = X$.
(b) A length of elastic string lies on the table without overlapping itself. You lift it up, stretch parts of it, shrink other parts, and put it down in such a way that it covers no points of the table other than those initially covered. Show that there is a point in the string that is in its original location.

19. Let f be a continuous function such that $f(f(x)) = x$ for all x. Prove that there is at least one X such that $f(X) = X$.

20. If f is a function, then by a *chord of* f we shall mean a line segment whose ends are on the graph of f. Now let f be continuous throughout $[0,1]$, and let $f(0) = f(1)$.
(a) Show why there is a horizontal chord of f of length $\frac{1}{2}$.
(b) Show why there is a horizontal chord of f of length $1/n$, where $n = 1, 2, 3, 4, \ldots$.
(c) Must there exist a horizontal chord of f of length $2/3$?
(d) What is the answer to (c) if we also demand that $f(x) \geqslant 0$ for all x in $[0,1]$?

21. Let f be continuous everywhere, and have a derivative at 0 and at 1. Assume also that $f'(0) = 0$ and $f'(1) = 1$. Show why there is a chord of f that has slope $\frac{1}{2}$. Generalize to other slopes. Must there be a chord of f having slope 0? Slope 1?

22. Let f be a continuous function defined on $[0,1]$ with values on $[0,1]$. Let $g(x) = x^2$. Prove that if $f(g(x)) = g(f(x))$ for all x in $[0,1]$, then there is X in $[0,1]$ such that $f(X) = X = g(X)$. (It is not known whether the conclusion holds if we ask merely that g be a continuous function such that $f(g(x)) = g(f(x))$ for all x in $[0,1]$ and $g(x)$ is in $[0,1]$ when x is in $[0,1]$.)

4. Precise definitions of limits. In speaking of "sums tending toward," or of "Δx approaching 0," or of "n growing arbitrarily large," we may mistakenly think of something traveling toward a number. The precise definitions of the definite integral, the derivative, or the limit of a sequence should not involve any suggestion of motion. They should be phrased only in terms of numbers, which are motionless.

This is an appropriate place to present precise definitions of the various limits. Such definitions are necessary to ensure understanding of the limit concept and for dealing with delicate properties concerning definite integrals, limits of functions, or limits of sequences. (For the problems in this book, however, intuition will usually suffice.)

We now define the definite integral, limit of a function of a real variable, and limit of a sequence in such a way as to emphasize their similarity.

DEFINITION: *The definite integral of f over $[a,b]$.* The number A is the definite integral of f over $[a,b]$ if for any positive number ε, however small, there is a positive number δ, depending on ε, such that any sum

$$\sum_{i=1}^{n} f(X_i)(x_i - x_{i-1})$$

formed with any partition of $[a,b]$ of mesh less than δ (no matter how X_i is chosen in $[X_{i-1}, X_i]$) differs from A by less than ε.

REMARKS. ε is read "epsilon" and δ "delta." Think of ε as the challenge, and δ the reply; the smaller ε is, the smaller will δ have to be chosen. The phrase "however small" in the definition could be omitted; it embodies an irrelevant human element.

The definition becomes much shorter if the absolute-value notation is used. It reads as follows: The number A is the definite integral of f over $[a,b]$ if for any positive number ε there is a positive number δ such that

$$\left| \sum_{i=1}^{n} f(X_i)(x_i - x_{i-1}) - A \right| < \varepsilon$$

for any sum formed with any partition of $[a,b]$ of mesh less than δ (no matter how X_i is chosen in $[x_{i-1}, x_i]$).

DEFINITION: *Limit of a function of a real variable.* The number A is *the limit of $f(x)$ as x approaches a* if for any positive number ε, however small, there is a positive number δ, depending on ε, such that $f(x)$ differs from A by less than ε when x differs from a by less than δ (except, perhaps, when $x = a$).

REMARK. We assume that f is defined in an interval around a, but make no reference to $f(a)$ itself, even if f is defined at a.

In terms of absolute values, the definition reads as follows: The number A is the limit of $f(x)$ as x approaches a if for any positive number ε there is a positive number δ, depending on ε, such that

$$|f(x) - A| < \varepsilon$$

whenever $|x - a| < \delta$ (except, perhaps, when $x = a$).

DEFINITION: $\lim\limits_{x \to \infty} f(x)$. The number A is the *limit of $f(x)$ as x approaches infinity* if for any positive number ε, however small, there is a number X, depending on ε, such that $f(x)$ differs from A by less than ε for any x greater than X.

The reader should contrast these last two definitions with their informal counterparts on page 77.

DEFINITION: *The limit of a sequence.* The number A is the *limit of the sequence* a_n, if for each positive number ε, however small, there is a positive integer N, depending on ε, such that a_n differs from A by less than ε, whenever n is larger than N.

REMARK. As the challenge ε shrinks, we would expect that the reply N would have to become larger. For instance, in a proof that $\lim\limits_{n \to \infty} 1/n^2 = 0$, it turns out that the reply, N, has to be larger than $1/\sqrt{\varepsilon}$. The definition can also be phrased thus: The number A is the limit of the sequence a_n if for each positive number ε there is a positive integer N, depending on ε, such that

$$|a_n - A| < \varepsilon$$

whenever $n > N$.

Keep in mind that in all these cases a function need not have a definite integral, nor a function have a limit, nor a sequence have a limit (see Examples 2, 5, and 2 on pages 26, 78, and 67, respectively).

With these definitions it is then possible to *prove* such assertions as

If $\lim\limits_{x \to a} f(x) = A$ and $\lim\limits_{x \to a} g(x) = B$, then it follows that $\lim\limits_{x \to a} [f(x) \cdot g(x)] = A \cdot B$,

$\lim\limits_{x \to a} [f(x) + g(x)] = A + B$, and (if $B \neq 0$) $\lim\limits_{x \to a} f(x)/g(x) = A/B$

assertions we have already used. (See Appendix F.) We shall illustrate the effectiveness of the precise definition of the definite integral by proving a theorem that may not be obvious. To do so we first define a *bounded function*.

DEFINITION: *Bounded function.* A function f, defined on $[a,b]$, is *bounded* over $[a,b]$ if there is a number B such that

$$-B \leqslant f(x) \leqslant B \qquad \text{for all } x \text{ in } [a,b]$$

In other words, $|f(x)|$ does not become arbitrarily large for x in $[a,b]$. As the maximum value theorem shows, any continuous function on $[a,b]$ is bounded there.

For example, x^2 is bounded on $[0,1]$, since $x^2 \leqslant 1$ for any x in $[0,1]$. On the other hand, the function f given by

$$f(0) = 0 \qquad f(x) = \frac{1}{x} \qquad \text{if } 0 < x \leqslant 1$$

is *not* bounded on $[0,1]$. The maximum value theorem assures us that any continuous f is bounded on $[a,b]$.

THEOREM. *If f has a definite integral over $[a,b]$, then f is bounded over $[a,b]$.*

PROOF. We prove this in the case $[a,b] = [0,1]$. Let A be the definite integral of f over $[0,1]$ and consider $\varepsilon = 1$. Then there is a δ such that any sum

$$\sum_{i=1}^{n} f(X_i)(x_i - x_{i-1})$$

differs from A by less than 1, as long as the mesh of the partition is less than δ. Select m, an integer such that $1/m < \delta$. Then, in particular,

$$\sum_{i=1}^{m} f\left(\frac{i}{m}\right)\frac{1}{m}$$

differs from A by less than 1, since it is a sum obtained from a partition of mesh $= 1/m$, which is less than δ.

We show first why f is bounded over $[0, 1/m]$. To do so, choose X_1 arbitrarily in $[0, 1/m]$, $X_2 = 2/m$, $X_3 = 3/m$, . . . , $X_m = m/m = 1$. Now,

$$\sum_{i=1}^{m} f(X_i)\frac{1}{m} \qquad \text{and} \qquad \sum_{i=1}^{m} f\left(\frac{i}{m}\right)\frac{1}{m}$$

both differ from A by less than 1. Therefore

$$\sum_{i=1}^{m} f(X_i)\frac{1}{m} \qquad \text{differs from} \qquad \sum_{i=1}^{m} f\left(\frac{i}{m}\right)\frac{1}{m}$$

by less than 2. That is,

$$-2 < \sum_{i=1}^{m} f(X_i)\frac{1}{m} - \sum_{i=1}^{m} f\left(\frac{i}{m}\right)\frac{1}{m} < 2$$

But in view of the special choice of X_1, X_2, . . . the preceding inequality reduces to

$$-2 < f(X_1)\frac{1}{m} - f\left(\frac{1}{m}\right)\frac{1}{m} < 2$$

Multiplying by m, we obtain

$$-2m < f(X_1) - f\left(\frac{1}{m}\right) < 2m$$

and thus
$$-2m + f\left(\frac{1}{m}\right) < f(X_1) < 2m + f\left(\frac{1}{m}\right)$$

Since X_1 was arbitrary in $\left[0, \dfrac{1}{m}\right]$, we see that f is bounded on $\left[0, \dfrac{1}{m}\right]$.

In a similar manner we can show that f is bounded on $[1/m, 2/m]$, on $[2/m, 3/m], \ldots$, and on $[(m-1)/m, 1]$. Thus f is bounded on $[0,1]$. The theorem is proved.

It takes a good deal of practice to feel at home with the style of such proofs. To appreciate it, one should try to "prove" the theorem without exploiting a precise definition of the definite integral. Other, simpler proofs in this style appear in Appendix F.

Using the precise definition of the definite integral, we can also prove such assertions as

$$\int_a^b cf(x)\,dx = c\int_a^b f(x)\,dx$$

where c is a constant factor;

$$\int_a^b [f(x) + g(x)]\,dx = \int_a^b f(x)\,dx + \int_a^b g(x)\,dx$$

and, if $f(x) \leqslant g(x)$ for all x in $[a,b]$,

$$\int_a^b f(x)\,dx \leqslant \int_a^b g(x)\,dx$$

(assuming, of course, that the various definite integrals in question exist.)

If we interpret the various functions as cross-sectional functions of some plane set, the three assertions are plausible. The first then says "If we magnify each vertical cross section of a plane set by the factor c, then we magnify the area by c." The second says "The area of a set that is cut into two sets is the sum of the areas of those two sets," and the third "If one set A lies within another set B, then the area of A is not larger than the area of B."

EXERCISES

1. Let $f(x) = 1/x$ if $x \neq 0$, and $f(0) = 3$. Show that for any fixed partition of $[0,1]$ you can choose X_1 in $[x_0, x_1]$ in such a way as to make $\sum_{i=1}^{n} f(X_i)(x_i - x_{i-1})$ as large as you please. In view of this fact, do you think $\int_0^1 f(x)$ exists? (Compare your opinion with the theorem in this section.)

2. Show explicitly why

$$\sum_{i=1}^{m} f(X_i)\frac{1}{m} - \sum_{i=1}^{m} f\left(\frac{1}{m}\right)\frac{1}{m} = f(X_1)\frac{1}{m} - f\left(\frac{1}{m}\right)\left(\frac{1}{m}\right),$$

as stated in the proof of the theorem.

3. In the proof of the theorem on page 88 did we have to choose $\varepsilon = 1$? Would $\varepsilon = 1,000$ have sufficed?

4. Showing all details, prove that f in the theorem on page 88 is bounded on $[1/m, 2/m]$.

5. Explain why the fact that f is bounded on each of

$$\left[0, \frac{1}{m}\right], \left[\frac{1}{m}, \frac{2}{m}\right], \left[\frac{2}{m}, \frac{3}{m}\right], \ldots, \left[\frac{m-1}{m}, 1\right]$$

implies that f is bounded on $[0,1]$.

□ □ □

6. Give a precise definition of $\lim\limits_{x \to -\infty} f(x)$.

7. (a) In the precise definition of the definite integral (page 86), an ε and a δ appear. In general, as ε shrinks what has to happen to δ?

(b) In the precise definition of $\lim\limits_{x \to \infty} f(x)$ appear an ε and an X. In general, as ε shrinks what has to happen to X?

8. Prove the theorem on page 88. (We proved it only for $[a,b] = [0,1]$.)

9. Prove that if a function has a definite integral over a square set, it is bounded there.

10. The symbols $\lim\limits_{x \to \infty} f(x) = \infty$ are supposed to suggest that as x gets arbitrarily large (and positive), so does $f(x)$. For instance, $\lim\limits_{x \to \infty} x^2 = \infty$. Devise a precise definition for this general concept.

11. The symbols $\lim\limits_{x \to a} f(x) = \infty$ are supposed to suggest that as x approaches a, the function $f(x)$ becomes and remains very large (and positive). (For instance, $\lim\limits_{x \to 0} (1/x)^2 = \infty$). Devise a precise definition for this general concept.

12. Using the precise definition of the definite integral, page 86, prove the following.

(a) If $\int_a^b f(x)\,dx = A$ and $\int_a^b g(x)\,dx = B$, then $\int_a^b [f(x)+ g(x)]\,dx$ exists and equals $A + B$.

(b) If $\int_a^b f(x)\,dx = A$, then $\int_a^b cf(x)\,dx$ exists and equals cA, where c is a constant factor.

13. Interpret the assertion "If $f(x) \leqslant g(x)$ for all x in $[a,b]$, then $\int_a^b f(x)\,dx \leqslant \int_a^b g(x)\,dx$" where (a) f and g are densities of matter on a line; (b) f and g are speeds of two cars.

5. Summary. This chapter made precise the ideas conveyed somewhat loosely in such phrases as "as n gets arbitrarily large, a_n approaches A," "as x approaches a, $f(x)$ approaches A," and "as the mesh approaches 0, $\sum_{i=1}^{n} f(X_i)(x_i - x_{i-1})$ approaches A." In each case, the precise definition is phrased in terms of the existence of a number that meets the challenge represented by the number $\varepsilon > 0$, and which usually depends on ε. We also defined a continuous function and a bounded function. As an illustration of precise definitions, we proved that a function that has a definite integral over an interval is bounded there.

4

The computation
of derivatives

In Chaps. 2 and 3 we computed a few derivatives, showing that $D(x^2) = 2x$, $D(x^3) = 3x^2$, $D(\sqrt{x}) = 1/(2\sqrt{x})$, and $D(x^5) = 5x^4$. We also attacked the problem of finding the derivatives of 10^x, $\log_{10} x$, and $\sin x$. Each time we went back to the definition of the derivative and examined

$$\lim_{\Delta x \to 0} \frac{\Delta y}{\Delta x}$$

with the aid of various algebraic or trigonometric identities. In view of the importance of the derivative, it will be convenient to be able to compute swiftly the derivatives of the common functions. This chapter will develop the necessary machinery, so that we shall be able to compute derivatives without having to examine limits each time.

92

1. The derivatives of some basic functions. Later in this chapter we will show that the derivatives of many functions can be computed if we know the derivatives of the following functions: the constant functions; the power functions x^n; the trigonometric functions, sin x and cos x; and the logarithmic function. In this section we compute the derivatives of these basic functions.

THEOREM 1. *The derivative of a constant function is 0. [Briefly, $D(c) = 0$.]*

PROOF. Let c be a number and let $f(x) = c$ for all x. Then for any $\Delta x \neq 0$ we have $\Delta f = f(x + \Delta x) - f(x) = c - c = 0$. Thus $\Delta f/\Delta x = 0/\Delta x = 0$, and $\lim_{\Delta x \to 0} (\Delta f/\Delta x) = 0$. The theorem is proved.

REMARK. From two points of view, Theorem 1 is not a surprise. After all, the graph of $f(x) = c$ is a horizontal line, and coincides with each of its tangent lines:

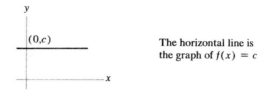

The horizontal line is the graph of $f(x) = c$

Also, if we think of x as time, and $f(x)$ as "position" of a particle, then Theorem 1 implies that a stationary particle has zero velocity.

THEOREM 2. *If n is a positive integer, $1, 2, 3, \ldots$, then the derivative of x^n is nx^{n-1}. [Briefly, $D(x^n) = nx^{n-1}$.]*

PROOF. Let $f(x) = x^n$. Then $\Delta f = f(x + \Delta x) - f(x) = (x + \Delta x)^n - x^n$. The binomial theorem asserts that

$$(x + \Delta x)^n = x^n + nx^{n-1} \Delta x + \frac{(n)(n-1)}{1 \cdot 2} x^{n-2} (\Delta x)^2$$

$$+ \frac{(n)(n-1)(n-2)}{1 \cdot 2 \cdot 3} x^{n-3} (\Delta x)^3 + \cdots + (\Delta x)^n$$

Thus

$(x + \Delta x)^n = x^n + nx^{n-1} \Delta x + (\Delta x)$ (sum of terms each of which has Δx as a factor)

and hence

$(x + \Delta x)^n - x^n = nx^{n-1} \Delta x + (\Delta x)$ (something approaching 0 as Δx approaches 0)

Now we examine $\Delta f/\Delta x$. We have

$$\frac{\Delta f}{\Delta x} = \frac{nx^{n-1} \Delta x + (\Delta x) \text{ (something approaching } 0 \text{ as } \Delta x \text{ approaches } 0)}{\Delta x}$$

Dividing numerator and denominator by Δx (which is not 0), we obtain

$$\lim_{\Delta x \to 0} \frac{\Delta f}{\Delta x} = \lim_{\Delta x \to 0} (nx^{n-1} + \text{something that approaches } 0)$$

$$= nx^{n-1} + 0 = nx^{n-1}$$

Theorem 2 is proved.

REMARKS. If $n = 1$, Theorem 2 asserts that $D(x^1) = 1x^0 = 1$. Thus Theorem 2 implies that $D(x) = 1$. This is not surprising, for the graph of $y = x$ is the straight line with slope 1:

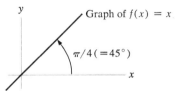

For $n = 2$, Theorem 2 says that $D(x^2) = 2x^1 = 2x$, a result found in Chap. 2. Similarly, it implies that $D(x^3) = 3x^2$ and $D(x^5) = 5x^4$.

THEOREM 3.   *The derivative of* $\sin x$ *is* $\cos x$.

PROOF.   In this case, $\Delta f = \sin(x + \Delta x) - \sin x$. But $\sin(x + \Delta x) = \sin x \cos \Delta x + \cos x \sin \Delta x$. Hence

$$\Delta f = \sin x \cos \Delta x + \cos x \sin \Delta x - \sin x$$

$$= \sin x (\cos \Delta x - 1) + \cos x \sin \Delta x$$

Thus

$$\frac{\Delta f}{\Delta x} = \sin x \frac{\cos \Delta x - 1}{\Delta x} + \cos x \frac{\sin \Delta x}{\Delta x}$$

Recall that we proved in Chap. 3 that

$$\lim_{\Delta x \to 0} \frac{1 - \cos \Delta x}{\Delta x} = 0 \quad \text{and} \quad \lim_{\Delta x \to 0} \frac{\sin \Delta x}{\Delta x} = 1$$

Rewriting $\dfrac{\Delta f}{\Delta x}$ as $(-\sin x) \dfrac{1 - \cos \Delta x}{\Delta x} + \cos x \dfrac{\sin \Delta x}{\Delta x}$, we obtain

$$\lim_{\Delta x \to 0} \frac{\Delta f}{\Delta x} = (-\sin x) \lim_{\Delta x \to 0} \frac{1 - \cos \Delta x}{\Delta x} + \cos x \lim_{\Delta x \to 0} \frac{\sin \Delta x}{\Delta x}$$

which is simply

$$(-\sin x)(0) + (\cos x)(1) = \cos x$$

Hence $\lim_{\Delta x \to 0} (\Delta f / \Delta x) = \cos x$. The theorem is proved.

REMARK.   In particular, $D(\sin x)$ for $x = 0$ is $\cos 0 = 1$. This implies that the graph of $y = \sin x$ cuts the x axis at the origin with slope 1, hence at an angle of $\pi/4$.

THEOREM 4. *The derivative of $\cos x$ is $-\sin x$.*

We omit the proof, which is similar to the proof of Theorem 3. It makes use of the trigonometric identity,

$$\cos (x + \Delta x) = \cos x \cos \Delta x - \sin x \sin \Delta x$$

Before we find the derivative of $\log_{10} x$, let us recall the definition of a logarithm.

DEFINITION: *Logarithm.* If a and c are positive numbers, and $a^b = c$, we call b the logarithm of c relative to the base a, and write

$$b = \log_a c$$

Thus $\log_2 8 = 3$, $\log_7 7 = 1$, $\log_\pi 1 = 0$, $\log_5 \frac{1}{5} = -1$, $\log_{10} 10 = 1$, $\log_e e = 1$, $\log_{10} 100 = 2$, $\log_{10} 0.1 = -1$, $5^{\log_5 27} = 27$.

In finding the derivative of the function $\log_{10} x$ we will assume these properties of the logarithm and exponential functions: If A and B are positive numbers and r and s are any real numbers, then $\log_{10} (A/B) = \log_{10} A - \log_{10} B$, $\log_{10} A^r = r \log_{10} A$, and $(A^r)^s = A^{rs}$. We also assume that $\lim_{h \to 0} (1 + h)^{1/h}$ exists (we denote it e, see Example 3, page 76), and that the function $\log_{10}$ is continuous.

THEOREM 5. *The derivative of $\log_{10} x$ is $(\log_{10} e)/x$ for $x > 0$.*

PROOF.   Here $\Delta f = \log_{10} (x + \Delta x) - \log_{10} x$. Since $\log_{10} A - \log_{10} B = \log_{10} (A/B)$, we have

$$\Delta f = \log_{10} \frac{x + \Delta x}{x} = \log_{10} \left(1 + \frac{\Delta x}{x} \right)$$

Then

$$\frac{\Delta f}{\Delta x} = \frac{1}{\Delta x} \log_{10} \left(1 + \frac{\Delta x}{x} \right)$$

Since $r \log_{10} A = \log_{10} (A^r)$, we have

$$\frac{\Delta f}{\Delta x} = \log_{10} \left(1 + \frac{\Delta x}{x} \right)^{1/\Delta x}$$

We now rewrite

$$\left(1 + \frac{\Delta x}{x} \right)^{1/\Delta x} \qquad \text{as} \qquad \left(1 + \frac{\Delta x}{x} \right)^{(x/\Delta x)\,(1/x)}$$

and the latter as

$$\left[\left(1 + \frac{\Delta x}{x} \right)^{x/\Delta x} \right]^{1/x}$$

which is of the form A^r, where

$$A = \left(1 + \frac{\Delta x}{x} \right)^{x/\Delta x} \qquad \text{and} \qquad r = \frac{1}{x}$$

Thus

$$\frac{\Delta f}{\Delta x} = \log_{10} \left[\left(1 + \frac{\Delta x}{x} \right)^{x/\Delta x} \right]^{1/x} = \frac{1}{x} \log_{10} \left(1 + \frac{\Delta x}{x} \right)^{x/\Delta x}$$

Now, if we call $(\Delta x)/x$ simply h, and observe that as Δx approaches 0, so does h, we have

$$\lim_{\Delta x \to 0} \frac{\Delta f}{\Delta x} = \frac{1}{x} \lim_{h \to 0} \left[\log_{10} (1 + h)^{\frac{1}{h}} \right]$$

But, since the logarithm function is continuous,

$$\lim_{h \to 0} \left[\log_{10} (1 + h)^{\frac{1}{h}} \right] = \log_{10} e$$

Thus
$$\lim_{\Delta x \to 0} \frac{\Delta f}{\Delta x} = \frac{1}{x} \log_{10} e$$

and the theorem is proved.

REMARKS. Since $e = 2.178 \ldots$, a table of logarithms to the base 10 yields $\log_{10} e = 0.434 \ldots$. Approximately,

$$D(\log_{10} x) = 0.434 \frac{1}{x}$$

The awkward "0.434" can be avoided if we compute logarithms to a base different from 10, as the next theorem shows.

THEOREM 6.   *The derivative of* $\log_a x$ *is* $(1/x) \log_a e$. *In particular,*

$$D(\log_e x) = \frac{1}{x}$$

PROOF. The proof of Theorem 6 is obtained from the proof of Theorem 5 by replacing 10 with a throughout. We assume that $\log_a x$ satisfies the same conditions as the function $\log_{10} x$; for example, $\log_a (A/B) = \log_a A - \log_a B$.

Note that e is the base that yields the simplest formula for the derivative of the resulting logarithm. For this reason we will generally use base e rather than base 10. We will write $\log_e x$ as $\ln x$ (the natural logarithm of x). (For purposes of arithmetic—such as using logarithms for multiplication—base 10 is preferable.) Most handbooks of mathematical tables include tables of $\log_{10} x$ ("common logarithm") and $\ln x$ ("natural logarithm"). It would be helpful at this point to browse through both tables. Though natural logarithms were introduced in the seventeenth century, the symbol "ln" was first used in 1893.

EXERCISES

1. (*a*) Let $f(x) = x$ for all x. Using only the definition of the derivative, prove that $f'(x) = 1$ for all x.
   (*b*) Let $f(x) = 4$ for all x. Using only the definition of the derivative, prove that $f'(x) = 0$ for all x.
2. Write out in detail a direct proof that $D(x^4) = 4x^3$, using as an outline the proof of Theorem 2. In particular, write out all five terms in the expansion of $(x + \Delta x)^4$.

3. Prove Theorem 4, which asserts that $d(\cos x)/dx = -\sin x$.

4. (a) Without the use of tables, compute $\log_{10} 1, \log_{10} 10, \log_{10} 100, \log_{10} 0.1, \log_{10} 0.01$.
(b) With the aid of (a), graph $y = \log_{10} x$.
(c) For which x is $\log_{10} x$ defined?

5. (a) (See Exercise 4.) Draw a tangent to the graph of $y = \log_{10} x$ at $(1,0)$.
(b) Estimate the slope of the line you drew.
(c) Is the number you obtained in (b) in reasonable agreement with the derivative of $\log_{10} x$ at $x = 1$?

6. Compute $\log_2 4$, $\log_4 2$, $\log_{10} \sqrt{10}$, $\log_3 \frac{1}{3}$, $\log_e 1$, $2^{\log_2 8}$, $e^{\ln x}$, $10^{\log_{10} 17}$, the father of the boy whose father is James.

7. (a) Taking 2.7 as an approximation of e, estimate e^2 and e^{-1}.
(b) Using (a) and, if you wish, a table of the exponential function e^x, graph e^x.
(c) Draw a tangent line to the graph of e^x at $(0,1)$. Estimate the slope of the line you drew.

8. (a) In the proof of Theorem 5, why did we change $(1 + \Delta x/x)^{1/\Delta x}$ to $[(1 + \Delta x/x)^{x/\Delta x}]^{1/x}$?
(b) How was the continuity of $\log_{10} x$ used?

9. Prove Theorem 6.

10. To draw a tangent to the curve $y = x^4$ at $(2,16)$, lay off the distance 16 three times on the y axis, beginning at $(0,0)$ and moving down, thereby obtaining the point $(0, -48)$. Then the line through $(0, -48)$ and $(2,16)$ will be tangent to $y = x^4$ at $(2,16)$. Why?

11. Using the definition of derivative, show that $D(x^3/3 + x^2/2 + x) = x^2 + x + 1$.

12. Knowing that $D(x^n) = nx^{n-1}$ for $n = 1, 2, \ldots$, find (a) the slope of the tangent line to the curve $y = x^6$ at $(1,1)$; (b) the density at $x = 3$ of a string whose left-hand x inches has a mass of x^4 ounces; (c) the speed at time $t = \frac{1}{2}$ of an object that travels t^8 miles in t hours; (d) the magnification at $x = 1$ of a lens that projects x onto x^{100}.

13. (a) What is the slope of the tangent line to the curve $y = \sin x$ at $(\pi/3, \sin (\pi/3))$?
(b) An object on a spring scale oscillates up and down and at time t has the y coordinate $\sin t$. How fast is it moving at $t = \pi/3$? Assume that distance is in feet and time in seconds.
(c) What is the derivative of $\sin x$ at $x = \pi/3$?

[Answer: (c) $\frac{1}{2}$]

14. Carry through the following alternative proof of Theorem 2.
(a) Prove, by multiplying out the left side, that

$$(y - x)(y^{n-1} + y^{n-2} x + y^{n-3} x^2 + \cdots + yx^{n-2} + x^{n-1}) = y^n - x^n$$

(b) Using (a), prove that $\lim_{x_2 \to x_1} (x_2^n - x_1^n)/(x_2 - x_1) = nx_1^{n-1}$.

15. Show that $D(\sin 2x) = 2 \cos 2x$. (Hint: Examine $\Delta y/\Delta x$.)

16. Show that $D(\ln 2x) = 1/x$.

17. Show that $d(e^{2x})/dx = 2e^{2x}$.

18. Show that $(\sin x^2)' = 2x \cos x^2$. (Hint: Examine $\Delta y/\Delta x$.)

19. Show that $d(\ln x^2)/dx = 2/x$.

2. The derivatives of the sum, difference, product, and quotient of functions. We know that $D(x^2) = 2x$, $D(x^3) = 3x^2$, $D(\sin x) = \cos x$. If we need the derivative of $(x^2 + x^3)/\sin x$, must we still go back to the definition of the derivative and study a quotient, $\Delta f/\Delta x$? The answer is no, and the following theorems provide short cuts for computing such derivatives.

THEOREM 1. *If we know df/dx and dg/dx, then we know that $f + g$ has a derivative and*

$$\frac{d(f + g)}{dx} = \frac{df}{dx} + \frac{dg}{dx}$$

PROOF. Give $f + g$ the name h. Then $h(x + \Delta x) = f(x + \Delta x) + g(x + \Delta x)$, and $h(x) = f(x) + g(x)$. Thus a little algebra shows that

$$h(x + \Delta x) - h(x) = [f(x + \Delta x) - f(x)] + [g(x + \Delta x) - g(x)]$$

or simply

$$\Delta h = \Delta f + \Delta g$$

and thus

$$\lim_{\Delta x \to 0} \frac{\Delta h}{\Delta x} = \lim_{\Delta x \to 0} \frac{\Delta f + \Delta g}{\Delta x} = \lim_{\Delta x \to 0} \left(\frac{\Delta f}{\Delta x} + \frac{\Delta g}{\Delta x} \right) = \lim_{\Delta x \to 0} \frac{\Delta f}{\Delta x} + \lim_{\Delta x \to 0} \frac{\Delta g}{\Delta x} = \frac{df}{dx} + \frac{dg}{dx}$$

In other words, the derivative of h is the sum of the derivatives of f and g. The theorem is proved.

Example 1. $D(x^2 + x^3) = D(x^2) + D(x^3) = 2x + 3x^2$.

Example 2. $D(\ln x + \cos x) = (1/x) - \sin x$.

The following theorems could all be phrased in the style of Theorem 1. However, we will state them tersely to emphasize their computational significance.

THEOREM 2.   *If f and g have derivatives, then $D(f - g) = Df - Dg$.*
The proof, similar to the one for Theorem 1, is omitted.

Example 3. $D(x^2 - \sin x) = 2x - \cos x$.

The following theorem concerning the derivative of the product of two functions may be surprising; it was *not* the first guess, in 1675, of Leibniz, who first obtained the basic properties of the derivative.

THEOREM 3.   *If f and g have derivatives, then $D(fg) = f D(g) + g D(f)$.*

Before we present the proof, we offer two examples.

Example 4. $D(x^2 \sin x) = (x^2)(\cos x) + (\sin x)(2x)$.

Example 5. $D(x^3 \cdot x^5) = (x^3)(5x^4) + (x^5)(3x^2)$, which simplifies to $5x^7 + 3x^7 = 8x^7$, in agreement with our previous result, $D(x^8) = 8x^7$.

PROOF OF THEOREM 3.   Call the function fg simply h. Thus

$$h(x + \Delta x) = f(x + \Delta x) g(x + \Delta x)$$

and $$h(x) = f(x)\, g(x)$$

Rather than subtract directly, we first write

$$f(x + \Delta x) = f(x) + \Delta f \qquad \text{and} \qquad g(x + \Delta x) = g(x) + \Delta g$$

Then

$$h(x + \Delta x) = [f(x) + \Delta f]\,[g(x) + \Delta g] = f(x)g(x) + f(x)\,\Delta g + g(x)\,\Delta f + \Delta f\,\Delta g$$

Hence $$\Delta h = f(x)\,\Delta g + g(x)\,\Delta f + \Delta f\,\Delta g$$

and $$\frac{\Delta h}{\Delta x} = f(x)\,\frac{\Delta g}{\Delta x} + g(x)\,\frac{\Delta f}{\Delta x} + \Delta f\,\frac{\Delta g}{\Delta x}$$

Taking limits, we obtain

$$\lim_{\Delta x \to 0} \frac{\Delta h}{\Delta x} = f(x)\, D(g) + g(x)\, D(f) + (0)\, D(g)$$

from which we conclude that

$$D(h) = f\, D(g) + g\, D(f)$$

and the theorem is proved.

COROLLARY TO THEOREM 3.   If f has a derivative and c is a constant, $D(cf) = c\, D(f)$.

PROOF.   Let g be the constant function given by

$$g(x) = c$$

By Theorem 1 of Sec. 1, we have $D(g) = 0$. By Theorem 3, we have $D(gf) = g\, D(f) + f\, D(g)$, which in the present case becomes $c\, D(f)$. This proves the corollary. (A direct proof is outlined in Exercise 5.)

Example 6. $D(6x^2) = 6D(x^2) = 6(2x) = 12x.$

THEOREM 4.   *If f and g have derivatives, then*

$$D\left(\frac{f}{g}\right) = \frac{g\, D(f) - f\, D(g)}{g^2} \qquad \text{where } g(x) \neq 0$$

PROOF.   Denote the quotient function f/g by h. Thus $h(x) = f(x)/g(x)$ and $h(x + \Delta x) = f(x + \Delta x)/g(x + \Delta x)$. [Since $g(x) \neq 0$ and g is continuous, for Δx sufficiently small, $g(x + \Delta x) \neq 0$.] Before we compute Δh, we write $f(x + \Delta x)$ as $f(x) + \Delta f$, and $g(x + \Delta x)$ as $g(x) + \Delta g$. Then we have

$$\Delta h = \frac{f(x) + \Delta f}{g(x) + \Delta g} - \frac{f(x)}{g(x)}$$

Putting the right side over a common denominator, we obtain

$$\Delta h = \frac{g(x)\,[f(x) + \Delta f] - f(x)\,[g(x) + \Delta g]}{g(x)\,[g(x) + \Delta g]}$$

which we can write as

$$\Delta h = \frac{g(x)f(x) + g(x)\,\Delta f - f(x)g(x) - f(x)\,\Delta g}{g(x)\,[g(x) + \Delta g]}$$

With the cancelation of $g(x)f(x)$ and $f(x)g(x)$, we obtain

$$\Delta h = \frac{g(x)\,\Delta f - f(x)\,\Delta g}{g(x)\,[g(x) + \Delta g]}$$

hence
$$\frac{\Delta h}{\Delta x} = \frac{g(x)\,(\Delta f/\Delta x) - f(x)\,(\Delta g/\Delta x)}{g(x)\,[g(x) + \Delta g]}$$

We are ready to examine $\lim\limits_{\Delta x \to 0} (\Delta h/\Delta x)$. Since $\lim\limits_{\Delta x \to 0} (\Delta f/\Delta x) = D(f)$, $\lim\limits_{\Delta x \to 0} \Delta g/\Delta x = D(g)$, and $\lim\limits_{\Delta x \to 0} \Delta g = 0$, we obtain

$$D(h) = \frac{g(x)\,D(f) - f(x)\,D(g)}{[g(x)]^2}$$

and the theorem is proved.

Example 7.
$$D\!\left(\frac{1 + x^2}{5 + x^3}\right) = \frac{(5 + x^3)\,D(1 + x^2) - (1 + x^2)\,D(5 + x^3)}{(5 + x^3)^2}$$

Now, $D(1 + x^2) = D(1) + D(x^2) = 0 + 2x$, and, similarly, $D(5 + x^3) = 3x^2$. Thus

$$D\!\left(\frac{1 + x^2}{5 + x^3}\right) = \frac{(5 + x^3)\,(2x) - (1 + x^2)\,(3x^2)}{(5 + x^3)^2}$$

which, in an emergency, could be simplified.

COROLLARY 1 TO THEOREM 4. $D(1/x) = -1/x^2$.

PROOF.   Apply Theorem 4 to the case in which $f(x) = 1$ for all x and $g(x) = x$ for all x;

$$D\!\left(\frac{1}{x}\right) = D\!\left(\frac{f}{g}\right) = \frac{g\,D(f) - f\,D(g)}{g^2}$$

which, in view of the fact that $D(f) = 0$ and $D(g) = 1$, gives

$$D\!\left(\frac{1}{x}\right) = -\frac{f\,D(g)}{g^2} = -\frac{(1)\,(1)}{x^2} = \frac{-1}{x^2}$$

More generally, we have the following result.

COROLLARY 2 TO THEOREM 4.   If n is a negative integer, $n = -1, -2, -3, \dots$, then $D(x^n) = nx^{n-1}$.

PROOF.   We write out the proof for only one case, say, $n = -3$. In this case,

$$D(x^n) = D(x^{-3}) = \underset{D(f/g)}{D\!\left(\frac{1}{x^3}\right)} = \frac{(x^3)\,D(1) - 1\,D(x^3)}{(x^3)^2} = \frac{(x^3)\,(0) - (1)\,(3x^2)}{x^6} = \frac{-3x^2}{x^6}$$

$$= \frac{-3}{x^4} = (-3)\,x^{-4} = (-3)\,x^{-3-1} = nx^{n-1}$$

A similar proof works for any negative integer.

REMARK.   In the preceding proof we put $D(f/g)$ below an equals sign as a short-hand justification for the equation. This is a handy device for keeping in mind what we are doing as we compute.

COROLLARY 3 TO THEOREM 4. $D\left(\dfrac{1}{f}\right) = -\dfrac{D(f)}{f^2}$.

The proof is left to the reader.

COROLLARY 4 TO THEOREM 4. $D(\tan x) = \sec^2 x$; $D(\sec x) = \sec x \tan x$; $D(\cot x) = -\csc^2 x$; $D(\csc x) = -\csc x \cot x$.

PROOF.   We prove only the first two statements.

$$D(\tan x) = D\left(\frac{\sin x}{\cos x}\right) = \frac{\cos x\, D(\sin x) - \sin x\, D(\cos x)}{\cos^2 x}$$

$$= \frac{(\cos x)(\cos x) - \sin x\,(-\sin x)}{\cos^2 x} = \frac{\cos^2 x + \sin^2 x}{\cos^2 x} = \frac{1}{\cos^2 x} = \sec^2 x$$

$$D(\sec x) = D\left(\frac{1}{\cos x}\right) = \frac{-D(\cos x)}{\cos^2 x} = \frac{\sin x}{\cos^2 x} = \frac{1}{\cos x}\frac{\sin x}{\cos x} = \sec x \tan x$$

Example 8.

$$
\begin{aligned}
D(5x^{-2} + \tan x + \ln x) &= \underset{D(f+g)}{D(5x^{-2} + \tan x) + D(\ln x)} \\
&= \underset{D(f+g)}{D(5x^{-2}) + D(\tan x) + D(\ln x)} \\
&= \underset{D(cf)}{5D(x^{-2}) + D(\tan x) + D(\ln x)} \\
&= 5(-2x^{-3}) + \sec^2 x + 1/x
\end{aligned}
$$

Example 8 points out that *the derivative of the sum of several functions is the sum of their derivatives.*

EXERCISES

1. (*a*) Compute $D(x^2 + x^3)$ without using Theorem 1.
   (*b*) Compute $D(x^2 + x^3)$ with the aid of Theorem 1.
2. (*a*) Compute $D(x^4 + 2)$ without using Theorem 1.
   (*b*) Compute $D(x^4 + 2)$ with the aid of Theorem 1.
3. With the aid of Theorem 1, compute $D(x^4 + x^6 + x^8)$.

   (Answer: $4x^3 + 6x^5 + 8x^7$)
4. With the aid of Theorem 1, compute $D(\cos x + x^2)$.
5. Prove, without the aid of Theorem 3, that $D(cf) = c\,D(f)$. [Hint: Call $cf = h$; then $h(x) = cf(x)$.]
6. Write out the proof of Corollary 2 to Theorem 4 for $n = -5$.
7. Justifying each step by placing the appropriate symbols below each equals sign in your computation, find with the aid of the various theorems (*a*) $D(5 + 6x^2)$; and (*b*) $D((1 + 3x)/(x^2 + \sin x))$ [Answer: (*a*) $12x$]

8. (See Exercise 7.) Justifying each step, compute (a) $D[(x^2 - \ln x)(x^5)]$.
(b) $D(\sin x/\cos x)$.

9. (a) Prove Corollary 3 to Theorem 4. (Hint: Use Theorem 4.)
(b) With the aid of Corollary 3 to Theorem 4, compute $D(1/(x^5 + 1))$, $D(1/\sin x)$, and $D[1/(x + \log_{10} x)]$.
    [Answer: (b) $-5x^4/(x^5 + 1)^2$; $-\cos x/\sin^2 x$; $-[1 + (1/x)\log_{10} e]/(x + \log_{10} x)^2$]

10. Complete the proof of Corollary 4 to Theorem 4.

11. Compute the derivative of (a) $1/(1 + x^2)$; (b) $(\sin x)/(1 + x^2)$; (c) $5 \ln x - 6 \sin x$.
    [Answer: (a) $-2x/(1 + x^2)^2$; (b) $[(1 + x^2)\cos x - 2x \sin x]/(1 + x^2)^2$;
    (c) $(5/x) - 6 \cos x$]

12. Compute the derivative of (a) $(1 + 2x)/(1 - 2x)$; (b) $4x^5 \cos x$; (c) $x^5 - \ln x$.

13. Compute the derivative of (a) $x^4 - \tan x$; (b) $x^4 + \tan x$; (c) $x^4/\tan x$; (d) $x^4 \tan x$.

14. (a) Assuming $D(x^5) = 5x^4$ and $D(x) = 1$, show how Theorem 3 then can be used to obtain $D(x^6)$.
(b) Show how one can use Theorem 3, together with $D(x) = 1$, to obtain, successively, $D(x^2) = 2x, D(x^3) = 3x^2$, and so on—in short, another proof that $D(x^n) = nx^{n-1}$ when n is a positive integer.

15. Without the aid of Theorem 3, prove that $D(x^2 \sin x) = x^2 \cos x + (\sin x)(2x)$.

16. Write out a general proof of Corollary 2 to Theorem 4.

17. (See Exercise 10, page 97.) Develop a way of drawing the tangent line to (x,y) on the curve $y = x^n$, where n is a positive integer.

18. (a) Using $\lim_{\theta \to 0} \sin \theta/\theta = 1$, prove that $\lim_{\theta \to 0} \tan \theta/\theta = 1$.
(b) Using (a) and the identity $\tan x - \tan y = (1 + \tan x \tan y)[\tan (x - y)]$, obtain a direct proof that $D(\tan x) = \sec^2 x$.

3. The chain rule. One way to find the derivative of $(1 + x^2)^{100}$ consists of first multiplying it out, expressing it as a polynomial of degree 200 with 101 terms, and then computing the derivative by methods we developed in Sec. 2. We will develop a much quicker technique.

We notice that $y = (1 + x^2)^{100}$ is built up in stages from the simpler functions,

$$y = u^{100} \qquad u = 1 + x^2$$

As another instance, $y = \sqrt[3]{\sin x}$ can be expressed as

$$y = \sqrt[3]{u} \qquad u = \sin x$$

These are special cases of

$$y = f(u) \qquad u = g(x)$$

Indirectly, then, y is a function of x, $y = f(g(x))$. This new function, the composition of f and g, we denote $f \circ g$; we have

$$y = (f \circ g)(x) = f(g(x))$$

(This concept of the composite function is discussed further in Appendix C.)

If we think of g as some complicated projection from a slide to a screen (see Chap. 2, page 42) and f as a projection from that screen to a second screen, then $f \circ g$ is the final projection from the slide to the second screen.

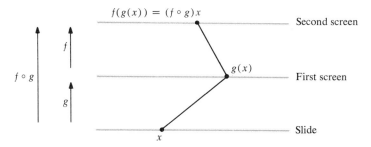

The question is this: If we know $D(g)$ and $D(f)$, how can we find $D(f \circ g)$? Let us use our optical intuition first. The projection g magnifies at x by a factor $D(g)$ evaluated at x. Then the projection f magnifies at $g(x)$ by a factor $D(f)$ evaluated at $g(x)$. Intuitively we might suspect that the magnification of $f \circ g$ is the *product* of the two successive magnifications. We conjecture that $D(f \circ g)$ at x is equal to $[f'$ at $g(x)]$ times $(g'$ at $x)$. The following theorem shows that our conjecture is correct.

THEOREM: *The chain rule.* $D(f \circ g)(x) = f'(g(x)) \cdot g'(x)$.

PROOF. We must compute $\lim_{\Delta x \to 0} \Delta(f \circ g)/\Delta x$. The computations will involve Δx, Δg, and $\Delta(f \circ g)$, which are shown in this diagram:

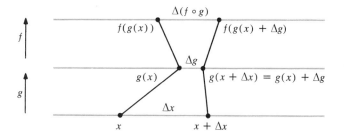

Since f is differentiable at $g(x)$, $\Delta(f \circ g) = f'(g(x)) \Delta g + (\varepsilon)(\Delta g)$, where $\varepsilon \to 0$ as $\Delta g \to 0$ (see page 79). We set $\varepsilon = 0$ if $\Delta g = 0$. Thus

$$\frac{\Delta(f \circ g)}{\Delta x} = f'(g(x)) \frac{\Delta g}{\Delta x} + \varepsilon \frac{\Delta g}{\Delta x}$$

and we have

$$(f \circ g)'(x) = \lim_{\Delta x \to 0} \frac{\Delta(f \circ g)}{\Delta x} = \lim_{\Delta x \to 0} \left[f'(g(x)) \frac{\Delta g}{\Delta x} + \varepsilon \frac{\Delta g}{\Delta x} \right]$$

$$= f'(g(x)) \lim_{\Delta x \to 0} \frac{\Delta g}{\Delta x} + \lim_{\Delta x \to 0} \varepsilon \lim_{\Delta x \to 0} \frac{\Delta g}{\Delta x} = f'(g(x)) g'(x) + 0 \, g'(x)$$

and thus
$$D(f \circ g)(x) = f'((g(x))\, g'(x)$$

The chain rule is proved.

Example 1. Let $f(x) = x^{100}$ and $g(x) = x^2 + 1$. Then $(f \circ g)(x) = f(g(x)) = f(x^2 + 1)$ $= (x^2 + 1)^{100}$. Then $f'(x) = 100x^{99}$ and $g'(x) = 2x$. The chain rule then asserts that

$$\underbrace{D[(x^2 + 1)^{100}]}_{(f \circ g)'(x)} = \underbrace{100(x^2 + 1)^{99}}_{f'(g(x))}\ \underbrace{(2x)}_{g'(x)}$$

Certainly this is faster than first expanding $(1 + x^2)^{100}$, as the reader may verify if he wishes.

Example 2. Find $D(\sin 2x)$. Here again we have a composite function, for if we let $y = \sin 2x$, then $y = \sin u$, where $u = 2x$. Since the derivative of the sine function is the cosine function, and $D(2x) = 2$, we have, by the chain rule,

$$D(\sin 2x) = (\cos 2x)\,(2).$$

In short, $D(\sin 2x) = 2 \cos 2x$.

REMARK. Example 2 shows that if we use the symbol u in the formula $y = \sin u$ simply as part of the description of the sine function—disregarding its use already in the formula $u = 2x$, our computation can be stated as follows:

The derivative of $\sin u$ with respect to x equals (derivative of $\sin u$ with respect to u) times (derivative of u with respect to x). This observation suggests another statement of the chain rule: If y is a certain function of x that can be expressed as

$$y = f(u) \qquad u = g(x)$$

then
$$\frac{dy}{dx} = \frac{dy}{du}\frac{du}{dx}$$

Example 3. Find dy/dx if $y = (x + 3x^5)^{15}$. Since

$$y = u^{15} \qquad u = x + 3x^5$$

we use the chain rule. We have

$$\frac{dy}{du} = 15u^{14} \qquad \text{and} \qquad \frac{du}{dx} = 1 + 15x^4$$

and the chain rule yields

$$\frac{dy}{dx} = 15u^{14}(1 + 15x^{14}) = 15(x + 3x^5)^{14}(1 + 15x^4)$$

Example 4. Find $D(\ln|x|)$, where $|x|$ denotes the absolute value of x. Here we let $y = \ln|x|$. Then

$$y = \ln u \qquad u = |x|$$

Now $dy/du = 1/u$ and $du/dx = 1$ if $x > 0$, and $du/dx = -1$ if $x < 0$. Then the chain rule gives

$$\frac{dy}{dx} = \frac{1}{u}\,1 = \frac{1}{|x|} = \frac{1}{x} \qquad x > 0$$

and $\qquad \dfrac{dy}{dx} = \dfrac{1}{u}(-1) = \dfrac{1}{|x|}(-1) = \dfrac{1}{-|x|} = \dfrac{1}{x} \qquad x < 0$

We have obtained an important result:

$$D(\ln|x|) = \frac{1}{x}$$

for any $x \neq 0$, negative or positive.

Example 5. We find the derivative of $[\sin(1 + x^2)]^3$. Here

$$y = v^3 \qquad v = \sin u \qquad \text{and} \qquad u = 1 + x^2$$

and we apply the chain rule twice, first to obtain dy/du:

$$\frac{dy}{du} = \frac{dy}{dv}\frac{dv}{du} = (3v^2)(\cos u)$$

and then to obtain dy/dx:

$$\frac{dy}{dx} = \frac{dy}{du}\frac{du}{dx} = (3v^2 \cos u)(2x)$$

Expressing everything in terms of x, we obtain

$$\frac{d\{[\sin(1 + x^2)]^3\}}{dx} = 3[\sin(1 + x^2)]^2[\cos(1 + x^2)](2x)$$

As these examples may suggest, *the chain rule is the most frequently used device for computing derivatives.*

Example 6. We find the derivative of $\ln[(1 + x^2)^3/x]$. Before we differentiate, let us simplify the formula by using properties of logarithms. We have

$$\ln \frac{(1 + x^2)^3}{x} = 3\ln(1 + x^2) - \ln x$$

The expression on the right of the equal sign is much easier to differentiate than the original one. We have $D(\ln x) = 1/x$ and using the chain rule, $D[3\ln(1 + x^2)] = 6x/(1 + x^2)$. Thus the derivative in question is $6x/(1 + x^2) - 1/x$.

EXERCISES

1. Express the function $y = x^{12}$ as a composite function in four different ways, and find dy/dx each time.
2. The function $y = 15x$ can be thought of as the composition, $f \circ g$, of the functions $f(x) = 3x$ and $g(x) = 5x$.
   (a) Compute $D(f \circ g)(x)$ without using the chain rule.
   (b) Compute $f'(g(x))$ and $g'(x)$.
   (c) Is $D(f \circ g)(x)$ equal to $Df'(g(x))g'(x)$, as the chain rule asserts?
3. (a) Compute $D((1 + x^2)^3)$ without the aid of the chain rule. (That is, first expand it and then find the derivative of the resulting polynomial of degree 6.)
   (b) Compute $D((1 + x^2)^3)$ with the aid of the chain rule.
   (c) Do the results in (a) and (b) agree?

4. Compute the derivatives of the following functions, and *justify* each step (to justify by the chain rule, place "C.R." below the equals sign): (a) $(3x^4 + x)^{10}$; (b) $(x^2 + 1)^5/x$; (c) $6x^2 + (x^3 - 5x)^{11}$.

   > [Answer: (a) $10(3x^4 + x)^9 (12x^3 + 1)$; (b) $[10x(x^2 + 1)^4 - (x^2 + 1)^5]/x^2$; (c) $12x + 11(x^3 - 5x)^{10} (3x^2 - 5)$]

5. Let $y = f(x)$ be some function of x. Using the chain rule, show that

$$\frac{d(y^2)}{dx} = 2y \frac{dy}{dx}$$

6. Compute the derivatives of the following functions, and *justify* each step. (a) $\ln (x^2 - 1)$; (b) $\ln|\cos x|$; (c) $\sec (x^2 + 1)$; (d) $\sin^3 (x^2 + 1)$; (e) $\cos^3 2x$; (f) $(2x + 1)^5 (3x + 1)^{17}$.

   > [Answer: (a) $2x/(x^2 - 1)$; (c) $2x \sec (x^2 + 1) \tan (x^2 + 1)$; (d) $6x \sin^2 (x^2 + 1) \cos (x^2 + 1)$]

7. Find the derivative of (a) $(5x^2 + x + 1)/(6x^2 + 2)$; (b) $[(5x^2 + x + 1)/(6x^2 + 2)]^{100}$; (c) $\log_{10} (x^4 + 1)$; (d) $\ln \sin x^2$; (e) $\tan^5 2x$; (f) $(3x^2 + 1)^{10} (5x^3 + 4)^{15}$.

8. (a) In which parts of Exercise 7 was the chain rule used?
   (b) In which parts of Exercise 7 was the chain rule used more than once?

9. The side s of a cube is increasing at the rate of 5 inches per second. At what rate is the volume V increasing when $s = 2$? When $s = 3$? [Suggestions: (a) Compute dV/ds; (b) Compute ds/dt; (c) In view of (a) and (b), and the chain rule, compute dV/dt; (d) Use (c) to solve the problem.]

10. The binomial coefficients, denoted $C_i{}^n$ or $\binom{n}{i}$, are the coefficients of the various powers of x when $(1 + x)^n$ is expanded. That is,

$$(1 + x)^n = 1 + \binom{n}{1} x + \binom{n}{2} x^2 + \cdots + \binom{n}{n-1} x^{n-1} + x^n$$

   Differentiate both sides of the above equation with respect to x.
   (a) What algebraic identity results?
   (b) Replace x by 1 in the identity of (a).
   (c) Check that the equation in (b) is true for $n = 4$ by doing the necessary arithmetic.
   (d) Replace x by -1 in the identity of (a).
   (e) Check that the equation in (d) is true for $n = 4$.

11. Graph $y = |x|$ and, using the graph, show that $dy/dx = 1$ if $x > 0$ and $dy/dx = -1$ if $x < 0$.

□ □ □

12. (a) Compute $D(\ln (1 + x))$ with the aid of the chain rule.
    (b) Compute $D(\ln (1 + x))$ without the aid of the chain rule.

13. (a) Compute $D(\ln (1 + x^2))$ with the aid of the chain rule.
    (b) Compute $D(\ln (1 + x^2))$ without the aid of the chain rule.

14. Find the hole in this alternative proof of the chain rule. We have

$$\frac{\Delta(f \circ g)}{\Delta x} = \frac{\Delta(f \circ g)}{\Delta g} \frac{\Delta g}{\Delta x}$$

Thus $\quad f'(g(x)) = \lim_{\Delta x \to 0} \dfrac{\Delta(f \circ g)}{\Delta g} \lim_{\Delta x \to 0} \dfrac{\Delta g}{\Delta x} = \lim_{\Delta g \to 0} \dfrac{\Delta(f \circ g)}{\Delta g} \lim_{\Delta x \to 0} \dfrac{\Delta g}{\Delta x} = f'(g(x)) g'(x)$

15. Show that the proof offered in Exercise 14 goes through smoothly if we make the additional assumption that $g'(x)$ is not 0.

16. (a) Using the trigonometric identity $\sin(A - B) = \sin A \cos B - \cos A \sin B$, prove that $\cos x = \sin(\pi/2 - x)$.

    (b) With the aid of the chain rule and $D(\sin x) = \cos x$, obtain another proof that $D(\cos x) = -\sin x$.

17. This exercise will show why solar stoves, radio-wave receivers, and reflectors behind arc lights or flashlight bulbs are parabolic. The focus of the parabola $y^2 = 4x$ is the point $(1,0)$. Prove that the angle between a tangent line to the parabola at (x,y) and the line through (x,y) and the focus equals the angle between the tangent line and the x axis. (Hence all light parallel to the x axis is reflected through a single point: the focus.) [Hint: The identity $\tan(A - B) = (\tan A - \tan B)/(1 + \tan A \tan B)$ shows that if m_1 and m_2 are the slopes of lines L_1 and L_2, and L_1 makes a larger angle with the positive x axis than L_2 does, then the angle between L_1 and L_2 has a tangent equal to $(m_1 - m_2)/(1 + m_1m_2)$.]

18. This exercise will show why a person standing at one focus of an elliptical "whispering" room can be heard easily at the other focus. Prove that the two lines from the foci of an ellipse to a point (x,y) on the ellipse make equal angles with the tangent line to the ellipse at (x,y).

4. The derivative of an inverse function.

Frequently, if y is a certain function of x, so that $y = f(x)$, we can solve for x *uniquely* in terms of y. When this is so, this process creates a second function, which we call the inverse function to f, and we write it f^{-1}; thus $x = f^{-1}(y)$. (This concept is discussed in Appendix C, pages 574–575.) We will exploit the relation between a function and its inverse to find the derivatives of several important functions. First, let us present a few examples of inverse functions.

Example 1. If $y = 3x$, then $x = y/3$. In this case, f multiplies the argument by 3, while f^{-1} divides the argument by 3. The inverse function could be written $z = w/3$, or $u = v/3$, or $x = y/3$, or $y = x/3$. It may seem odd to have $y = 3x$ and then $y = x/3$, but there is no contradiction. The expression $y = 3x$ is a description of the function "multiply by 3" and has the same meaning as $S = 3P$; the expression $y = x/3$ is a description of the function "divide by 3." For three centuries the x axis has been horizontal and the y axis vertical. And tradition prefers that we show the function values ("dependent variable") as the vertical coordinate and the domain where the function is defined ("independent variable") as the horizontal coordinate. For this reason we write the original function $y = 3x$ and its inverse function $y = x/3$. The graphs of f and f^{-1} in this case are as shown

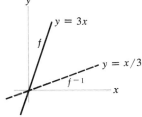

If a function has the formula $y = 3x + 4$, then we still obtain a unique solution for x, namely, $x = (y - 4)/3$. Hence $y = (x - 4)/3$ is the formula for the inverse function in this case.

Example 2. If $y = x^3$, then $x = \sqrt[3]{y}$. In this case $f(x) = x^3$ and $f^{-1}(x) = \sqrt[3]{x}$. This shows f and f^{-1} pictorially:

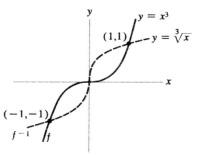

Example 3. If $y = \log_{10} x$, then $x = 10^y$. The inverse of the logarithm function is the exponential function, $y = 10^x$. Here $f(x) = \log_{10} x$, and $f^{-1}(x) = 10^x$. The graphs are as shown:

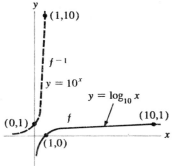

Note that for $a > 1$ the graph of a^x rises as we move to the right and passes through $(0,1)$, since $a^0 = 1$.

Example 4. If $y = x^2$, then when we solve for x, we generally obtain two solutions $\sqrt{y}$ and $-\sqrt{y}$. However, if we consider $y = x^2$ only for $x \geqslant 0$, then we can solve for x uniquely, $x = \sqrt{y}$. In that case, we graph $f(x) = x^2$ and $f^{-1}(x) = \sqrt{x}$.

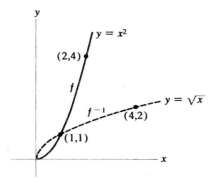

Generally, if n is even, we will interpret the symbol $x^{1/n}$ as denoting the function $\sqrt[n]{x}$, which has positive values when x is positive.

Example 5. Consider $y = \tan x$. We cannot solve for x uniquely since, for example, $\tan \pi = \tan 0 = 0$. In fact, since $\tan (x + \pi) = \tan x$, there are an infinite number of solutions for x. However, there is *only one* solution if we restrict x by the demand that $-\pi/2 < x < \pi/2$. If $y = \tan x$, then we write $x = \tan^{-1} y$ and insist that x is in the open interval $(-\pi/2, \pi/2)$. We say "x is the angle whose tangent is y" or "x is the arctan of y." The graphs of $y = \tan x$ and $y = \tan^{-1} x$ are sketched here:

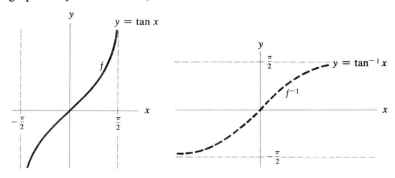

It is easier, however, to think of $y = \tan x$ and $y = \tan^{-1} x$ in terms of the unit circle.

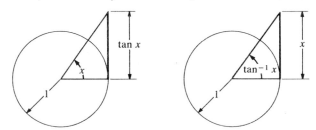

Note that as x shrinks from being large and positive down to 0, then to being large and negative, the angle $\tan^{-1} x$ moves from values near $\pi/2$ to 0, then to values near $-\pi/2$. For example, $\tan^{-1}(1) = \pi/4$, $\tan^{-1}(0) = 0$, $\tan^{-1}(-1) = -\pi/4$, as we can see by inspection of the diagram of the unit circle on the right.

Example 6. Consider $y = \sin x$, whose graph is

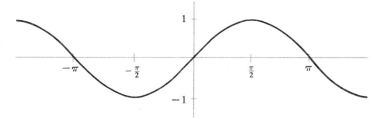

As the graph shows, we obtain an infinite set of solutions for x to the equation $y = \sin x$. A horizontal line meets the graph an infinite number of times if it meets it at all. For instance, if we solve the equation $0 = \sin x$, we obtain $x = 0, \pm\pi, \pm 2\pi, \ldots$. However, if we restrict x by the demand $-\pi/2 \leqslant x \leqslant \pi/2$, we do obtain a unique solution x to the equation $y = \sin x$. This solution we call "the arcsine of y" or "the angle whose sine is y" and write it $\sin^{-1} y$. Keeping in mind that x is in $[-\pi/2, \pi/2]$, we draw the graphs of the sine and arcsine functions:

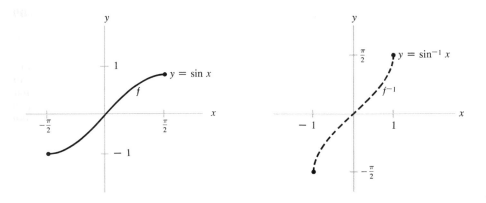

Now, if we think of f as the projection from a slide to a screen,

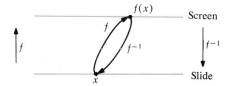

then f^{-1} assigns to each point on the screen the point on the slide that projects onto it. If f magnifies by a certain ratio at x, say 3, then we expect f^{-1} to *shrink* by a factor 3 at $f(x)$, that is, "magnify" by a factor $\frac{1}{3}$. Intuitively, if f has a derivative at x, we expect f^{-1} to have a derivative at the number $f(x)$, and in fact,

$$(f^{-1})'(f(x)) = \frac{1}{f'(x)} \qquad f'(x) \neq 0$$

We shall not prove this fact, but only assume that if f is differentiable, then so is f^{-1}, if $f'(x) \neq 0$. With this assumption we now obtain the derivatives of several important functions.

THEOREM 1. $D(x^{1/n}) = \dfrac{1}{n} x^{(1/n)-1}$ *for any positive integer n.*

PROOF. We present the proof in the case $n = 3$. In this case let $y = x^{1/3}$. We want to compute dy/dx. Now, $x^{1/3} = \sqrt[3]{x}$, the function inverse to the cubing function. We have $y = x^{1/3}$, $x = y^3$. Thus

$$1 = \frac{d(x)}{dx} = \underset{\text{C.R.}}{=} \frac{d(y^3)}{dx} = \frac{d(y^3)}{dy}\frac{dy}{dx} = 3y^2 \frac{dy}{dx}$$

Hence
$$1 = 3y^2 \frac{dy}{dx}$$

and we have
$$\frac{dy}{dx} = \frac{1}{3y^2} = \frac{y^{-2}}{3} = \tfrac{1}{3}(x^{1/3})^{-2} = \tfrac{1}{3}x^{-2/3}$$

Thus $d(x^{1/3})/dx = (\tfrac{1}{3})\,x^{-2/3}$, which can be written $(\tfrac{1}{3})\,x^{(1/3)-1}$, in agreement with the theorem.

REMARK. The function $y = x^{1/3}$ is defined for all x; for instance, $(-1)^{1/3} = -1$, $1^{1/3} = 1$. However, the function $y = x^{1/2}$ or, more generally, $x^{1/n}$, n even, is defined only for $x \geqslant 0$.

THEOREM 2. $D(x^{m/n}) = (m/n)\,x^{(m/n)-1}$, *where m/n is a rational number.*

PROOF. Let $y = x^{m/n}$. Then $y = (x^{1/n})^m$, and we are in a position to use the chain rule and Theorem 1, for
$$y = u^m \qquad u = x^{1/n}$$

Then
$$\frac{dy}{dx} = \frac{d(u^m)}{du}\frac{d(x^{1/n})}{dx} = (mu^{m-1})\frac{1}{n}x^{1/n-1}$$

Replacing u by $x^{1/n}$, we obtain
$$\frac{dy}{dx} = m(x^{1/n})^{m-1}\frac{1}{n}x^{1/n-1} = \frac{m}{n}x^{(m-1)/n}x^{1/n-1} = \frac{m}{n}x^{(m-1)/n+(1/n)-1} = \frac{m}{n}x^{(m/n)-1}$$

and the theorem is proved.

Theorems 1 and 2 and the theorem that asserts that if n is an integer, $D(x^n) = nx^{n-1}$, are all summarized in the single assertion: *If a is a rational number, then $D(x^a) = ax^{a-1}$.*

THEOREM 3. $D(10^x) = \dfrac{1}{\log_{10} e}\,10^x = (2.30)\,10^x.$

PROOF. Let $y = 10^x$. Since the function 10^x is the inverse of the $\log_{10} x$ function, we can assume that the derivative of y exists. Now, $x = \log_{10} y$, and thus
$$1 = \frac{dx}{dx} = \frac{d(\log_{10} y)}{dx} = (\log_{10} e)\frac{1}{y}\frac{dy}{dx}$$

by the chain rule; hence
$$1 = (\log_{10} e)\frac{1}{y}\frac{dy}{dx}$$

and
$$\frac{dy}{dx} = \frac{1}{\log_{10} e}y = \frac{1}{\log_{10} e}10^x$$

The theorem is proved.

THEOREM 4. $D(e^x) = e^x$, where $e = \lim\limits_{h \to 0} (1 + h)^{1/h}$.

PROOF.   Let $y = e^x$; then $x = \ln y$. We have

$$1 = \frac{dx}{dx} = \frac{d(\ln y)}{dx} = \frac{1}{y}\frac{dy}{dx}$$

hence

$$1 = \frac{1}{y}\frac{dy}{dx}$$

Thus

$$\frac{dy}{dx} = y = e^x$$

THEOREM 5. $D(\tan^{-1} x) = \dfrac{1}{1 + x^2}$.

PROOF.   Let $y = \tan^{-1} x$; then $x = \tan y$. We have

$$1 = \frac{dx}{dx} = \frac{d(\tan y)}{dx} = \sec^2 y \frac{dy}{dx} = (1 + \tan^2 y)\frac{dy}{dx}$$

Thus

$$1 = (1 + \tan^2 y)\frac{dy}{dx}$$

and we obtain

$$\frac{dy}{dx} = \frac{1}{1 + \tan^2 y} = \frac{1}{1 + x^2}$$

THEOREM 6. $D(\sin^{-1} x) = \dfrac{1}{\sqrt{1 - x^2}}$.

PROOF.   Let $y = \sin^{-1} x$; then $x = \sin y$. We have

$$1 = \frac{dx}{dx} = \frac{d(\sin y)}{dx} = \cos y \frac{dy}{dx}$$

hence

$$\frac{dy}{dx} = \frac{1}{\cos y}$$

But $\cos^2 y + \sin^2 y = 1$ and $\cos y \geqslant 0$ for $y = \sin^{-1} x$; thus $\cos y = \sqrt{1 - \sin^2 y}$ and

$$\frac{1}{\cos y} = \frac{1}{\sqrt{1 - \sin^2 y}} = \frac{1}{\sqrt{1 - x^2}}$$

We can also define $\cos^{-1} x$, $\csc^{-1} x$, $\cot^{-1} x$, stipulating that $0 \leqslant \cos^{-1} x \leqslant \pi$, $0 \leqslant \sec^{-1} x \leqslant \pi$, $-\pi/2 \leqslant \csc^{-1} x \leqslant \pi/2$, $0 \leqslant \cot^{-1} x \leqslant \pi$. The proof of the next theorem is similar to the proofs of the preceding theorems and is omitted.

THEOREM 7. $D(\cos^{-1} x) = \dfrac{-1}{\sqrt{1 - x^2}}$

$$D(\sec^{-1} x) = \frac{1}{|x|\sqrt{x^2 - 1}}$$

$$D(\csc^{-1} x) = \frac{-1}{|x|\sqrt{x^2 - 1}}$$

$$D(\cot^{-1} x) = \frac{-1}{1 + x^2}$$

We are now in a position to compute the derivative of any function likely to occur in practical situations.

Example 7. We compute $D(\sqrt{1 + x^2})$ as follows. For clarity, let

$$y = \sqrt{1 + x^2}$$

Then $y = \sqrt{u}$, where $u = 1 + x^2$. By Theorem 1 (or Theorem 2),

$$\frac{dy}{du} = \frac{1}{2} u^{-\frac{1}{2}} = \frac{1}{2\sqrt{u}}$$

also, $du/dx = 2x$. By the chain rule,

$$\frac{dy}{dx} = \frac{1}{2\sqrt{u}} 2x = \frac{x}{\sqrt{u}} = \frac{x}{\sqrt{1 + x^2}}$$

Example 8. We compute $D(2^{x^2})$. Let us write $y = 2^{x^2}$. It is a good habit to express an exponential function as a power of e, because of the simplicity of the formula $D(e^x) = e^x$. This we do by expressing 2 as $e^{\ln 2}$. Thus

$$y = (e^{\ln 2})^{x^2} = e^{(\ln 2)(x^2)}$$

Since $y = e^{(\ln 2)(x^2)}$, we again have occasion to use the chain rule: $y = e^u$, where $u = (\ln 2)(x^2)$. By Theorem 4, we have $du/dx = (\ln 2)(2x) = 2(\ln 2)(x)$. By virtue of the chain rule,

$$\frac{dy}{dx} = e^u (2 \ln 2) x = e^{(\ln 2)x^2} (2 \ln 2) x = 2^{x^2} (2 \ln 2) x$$

which is usually written with the constants in front, $(2 \ln 2) 2^{x^2} x$.

Example 9. We compute $D(\tan^{-1}(e^{x^2}))$. This time we will need the chain rule twice. If $y = \tan^{-1}(e^{x^2})$, we have $y = \tan^{-1} u$, where $u = e^v$, and $v = x^2$. By Theorem 5 of Sec. 1, $dv/dx = 2x$. Two applications of the chain rule yield

$$\frac{dy}{dx} = \frac{dy}{du}\frac{du}{dv}\frac{dv}{dx} = \frac{1}{1 + u^2} e^v 2x$$

which we express in terms of x,

$$\frac{dy}{dx} = \frac{1}{1 + (e^{x^2})^2} e^{x^2} 2x$$

Finally, this can be written

$$\frac{dy}{dx} = \frac{2xe^{x^2}}{1 + e^{2x^2}}$$

With a little practice we will be able to compute such derivatives without naming the various functions involved in the chain rule. Eventually, we should memorize the facts in the accompanying table, which records the results in this chapter and calls attention to certain functions.

f	Derivative of f	Comment
Constant function "c"	0	
x^a	ax^{a-1}	
$\sqrt{x}$	$1/(2\sqrt{x})$	
$1/x$	$-1/x^2$	
$\sqrt{1+x^2}$	$x/\sqrt{1+x^2}$	
$\sin x$	$\cos x$	
$\cos x$	$-\sin x$	Remember the minus sign
$\tan x$	$\sec^2 x$	
$\sec x$	$\sec x \tan x$	
$\csc x$	$-\csc x \cot x$	Not common
$\cot x$	$-\csc^2 x$	Not common
$\ln|x|$	$1/x$	Note that these hold even if x is negative
$\log_{10}|x|$	$\log_{10}(e)/x$	
$\log_a|x|$	$\log_a(e)/x$	
e^x	e^x	
e^{kx}	ke^{kx}	
e^{-x}	$-e^{-x}$	
a^x	Write $a^x = e^{x \ln a}$	Don't memorize a formula for $d(a^x)/dx$
$\sin^{-1} x$	$1/\sqrt{1-x^2}$	
$\cos^{-1} x$	$-1/\sqrt{1-x^2}$	
$\tan^{-1} x$	$1/(1+x^2)$	
$\sec^{-1} x$	$1/(|x|\sqrt{x^2-1})$	
$\csc^{-1} x$	$-1/(|x|\sqrt{x^2-1})$	Not common
$\cot^{-1} x$	$-1/(1+x^2)$	Not common

Techniques for finding derivatives

$$(f + g)' = f' + g' \qquad (cf)' = cf' \qquad (f - g)' = f' - g'$$

$$(fg)' = fg' + gf' \qquad \left(\frac{1}{f}\right)' = \frac{-f'}{f^2} \qquad \left(\frac{f}{g}\right)' = \frac{gf' - fg'}{g^2}$$

and, *most important of all the tools*, the chain rule:

$$\frac{dy}{dx} = \frac{dy}{du}\frac{du}{dx}$$

EXERCISES

1. (a) Graph $y = \sqrt[3]{x}$ and draw tangent lines at $(1,1)$ and $(-1,-1)$.
   (b) Compare the slopes of the lines you drew with $D(\sqrt[3]{x})$ at $x = 1$ and $x = -1$.
2. (a) Graph $y = e^x$ and draw a tangent line at each of the points $(0,1)$, $(1,e)$, $(-1, 1/e)$.
   (b) Compare the slopes of the lines you drew in (a) to the derivatives of e^x at 0, 1, and -1, respectively.
3. Using radian measure, evaluate (a) $\sin^{-1}(1)$; (b) $\tan^{-1}(1)$; (c) $\cos^{-1}(1)$; (d) $\cos^{-1}(\frac{1}{2})$; (e) $\sec^{-1}(2)$, and draw the appropriate diagram on a unit circle in each case.
   [Answer: (a) $\pi/2$; (b) $\pi/4$; (c) 0; (d) $\pi/3$; (e) $\pi/3$]
4. Complete the table, and graph $y = \cos^{-1}x$.

x	0	$\frac{1}{2}$	1	$-\frac{1}{2}$	-1
$\cos^{-1}x$					

5. Prove that $D(\cos^{-1}x) = -1/\sqrt{1 - x^2}$.
6. A beachcomber walks 2 miles per hour along the shore. A rotating light 3 miles offshore follows the beachcomber.
   (a) Intuitively, what do you think happens to the rate at which the light rotates as the beachcomber walks further and further along the shore away from the lighthouse?
   (b) Letting x describe the position of the beachcomber and θ the angle of the light, express θ as a function of x.

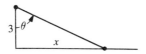

   (c) Find $d\theta/dx$ and dx/dt, where t denotes time.
   (d) With the aid of (c) show that $d\theta/dt = 6/(9 + x^2)$ (radians per minute).
   (e) Does the formula in (d) agree with your guess in (a)?

7. Use Theorem 3 to compute $\lim_{h \to 0} (10^h - 1)/h$. (Hint: Relate the limit to the derivative.)

(Answer: $\ln 10 = 2.303$)

8. Prove that the function ke^x is equal to its own derivative (k is a constant).

9. Occasionally the derivative of a function has a simpler formula than the original function, as these examples illustrate. Show that
   (a) $D[\ln(x + \sqrt{x^2 + 1})] = 1/\sqrt{x^2 + 1}$; (b) $D(xe^x - e^x) = xe^x$;
   (c) $D[(\frac{1}{2}) \ln ((1 + x)/(1 - x))] = 1/(1 - x^2)$.

10. (a) Show that $D[x - \ln(x + 1)] = x/(x + 1)$.
    (b) Show that $D(2\sqrt{3x + 5})/3 = 1/\sqrt{3x + 5}$.

11. Determine and express as a decimal (a) $\lim_{\Delta x \to 0} \dfrac{e^{2 + \Delta x} - e^2}{\Delta x}$; (b) $\lim_{x \to 2} \dfrac{e^x - e^2}{x - 2}$.

12. Compute the derivatives of the following functions, each time first writing the function in the form $e^{f(x)}$.
    (a) $10^{\sin^{-1} x}$; (b) $2^{\sin^{-1} x}$; (c) $10^{1/x}$.

    [Answer: (a) $(\ln 10)(10^{\sin^{-1} x})/\sqrt{1 - x^2}$]

13. Compute the derivatives of (a) $\log_{10}(1 + 3x^4)$; (b) $\ln(1 + 3x^4)$; (c) $\tan^{-1}(e^x)$;
    (d) $(\tan x) - x$.   [Answer: (b) $12x^3/(1 + 3x^4)$; (d) $\tan^2 x$]

14. Show that (a) $D(\sec^{-1} 15x) = \dfrac{1}{|x|\sqrt{225x^2 - 1}}$;

    (b) $D\left(\frac{1}{2} \ln \dfrac{x}{2 + \sqrt{x^2 + 4}}\right) = \dfrac{1}{x\sqrt{x^2 + 4}}$;

    (c) $D[\sin^{-1}(3x - 1)] = \dfrac{3}{\sqrt{6x - 9x^2}}$.

15. Show that (a) $D\left(\sin^{-1} \dfrac{2x - 3}{\sqrt{13}}\right) = \dfrac{1}{\sqrt{-x^2 + 3x + 1}}$;

    (b) $D[\ln(2x + 3 + 2\sqrt{x^2 + 3x + 1})] = \dfrac{1}{\sqrt{x^2 + 3x + 1}}$.

16. Show that (a) $D[e^x(x^2 - 2x + 2)] = x^2 e^x$; (b) $D[x(\ln x)^2 - 2x \ln x + 2x] = \ln^2 x$;
    (c) $D[(18x^2 - 1)(\sin^{-1} 3x) + 3x\sqrt{1 - 9x^2}] = 36x \sin^{-1} 3x$.

17. Show that if p is any constant,
$$D\left(-\frac{1}{p} \ln \frac{p + \sqrt{p^2 + x^2}}{x}\right) = \frac{1}{x\sqrt{p^2 + x^2}}$$

18. Show that if a and c are constants, $c > 0$, then
$$D\left(\frac{1}{\sqrt{c}} \ln \frac{\sqrt{ax^2 + c} + \sqrt{c}}{x}\right) = \frac{1}{x\sqrt{ax^2 + c}}$$

19. Compute the differential of (a) e^{x^2}; (b) $\ln|1 + x|$; (c) $\tan^{-1} 6x$; (d) $\sqrt[3]{x}$.
    [Answer: (a) $2xe^{x^2} dx$; (b) $dx/(1 + x)$; (c) $6 dx/(1 + 36x^2)$; (d) $(\frac{1}{3}) x^{-2/3} dx$]

20. (a) Compute the derivative of $y = \sqrt{9 + x^2}$ at $x = 4$.
    (b) Find the slope of the tangent line to the curve $y = \sqrt{9 + x^2}$ at $(4, 5)$.
    (c) Find the velocity of a particle at time $t = 4$ whose position on a line at time t is $y = \sqrt{9 + t^2}$.

(d) Find the magnification at $x = 4$ of a lens that projects x onto $\sqrt{9 + x^2}$.

(e) Find the density at $x = 4$ of a string whose left-hand x inches has a mass $\sqrt{9 + x^2}$ ounces.

(f) Using differentials, estimate $\sqrt{9 + (4.1)^2}$ and $\sqrt{9 + (3.9)^2}$.

Verify the equations in Exercises 21 through 26.

21. $\dfrac{x}{(ax + b)^3} = D\left[\dfrac{b}{2a^2(ax + b)^2} - \dfrac{1}{a^2(ax + b)}\right].$

22. $\dfrac{x^2}{(ax + b)^3} = D\left\{\dfrac{1}{a^3}\left[\ln(ax + b) + \dfrac{2b}{ax + b} - \dfrac{b^2}{2(ax + b)^2}\right]\right\}.$

23. $\dfrac{1}{x^3(ax + b)} = D\left[\dfrac{2ax - b}{2b^2 x^2} + \dfrac{a^2}{b^3}\ln\dfrac{x}{ax + b}\right].$

24. (a) $\dfrac{1}{x\sqrt{ax + b}} = D\left[\dfrac{1}{\sqrt{b}}\ln\dfrac{\sqrt{ax + b} - \sqrt{b}}{\sqrt{ax + b} + \sqrt{b}}\right], \qquad b > 0.$

(b) $\dfrac{1}{x\sqrt{ax + b}} = D\left[\dfrac{2}{\sqrt{-b}}\tan^{-1}\sqrt{\dfrac{ax + b}{-b}}\right], \qquad b < 0.$

25. $\dfrac{1}{(ax + b)^2(cx + d)} = D\left[\dfrac{1}{bc - ad}\left(\dfrac{1}{ax + b} + \dfrac{c}{bc - ad}\ln\dfrac{cx + d}{ax + b}\right)\right], \qquad bc - ad \neq 0.$

26. (a) $\dfrac{1}{ax^2 + c} = D\left[\dfrac{1}{2\sqrt{-ac}}\ln\dfrac{x\sqrt{a} - \sqrt{-c}}{x\sqrt{a} + \sqrt{-c}}\right], \qquad a > 0,\, c < 0.$

(b) $\dfrac{1}{ax^2 + c} = D\left[\dfrac{1}{2\sqrt{-ac}}\ln\dfrac{\sqrt{c} + x\sqrt{-a}}{\sqrt{c} - x\sqrt{-a}}\right], \qquad a < 0,\, c > 0.$

(c) $\dfrac{1}{ax^2 + c} = D\left[\dfrac{1}{\sqrt{ac}}\tan^{-1}\left(x\sqrt{\dfrac{a}{c}}\right)\right], \qquad a > 0,\, c > 0.$

□ □ □

27. Sometimes a function is given in such an indirect manner that we can not find a formula for it. For instance, say that $y = f(x)$ satisfies the equation $y^5 - x^3 y^3 + yx^2 - 26 = 0$ and that $f(1) = 2$. To find dy/dx in such a case, differentiate both sides of the equation with respect to x, keeping in mind that $d(y^n)/dx = ny^{n-1}\,dy/dx$. (a) Verify that $x = 1$, $y = 2$ satisfies the equation. (b) Find dy/dx in terms of x and y. (c) Find dy/dx at $x = 1$, $y = 2$.

[Answer: (b) $(2xy + 3x^2 y^3)/(5y^4 - 3y^2 x^3 - x^2)$; (c) $28/67$]

28. Assume that f^{-1} has a derivative. Use the chain rule and the identity $x = f^{-1}(f(x))$ to obtain a proof that $(f^{-1})'(f(x)) = 1/f'(x)$ if $f'(x) \neq 0$.

29. If x is positive, then by the definition of $\ln x$, we have $x = e^{\ln x}$. Use this fact to obtain an alternative proof that $D(x^a) = ax^{a-1}$. Incidentally, note that in your proof a may be rational or irrational, whereas the theorem in the text disposes only of rational exponents.

30. (a) Graph $y = \sec^{-1} x$, and (b) prove that $D(\sec^{-1} x) = \dfrac{1}{|x|\sqrt{x^2 - 1}}$. (Examine the cases $x > 0$ and $x < 0$ separately.)

31. Comment on this treatment of $D(f^{-1})$. In particular, discuss the replacement of $\Delta y \to 0$ by $\Delta x \to 0$.

PROOF. $(f^{-1})'(f(x)) = \lim_{\Delta y \to 0} \dfrac{\Delta x}{\Delta y} = \lim_{\Delta x \to 0} \dfrac{\Delta x}{\Delta y} = \lim_{\Delta x \to 0} \dfrac{1}{(\Delta y / \Delta x)} = \dfrac{1}{f'(x)}$.

32. Prove that $\lim_{h \to 0} (1 + 2h)^{1/h} = e^2$.

33. (See Exercise 27.) If $y + e^{xy} = x + e$, find dy/dx at $(1,1)$.

[Answer: $(1 - e)/(1 + e)$]

5. Summary. We have developed formulas and rules that enable us to compute the derivatives of many functions rapidly. It will no longer be necessary to study the behavior of $\Delta y/\Delta x$ each time we want to compute a derivative. The tables on pages 114, 115 are therefore of the utmost importance and should be memorized, for they play as important a role in the calculus as the multiplication table does in arithmetic. Practice will make them second nature. Bear in mind, however, that *the derivative is the limit of a certain quotient*, and that each statement in the tables is a theorem about this limit.

5

The law of the mean

In Chap. 1 we defined the definite integral and in Chap. 2 the derivative. In this chapter we develop the law of the mean. In Chap. 6 we use it to show that derivatives are the key to the easy computation of many definite integrals.

1. Rolle's theorem. We will develop two theorems in this section. The first, used in proving the second, has other applications as well; we will use the second in proving the law of the mean.

The first theorem asserts that at a number X, where a differentiable function assumes a maximum (or minimum) value in an interval $[a,b]$, $X \neq a$, $X \neq b$, the tangent line to the graph of f must be horizontal:

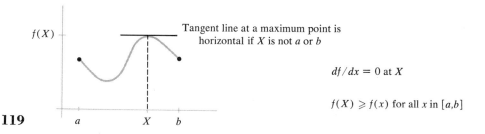

$f(X)$

Tangent line at a maximum point is horizontal if X is not a or b

$df/dx = 0$ at X

$f(X) \geqslant f(x)$ for all x in $[a,b]$

119

a X b

Note the restriction that X not be one of the end points of the interval under discussion. For example, for $f(x) = x^2$, and $[a,b] = [0,2]$, the maximum of f occurs at an end of the interval, 2; there the derivative, $2x$, is 4.

For x in $[0,2]$ $f(x)$ is a maximum at $x = 2$, yet the tangent line there is not horizontal

Though from a geometric point of view the theorem is reasonable, it is safest to state and prove it without any picture, using only the definition of the derivative in its proof, rather than any of its various applications. A formal statement of the theorem and its proof follows.

THEOREM 1.   *Let f be a function defined on* $[a,b]$. *If* $f(x)$ *takes on a maximum (or minimum) value for x in* $[a,b]$ *at a number X other than a or b, and if* $f'(X)$ *exists, then* $f'(X)$ *must be* 0.

PROOF.   We present a proof by contradiction for the case in which $f(X)$ is a maximum. Let us assume that $f'(X)$ is not 0; say that it is greater than 0. From this we shall deduce that $f(X)$ is not the largest value of $f(x)$ for x in $[a,b]$. [A similar contradiction will result if we assume $f'(X) < 0$.]

If $f'(X) > 0$, then $[f(x) - f(X)]/(x - X)$ must be positive for x close to X, since it is an estimate of $f'(X)$. In particular, when x is close to X and to the *right* of X, we have both

$$\frac{f(x) - f(X)}{x - X} > 0 \quad \text{and} \quad x - X > 0$$

Since the product of two positive numbers is positive, we obtain

$$f(x) - f(X) = \frac{f(x) - f(X)}{x - X}(x - X) > 0$$

Hence $f(x) - f(X) > 0$ or, equivalently,

$$f(x) > f(X)$$

in violation of the hypothesis on $f(X)$. If the reader disposes of the case $f'(X) < 0$, the proof will be complete. The "minimum" case is treated similarly.

If the graph of a well-behaved function f has a horizontal chord, then it seems likely that it has at least one horizontal tangent line.

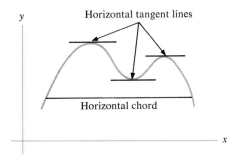

This naive observation is made precise in the next theorem.

THEOREM 2: *Rolle's theorem.* Let f be a continuous function on $[a,b]$ and have a derivative at all x in $[a,b]$ except perhaps at $x = a$ and $x = b$. If $f(a) = f(b)$, then there is at least one argument X such that $f'(X) = 0$ and $a < X < b$.

PROOF. Since f is continuous on $[a,b]$, it takes on a maximum value M and a minimum value m for the interval $[a,b]$. Clearly we have

$$m \leqslant f(a) = f(b) \leqslant M$$

If $m = M$, then f is constant, and $f'(x) = 0$ throughout the interval. Then certainly there is, as the theorem asserts, at least one X such that $f'(X) = 0$.

If $m \neq M$, then we must have at least one of these situations:

$$m < f(a) = f(b) \qquad \text{or} \qquad M > f(a) = f(b)$$

If $M > f(a)$, then let X be an argument such that

$$f(X) = M$$

Clearly $X \neq a$, $X \neq b$. By Theorem 1, $f'(X) = 0$.

If $m < f(a)$, a similar argument assures the existence of the X promised by the theorem. This concludes the proof.

Example 1. Let $f(x) = x^2 - 2x + 5$, and $[a,b] = [0,2]$. Note that $f(0) = 5 = f(2)$. Also, f is continuous and f' exists (even at a and b). According to Rolle's theorem, there is an X for which $f'(X) = 0$ and $0 < X < 2$. It is easy to find such an X for this function, since $f'(x) = 2x - 2$. Setting $2x - 2 = 0$, we see that $X = 1$; in this case X is unique.

Example 2. Let $f(x) = \sqrt{1 - x^2}$ and $[a,b] = [-1,1]$. Observe that $f(-1) = 0 = f(1)$, that f is continuous, and that $f'(x) = -x/\sqrt{1 - x^2}$, which is defined for all x in $[-1,1]$ except at -1 and 1. Rolle's theorem then guarantees that there is at least one X, where $-1 < X < 1$, such that $f'(X) = 0$. For this function f we can find X by setting $-x/\sqrt{1 - x^2} = 0$; thus $X = 0$ and is unique.

EXERCISES

1. (a) Using Theorem 1, find the minimum value and the maximum value of $f(x) = x^3 - 12x + 12$ over [0,1]; over [0,3].
   (b) Graph f.

   [Answer: (a) 1 and 12; -4 and 12]

2. Translate Theorem 1 into a statement about a particle moving on a line. [Let $f(x)$ be its position at time x.] Is the conclusion of Theorem 1 reasonable?

3. Translate Rolle's theorem into a statement about a particle moving on a line. [Interpret x as time and $f(x)$ as position.] Is the conclusion reasonable?

4. In the proof of Theorem 1 we did not examine the case $f'(X) < 0$. Write out the details for this case.

5. In the proof of Rolle's theorem we did not examine the case $m < f(a)$. Write out the details for this case.

6. Consider $f(x) = x^4 - 2x^2 + 1$. Show that $f(-2) = f(2)$. Do the hypotheses of Rolle's theorem hold, with $[a,b] = [-2,2]$? If so, find all the X's in $[-2,2]$ that satisfy the conclusion of Rolle's theorem.

7. (a) Let $f(x) = |x|$. Note that $f(2) = f(-2)$. Does Rolle's theorem say anything about f? Can you find an X such that $f'(X) = 0$? (b) Proceed as in (a), but let $f(x) = (x^2 - 4)/(x + \frac{1}{2})$.

□ □ □

8. (a) Assume that every polynomial of degree 5 has at most five real roots. Use Rolle's theorem to prove that every polynomial of degree 6 has at most six real roots.
   (b) Use the technique of (a) to prove that a polynomial of degree n has at most n real roots.

9. Prove that if $a_0, \ldots, a_n$ are numbers such that

$$\frac{a_0}{1} + \frac{a_1}{2} + \frac{a_2}{3} + \cdots + \frac{a_n}{n+1} = 0$$

   then the polynomial $f(x) = a_0 + a_1 x + a_2 x^2 + \cdots + a_n x^n$ has at least one root between 0 and 1. [That is, prove there is a number X such that $f(X) = 0$ and $0 < X < 1$.] Give an example of such a polynomial f.

10. Find the minimum and maximum of $x^3 - 6x^2 + 11x - 4$ for x in [1,3].

   (Answer: $2 - 2\sqrt{3}/9$ and $2 + 2\sqrt{3}/9$)

2. The law of the mean. The law of the mean generalizes Rolle's theorem. In geometric terms it asserts that if you draw a chord for the graph of a well-behaved function, then somewhere above or below that chord the graph has a tangent line parallel to the chord:

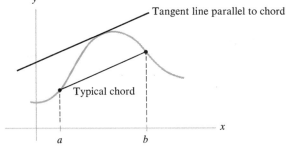

In the language of functions, freed from any particular interpretation, we have the following major result.

THEOREM: *Law of the mean.*   Let f be a continuous function on $[a,b]$ and have a derivative at all x in $[a,b]$ except perhaps at $x = a$ and $x = b$. Then there is at least one argument X such that $a < X < b$ and

$$f'(X) = \frac{f(b) - f(a)}{b - a}$$

PROOF.   We shall prove the theorem by introducing a function to which we can apply Rolle's theorem. This diagram, in which L is the line on the given chord, suggests such a function:

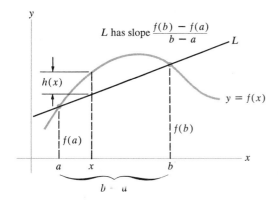

L has slope $\dfrac{f(b) - f(a)}{b - a}$

Let $h(x) =$ vertical distance from line L to the curve. Note that $h(a) = 0$ and $h(b) = 0$

We define a new function, h, by $h(x) = f(x) - L(x)$, where $L(x)$ is the ordinate on L. Since the straight line L has slope $[f(b) - f(a)]/(b - a)$, we have

$$h'(x) = f'(x) - L'(x) = f'(x) - \frac{f(b) - f(a)}{b - a}$$

Since $h(a) = 0 = h(b)$, and h is continuous on $[a,b]$ and differentiable except perhaps at a and b, we can apply Rolle's theorem to h. There is a number X, satisfying $a < X < b$, and such that $h'(X) = 0$. In terms of f, this asserts that

$$f'(X) - \frac{f(b) - f(a)}{b - a} = 0$$

The law of the mean is proved.

Example 1.   Let $f(x) = e^x$, let $a = 0$, and let b be any positive number. Then $f'(x) = e^x$, and the law of the mean asserts that there is a number X satisfying $0 < X < b$, and such that

$$e^X = \frac{e^b - e^0}{b - 0}$$

In other words, $e^X = (e^b - 1)/b$. Rewriting this as $e^b - 1 = be^X$, with $0 < X < b$, we obtain

$$e^b = 1 + be^X$$

Since $X > 0$, we have $e^X > 1$. We have proved that $e^b > 1 + b$ if $b > 0$. (Example 5 and Exercise 13 draw an interesting conclusion from this inequality.)

There are several ways of writing the law of the mean. Which one we use will depend on our need. For example, if $a \neq b$, the equation $f'(X) = [f(b) - f(a)]/(b - a)$ is equivalent to

$$f(b) - f(a) = (b - a) f'(X)$$

hence to $f(b) = f(a) + (b - a) f'(X)$ for some X, $a < X < b$

In this form, the law of the mean tells us that $f(b)$ is equal to $f(a)$ plus a quantity that involves f'. We exploit this in the next example.

Example 2. We can use the law of the mean to estimate $\sqrt{17}$. Let $f(x) = \sqrt{x}$ with $a = 16$ and $b = 17$. Then $f(a) = 4$ and $f'(x) = 1/(2\sqrt{x})$, and the assertion $f(b) = f(a) + (b - a) f'(X)$ becomes $\sqrt{17} = 4 + (17 - 16) [1/(2\sqrt{X})]$, for some number X such that $16 < X < 17$. Thus $\sqrt{17} = 4 + 1/(2\sqrt{X})$, with $16 < X < 17$. Since $16 < X < 17$, we have

$$4 + \frac{1}{2\sqrt{17}} < \sqrt{17} < 4 + \frac{1}{2\sqrt{16}} = 4 + \frac{1}{8}$$

Even though the expression $4 + 1/(2\sqrt{17})$ contains $\sqrt{17}$, the quantity we are estimating, it is still of use, for

$$4 + \frac{1}{2\sqrt{25}} < 4 + \frac{1}{2\sqrt{17}}$$

and (since we chose 25 wisely) we can compute $4 + 1/(2\sqrt{25}) = 4 + \frac{1}{10}$. Thus

$$4.100 = 4 + \frac{1}{10} < \sqrt{17} < 4 + \frac{1}{8} = 4.125$$

For later use we deduce several corollaries from the law of the mean.

COROLLARY 1 TO LAW OF THE MEAN.   If $f'(x) = 0$ for all x, then f is constant.

PROOF.   Let a and b be two numbers. We wish to prove that $f(b) = f(a)$ [in other words, that $f(b) - f(a) = 0$]. Now, by the law of the mean,

$$f(b) - f(a) = (b - a) f'(X)   a < X < b$$

But $f'(X) = 0$. Thus

$$f(b) - f(a) = (b - a) (0) = 0$$

and we have proved the corollary.

In the next example we solve a differential equation, that is, an equation involving the derivative of a function.

Example 3. Many biological, physical, and economic variables grow or shrink at a rate proportional to the amount present. For this reason it is of interest to know what functions f have the property that $f'(x)$ is proportional to $f(x)$. For instance, any function of the form $f(x) = Ae^{kx}$, where A and k are constants, has this property, since

$$f'(x) = D(Ae^{kx}) = Ake^{kx} = kAe^{kx} = kf(x)$$

With the aid of Corollary 1 we now show that Ae^{kx} is *the only type of function with the property of having its derivative proportional to itself.*

To do so, consider any function f such that $f'(x) = kf(x)$ for all x. We will show that the function $g(x) = f(x)/e^{kx}$ is constant. In view of Corollary 1, it suffices to show that $g'(x) = 0$ for all x. Now,

$$g'(x) = \frac{e^{kx} f'(x) - f(x) ke^{kx}}{(e^{kx})^2} = \frac{e^{kx} kf(x) - f(x) ke^{kx}}{(e^{kx})^2} = \frac{0}{(e^{kx})^2} = 0$$

Thus $f(x)/e^{kx} = A$, where A is fixed; that is, $f(x)$ has the form Ae^{kx}. Many applications of this important result are to be found in Chap. 21.

COROLLARY 2 TO LAW OF THE MEAN. If two functions have the same derivative, then they differ by a constant. That is, if $f'(x) = g'(x)$ for all x, then there is a constant C, such that $f(x) = g(x) + C$, for all x.

PROOF. Define a third function, h, by $h(x) = f(x) - g(x)$. Then we have $h'(x) = f'(x) - g'(x) = 0$ for all x. By Corollary 1, we know that h is a constant function. Thus $h(x) = C$ for all x. Hence $C = f(x) - g(x)$ for all x, and the corollary is proved.

Example 4. Let f be a function such that $f(0) = 5$ and $f'(x) = 2x$ for all x. Corollary 2 enables us to describe f explicitly. Since $f(x)$ and the function $g(x) = x^2$ have the same derivatives, $f(x) = x^2 + C$, for some constant C. But $f(0) = 5$. Thus $5 = 0^2 + C$. Hence $C = 5$ and we see that $f(x) = x^2 + 5$.

COROLLARY 3 TO LAW OF THE MEAN. If f is continuous, and $f'(x) > 0$ for all $x > a$, then f is an increasing function for $x \geqslant a$; that is, if $x_1 > x_2 \geqslant a$, then $f(x_1) > f(x_2)$.

PROOF. By the law of the mean, there is a number X such that

$$f(x_1) - f(x_2) = f'(X)(x_1 - x_2) \qquad \text{and} \qquad x_1 > X > x_2$$

Since both $f'(X)$ and $x_1 - x_2$ are positive, their product, $f(x_1) - f(x_2)$, is positive. This proves the corollary.

Example 5. In Example 1 we showed that if $x > 0$, then $e^x > 1 + x$ Using Corollary 3, we will strengthen this to $e^x > 1 + x + (x^2/2)$. To do so, consider the function $f(x) = e^x - 1 - x - (x^2/2)$. Observe that $f(0) = e^0 - 1 - 0 - 0 = 0$ and that $f'(x) = e^x - 1 - x$, which by Example 1 is positive if $x > 0$. Corollary 3 assures us that f is an increasing function for positive x. In particular, if $x > 0$, then we have $f(x) > f(0)$; that is,

$$e^x - 1 - x - \frac{x^2}{2} > 0$$

from which it follows that $e^x > 1 + x + (x^2/2)$ when x is positive.

Thus, for positive x, we see that $e^x > x^2/2$. From this we will show that e^x grows faster than any fixed power of x, a result that we will need later. More precisely, we will show that $\lim\limits_{x \to \infty} x^a/e^x = 0$ for any fixed number a. In the case $a = 1$ we have

$$\frac{x}{e^x} < \frac{x}{x^2/2} = \frac{2}{x}$$

hence

$$\lim_{x \to \infty} \frac{x}{e^x} = 0$$

The general case for any positive a may be reduced to the case $a = 1$ with the aid of the variable y defined by $x = ay$. We then have

$$\frac{x^a}{e^x} = \frac{(ay)^a}{e^{ay}} = \frac{y^a \, a^a}{(e^y)^a} = \left(\frac{y}{e^y}\right)^a a^a$$

Since a^a is fixed and, as we have just shown, $\lim\limits_{x \to \infty} (y/e^y) = 0$, we conclude that $\lim\limits_{x \to \infty} x^a/e^x = 0$. The case $a < 0$ is easy since then $\lim\limits_{x \to \infty} x^a = 0$, as well as $\lim\limits_{x \to \infty} 1/e^x = 0$.

COROLLARY 4 TO LAW OF THE MEAN.   If $f'(x) < 0$ for all $x > a$, then f is a decreasing function for $x \geqslant a$; that is, if $x_1 > x_2 \geqslant a$, then $f(x_1) < f(x_2)$.

We omit the proof, which is similar to that for Corollary 3. Stated geometrically, Corollaries 3 and 4 are quite reasonable. For example, Corollary 3 asserts that if at every point the graph has a tangent line with positive slope, then the curve ascends as we move to the right.

The law of the mean can also be written this way: If F is a continuous function on $[a,b]$ and has a derivative $f(=F')$ for all x in $[a,b]$, except perhaps for $x = a$ and $x = b$, then there is a number X, with $a < X < b$, such that

$$F(b) - F(a) = f(X)(b - a)$$

The next corollary generalizes this fact, and *will be of great importance in relating the derivative to the definite integral.*

COROLLARY 5 TO LAW OF THE MEAN.   Let F be continuous on $[a,b]$ and have a derivative f for all x in $[a,b]$, except perhaps at $x = a$ and $x = b$. Let

$$x_0 = a, x_1, \ldots, x_{i-1}, x_i, \ldots, x_n = b$$

be any partition of $[a,b]$. Then it is possible to choose X_1 in $[x_0, x_1]$, X_2 in $[x_1, x_2]$, $\ldots$, X_n in $[x_{n-1}, x_n]$ in such a way that

$$\sum_{i=1}^{n} f(X_i)(x_i - x_{i-1}) = F(b) - F(a)$$

PROOF.   Observe first that

$$F(b) - F(a) = F(x_n) - F(x_0)$$

and then that

$$F(x_n) - F(x_0) = [F(x_n) - F(x_{n-1})] + [F(x_{n-1}) - F(x_{n-2})] + \cdots + [F(x_1) - F(x_0)]$$

We rewrite the typical summand $[F(x_i) - F(x_{i-1})]$ with the aid of the law of the mean. We have

$$F(x_i) - F(x_{i-1}) = F'(X_i)(x_i - x_{i-1})$$

for some X_i, with $x_{i-1} < X_i < x_i$. Since we have given F' the name f, we have

$$F(x_i) - F(x_{i-1}) = f(X_i)(x_i - x_{i-1})$$

Thus
$$F(b) - F(a) = F(x_n) - F(x_0) = \sum_{i=1}^{n} f(X_i)(x_i - x_{i-1})$$

and the corollary is proved.

Example 6. As an illustration of Corollary 5, let us take $F(x) = x^3/3$, with $a = 0$ and $b = 3$. Then $f(x) = D(x^3/3) = x^2$, and the corollary asserts that for any partition of $[0,3]$ we can find numbers $X_1, X_2, \ldots, X_n$ such that $\sum_{i=1}^{n} X_i^2(x_i - x_{i-1})$ equals $3^3/3 - 0^3/3$ (that is, 9). This might remind us of Problem 1, page 4, where we eventually showed that the area of that region is 9. Corollary 5 implies that no matter what partition of $[0,3]$ we use, we can always find $X_1, X_2, \ldots, X_n$ such that the rectangles they determine have a total area equal to 9. A glance at the graph of $y = x^2$ will persuade us that this is true, without any reference to Corollary 5.

The full strength of Corollary 5 will manifest itself in Chap. 6.

EXERCISES

The answers to Exercises 1, 2, and 3 should be phrased in colloquial English. No mathematical terms or symbols should be used.

1. State the law of the mean in terms of a particle moving on a line. Let x be time and $f(x)$ position. In these terms, does the law of the mean seem reasonable?
2. State the law of the mean in terms of density and mass. Let x be the distance from the left end of a string and $f(x)$ the mass of the string from 0 to x. When stated in these terms, does the law of the mean seem reasonable?
3. State the law of the mean in terms of a slide and screen. Let x denote the position on the (linear) slide and $f(x)$ denote the position of the image on the screen. In optical terms, what does the law of the mean say? (For the optical interpretation of f', see Chap. 2.)
4. (a) Recall the definition of $L(x)$ in the proof of the law of the mean, and show that

$$L(x) = f(a) + \frac{x - a}{b - a}[f(b) - f(a)]$$

   (b) Using (a), show that
$$L'(x) = \frac{f(b) - f(a)}{b - a}$$

5. (a) Use the law of the mean to prove that $4.300 < \sqrt{19} < 4.375$.
   (b) Using differentials, estimate $\sqrt{19}$.

6. Let f have a derivative for all x.
   (a) Is every chord of the graph of f parallel to some tangent to the graph of f?
   (b) Is every tangent to the graph of f parallel to some chord of the graph of f?
7. Assume that f has a derivative for all x, that $f(3) = 7$, and that $f(8) = 17$. What can we conclude about f'?
8. Which of the five corollaries implies (a) that if two cars on a straight road have the same velocity at every instant, they remain a fixed distance apart? (b) that if a car travels 0 miles per hour, it doesn't move? (c) that if all the tangents to a curve are horizontal, the curve is a horizontal straight line? (d) that if two curves have parallel tangent lines at any two points with the same abscissa, one curve is obtainable from the other by raising or lowering it?
9. What does Corollary 5 say concerning (a) the string on page 4; (b) the engineer on page 4; (c) the tent on page 4? (Hint: See Example 6.)
10. A student, inspired by Corollary 5, proposes this theorem and proof. Alleged theorem: If $f(x) = F'(x)$ for all x, then $\int_a^b f(x)\,dx$ is equal to $F(b) - F(a)$. Alleged proof: This is an obvious consequence of Corollary 5.
    (a) Explain why the alleged proof is not valid.
    (b) What extra hypothesis should the student include in his theorem?
11. (a) Show that the derivative of 10^x is proportional to 10^x.
    (b) Does this contradict our assertion in Example 3 that the only functions whose derivative is proportional to the function itself must have the form Ae^{kx}? Explain.
12. Using the technique we employed in Example 5, show that if x is positive, then $e^{-x} > 1 - x$. Graph $y = e^{-x}$ and $y = 1 - x$.
13. (a) Using the inequality $e^x > 1 + x$ for $x > 0$, prove this theorem: If $u_1, u_2, u_3, \ldots$ is a sequence of positive numbers such that the sequence of sums $u_1, u_1 + u_2, u_1 + u_2 + u_3, \ldots$ converges, then the sequence of products $(1 + u_1), (1 + u_1)(1 + u_2), (1 + u_1)(1 + u_2)(1 + u_3), \ldots$ also converges.
    (b) Prove the converse.
14. Prove that if $|f'(x)| \leqslant 6$ for all x, then $|f(x_1) - f(x_2)| \leqslant 6|x_1 - x_2|$ for all numbers x_1 and x_2.
15. (a) Use the law of the mean to show that

$$0.167 = \tfrac{1}{6} < \ln(1.2) < \tfrac{1}{5} = 0.200$$

    (b) Use differentials to estimate $\ln(1.2)$.
    (c) Find $\ln(1.2)$ in a table.
16. (a) Use the law of the mean to show that

$$\frac{\pi}{4} - \frac{0.1}{1 + 1^2} > \tan^{-1} 0.9 > \frac{\pi}{4} - \frac{0.1}{1 + (0.9)^2}$$

hence
$$\frac{\pi}{4} - 0.05 > \tan^{-1} 0.9 > \frac{\pi}{4} - 0.06$$

    (b) Find $\tan^{-1} 0.9$ with the aid of a table.
17. Prove Corollary 4.
18. This illustrates Corollary 5: Let $F(x) = x^3$ [hence $f(x) = 3x^2$] and $a = 1$, $b = 4$. Let the partition be $x_0 = 1$, $x_1 = 2$, $x_2 = 3$, $x_3 = 4$. Find X_1, X_2, X_3.

[Answer: $X_1 = \sqrt{\tfrac{7}{3}}$; $X_2 = \sqrt{\tfrac{19}{3}}$; $X_3 = \sqrt{\tfrac{37}{3}}$]

19. This illustrates Corollary 5: Let $F(x) = x^2$; hence $f(x) = 2x$. Consider $a = 1$, $b = 6$, and the partition $x_0 = 1$, $x_1 = 3$, $x_2 = 4$, $x_3 = 5$, $x_4 = 6$. Find the X_1, X_2, X_3, X_4 guaranteed by Corollary 5.
20. This illustrates Corollary 5: Let $F(x) = 1/x$; hence $f(x) = -1/x^2$. Verify that

$$\sum_{i=1}^{4} f(X_i)(x_i - x_{i-1}) = F(5) - F(1) \text{ for the partition } x_0 = 1,\ x_1 = 2,\ x_2 = 3,\ x_3 = 4,$$

$x_4 = 5$, and $X_1 = \sqrt{2}$, $X_2 = \sqrt{6}$, $X_3 = \sqrt{12}$, $X_4 = \sqrt{20}$.
21. Prove that $e^x > 1 + x + x^2/2 + x^3/6$ for positive x. (Hint: See Example 5.)

22. Let f and g be two functions defined for all x. Assume that g is continuous and that for any two numbers x_1 and x_2 there is a number X, with $x_1 < X < x_2$, such that

$$\frac{f(x_1) - f(x_2)}{x_1 - x_2} = g(X)$$

Prove that f is differentiable. What is its derivative?
23. (a) Graph f if $f(x) = x^2 \sin(1/x)$ for $x \neq 0$ and $f(0) = 0$.
    (b) Show that f has a derivative at all x. In particular, show that $f'(0) = 0$.
    (c) Show that f' is not continuous at 0.
24. Let f be differentiable everywhere. Assume that $f'(a) = 0$ and $f'(b) = 1$. Prove that there is a number X, with $a < X < b$, such that $f'(X) = \frac{1}{2}$. (Warning: As Exercise 23 shows, f' need not be continuous.)
25. Generalize Exercise 24.
26. Proposed theorem: If f is a differentiable increasing function, then $f'(x) > 0$ for all x. Proposed proof: Let x be fixed and $y > x$. Then $[f(y) - f(x)]/(y - x) = f'(X)$ for some number X, with $x < X < y$. But $f(y) - f(x) > 0$ and $y > x$. Thus $f'(X) > 0$. Yet y can be chosen as close as we please to x; hence X is arbitrarily close to x. Thus $f'(x) > 0$.
    (a) What do you think of this proposed converse of Corollary 3?
    (b) Show that x^3 is an increasing function, but its derivative is not always > 0.
    (c) How should the proposed theorem be revised?
27. Prove that if a continuous function f is defined for all x and f' is defined for all x (except possibly at $x = 1$), and if $\lim_{x \to 1} f'(x)$ exists, then f' exists at 1. If we omit the assumption that f is continuous, is the conclusion still true?
28. If f and g are differentiable functions, with $f(0) = g(0)$ and $f'(x) \geqslant g'(x)$ for all x, is $f(x) \geqslant g(x)$ for all x? For all positive x? Explain.
29. If f is defined for all x, with $f(0) = 0$, and $f'(x) \geqslant 1$ for all x, what is the most we can say about $f(3)$? Prove it.
30. Let f have a derivative everywhere, such that $D(f) = f$, and $f(0) = 1$. In answering the following, *do not* make use of the explicit formula for f, $f(x) = Ae^x$, obtained in Example 3.
    (a) Show that for any constant k we have $D(f(x)\,f(k-x)) = 0$.
    (b) In view of Corollary 1, what kind of function must $f(x)\,f(k-x)$ be?
    (c) Prove that $f(x)\,f(k-x) = f(k)$ for all x.
    (d) From (c), prove that $f(x+y) = f(x)\,f(y)$ for all x and y.
31. Let f have a derivative at all $x > 0$, with $f'(x) = 1/x$ and $f(1) = 0$.

(a) Prove that $f(xy) = f(x) + f(y)$ without referring to the function $\ln x$. (Hint: Modify the technique used in Exercise 30.)

(b) Without using (a), prove that $f(x) = \ln x$.

32. Prove that $(\tan x) - x$ is an increasing function of x, when $0 \leqslant x < \dfrac{\pi}{2}$.

(b) Deduce that $\tan x > x$ for $0 < x < \dfrac{\pi}{2}$.

(c) From (b) obtain $x \cos x - \sin x < 0$, if $0 < x < \dfrac{\pi}{2}$.

(d) Prove that $(\sin x)/x$ is a decreasing function if $0 < x < \dfrac{\pi}{2}$.

33. Proposed theorem: If f and g are differentiable, $f(a) = g(a)$ and $f(b) = g(b)$, then there is at least one X between a and b, where $f'(X) = g'(X)$. Proposed proof: By the law of the mean, there is a number X between a and b, such that

$$f'(X) = \frac{f(b) - f(a)}{b - a} \qquad \text{and} \qquad g'(X) = \frac{g(b) - g(a)}{b - a}$$

Since $f(b) - f(a) = g(b) - g(a)$, the theorem is proved.

(a) Is the proposed theorem true?

(b) Is the proposed proof correct? If not, devise a valid proof.

(c) In geometrical terms, what does the proposed theorem say?

(d) In terms of two moving particles, what does the proposed theorem say?

34. Let $u_1, u_2, u_3, \ldots$ be a sequence such that $0 < u_n < 1$ for each n. Show that if the sequence of sums $u_1, u_1 + u_2, u_1 + u_2 + u_3, \ldots$ diverges, then the sequence of products $(1 - u_1), (1 - u_1)(1 - u_2), (1 - u_1)(1 - u_2)(1 - u_3), \ldots$ converges to 0. (Hint: See Exercise 12.)

35. (See Exercise 34.) Let $u_1, u_2, u_3, \ldots$ be a sequence such that $0 < u_n < 1$ for each n. An optimist, hoping to travel arbitrarily far, travels u_n inches on his nth step. A pessimist, content to reach a chair a foot away, covers on his nth step a u_nth of the distance remaining between him and the chair. Show that if the optimist can travel as far as he wishes, then the pessimist can get as close to the chair as he wishes.

36. Show that if $0 < x < 1$, then $|\ln (1 - x)| < x/(1 - x)$. (Hint: Use the technique employed in Example 5.

37. Let $u_1, u_2, u_3, \ldots$ be a sequence such that $0 < u_n < 1$ for each n.

(a) Show that if the sequence $u_1, u_1 + u_2, u_1 + u_2 + u_3, \ldots$ converges, then the sequence $\ln (1 - u_1), \ln (1 - u_1) + \ln (1 - u_2), \ln (1 - u_1) + \ln (1 - u_2) + \ln (1 - u_3)$, . . . converges. (Hint: See Exercise 36.)

(b) From the same assumption used in (a), deduce that the sequence of products $(1 - u_1), (1 - u_1)(1 - u_2), (1 - u_1)(1 - u_2)(1 - u_3), \ldots$ cannot approach 0.

(c) What does (b) tell us about the optimist and pessimist in Exercise 35?

38. Show that if f has a derivative everywhere and $f'(x) \geqslant 0$ when $x \neq 0$, then $f'(0)$ cannot be negative. (Warning: as Exercise 23 shows, a derivative need not be continuous.)

3. Summary. The main theorem in this chapter is the law of the mean (page 123), which asserts that if f is continuous on $[a,b]$ and differentiable on (a,b), then there is at least one number X in (a,b) such that

$$f'(X) = \frac{f(b) - f(a)}{b - a}$$

Rewriting this equation as $f(b) = f(a) + (b - a)f'(X)$, we see that it may give us information about $f(b)$ if we know $f(a)$ (Examples 1 and 2, pages 123–124). From the law of the mean, it follows that if a function has derivative 0 everywhere, then it is constant (Corollary 1, page 124); that two functions that have the same derivative everywhere differ by a constant (Corollary 2, page 125); and that a function whose derivative is positive is increasing (Corollary 3, page 125). In Corollary 5 (page 126) the law of the mean relates the derivative to sums of the type met in the definition of the definite integral. We shall need this corollary in Chap. 6, where the two basic concepts of the calculus, the derivative and the definite integral, meet in the fundamental theorem of calculus.

6

The fundamental theorem
of calculus

IN Chaps. 1 and 2 we saw that the definite integral of velocity is the change in position, and that velocity is the derivative of the position function. Similarly, the definite integral of density is mass, and density is the derivative of the mass function. These observations suggest that there is a close relation between the definite integral and the derivative.

This relation, which we examine in this chapter, provides an efficient technique for computing many definite integrals over intervals.

1. Various forms of the fundamental theorem of calculus. First we translate our introductory remarks into mathematical symbols and equations. If we let x denote time and $F(x)$ denote the coordinate of a particle moving on a line, then

$F'(x)$ is the velocity at time x, and the assertion "the definite integral of velocity is change in position" now reads

$$\int_a^b F'(x)\,dx = F(b) - F(a)$$

where a represents the initial time and b the terminal time. This generalizes the assertion "rate $\times$ time $=$ distance," valid for an object moving at a constant rate.

Similarly, if we let x denote the distance of a point from the left end of a string whose density may not be constant, and $F(x)$ the mass of the part of the string to the left of x, then $F'(x)$ is the density at x, and the assertion "the definite integral of density is mass" now reads

$$\int_a^b F'(x)\,dx = F(b) - F(a)$$

where a and b describe the end points of a typical section of string:

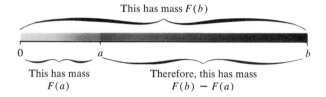

This has mass $F(b)$

0 a b

This has mass   Therefore, this has mass
$F(a)$ $F(b) - F(a)$

These two physical situations suggest that there is a purely mathematical theorem lurking in the background. It is this theorem, the fundamental theorem of calculus, which we investigate in this chapter.

To express the fundamental theorem of calculus in its most useful form, let us rewrite the equation

$$\int_a^b F'(x)\,dx = F(b) - F(a)$$

in the form
$$\int_a^b f(x)\,dx = F(b) - F(a) \qquad f = F'$$

Unfortunately, as it stands, it is not generally true. Example 1 presents a function F, which has a derivative $f = F'$, yet for which $\int_0^1 f(x)\,dx$ does not exist.

Example 1. We now exhibit a differentiable function F, *such that* $\int_0^1 F'(x)\,dx$ *does not exist.* To put it another way, we exhibit a function f, which is a derivative, yet $\int_0^1 f(x)\,dx$ does not exist. Let $F(x) = (\frac{1}{2})\,x^2 \sin(1/x^2)$ if $x \neq 0$ and $F(0) = 0$, and let $f = F'$.

The graph of F oscillates infinitely often near $(0,0)$ between the curves $y = \frac{1}{2}x^2$ and $y = -\frac{1}{2}x^2$, and has arbitrarily steep tangent lines near $(0,0)$ but a horizontal tangent line at $(0,0)$.

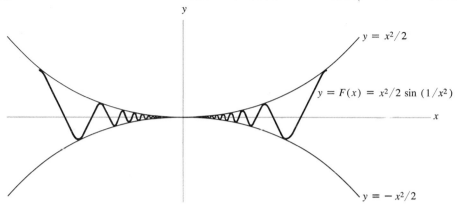

We justify the above assertions by examining F and $f = F'$. First of all, whenever $\sin(1/x^2) = 1$, the graph of $y = F(x)$ meets the graph of $y = x^2/2$. Now, $\sin(1/x^2) = 1$ whenever $1/x^2 = (2n + \frac{1}{2})\pi$, hence whenever $x = \pm\sqrt{1/[(2n + \frac{1}{2})\pi]}$. Thus the curve $y = F(x)$ meets the curve $y = x^2/2$ infinitely often near $(0,0)$. Similarly it meets the curve $y = -x^2/2$ infinitely often near $(0,0)$. Thus the graph of $y = F(x)$ oscillates infinitely often near $(0,0)$.

A simple calculation shows that

$$F'(x) = x\sin\frac{1}{x^2} - \frac{1}{x}\cos\frac{1}{x^2} \qquad x \neq 0$$

and an examination of $\Delta F/\Delta x$ shows that

$$F'(0) = 0$$

Consider the behavior of $f(x) = F'(x)$ for x in $[0,1]$. The part $x\sin(1/x^2)$ is continuous; moreover, since $|\sin\theta| \leqslant 1$ for any θ, $|x\sin(1/x^2)| \leqslant x \leqslant 1$ for x in $[0,1]$. But when $1/x^2$ is some integral multiple of 2π, say $2n\pi$, where n is an integer, we have

$$\left(\frac{1}{x}\right)\cos\left(\frac{1}{x^2}\right) = \frac{1}{x}\cos(2n\pi) = \left(\frac{1}{x}\right)(1) = \frac{1}{x} = \sqrt{2n\pi}$$

as large a number as we please. Thus f is unbounded on $[0,1]$; but as shown on page 88, a function that is unbounded on $[0,1]$ cannot have a definite integral over $[0,1]$. This concludes Example 1.

Clearly our conjecture, $\int_a^b F'(x)\,dx = F(b) - F(a)$, motivated by physical intuition, must be made more precise. We must impose some condition on the function F' to guarantee that $\int_a^b F'(x)\,dx$ exists, some condition which, presumably, the velocity and density functions in physics satisfy. This we now do as we state the fundamental theorem of calculus.

THEOREM 1: *Fundamental theorem of calculus.* If f is continuous on $[a,b]$, then $\int_a^b f(x)\,dx$ exists. Furthermore, if $f = F'$, then $\int_a^b f(x)\,dx$ is equal to $F(b) - F(a)$.

Note that the assumption that f is continuous excludes the function f in Example 1. A partial proof of Theorem 1 will be given later in this chapter. However, we will give in Sec. 2 a complete proof of the following special case of the fundamental theorem of calculus.

THEOREM 2: *Fundamental theorem of calculus, special case.* If f is an increasing or decreasing function on $[a,b]$ and $f = F'$, then $\int_a^b f(x)\,dx$ exists and is equal to $F(b) - F(a)$.

We illustrate the usefulness of the fundamental theorem of calculus by several examples:

Example 2. In Chap. 1 we met four problems whose answers involved $\int_0^3 x^2\,dx$. Now we can compute this definite integral without observing that three pyramids form a cube. In this case $a = 0$, $b = 3$, and $f(x) = x^2$. We call on our experience with derivatives to discover an F such that $F'(x) = x^2$. For instance, $F(x) = x^3/3$ suffices. We then have

$$\int_0^3 x^2\,dx \underset{\text{FTC}}{=} F(3) - F(0) = \frac{3^3}{3} - \frac{0^3}{3} = \frac{27}{3} - \frac{0}{3} = 9$$

in agreement with our work in Chap. 1. The FTC under the equals sign reminds us that we are making use of the fundamental theorem of calculus. (In this case, since x^2 is increasing on $[0,3]$, Theorem 2 is sufficient.)

Example 3. Let us compute the area under the curve $y = \cos x$, above the x axis, and between $x = 0$ and $x = \dfrac{\pi}{2}$:

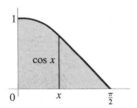

As we showed in Chap. 1, area is the definite integral of a cross section, in this case,

$$\text{Area} = \int_0^{\pi/2} \cos x\,dx$$

We must discover a function F such that $F'(x) = \cos x$. Our knowledge of derivatives suggests $F(x) = \sin x$. Thus

$$\int_0^{\pi/2} \cos x\,dx \underset{\text{FTC}}{=} F\left(\frac{\pi}{2}\right) - F(0) = \sin\frac{\pi}{2} - \sin 0 = 1 - 0 = 1$$

The area in question is 1.

Example 4. We find the volume of a sphere of radius r. Recalling that volume is the definite integral of the area of cross section, we begin by computing $A(x)$, the cross-sectional area as a function of x:

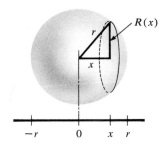

Since the cross section is a circle, its area is $\pi(R(x))^2$, where $R(x)$ is its radius. The right triangle in the diagram shows that $[R(x)]^2 = r^2 - x^2$. Thus $A(x) = \pi(r^2 - x^2)$, and the volume of the sphere is $\int_{-r}^{r} \pi(r^2 - x^2)\, dx$. To apply the fundamental theorem of calculus *we must find a function F of which $\pi(r^2 - x^2)$ is the derivative.* One such F is $\pi(r^2 x - x^3/3)$. Theorem 1 asserts that

$$\int_{-r}^{r} \pi(r^2 - x^2)\, dx \underset{\text{FTC}}{=} F(r) - F(-r) = \pi\left(r^2 \cdot r - \frac{r^3}{3}\right) - \pi\left[r^2(-r) - \left(\frac{-r}{3}\right)^3\right]$$

which reduces to $(\tfrac{4}{3})\pi r^3$. Note that we could also have used $F(r) = \pi(r^2 x - x^3/3) + 1492$.

The next two examples form a fable whose moral should not be forgotten.

Example 5. We compute $\int_{0}^{1} e^{\sqrt{x}}\, dx$. Since $e^{\sqrt{x}}$ is an increasing function we hope to apply Theorem 2. To do so we must find F such that $F'(x) = e^{\sqrt{x}}$. It happens that $F(x) = 2e^{\sqrt{x}}(\sqrt{x} - 1)$ works, as the reader can check by computing F' from the formula for F. (We show how to find this F in Chap. 7, where techniques for finding a function that has a prescribed derivative are presented.) Thus

$$\int_{0}^{1} e^{\sqrt{x}}\, dx \underset{\text{FTC}}{=} [2e^{\sqrt{1}}(\sqrt{1} - 1)] - [2e^{\sqrt{0}}(\sqrt{0} - 1)] = 2e^1(0) - 2e^0(-1) = 0 + 2 = 2$$

Example 6. We try to compute $\int_{0}^{1} e^{-x^2}\, dx$. Proceeding as in the previous example, we reach a point at which we seek F such that $F'(x) = e^{-x^2}$. As we will show in Sec. 2, there is such an F. However, as Liouville proved in 1835, F cannot be expressed as a finite combination or composition of the functions we studied in Chap. 4: polynomials, logarithms, exponentials, and trigonometric functions. We are blocked, for the fundamental theorem of calculus is of use only if f is so well behaved that there is a function F, expressible in terms of the functions in Chap. 4, such that $F' = f$.

Let us call a function *elementary* if it can be obtained from the functions in Chap. 4 by composition, addition, multiplication, subtraction, and division. In

Chap. 4 we showed that an elementary function has an elementary derivative, but Liouville proved that an elementary function need not be tne derivative of an elementary function. As an example, we have e^{-x^2}. Therefore the fundamental theorem of calculus is of no use in computing $\int_0^1 e^{-x^2} dx$.

The moral is this: it is not easy to tell by glancing at f whether the desired F is elementary. After all, $e^{\sqrt{x}}$ looks fancier than e^{-x^2} yet is the derivative of an elementary function, while e^{-x^2} is not.

Incidentally $(1/\sqrt{2\pi}) \int_0^b e^{-x^2/2} dx$ is an important quantity in statistics. Most handbooks tabulate it (as a function of b) under the title "Area of the Normal Curve of Error."

EXERCISES

1. Show that the function F of Example 1 has $F'(0) = 0$. (Hint: Examine $\Delta F/\Delta x$.)
2. Find a number x_0 such that $F'(x_0) > 2000$, where F is given in Example 1.
3. Find an x such that $(1/x) \cos (1/x^2) > 1000$.
4. (a) Set up a definite integral, $\int_a^b f(x) dx$, equal to the area under $y = 1/(1 + x^2)$, above the x axis, between $x = 0$ and $x = 1$.

   (b) Evaluate the area in (a) with the aid of the fundamental theorem of calculus. [Answer: (b) $\pi/4$]
5. (a) Proceed as in Exercise 4(a), but use the area between $x = 0$ and $x = b$, instead of $x = 0$ and $x = 1$.

   (b) Using $A(b)$ to denote the answer to (a), find $\lim_{b \to \infty} A(b)$. [Answer: (b) $\pi/2$]
6. Compute (a) $\int_1^3 x^4 dx$; (b) $\int_0^\pi \sin x\, dx$; (c) $\int_{1/2}^{\sqrt{3}/2} (1/\sqrt{1 - x^2}) dx$.

   (d) Which of (a), (b), (c) is not directly computable with the aid of Theorem 2? [Answer: (a) $242\tfrac{2}{5}$; (b) 2; (c) $\pi/6$]
7. Compute (a) $\int_0^1 x e^{x^2} dx$; (b) $\int_1^4 (5x^2 - 7) dx$; (c) $\int_1^5 (2/x) dx$.

   [Answer: (a) $(e - 1)/2$; (b) $252\tfrac{2}{3}$; (c) $2 \ln 5$]
8. (a) For a function F, with $F'(x) = x^2$, we used $(\tfrac{1}{3}) x^3$. Show that $(\tfrac{1}{3}) x^3 + 121$ also has a derivative equal to x^2.

   (b) What result obtained in Chap. 5 assures us that if $F' = f$ and $G' = f$, then G differs from F by a constant?
9. Using a table of e^x or e^{-x}, estimate $\int_0^1 e^{-x^2} dx$. Specifically, letting $f(x) = e^{-x^2}$, compute $\sum_{i=1}^3 f(X_i)(x_i - x_{i-1})$ for the partition $x_0 = 0$, $x_1 = \tfrac{1}{3}$, $x_2 = \tfrac{2}{3}$, $x_3 = 1$, and $X_1 = 0.3$, $X_2 = 0.4$, $X_3 = 0.8$. (Answer: 0.764)
10. Check that $D[2e^{\sqrt[3]{x}} (\sqrt{x} - 1)] = e^{\sqrt[3]{x}}$.
11. Check that $D[3e^{\sqrt[3]{x}} (x^{2/3} - 2\sqrt[3]{x} + 2)] = e^{\sqrt[3]{x}}$.

12. Find F such that $F'(x)$ is equal to (a) $e^{x^5} x^4$; (b) $1/x^2$; (c) e^{-x}.

13. Let $a_n = \dfrac{1^3 + 2^3 + 3^3 + 4^3 + \cdots + n^3}{n^4}$.

   (a) Compute a_1, a_2, a_3.

   (b) Show that a_n is an approximation to $\displaystyle\int_0^1 x^3 \, dx$.

   (c) Using the fundamental theorem of calculus, prove that $\lim\limits_{n \to \infty} a_n = \tfrac{1}{4}$.

   (d) Which of Theorems 1 and 2 can be used in (c)?   [Answer: (a) 1, 0.563, 0.444]

14. (See Exercise 13.) Prove that for any positive rational number r,

$$\lim_{n \to \infty} \frac{1^r + 2^r + 3^r + \cdots + n^r}{n^{r+1}} = \frac{1}{r+1}.$$

15. Let $f(x) = 0$ if $x \neq 1$, and let $f(1) = 3$.

   (a) Show that $\displaystyle\int_0^2 f(x) \, dx$ exists and is equal to 0.

   (b) Show that there is no function F such that $f = F'$.

   (c) What is the moral that is implicit in parts (a) and (b)?

□ □ □

16. (a) Let $a_n = n \left(\dfrac{1}{n^2 + 1^2} + \dfrac{1}{n^2 + 2^2} + \dfrac{1}{n^2 + 3^2} + \cdots + \dfrac{1}{n^2 + n^2} \right)$

   Compute a_1, a_2, a_3.

   (b) Show that a_n is a disguised version of a sum approximating $\displaystyle\int_0^1 1/(1 + x^2) \, dx$.

   (c) In view of (b), compute $\lim\limits_{n \to \infty} a_n$.
                [Answer: (a) $a_1 = \tfrac{1}{2} = 0.500$, $a_2 = \tfrac{13}{20} = 0.650$, $a_3 = \tfrac{136}{195} = 0.697$]

17. Let $F(x) = x \sin(1/x)$ if $x \neq 0$, and $F(0) = 0$.
   (a) Graph F.
   (b) Does $F'(0)$ exist? Explain.

18. (a) If f is increasing on $[0,1]$, and $f = F'$, show that f is continuous. (Exercises 24 and 25 on page 129 give further information about f.)
   (b) Is an increasing function necessarily continuous?
   (c) Show that if the hypothesis of Theorem 2 is satisfied, then the hypothesis of Theorem 1 is satisfied.

19. Evaluate $\displaystyle\int_{-1}^1 x^{15} e^{-x^4} \, dx$. [Hint: Do not try to find F such that $F'(x) = x^{15} e^{-x^4}$.]

20. (See Exercise 24, page 73.)
   (a) If the needle falls at an angle θ to the lines ($0 \leqslant \theta < \pi$), as shown in the following diagram, show that the probability of its meeting a line is $\sin \theta$.

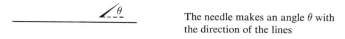

The needle makes an angle θ with the direction of the lines

(b) Why would $\left(\int_0^\pi \sin\theta\, d\theta\right)/\pi$ be a reasonable representation of the probability of the needle's meeting a line?

(c) Compute $\left(\int_0^\pi \sin\theta\, d\theta\right)/\pi$.

[Answer: (c) $2/\pi$]

21. Let $f(x) = -x^2\cos(1/x) + 4x^3\sin(1/x)$, if $x \neq 0$ and $f(0) = 0$; let $F(x) = x^4\sin(1/x)$ if $x \neq 0$ and $F(0) = 0$.
    (a) Show that $f = F'$.
    (b) Show that Theorem 1 applies for $a = 0$ and $b = 1$, but not Theorem 2.

2. Proof of a special case of the fundamental theorem of calculus.

We now prove Theorem 2 of Sec. 1. Though in practice we will use the more general Theorem 1 we include Theorem 2 and its proof for several reasons: (1) We will not be able to present a complete proof of Theorem 1; (2) in practice Theorem 2 is frequently sufficient; (3) understanding a proof of Theorem 2 will help us appreciate both Theorems 1 and 2.

For convenience we repeat Theorem 2.

THEOREM 2: *Fundamental theorem of calculus, special case.* If f is an increasing or decreasing function on $[a,b]$ and $f = F'$, then $\int_a^b f(x)\, dx$ exists and is equal to $F(b) - F(a)$.

PROOF. We consider only the case in which f is increasing. By Corollary 5, page 126, no matter how fine the mesh of the partition, we can always construct for it an approximating sum, $\sum_{i=1}^n f(X_i^*)(x_i - x_{i-1})$, equal to $F(b) - F(a)$. (We use the symbol X_i^* rather than X_i because we want to reserve X_i to denote, as usual, an arbitrary number in $[x_{i-1}, x_i]$.) Thus if *all* the sums of the form $\sum_{i=1}^n f(X_i)(x_i - x_{i-1})$ tend to be near a certain number when the mesh is small, that number must be $F(b) - F(a)$. In other words, if the definite integral of f over $[a,b]$ exists, it must have the value $F(b) - F(a)$. This suggests that we prove both assertions in Theorem 2 by showing that *any* sum $\sum_{i=1}^n f(X_i)(x_i - x_{i-1})$ formed on a sufficiently fine partition is close to $F(b) - F(a)$.

Since f is increasing,

(1) $\qquad \sum_{i=1}^n f(x_{i-1})(x_i - x_{i-1}) \leqslant \sum_{i=1}^n f(X_i)(x_i - x_{i-1}) \leqslant \sum_{i=1}^n f(x_i)(x_i - x_{i-1})$

Also, for the same partition, let $X_1^*, \ldots, X_n^*$ be chosen in accord with Corollary 5, page 126. Since f is increasing, we have $f(x_{i-1}) \leqslant f(X_i^*) \leqslant f(x_i)$, and thus

(2) $$\sum_{i=1}^{n} f(x_{i-1})(x_i - x_{i-1}) \leqslant F(b) - F(a) \leqslant \sum_{i=1}^{n} f(x_i)(x_i - x_{i-1})$$

In view of (1) and (2), $\sum_{i=1}^{n} f(X_i)(x_i - x_{i-1})$ differs from $F(b) - F(a)$ by at most the difference between $\sum_{i=1}^{n} f(x_i)(x_i - x_{i-1})$ and $\sum_{i=1}^{n} f(x_{i-1})(x_i - x_{i-1})$. All that remains to be shown, therefore, is that when the mesh is small,

(3) $$\sum_{i=1}^{n} f(x_i)(x_i - x_{i-1}) - \sum_{i=1}^{n} f(x_{i-1})(x_i - x_{i-1})$$

is also small.

To show that (3) is small, we rewrite it as

$$\sum_{i=1}^{n} [f(x_i) - f(x_{i-1})](x_i - x_{i-1})$$

Since f is increasing, we have

$$0 < f(x_i) - f(x_{i-1}) \qquad \text{for each } i = 1, 2, \ldots, n$$

Also, if we denote the mesh of the partition by p, we have

$$x_i - x_{i-1} \leqslant p \qquad \text{for each } i$$

Hence $$\sum_{i=1}^{n} [f(x_i) - f(x_{i-1})](x_i - x_{i-1}) \leqslant \sum_{i=1}^{n} [f(x_i) - f(x_{i-1})] p$$

and the right-hand side is equal to

$$p \sum_{i=1}^{n} [f(x_i) - f(x_{i-1})]$$

Now, we have

$$\sum_{i=1}^{n} [f(x_i) - f(x_{i-1})] = [f(x_1) - f(x_0)] + [f(x_2) - f(x_1)] + \cdots + [f(x_n) - f(x_{n-1})]$$

which, after cancelations, reduces to $f(x_n) - f(x_0)$, or simply to

$$f(b) - f(a)$$

Thus $$\sum_{i=1}^{n} [f(x_i) - f(x_{i-1})](x_i - x_{i-1}) \leqslant [f(b) - f(a)] p$$

which is small when p is small.

Hence we have shown that any sum $\sum_{i=1}^{n} f(X_i)(x_i - x_{i-1})$ differs from $F(b) - F(a)$ by less than $[f(b) - f(a)] p$, a quantity that is small when p is small. This proves the theorem. (The case in which f is decreasing is left to the reader.)

EXERCISES

1. In the proof of Theorem 2 we went from the assertion $x_i - x_{i-1} \leqslant p$ to

$$\sum_{i=1}^{n} [f(x_i) - f(x_{i-1})] (x_i - x_{i-1}) \leqslant p \sum_{i=1}^{n} [f(x_i) - f(x_{i-1})]$$

   Explain how this was done. In particular show how we used the assumption that f is increasing.
2. With the book closed, prove Theorem 2.
3. Prove Theorem 2 with the assumption that f is decreasing.
4. How fine should a partition of $[1,5]$ be to assure us that any approximating sum to

$$\int_{1}^{5} (1/x) \, dx \text{ formed with it differs from } \int_{1}^{5} (1/x) \, dx \text{ by less than } 0.01? \text{ Explain.}$$

   (Answer: 0.0125)
5. In Sec. 3 we prove that there is a function F such that $e^{x^2} = F'(x)$ (F is not an elementary function). Show that any approximating sum for $\int_{0}^{1} e^{x^2} \, dx$ formed by using

   a mesh $\leqslant 0.1$ differs from $\int_{0}^{1} e^{x^2} \, dx$ by less than 0.18.
6. Let f satisfy the hypothesis of Theorem 2 with $[a,b] = [0,1]$. How close is

$$\sum_{i=1}^{n} f(i/n) (1/n) \text{ to } \int_{0}^{1} f(x) \, dx?$$

7. Is this a true theorem: If $f = F'$ throughout $[a,b]$ and $\int_{a}^{b} f(x) \, dx$ exists, then

   $\int_{a}^{b} f(x) \, dx = F(b) - F(a)$? Explain.

8. The speed of a certain particle t minutes after it starts to move is t^4 feet per minute. How far does it travel during (a) the first minute; (b) the third minute?
   [Answer: (a) 0.2 feet; (b) 42.2 feet]
9. A certain bacterial population grows at the increasing rate of e^t members per minute t minutes after the experiment begins. How much does the population increase during the third minute?
10. Consider the region bounded by $y = \sqrt{\sin x}$, and the x axis, from $x = 0$ to $x = \pi/2$. Which is easier, to find its area or to find the volume of the "bowl" formed by rotating this region around the x axis? Solve the easier problem.
    [Answer (to easier problem): π]
11. (a) Graph $y = e^{-x}$.
    (b) For any number $b > 1$ find the area of the region below $y = e^{-x}$ and above $[1,b]$.
    (c) What happens to this area as b increases? [Answer: (c) It approaches 1]
12. Repeat Exercise 11 for the curve $y = 1/\sqrt{x}$.
13. (a) Which of these two definite integrals is easier to evaluate:

$$\int_{0}^{\sqrt{\pi}} 2x \sin x^2 \, dx \quad \text{or} \quad \int_{0}^{\sqrt{\pi}} 2 \sin x^2 \, dx$$

    (b) Evaluate the easier one.

    [Answer: (b) 2]

14. Let $a_n = n/(n + 1)^2 + n/(n + 2)^2 + \cdots + n/(n + n)^2$.

(a) Compute a_n for $n = 1, 2$, and 3.

(b) Rewrite a_n in such a way that it becomes an approximating sum to a certain definite integral.

(c) With the aid of (b), find $\lim_{n \to \infty} a_n$.

[Answer: (c) ½]

□   □   □

15. Prove that if $f = F'$ and f is differentiable, and if f' is bounded in $[a,b]$, then $\int_a^b f(x)\,dx$ exists and is equal to $F(b) - F(a)$. Do not use Theorem 1.

16. (See Exercise 15.) Show that the theorem proved in Exercise 15 applies to the f and F of Exercise 21, page 139.

17. This is suggested by Exercise 15. Devise two functions f and g such that $|f'(x)| \leqslant 1$, $|g'(x)| \leqslant 1$ for all x, yet the derivative of $f(x) \cdot g(x)$ is unbounded.

18. Prove that if $f = F'$ and f has a continuous derivative, then $\int_a^b f(x)\,dx$ exists and is equal to $F(b) - F(a)$. Do not use Theorem 1. (See Exercise 15.)

3. A different view of the fundamental theorem of calculus.

Theorem 2 is a special case of Theorem 1. The difficult part of Theorem 1 is the proof that $\int_a^b f(x)\,dx$ exists for any continuous f. *We shall assume that* $\int_a^b f(x)\,dx$ *exists if f is continuous*, and with this assumption, prove Theorem 1. The proof will give us a fresh perspective on the fundamental theorem of calculus; it does *not* use the law of the mean.

Before we consider the theorem and its proof, we examine some basic properties of the definite integral, properties that will be of use in the proof and elsewhere. We begin with two definitions.

DEFINITION: *The integral from a to b, with $b < a$.* If b is less than a, then

$$\int_a^b f(x)\,dx = -\int_b^a f(x)\,dx.$$

Example. Observe that the symbol $\int_3^0 x^2\,dx$, which we may read as the integral of x^2 from 3 to 0, is not defined as a definite integral. It is the negative of the definite integral, $\int_0^3 x^2\,dx$, which, as we saw in Chap. 1, equals 9. Thus $\int_3^0 x^2\,dx = -9$.

DEFINITION: *The integral from a to a.* $\int_a^a f(x)\,dx = 0$.

REMARK. We defined definite integrals over intervals $[a,b]$, where $a < b$, with the aid of partitions, $x_0 < x_1 < \cdots < x_n$. Rather than allow partitions to have repeated x_i, we simply make the above definition.

LEMMA 1.   If a, b, and c are numbers and $\int_a^c f(x)\,dx$ and $\int_c^b f(x)\,dx$ exist, then $\int_a^b f(x)\,dx$ exists, and we have

$$\int_a^c f(x)\,dx + \int_b^c f(x)\,dx = \int_a^b f(x)\,dx$$

A sketch of part of the proof of this lemma is to be found in Exercise 13. Geometrically speaking, the lemma is reasonable. For instance, if $a < b < c$, and if $f(x)$ is positive, it asserts that the area of the region under the curve $y = f(x)$ and above $[a,b]$ is the sum of the areas of the regions below the curve and above the intervals $[a,c]$ and $[c,b]$.

LEMMA 2.   If $\int_a^b f(x)\,dx$ exists, and if $m \leqslant f(x) \leqslant M$ for all x in $[a,b]$, then

$$m(b-a) \leqslant \int_a^b f(x)\,dx \leqslant M(b-a) \qquad a < b$$

or

$$m(b-a) \geqslant \int_a^b f(x)\,dx \geqslant M(b-a) \qquad b < a$$

PROOF.   We prove this for the case $a < b$.

Since $m \leqslant f(X_i) \leqslant M$ if X_i is in $[a,b]$, we have for any approximating sum based on a partition of $[a,b]$,

$$m \sum_{i=1}^n (x_i - x_{i-1}) \leqslant \sum_{i=1}^n f(X_i)(x_i - x_{i-1}) \leqslant M \sum_{i=1}^n (x_i - x_{i-1})$$

But $\sum_{i=1}^n (x_i - x_{i-1}) = b - a$. Therefore any approximating sum for $\int_a^b f(x)\,dx$ is between $m(b-a)$ and $M(b-a)$. This concludes the proof. (The case $b < a$ can be deduced from the case $a < b$ and the first definition above.)

LEMMA 3.   Let a and b be numbers and f a continuous function. Then there is a number X between a and b, such that

$$\int_a^b f(x)\,dx = f(X)(b-a)$$

PROOF.   We prove this for the case $a < b$. Let M be the maximum and m the minimum of $f(x)$ for x in $[a,b]$. (Recall the maximum value theorem and the minimum value theorem, page 84.) By Lemma 2 we have

$$m \leqslant \frac{\displaystyle\int_a^b f(x)\,dx}{b-a} \leqslant M$$

By the intermediate value theorem, page 83, there is a number X in $[a,b]$ such that

$$f(X) = \frac{\int_a^b f(x)\,dx}{b-a}$$

and the lemma is proved. (The case $b < a$ can be derived from the case $a < b$.)

If $f(x)$ is positive, and we interpret $\int_a^b f(x)\,dx$ as the area of the region below $y = f(x)$ and above $[a,b]$, then Lemma 3 asserts that there is a rectangle whose base is $[a,b]$ and whose height is $f(X)$, such that it has the same area as the region:

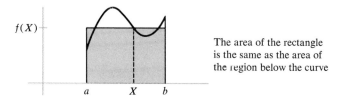

The area of the rectangle is the same as the area of the region below the curve

With these lemmas and the assumption that a continuous function has a definite integral, we are prepared to prove Theorem 1.

THEOREM 1: *Fundamental theorem of calculus.* If f is continuous on $[a,b]$, then $\int_a^b f(x)\,dx$ exists. Furthermore, if $f = F'$, then $\int_a^b f(x)\,dx$ is equal to $F(b) - F(a)$.

PROOF. We begin by constructing a particular function G of which f is the derivative. To do this, we define $G(t)$ to equal $\int_a^t f(x)\,dx$. For instance, $G(a) = \int_a^a f(x)\,dx = 0$, and $G(b) = \int_a^b f(x)\,dx$. We will show that $G' = f$. Once we have this information, we will easily prove the theorem.

We must examine

$$\frac{\Delta G}{\Delta t} = \frac{G(t + \Delta t) - G(t)}{\Delta t}$$

where Δt can be positive or negative.

By Lemma 1

$$G(t + \Delta t) - G(t) = \int_a^{t + \Delta t} f(x)\,dx - \int_a^t f(x)\,dx = \int_t^{t + \Delta t} f(x)\,dx$$

By Lemma 3 there is a number T, such that T is between t and $t + \Delta t$, and

$$\Delta G = \int_t^{t + \Delta t} f(x)\,dx = f(T)\,[(t + \Delta t) - t] = f(T)\,(\Delta t)$$

In other words,
$$\frac{\Delta G}{\Delta t} = f(T)$$

where T is between t and $t + \Delta t$.

This is enough information to enable us to compute $\lim_{\Delta t \to 0} \Delta G / \Delta t$. Since f is continuous, $\lim_{\Delta t \to 0} f(T) = f(t)$. Thus

$$\lim_{\Delta t \to 0} \frac{\Delta G}{\Delta t} = \lim_{\Delta t \to 0} f(T) = f(t)$$

and we have shown that $G'(t) = f(t)$.

Before we consider any F such that $F' = f$, let us observe that for the function G we have

$$G(b) - G(a) = \int_a^b f(x)\,dx - 0 = \int_a^b f(x)\,dx$$

Now let F be any function such that $F' = f$. Since G and F have the same derivative, they differ by a constant (see Corollary 2, page 125). Thus $F(t) = G(t) + C$, where C is fixed. Then

$$F(b) - F(a) = [G(b) + C] - [G(a) + C] = G(b) - G(a) + (C - C) = G(b) - G(a)$$

which we have already shown to be equal to $\int_a^b f(x)\,dx$. This completes the proof of Theorem 1.

REMARK.   If $f(x)$ is positive for all x in $[a,b]$, then we can interpret $G(t)$ as the area under the curve $y = f(x)$, from a to t:

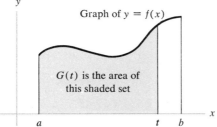

Graph of $y = f(x)$

$G(t)$ is the area of this shaded set

Then for $\Delta t > 0$, $G(t + \Delta t) - G(t) = \Delta G$ represents the area of a narrow strip, and T is chosen in such a way that the rectangle with base Δt and height $f(T)$ has an area equal to the area of the shaded strip.

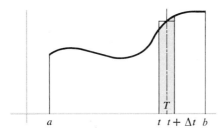

ΔG is the area of the shaded strip

Then $\Delta G/\Delta t = f(T)$, the height of the rectangle chosen as described. As Δt approaches 0, we see that $f(T)$ approaches $f(t)$, since f is continuous.

The crucial part of the preceding proof is the demonstration that the function G defined by $G(t) = \int_a^t f(x)\,dx$ has a derivative equal to f. From a theoretical point of view, this is the heart of the fundamental theorem of calculus. Since it is also of practical importance, we state it as a theorem for ease of reference.

THEOREM 3.   *If f is a continuous function, then*

$$\frac{d\left(\int_a^t f(x)\,dx\right)}{dt} = f(t)$$

In crude geometric terms Theorem 3 tells us that *the derivative of area is the ordinate* and *the derivative of volume is the cross-sectional area.*

Example 1.   As a stone is lowered into water, we record the volume of water it displaces. When x inches are submerged, the stone displaces $V(x)$ cubic inches of water. How can we find the area of the cross section of the stone made by the plane of the surface of the water when it is submerged to a depth of x inches?

If we call this area $A(x)$, then we have $V(t) = \int_a^t A(x)\,dx$. Theorem 3 then asserts that $A(t) = dV/dt$. In other words, to find the cross-sectional area simply differentiate the volume function.

Example 2.   According to Theorem 3,

$$\frac{d\left(\int_0^t e^{x^2}\,dx\right)}{dt} = e^{t^2}.$$

There is therefore a function F such that $dF/dx = e^{x^2}$. However, as Liouville proved, F is not an elementary function.

EXERCISES

1. (*a*) Prove that if f is continuous, then $\int_t^b f(x)\,dx$, a function of t, has a derivative equal to $-f(t)$. Model your proof on part of the proof of Theorem 1.

   (*b*) Verify (*a*) for $\int_t^b x^2\,dx$.

   (*c*) If $f(x)$ is positive, and we think of $\int_t^b f(x)\,dx$ as area, then is it reasonable that the derivative of $\int_t^b f(x)\,dx$ be negative? Explain.

2. (*a*) Show that $D\left(\int_0^x 6e^{t^2}\,dt\right) = 6e^{x^2}$.

(b) Show that $D\left(\int_0^{x^3} e^{t^2} dt\right) = 3x^2 e^{x^6}$.

3. (a) Show that the area of a circle of radius a is equal to $4\int_0^a \sqrt{a^2 - x^2}\, dx$.

(b) Verify that

$$D\left(\frac{x}{2}\sqrt{a^2 - x^2} + \frac{a^2}{2}\sin^{-1}\frac{x}{a}\right) = \sqrt{a^2 - x^2}$$

(c) Use (b) to compute the area of the circle.

4. Find

$$\lim_{x_2 \to x_1} \frac{\int_0^{x_2} e^{t^2} dt - \int_0^{x_1} e^{t^2} dt}{x_2 - x_1}$$

5. How often should a machine be overhauled? This depends on the rate $f(t)$ at which it depreciates and the cost A of overhaul. Denote the time interval between overhauls by T.

(a) Explain why you would like to minimize $g(T) = [A + \int_0^T f(t)\, dt]/T$.

(b) Find dg/dT.

(c) Show that when $dg/dT = 0$ we have $f(T) = g(T)$.

(d) Is this reasonable?

6. Let $f(x) = x^2/(1 + x^4)$. Compute $\int_0^1 (df/dx)\, dx$.   (Answer: ½)

7. Prove Lemma 1 in the special cases (a) $a = b$; (b) $a = c$.

8. Using Theorem 2 only, show that if f satisfies the hypotheses of Theorem 2, then the derivative of $\int_a^b f(x)\, dx$ with respect to b is $f(b)$, and with respect to a is $-f(a)$.

9. Find a function f such that $\int_0^t f(x)\, dx = (\sin t)/(1 + t^2)$ for all t.

10. A company is founded with a capital investment A. The plan is to have its rate of investment proportional to its total investment at any time. Let $f(t)$ denote rate of investment at time t.

(a) Show that there is a constant k such that $f(t) = k\left(A + \int_0^t f(x)\, dx\right)$ for any $t \geqslant 0$.

(b) Differentiate the relation in (a), and with the aid of the equation you obtain, find the form of f.

11. Theorem 3 offers this alternative approach to finding the derivative of $\sin x$ and $\sin^{-1} x$. Consider this diagram:

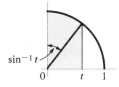

$\sin^{-1} t$

$0 \qquad t \qquad 1$

(a) By considering the area of the shaded region, show that

$$\int_0^t \sqrt{1 - x^2}\, dx = \frac{1}{2}\sin^{-1} t + \frac{t}{2}\sqrt{1 - t^2}$$

(b) From (a) we obtain

$$\sin^{-1} t = 2\int_0^t \sqrt{1 - x^2}\, dx - t\sqrt{1 - t^2}$$

Differentiate the expression on the right, and obtain a new proof that $D(\sin^{-1} t)$ $= 1/\sqrt{1 - t^2}$.

12. (See Exercise 11.) (a) Using the fact that $D(\sin^{-1} t) = \sqrt{1 - t^2}$, prove that $D(\sin x)$ $= \cos x$.

(b) From (a) prove that $\lim_{x \to 0} (\sin x/x) = 1$. (Observe that Exercises 11 and 12 obtain the basic properties of $\sin x$ and $\sin^{-1} x$ in the order opposite to that followed in Sections 1 and 4 of Chap. 4.)

13. We outline a proof that if $\int_a^c f(x)\, dx = A$ and $\int_c^b f(x)\, dx = B$, then $\int_a^b f(x)\, dx$ exists and equals $A + B$, for the case $a < c < b$.

(a) Show that for a fine partition of $[a,b]$ that includes c as one of its x_i's, any approximating sum formed on it is close to $A + B$.

(b) If c is not one of the x_i in a certain partition of $[a,b]$, introduce c as a new point of the partition. If c lies in $[x_i, x_{i-1}]$, introduce X^* in $[c, x_{i-1}]$ and X^{**} in $[x_i, c]$ in order to form an approximating sum for this partition. Why is the new sum close to the old sum? (Recall that if $\int_a^b f(x)\, dx$ exists, f is bounded on $[a,b]$.)

The proof that if $\int_a^b f(x)\, dx$ exists, then so do $\int_a^c f(x)\, dx$ and $\int_c^b f(x)\, dx$, is much more involved, and we omit it.

14. A particle moves along a line in such a way that its average velocity over *any* interval of time, $[a,b]$, is the same as its velocity at time $(a + b)/2$. Prove that the velocity $v(t)$ must be of the form $ct + d$ for appropriate constants c and d. [Hint: Begin by differentiating the relation $\int_a^b v(t)\, dt = [v((a + b)/2)](b - a)$ with respect to b and with respect to a.]

15. A particle moves along a line in such a way that the average velocity over any interval of time $[a,b]$ is equal to the average of its velocities at the beginning and end of the interval of time. Prove that the velocity $v(t)$ must be of the form $ct + d$ for appropriate constants c and d. (Hint: Begin by differentiating the relation

$$\int_a^b v(t)\, dt = \frac{v(a) + v(b)}{2}(b - a)$$

with respect to a and with respect to b.)

16. (*a*) Show that the average distance between vertices of a regular polygon of *n* sides inscribed in the unit circle is

$$A_n = \frac{2}{n-1} \cdot \sum_{k=1}^{n-1} \sin \frac{k\pi}{n}$$

(*b*) By relating A_n to an approximating sum for $\int_0^\pi \sin x \, dx$, prove that $\lim_{n \to \infty} A_n = 4/\pi$.

17. Using Theorem 2 and other results we have obtained (but not Theorems 1 or 3), prove this theorem: If $f = F'$ and f has a continuous derivative, and $f'(x) = 0$ for only a finite number of x in $[a,b]$, then $\int_a^b f(x) \, dx$ exists and is equal to $F(b) - F(a)$.

This theorem covers most cases that arise in practice.

18. (*a*) Show that $\int_1^{ab} (1/x) \, dx = \int_1^a (1/x) \, dx + \int_1^b (1/x) \, dx$ for $a > 0$ and $b > 0$.

(*b*) Find all continuous functions f such that $\int_1^{ab} f(x) \, dx = \int_1^a f(x) \, dx + \int_1^b f(x) \, dx$

for all $a > 0$ and $b > 0$.

4. An alternative approach to the logarithm and exponential functions.

Let us recall how the logarithm and exponential functions are usually defined. First the exponential function a^x $(a > 0)$ is built up in stages as follows: $a^n = a \cdot a \cdot a \cdot \cdots \cdot a$ (n times) for $n = 1, 2, 3, \ldots$; $a^{-n} = 1/a^n$ for $n = 1, 2, 3, \ldots$; $a^0 = 1$; $a^{1/n} = $ positive nth root for a for $n = 1, 2, 3, \ldots$; $a^{m/n} = (a^{1/n})^m$ for m an integer and $n = 1, 2, 3, \ldots$; and finally $a^x = \lim_{m/n \to x} a^{m/n}$ for irrational x.

A thorough treatment of the exponential function based on this approach is beset with many difficulties, such as: How do we know that a has an nth root? If $m/n = m'/n'$, is $(a^{1/n})^m = (a^{1/n'})^{m'}$? Does $\lim_{m/n \to x} a^{m/n}$ exist? After settling these questions, we would still have to prove that the exponential function is continuous and establish the important identities $a^{x+y} = a^x a^y$ and $a^{xy} = (a^x)^y$.

We present another approach, one which avoids the difficulties mentioned above and is based on the single assumption that a continuous function has a definite integral. We first define a function L, which will turn out to be the "logarithm to the base e" function, then a function E as the inverse of the function L. E will coincide with the "exponential with the base e" function, that is, $E(x) = e^x$. With the aid of the function E it is then a simple matter to define the functions a^x and $\log_a x$.

We begin by defining a function L which will turn out to coincide with the natural logarithm.

DEFINITION: *The function L.* $L(t) = \int_1^t (1/x)\,dx$ for $t > 0$.

Observe that $L(1) = \int_1^1 (1/x)\,dx = 0$; if $t > 1$, $L(t) > 0$ and is the area of this shaded set:

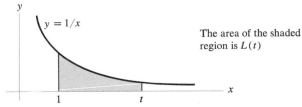

The area of the shaded region is $L(t)$

If $0 < t < 1$, then $L(t) = \int_1^t (1/x)\,dx = -\int_t^1 (1/x)\,dx$, the negative of the area of this shaded set:

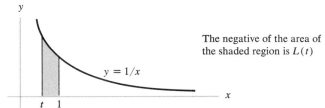

The negative of the area of the shaded region is $L(t)$

Thus, if $0 < t < 1$, we have $L(t) < 0$. $L(t)$ resembles a logarithm function also in that $L(t)$ is defined only for $t > 0$.

By Theorem 3, page 146, $L'(t) = 1/t$. With this information, we obtain some basic properties of the function L.

LEMMA 1. $L(xy) = L(x) + L(y)$ for $x,y > 0$.

PROOF.   Let $y > 0$ be fixed throughout this proof. Let $f(x) = L(xy) - L(x)$. Then we have $f'(x) = [L(xy)]' - [L(x)]' = (1/xy)(y) - 1/x = 1/x - 1/x = 0$. Thus f is constant. But $f(1) = L(1y) - L(1) = L(y) - L(1) = L(y)$, since $L(1) = 0$. Hence $f(x) = L(y)$ for all $x > 0$. In other words,

$$L(xy) - L(x) = L(y)$$

or equivalently $L(xy) = L(x) + L(y)$

and the theorem is proved.

Though we will not assume the existence of the exponential function a^x (since we wish to provide a new definition for it), we will need and define $a^n = a \cdot a \cdot \cdots \cdot a$ (n times), $a^{-n} = 1/a^n$, for $n = 1, 2, 3, \ldots$, and $a^0 = 1$.

LEMMA 2. $L(1/t) = -L(t)$ and $L(t^n) = nL(t)$ if n is an integer.

PROOF. $L(t) + L(1/t) = L(t(1/t)) = L(1) = 0$. Thus $L(1/t) = -L(t)$. For the second assertion, observe that $L(t^2) = L(t \cdot t) = L(t) + L(t) = 2L(t)$. Similarly,

$L(t^3) = L(t \cdot t^2) = L(t) + L(t^2) = L(t) + 2L(t) = 3L(t)$. A similar argument shows that $L(t^{-2}) = -2L(t)$, $L(t^{-3}) = -3L(t)$. An inductive argument shows that the lemma holds for all n, not just for 2, 3, -2, and -3.

Let us apply Lemma 2 to $t = 2$, say. Since $L(2)$ is positive, and $L(2^n) = nL(2)$, we conclude that $L(2^n)$ becomes arbitrarily large for large positive integers n. Similarly, since $L(2^{-n}) = -nL(2)$, $L(2^{-n})$ becomes arbitrarily large (and negative) for large positive integers n. Thus $\lim_{x \to 0} L(x) = -\infty$ and $\lim_{x \to \infty} L(x) = \infty$. From these two facts it follows that the range of L consists of all real numbers. Thus L is a one-to-one correspondence between the set of positive real numbers and the set of all real numbers. L therefore has an inverse function which we denote E. (For each real number x, $E(x)$ is positive; moreover $E[L(t)] = t$ for all positive real numbers t and $L[E(x)] = x$ for all real numbers x.)

LEMMA 3.   For all positive real numbers x, $L(x) = \ln x$.

PROOF.   Since the functions $L(x)$ and $\ln x$ have the same derivative, $1/x$, there is a constant C such that $L(x) = C + \ln x$. Since $L(1) = 0 = \ln 1$ it follows that $C = 0$, and therefore $L(x) = \ln x$ for all positive x.

LEMMA 4. $E(x) = e^x$ for all real numbers x.

PROOF. E is the inverse of the function L. Also, the exponential function e^x is the inverse of the function $\ln x$. In view of the preceding lemma, $E(x) = e^x$.

Starting with the function L we have reached the function e^x. We next define the exponential function a^x (where a is positive) in terms of the functions L and E as follows. (The definition is suggested by the equation $a^x = e^{x \ln a}$ of the traditional approach.)

DEFINITION: *Exponential function with base a; $a > 0$. $a^x = E[xL(a)]$.*

Finally, we define $\log_a x$.

DEFINITION: *Logarithm function with base a; $a > 0$, $a \neq 1$. If $a^y = x$, then $y = \log_a x$.* That is, the "logarithm function with the base a" is the inverse of the "exponential function with base a."

The next lemma assures us that the exponential function, as defined in the preceding paragraph, satisfies the identities with which we are familiar.

LEMMA 5.   (1) $E(x + y) = E(x)E(y)$ (2) $a^{x+y} = a^x a^y$

(3) $L(a^x) = xL(a)$ (4) $a^{xy} = (a^x)^y$

PROOF.   For (1), write x as $L(u)$ and y as $L(v)$. Then

$$E(x + y) = E[L(u) + L(v)] = E[L(uv)] = uv = E(x)E(y)$$

For (2) we have

$$a^{x+y} = E[(x + y) L(a)] = E[xL(a) + yL(a)] = E[xL(a)] \cdot E[yL(a)] = a^x a^y$$

The proofs of (3) and (4) are left to the reader.

The machinery now available enables us to give a quick proof that $\lim_{n \to \infty} (1 + 1/n)^n$ exists. (This proof should be contrasted with the proof outlined in Exercise 28, page 73.) In the proof we will make use of the fact that if f is a continuous increasing function and $\lim_{n \to \infty} f(a_n)$ exists, then $\lim_{n \to \infty} a_n$ exists. (A sketch of the graph of f will show that the assertion is plausible.)

LEMMA 6. $\lim_{n \to \infty} (1 + 1/n)^n$ exists. Denoting it e, we have $L(e) = 1$.

PROOF.   The derivative of the function L has a value $1/1 = 1$ at 1. Thus

$$\lim_{n \to \infty} \frac{L(1 + 1/n) - L(1)}{1/n} = 1$$

Since $L(1) = 0$, this reduces to $\lim_{n \to \infty} nL(1 + 1/n) = 1$ or $\lim_{n \to \infty} L[(1 + 1/n)^n] = 1$. Since L is a continuous increasing function it follows that $\lim_{n \to \infty} (1 + 1/n)^n$ exists. Denote this limit e. Since L is continuous, $L(e) = 1$.

EXERCISES

1. How do we know that $L(x)$ is continuous and increasing?
2. (a) Compute the area of these eight rectangles of the same width.

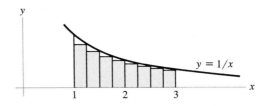

(b) From (a) deduce that $L(3) > 1$.
(c) From (b) and Lemma 6, deduce that $e < 3$.

[Answer: (a) 1.019]

3. (See Exercise 18, page 149, and Exercise 25, page 24.)

(a) Prove that for $b > 1$, we have $\int_a^{ab} (1/x)\,dx = \int_1^b (1/x)\,dx$ by observing that if

$\sum_{i=1}^n (1/X_i) (x_i - x_{i-1})$ is an approximation of $\int_1^b (1/x)\,dx$, then $\sum_{i=1}^n (1/ax_i)(ax_i - ax_{i-1})$

is an approximation of $\int_a^{ab} (1/x)\,dx$.

(b) If $a, b > 1$ deduce that $\int_a^{ab} (1/x)\,dx - \int_1^a (1/x)\,dx = \int_1^b (1/x)\,dx$.

(c) From (b), show that if $a, b > 1$, then $L(ab) = L(a) + L(b)$.

4. (a) Review the proof in Chap. 4, that $D(\ln x) = 1/x$. (b) Note in particular where we assumed that $\lim_{h \to 0} (1 + h)^{1/h}$ exists.

5. Prove that $L(a^{-4}) = -4L(a)$, as is asserted in Lemma 2.

6. Using the technique employed in the proof of Lemma 6, prove that
$\lim_{n \to \infty} (1 - 1/n)^{-n} = e$.

7. (a) Prove that $\lim_{n \to \infty} (1 + 2/n)^n = e^2$. (Hint: $(1 + 2/n)^n = [(1 + 2/n)^{n/2}]^2$.)

(b) Prove that $\lim_{n \to \infty} (1 + 1/n^2)^n = 1$.

8. Prove that $\lim_{n \to \infty} [1/(n + 1) + \cdots + 1/2n] = L(2)$.

9. By comparing the area of appropriate rectangles with the area under $y = 1/x$, prove that

$$\ln\left(\frac{n + 1}{2}\right) < \frac{1}{2} + \frac{1}{3} + \cdots + \frac{1}{n} < \ln n.$$

10. (a) Drawing an appropriate region under the curve $y = 1/x$, show that

$$x/(1 + x) < \ln(1 + x) < x, \text{ if } x > 0.$$

(b) Using differentials, estimate $\ln(1 + x)$.

(c) Using the law of the mean, prove that for $x > 0$, $x/(1 + x) < \ln(1 + x) < x$.

[Answer: (b) x]

11. (a) Exercise 10 suggests that when x is small, x is a good estimate of $\ln(1 + x)$. Use this as a shortcut to estimate the solution of the equation $(1 + 0.04)^n = 2$. (Hint: Take logarithms first.)

(b) Taking 0.7 as an estimate of $\ln 2$, show that the number of years required to double a dollar at compound interest is about (0.7) (the number of years required to double at simple interest).

[Answer: (a) 25 ln 2]

12. Using the fact that E is the inverse function of L, prove that $E'(x) = E(x)$.

□ □ □

13. (See Exercise 2.) (a) Show that $L(2) < 1$. (b) From (a) deduce that $e > 2$.

14. Complete the inductive argument in the proof of Lemma 2.

15. Using the technique employed in the proof of Lemma 6, prove that $\lim_{x \to 0} (1 + x)^{1/x}$ exists.

16. Show that $\lim_{n \to \infty} (1 - \tfrac{1}{2} + \tfrac{1}{3} - \cdots + (-1)^{n+1} 1/n) = \ln 2$. (Hint: Show $1/(n + 1)$
$+ 1/(n + 2) + \cdots + 1/2n = 1 - \tfrac{1}{2} + \tfrac{1}{3} - \cdots - 1/2n$, and use Exercise 8.)

17. (See Exercise 16.) Let $a_n = 1 - \tfrac{1}{2} + \tfrac{1}{3} - \cdots + (-1)^{n+1} 1/n$.

(a) Compute a_1, a_2, a_3, a_4 to three decimal places.

(b) Sketch a graph of a_n as a function of n.

(c) Using Exercise 16, show that $0.6 < \ln 2 < 0.8$.

18. Let $S_n = \frac{1}{2} + \cdots + 1/n$, for $n \geqslant 2$. As Exercise 9 shows, S_n behaves very much like $\ln n$. Since $\ln p + \ln q = \ln pq$, we might expect $S_p + S_q$ to be close to S_{pq}. Letting $(p,q) = S_p + S_q - S_{pq}$, prove that (a) $(p,q) = (q,p)$; (b) $(p,q) - (p-1,q) < 0$; (c) $(2,2) = -\frac{1}{12}$; and (d) in view of (a), (b), and (c), $(p,q) \leqslant -\frac{1}{12}$. Define a_n for $n \geqslant 2$ by $S_n = (\ln n) - a_n$. (e) Using a picture, show that $0 < a_n < -\frac{1}{2}$. (f) Using (e) prove that $(p,q) > -\frac{1}{2}$.

19. Prove that $L(a^x) = xL(a)$, as asserted in Lemma 5.

20. Prove that $a^{xy} = (a^x)^y$, as asserted in Lemma 5.

5. The antiderivative.

As the fundamental theorem of calculus shows, it is sometimes of importance to find a function with a prescribed derivative. If $F' = f$, we shall call F an *antiderivative* of f. Thus x^3 and $x^3 + 17$ are antiderivatives of $3x^2$.

Frequently the antiderivative is called the *integral* or *indefinite integral*. There is a danger that "integral" will become confused with "definite integral." It should be kept in mind that the definite integral $\int_a^b f(x)\,dx$ is a *number*, a limit of certain sums, while the integral or antiderivative is a function. Sometimes, in applications, both the definite integral and the indefinite integral are called the "integral"; it takes a clear mind and mastery of the definitions to keep the ideas separate. The "table of integrals" in a mathematical handbook is primarily a table of antiderivatives (functions); it is usually followed by a short section that lists the values of a few common definite integrals (numbers).

NOTATION. An antiderivative of f is denoted by $\int f(x)\,dx$.

Thus if $F' = f$, we write $F = \int f(x)\,dx$ and say "F is an antiderivative of f" or, for convenience, "$F(x)$ is an antiderivative of $f(x)$." For instance, we say, "x^3 is an antiderivative of $3x^2$." Observe that if F is an antiderivative of f, then so is the function whose value at x is $F(x) + C$, where C is constant.

Example 1. $x^3 + 17 = \int 3x^2\,dx$; $x^3 - 1 = \int 3x^2\,dx$; $x^3 = \int 3x^2\,dx$. Think of the equals sign in these equations as "is an."

NOTATION. We abbreviate $F(b) - F(a)$ to $F(x)\Big|_a^b$.

Example 2. By the fundamental theorem of calculus,

$$\int_1^2 \frac{1}{x^2}\,dx = \frac{-1}{x}\Big|_1^2 = \frac{-1}{2} - \frac{-1}{1} = \frac{1}{2}$$

WARNING. The fundamental theorem of calculus asserts, for instance, that

$$\underbrace{\int_1^2 \frac{1}{x^2}\,dx}_{\substack{\text{The definite} \\ \text{integral: a} \\ \text{limit of sums}}} = \underbrace{\int \frac{1}{x^2}\,dx}_{\substack{\text{The antiderivative:} \\ \text{a function; the value} \\ \text{of this function at 1} \\ \text{is subtracted from} \\ \text{its value at 2}}} \Big|_1^2$$

The symbols on the right and left of the equal sign are so similar that we might be tempted to think that the equation "is obvious" or "says nothing whatever." Beware: that compact equation is an application of the fundamental theorem of the calculus.

DEFINITION: *Integrand.* In the definite integral, $\int_a^b f(x)\,dx$, and in the antiderivative, $\int f(x)\,dx$, we call $f(x)$ the *integrand.*

The related processes of computing $\int_a^b f(x)\,dx$ and of finding an antiderivative, $\int f(x)\,dx$, are both called *integrating* $f(x)$.

Thus integration refers to two separate but related problems: computing a number, $\int_a^b f(x)\,dx$, or finding a function, $\int f(x)\,dx$. The fundamental theorem of calculus states that the second process is frequently of use in computing $\int_a^b f(x)\,dx$.

EXERCISES

1. Find the error in this reasoning.

$$\int_{-1}^1 \frac{1}{x^2}\,dx = \frac{-1}{x}\Big|_{-1}^1 = \frac{-1}{1} - \left(\frac{-1}{-1}\right) = -2. \qquad \left(\text{Suggestion: Graph } y = \frac{1}{x^2}\right)$$

2. (a) What guarantees that $\displaystyle\int_0^{\pi/2} \sin x\,dx = \int \sin x\,dx\,\Big|_0^{\pi/2}$?

   (b) Find $\displaystyle\int \sin x\,dx$ and use it to compute $\displaystyle\int_0^{\pi/2} \sin x\,dx$.

   [Answer: (b) $-\cos x$ and 1]

3. Give two antiderivatives for each of these functions: (a) e^x; (b) $\sqrt{x}$; (c) x^7.
4. Prove that if $F = \int f(x)\,dx$ and $G = \int f(x)\,dx$, then F and G differ by a constant, perhaps 0.
5. Compute (a) $\displaystyle\int x^2\,dx\,\Big|_1^2$; (b) $\displaystyle\int \frac{1}{x}\,dx\,\Big|_1^2$; (c) $\displaystyle\int \frac{1}{1+x^2}\,dx\,\Big|_0^1$.

6. Compute (a) $\displaystyle\int \cos x\,dx\,\Big|_0^{\pi/4}$; (b) $\displaystyle\int \frac{x}{1+x^2}\,dx\,\Big|_0^1$; (c) $\displaystyle\int \frac{1}{\sqrt[3]{x}}\,dx\,\Big|_1^2$.

   [Answer: (a) $\sqrt{2}/2$; (b) $(\frac{1}{2})\ln 2$; (c) $(\frac{3}{2})(\sqrt[3]{4} - 1)$]

7. (a) Which of these two numbers is defined as a limit of sums: $\displaystyle\int x^2\,dx\,\Big|_1^3$ or $\displaystyle\int_1^3 x^2\,dx$?

   (b) Why are the two numbers in (a) equal?
8. (a) Is there a relation between $\int f(x)\,dx$, $\int g(x)\,dx$, and $\int [f(x) - g(x)]\,dx$? Explain.
   (b) Is there a relation between $\int f(x)\,dx$, $\int g(x)\,dx$, and $\int [f(x)\,g(x)]\,dx$? Explain.
9. Compute (a) $D(\int x^5\,dx)$; (b) $D(\int \sin x^5\,dx)$.

□ □ □

10. Let f be continuous in $[0,1]$ and $f(x) \geqslant 0$ for all x in $[0,1]$. Prove that if $\int_0^t f(x)\, dx \geqslant f(t)$ for all t in $[0,1]$, then $f(x) = 0$ for all x in $[0,1]$.

11. Let f and g be continuous, and let $f(0) = 0$. Show why these three assertions are equivalent: (a) $g = df/dx$; (b) For each x and y, with $x \neq y$, there is T between x and y, such that $f(x) - f(y) = g(T)\,(x - y)$; (c) $f(x) = \int_0^x g(t)\, dt$.

6. Summary. We have shown the relation between the derivative and the definite integral as expressed in the fundamental theorem of calculus. This theorem tells us that if we are fortunate enough to know of a function F whose derivative is a given f, we can evaluate $\int_a^b f(x)\, dx$ by simply subtracting $F(a)$ from $F(b)$. Theorem 2, a special case of the fundamental theorem, was proved in detail. We include it because in our proof of the more general Theorem 1 we had to make a major assumption: that a continuous function has a definite integral. We also emphasized that

$$\frac{d\left[\int_a^t f(x)\, dx\right]}{dt}$$

is equal to $f(t)$, an assertion which is implicit in the fundamental theorem of calculus, but which is singled out in Theorem 3. Also, we obtained a new view of the logarithm function.

Glancing back at the opening four problems in Chap. 1 and the four in Chap. 2 and relating them to the fundamental theorem of calculus would provide a broad perspective on what we have accomplished.

7

Computing antiderivatives

In Chap. 4 we developed an automatic procedure for computing the derivative of any elementary function. In Chap. 6 we reduced the computation of many definite integrals to the computation of antiderivatives. We will present in this chapter a few techniques for finding antiderivatives.

There is no automatic procedure for finding antiderivatives. Moreover, some functions, such as e^{x^2}, have no elementary antiderivatives. It should be kept in mind that a slight alteration of an integrand can cause a great change in the form of an antiderivative; for instance,

$$\int \frac{1}{x^2+1}\,dx = \tan^{-1} x \qquad \text{and} \qquad \int \frac{x}{x^2+1}\,dx = \tfrac{1}{2}\ln(x^2+1)$$

A few moments of browsing through a table of antiderivatives (usually called a "table of integrals") will yield many such examples.

157

To be convenient, a table of antiderivatives should be short; it should not try to anticipate every antiderivative that may arise in practice. Sometimes we have to transform a problem into one listed in the table, or else solve it without the aid of the table. For this reason we present a few techniques for transforming problems and finding antiderivatives. It will sometimes be quicker to use these techniques than to thumb through the pages of the table, even though the table may list the answer.

For any constant C we have $\int [1/(x^2 + 1)]\,dx = \tan^{-1}(x) + C$. Since we require only one antiderivative to apply the fundamental theorem of calculus, it suffices to take C to be 0. Hence we will generally omit the C. In Parts II and III, where we meet a few differential equations, we will need the arbitrary C.

1. Some basic facts. Since $D(x^{n+1}) = (n+1)x^n$, it is easy to check that $\int x^n\,dx = x^{n+1}/(n+1)$ if $n \neq -1$. For instance, $\int x^2\,dx = x^3/3$ and $\int (1/x^2)\,dx = -1/x$. Indeed, any formula for a derivative yields a corresponding formula for an antiderivative.

For ease of reference we provide a miniature table of antiderivatives, deduced from the table of derivatives on page 114.

$$\int x^a\,dx = \frac{x^{a+1}}{a+1} \text{ for } a \neq -1 \qquad \int \frac{1}{x}\,dx = \ln|x| \qquad \int e^x\,dx = e^x$$

$$\int \sin x\,dx = -\cos x \qquad \int \cos x\,dx = \sin x$$

$$\int \frac{1}{\sqrt{1-x^2}}\,dx = \sin^{-1}x \qquad \int \frac{1}{1+x^2}\,dx = \tan^{-1}x$$

Moreover, if $F = \int f(x)\,dx$, and c is a constant, we have $(cF)' = cF' = cf$. In other words, if c is a constant factor,

$$\int cf(x)\,dx = c \int f(x)\,dx$$

That is, we can move a constant past the integral sign.

Also, we show that $\int [f(x) + g(x)]\,dx = \int f(x)\,dx + \int g(x)\,dx$. To do so, let

$$F' = f \qquad \text{and} \qquad G' = g$$

Then $$(F + G)' = F' + G' = f + g$$

That is, $F + G$ is an antiderivative of $f + g$, and

$$\int f(x)\,dx + \int g(x)\,dx = \int [f(x) + g(x)]\,dx$$

Example. With the above observations we obtain

$$\int \left(\frac{3}{x^2} + \frac{5}{\sqrt{1-x^2}}\right)dx = 3\int \frac{1}{x^2}\,dx + 5\int \frac{1}{\sqrt{1-x^2}}\,dx = 3\left(\frac{-1}{x}\right) + 5\sin^{-1}x$$

EXERCISES

1. Compute (a) $\int x^3\, dx$; (b) $\int 5x^3\, dx$; (c) $\int 8x^7\, dx$; (d) $\int x^7\, dx$.
2. Compute (a) $\int (1/\sqrt{x})\, dx$; (b) $\int (1/\sqrt[3]{x})\, dx$; (c) $\int x^2\, dx$; (d) $\int x\, dx$.
   [Answer: (a) $2\sqrt{x}$; (b) $(3/2)\, x^{2/3}$; (c) $x^3/3$; (d) $x^2/2$]
3. Compute (a) $\int (\cos x + 2 \sin x)\, dx$; (b) $\int [5/(1 + x^2)]\, dx$.
4. Compute (a) $\int 6e^x\, dx$; (b) $\int 6e^{-x}\, dx$; (c) $\int 5 \sin 2x\, dx$.
5. Compute (a) $\int (1 + x^2 - 6x)\, dx$; (b) $\int (x^2 \cdot x^3)\, dx$; (c) $\int (1 + x^2)^2\, dx$.
6. Compute (a) $\int (3 + 4x)\, dx$; (b) $\int 5x^2\, dx$; (c) $\int (x/\sqrt{1 - x^2})\, dx$; (d) $\int (1/x^2)\, dx$.

7. Give an example showing that $\int f(x)\, g(x)\, dx$ is not necessarily $[\int f(x)\, dx]\,[\int g(x)\, dx]$.
8. (a) Are the following three equations valid?

$$\int x^2\, dx = (x^3/3) + 19 \qquad \int x\, dx = x^2/2 \qquad \int (x^2 + x)\, dx = (x^3/3) + (x^2/2) + 1{,}000$$

(b) Considering part (a), would you still say that $\int x^2\, dx + \int x\, dx = \int (x^2 + x)\, dx$, as we showed on page 158? Explain.

2. The substitution technique.

2. The substitution technique. The technique of *substitution* or *change of variable* transforms one antidifferentiation problem into another which may be easier to solve or which may be listed in a table of integrals. The chain rule, the most important technique for computing derivatives, is the basis of this method.

For our present purposes we restate the chain rule, page 103, in different symbols, as follows:

If $G' = g$, $u = h(x)$, and $F(x) = G(h(x))$, then

$$\frac{dF}{dx} = g(h(x))\frac{du}{dx}$$

Expressing this in terms of antiderivatives, we have the following.

Let $G = \int g(u)\, du$ and $u = h(x)$. Then the function F defined by $F(x) = G(h(x))$ is an antiderivative of $g(h(x))\, (du/dx)$,

$$F = \int g(h(x))\frac{du}{dx}\, dx$$

For instance, we know that $u^{10} = \int 10\, u^9\, du$. If we let $u = x^3 + 1$, then according to the preceding remarks, $(x^3 + 1)^{10} = \int 10(x^3 + 1)^9\, 3x^2\, dx$. In this case, $G(u) = u^{10}$, $g(u) = 10\, u^9$, $h(x) = x^3 + 1$, and $F(x) = (x^3 + 1)^{10}$. The chain rule enabled us to relate $\int 10(x^3 + 1)^9\, 3x^2\, dx$ to $\int 10\, u^9\, du$.

The bookkeeping for integration by substitution is simplified if we use the symbolism of the differential. The purely formal procedure we will describe is justified by the chain rule, just as the procedure "invert and multiply" is justified by theorems about fractions.

When we introduce $u = x^3 + 1$ and $du = 3x^2\,dx$, the formal expression $10(x^3 + 1)^9\,3x^2\,dx$ takes the form $10\,u^9\,du$. The chain rule assures us that if we replace u by $x^3 + 1$ and du by $3x^2\,dx$ in the assertion

$$u^{10} = \int 10\,u^9\,du$$

then we obtain a *valid* equation,

$$(x^3 + 1)^{10} = \int 10(x^3 + 1)^9\,3x^2\,dx$$

For practical purposes we summarize our observations in the differential notation.

THEOREM 1: *Integration by substitution.* If the expression $f(x)\,dx$ takes the form $g(u)\,du$ when we introduce the differentiable function $u = h(x)$ and $du = (du/dx)\,dx$, then

$$\int f(x)\,dx = \int g(u)\,du$$

A few examples will show how the bookkeeping is done; we do not have to think through the chain rule each time.

Example 1. Consider $\int e^{x^2} x\,dx$. The factor x is very nearly the derivative of x^2. To exploit this resemblance, let us make use of the relation

$$\int e^{x^2} x\,dx = \tfrac{1}{2} \int e^{x^2} 2x\,dx$$

We deal with $\int e^{x^2} 2x\,dx$ by the substitution $u = x^2$; hence $du = 2x\,dx$. By the substitution method,

$$\int e^{x^2} 2x\,dx = \int e^u\,du$$

But it is easy to see that $\int e^u\,du = e^u$. We conclude that $\int e^{x^2} 2x\,dx = e^{x^2}$ and thus $\int e^{x^2} x\,dx = \tfrac{1}{2} e^{x^2}$, a result that can be checked by differentiating $\tfrac{1}{2} e^{x^2}$.

It is illuminating to contrast $\int e^{x^2} x\,dx$, which is easy to find, with $\int e^{x^2} dx$, which is not an elementary function.

Example 2. Consider $\int 3x^2/(x^3 + 1)\,dx$. We observe that $3x^2 = D(x^3 + 1)$. If we make the substitution $u = x^3 + 1$, hence $du = 3x^2\,dx$, we obtain

$$\int \frac{3x^2}{x^3 + 1}\,dx = \int \frac{du}{u}$$

But $\int du/u = \ln|u|$. Thus

$$\int \frac{3x^2}{x^3 + 1}\,dx = \ln|x^3 + 1|$$

Example 2 is an illustration of the very useful rule,

$$\int \frac{\text{derivative of } f}{f}\,dx = \ln|f|$$

Another illustration of this rule is

$$\int \tan \theta\,d\theta = \int \frac{\sin \theta}{\cos \theta}\,d\theta = -\int \frac{D(\cos \theta)}{\cos \theta}\,d\theta = -\ln|\cos \theta| = \ln|\sec \theta|.$$

Example 3.   Consider $\int \sin^2 \theta \cos \theta \, d\theta$. Recalling that $\cos \theta = D(\sin \theta)$, we make the substitution $u = \sin \theta$, hence $du = \cos \theta \, d\theta$. Again using the substitution theorem, we have

$$\int \sin^2 \theta \cos \theta \, d\theta = \int u^2 \, du$$

Since $\int u^2 \, du = u^3/3$ we conclude that $\int \sin^2 \theta \cos \theta \, d\theta = (\sin \theta)^3/3$.

Example 4.   Consider $\int (x/\sqrt{1+x}) \, dx$. The denominator is rather complicated. Perhaps it will simplify matters to set $u = 1 + x$, hence $du = D(1+x) \, dx = 1 \, dx = dx$. To express x in the numerator of the integrand in terms of u, we solve the equation $u = x + 1$ for x, and obtain $x = u - 1$. Hence

$$\int \frac{x}{\sqrt{1+x}} \, dx = \int \frac{u-1}{\sqrt{u}} \, du$$

But integration of the latter is not difficult:

$$\int \frac{u-1}{\sqrt{u}} \, du = \int \left(\frac{u}{\sqrt{u}} - \frac{1}{\sqrt{u}} \right) du = \int \left(\sqrt{u} - \frac{1}{\sqrt{u}} \right) du = \frac{u^{3/2}}{3/2} - \frac{u^{1/2}}{1/2} = \tfrac{2}{3} u^{3/2} - 2u^{1/2}$$

Hence
$$\int \frac{x}{\sqrt{1+x}} \, dx = \tfrac{2}{3} (1+x)^{3/2} - 2\sqrt{1+x}$$

as we may check by differentiation.

Example 5.   Consider $\int x^3/(1+x^4) \, dx$. Combining the methods of Examples 1 and 2, we have

$$\int \frac{x^3}{1+x^4} \, dx = \tfrac{1}{4} \int \frac{4x^3}{1+x^4} \, dx = \tfrac{1}{4} \ln|1+x^4|$$

which can be written $(\tfrac{1}{4}) \ln (1+x^4)$, since $1+x^4$ is positive.

Example 6.   (This example should be contrasted with Example 5.) Consider $\int [x \, dx/(1+x^4)]$. In this case the substitution $u = x^2$ is suggested, since $du = 2x \, dx$, and we have $x \, dx$ already present. Rather than rewrite the problem as $\tfrac{1}{2} \int [2x \, dx/(1+x^4)]$, let us simply note that $x \, dx = \tfrac{1}{2} \, du$. Hence

$$\int \frac{x \, dx}{1+x^4} = \int \frac{\tfrac{1}{2} \, du}{1+u^2} = \tfrac{1}{2} \int \frac{du}{1+u^2} = \tfrac{1}{2} \tan^{-1} u = \tfrac{1}{2} \tan^{-1} x^2$$

Example 7.   What happens if we make the substitution $u = x^4$ in Example 6? In this case $du = 4x^3 \, dx$, and we have

$$x \, dx = \frac{du}{4x^2} = \frac{du}{4\sqrt{u}}$$

We then obtain

$$\int \frac{x}{1+x^4} \, dx = \int \frac{1}{1+u} \frac{du}{4\sqrt{u}} = \tfrac{1}{4} \int \frac{1}{\sqrt{u} + u\sqrt{u}} \, du$$

In this case our substitution created a harder problem than the original. Skill in finding substitutions which simplify rather than complicate comes with practice.

EXERCISES

1. Check the solutions in Examples 2, 4, and 6 by differentiating them.
2. (a) Make an appropriate substitution to compute $\int (1 + x^2)^{10}\, x\, dx$,

$$\int \frac{5x^4}{x^5 + 1}\, dx, \text{ and } \int \frac{x^4}{x^5 + 1}\, dx.$$

   (b) Check your answers by differentiation.

3. (a) Compute $\int \sqrt{2x + 5}\, dx$, $\int \frac{1}{4x + 7}\, dx$, $\int \frac{2x}{\sqrt{1 + x^2}}\, dx$, $\int \frac{x}{\sqrt{1 - x^2}}\, dx$.

   (b) Check your answers by differentiation.

4. (a) Compute $\int \frac{2x}{(x^2 + 1)^4}\, dx$, $\int \frac{x}{(5x^2 + 1)^2}\, dx$, $\int \cos^3 x \sin x\, dx$.

   (b) Check your answers by differentiation.

5. Compute (a) $\int e^{-x}\, dx$; (b) $\int e^{3x}\, dx$; (c) $\int 10^x\, dx$; (d) $\int 2^x\, dx$. [Hint for (c) and (d): Write $10^x = (e^{\ln 10})^x$, $2^x = (e^{\ln 2})^x$.]

6. One of these two antiderivatives is not an elementary function: $\int (e^{1/x}/x)\, dx$, $\int (e^{1/x}/x^2)\, dx$. Compute the one that is elementary.

7. Showing your substitution $u = h(x)$, compute

   (a) $\int \frac{x}{\sqrt{2x + 1}}\, dx$; (b) $\int \frac{1}{\sqrt{2x + 1}}\, dx$; (c) $\int \frac{x^2}{\sqrt{2x + 1}}\, dx$; (d) $\int \frac{x^2}{\sqrt{3x + 4}}\, dx$.

8. Solve the easiest two of these three problems (one of the indicated antiderivatives is not an elementary function).

   (a) $\int \frac{x}{\ln x}\, dx$; (b) $\int \frac{\ln (x^2)}{x}\, dx$; (c) $\int \frac{\ln x}{x}\, dx$.

9. Give an example of an exponent a, such that each of the following antiderivatives is easy to compute. Carry out the computation in that case.

   (a) $\int \frac{x^a}{\sqrt{1 + x^3}}\, dx$; (b) $\int x^a \ln x\, dx$; (c) $\int x^a\, e^{\sqrt{x}}\, dx$.

   (Note: a might be different in each of the three cases.)

10. Compute (a) $\int \tan 5x \sec^2 5x\, dx$; (b) $\int \frac{1}{e^{7x}}\, dx$; (c) $\int \frac{1}{x} \ln (x^5)\, dx$.

11. Compute (a) $\int \frac{1}{1 + x^2}\, dx$; (b) $\int \frac{1}{1 + 9x^2}\, dx$; (c) $\int \frac{1}{1 + 5x^2}\, dx$; (d) $\int \frac{1}{5 + x^2}\, dx$.

12. Can we move an x past the integral sign? Is $\int (x \cdot x^2)\, dx$ equal to $x \int x^2\, dx$?

□ □ □

13. Combining Examples 6 and 7, compute $\int \frac{1}{\sqrt{x}\,(1 + x)}\, dx$.

14. $\int e^{x^2}\, dx$ is not an elementary function. From this fact deduce that $\int (e^x/\sqrt{x})\, dx$ is not an elementary function.

15. $\int (e^x/x)\,dx$ is not an elementary function. From this fact deduce that $\int (1/\ln x)\,dx$ is not an elementary function.

16. Liouville proved that if f and g are rational functions, and if $\int e^{f(x)} g(x)\,dx$ is an elementary function, then $\int e^{f(x)} g(x)\,dx$ can be expressed in the form $e^{f(x)} w(x)$, where $w(x)$ is a rational function. With the aid of this result, prove that $\int (e^x/x)\,dx$ is not an elementary function. [Hint: Assume $[e^x (p/q)]' = e^x/x$, where p and q are relatively prime polynomials. Write $q = x^i r$, where $i \geqslant 0$ and x does not divide the polynomial r.]

17. (a) Find $\int \ln x\,dx$ in a table of integrals. (b) Do you find $\int \ln (x + 7)\,dx$ in the table? (c) With the aid of (a), find $\int \ln (x + 7)\,dx$.

18. Show that if we can solve one of these three problems, we can solve the others:

$$\int \frac{x^2}{1 + x^4}\,dx \qquad \int \frac{\sqrt{x}}{1 + x^2}\,dx \qquad \int \sqrt{\tan \theta}\,d\theta$$

(We will develop in this chapter a method for integrating any rational function, in particular $x^2/(1 + x^4)$.)

3. Integration by parts. The chain rule was the basis for integration by substitution. The formula for the derivative of a product is the basis for another method of finding antiderivatives, integration by parts.

To describe this method, we begin with the equation

$$\frac{d(uv)}{dx} = u\frac{dv}{dx} + v\frac{du}{dx}$$

valid for any two differentiable functions, u and v. Now, let G be an antiderivative of $v(du/dx)$; that is, $dG/dx = v(du/dx)$. Then we assert that $uv - G$ is an antiderivative of $u(dv/dx)$. This assertion is verified by the following computation:

$$\frac{d(uv - G)}{dx} = \frac{d(uv)}{dx} - \frac{dG}{dx} = u\frac{dv}{dx} + v\frac{du}{dx} - v\frac{du}{dx} = u\frac{dv}{dx}$$

Expressing this in the notation of antiderivatives, we have

$$\int u\frac{dv}{dx}\,dx = uv - \int v\frac{du}{dx}\,dx$$

For bookkeeping purposes it is convenient to use (as in the preceding section) the notation du for the expression $(du/dx)\,dx$ and dv for $(dv/dx)\,dx$. We summarize the preceding remarks in a theorem.

THEOREM 2: *Integration by parts.* If u and v are differentiable functions, then

$$\int u\,dv = uv - \int v\,du$$

A few examples will show how Theorem 2 is used.

Example 1. We find $\int xe^{-x}\,dx$. In this case let us try $u = x$ and hence $dv = e^{-x}\,dx$. We must then compute du and v. We have $du = dx$ and $v = -e^{-x}$. (Of course, $-e^{-x} + C$, where C is a constant, would also serve as v, but we choose the simplest v.) Using integration by parts, we obtain

$$\int \overset{u}{\overbrace{x}} \overset{dv}{\overbrace{e^{-x}\,dx}} = \overset{u}{\overbrace{x}}\,\overset{v}{\overbrace{(-e^{-x})}} - \int \overset{v}{\overbrace{(-e^{-x})}}\,\overset{du}{\overbrace{dx}}$$

Fortunately $\int v\,du$ is easier to find than $\int u\,dv$. We have $\int (-e^{-x})\,dx = e^{-x}$. Hence

$$\int xe^{-x}\,dx = x(-e^{-x}) - (e^{-x}) = e^{-x}(-1-x)$$

a result which is easy to check by differentiation.

Example 2. Let us find $\int x^2 e^{-x}\,dx$. This time let us put $u = x^2$ and $dv = e^{-x}\,dx$. Then $du = 2x\,dx$ and $v = -e^{-x}$. Integration by parts yields

$$\int \overset{u}{\overbrace{x^2}}\,\overset{dv}{\overbrace{e^{-x}\,dx}} = \overset{u}{\overbrace{x^2}}\,\overset{v}{\overbrace{(-e^{-x})}} - \int \overset{v}{\overbrace{-e^{-x}}}\,\overset{du}{\overbrace{2x\,dx}} = -x^2 e^{-x} + 2\int e^{-x}x\,dx$$

Example 1 shows that

$$\int e^{-x}x\,dx = e^{-x}(-1-x)$$

Thus $\int x^2 x^{-x}\,dx = -x^2 e^{-x} + 2e^{-x}(-1-x) = e^{-x}(-2-2x-x^2)$

It is instructive to check this answer by differentiation.

Example 3. Consider $\int \tan^{-1} x\,dx$. Recalling that the derivative of $\tan^{-1} x$ is $1/(1+x^2)$, a much simpler function than $\tan^{-1} x$, let us set $u = \tan^{-1} x$ and $dv = dx$. Then $du = [1/(1+x^2)]\,dx$, and $v = x$. Integration by parts yields

$$\int \overset{u}{\overbrace{\tan^{-1}x}}\,\overset{dv}{\overbrace{dx}} = \overset{u}{\overbrace{\tan^{-1}x}}\,\overset{v}{\overbrace{x}} - \int \overset{v}{\overbrace{x}}\,\overset{du}{\overbrace{\frac{1}{1+x^2}}}\,dx$$

Now, $\int v\,du$ is easier than our original problem. We have

$$\int \frac{x}{1+x^2}\,dx = \tfrac{1}{2}\int \frac{2x}{1+x^2}\,dx = \tfrac{1}{2}\ln(1+x^2)$$

Hence $\int \tan^{-1} x\,dx = x\tan^{-1} x - \tfrac{1}{2}\ln(1+x^2)$

Example 4. Many formulas in a table of integrals express the integral of a function that involves the nth power of some expression in terms of the integral of a function that involves the $(n-1)$th or lower power of the same expression. These are *reduction* formulas. Usually they are obtained by an integration by parts. For instance, let us show how to derive the formula

$$\int \sin^n x\,dx = -\frac{\sin^{n-1} x \cos x}{n} + \frac{n-1}{n}\int \sin^{n-2} x\,dx \qquad n \geqslant 2$$

We first write $\int \sin^n x\,dx$ as $\int \sin^{n-1} x \sin x\,dx$. Then we let $u = \sin^{n-1} x$ and $dv = \sin x\,dx$. Thus

$$du = (n-1)\sin^{n-2} x \cos x\,dx \qquad \text{and} \qquad v = -\cos x$$

Integration by parts asserts that

$$\int \overset{u}{\overbrace{\sin^{n-1}x}}\,\overset{dv}{\overbrace{\sin x\,dx}} = \overset{u}{\overbrace{(\sin^{n-1}x)}}\,\overset{v}{\overbrace{(-\cos x)}} - \int \overset{v}{\overbrace{(-\cos x)}}\,\overset{du}{\overbrace{(n-1)\sin^{n-2}x\cos x\,dx}}$$

But the integral on the right of the above equation is equal to

$$\int (1 - n) \cos^2 x \sin^{n-2} x \, dx = (1 - n) \int (1 - \sin^2 x) \sin^{n-2} x \, dx$$
$$= (1 - n) \int \sin^{n-2} x \, dx - (1 - n) \int \sin^n x \, dx$$

We thus have

$$\int \sin^n x \, dx = -\sin^{n-1} x \cos x + (n - 1) \int \sin^{n-2} x \, dx - (n - 1) \int \sin^n x \, dx$$

Rather than being dismayed by the reappearance of $\int \sin^n x \, dx$, let us collect like terms:

$$n \int \sin^n x \, dx = -\sin^{n-1} x \cos x + (n - 1) \int \sin^{n-2} x \, dx$$

from which the quoted formula follows.

Any table of integrals contains the formulas we derived in these four examples. There is no need to memorize them.

EXERCISES

In Exercises 1 through 7 find the indicated antiderivative:

1. (a) $\int xe^x \, dx$; (b) $\int x^2 e^x \, dx$.
2. $\int \ln (x + 1) \, dx$ (a) using $u = \ln (x + 1)$, $dv = dx$, $v = x$; (b) using $u = \ln (x + 1)$, $dv = dx$, $v = x + 1$. (c) Which is easier?
3. $\int \sin^{-1} x \, dx$.
4. $\int (\ln x)^2 \, dx$.
5. (a) $\int xe^{-kx} \, dx$; (b) $\int x^2 ex^{-kx} \, dx$ (where k is fixed).
6. (a) $\int x \sin x \, dx$; (b) $\int x^2 \cos x \, dx$.
7. $\int \ln (4 + x^2) \, dx$.
8. Use the formula of Example 4 to compute $\int \sin^2 x \, dx$, $\int \sin^3 x \, dx$, $\int \sin^4 x \, dx$, $\int \sin^5 x \, dx$.
9. Where is the error in this proof that $0 = -1$?

$$\int x^{-1} \, dx = \int \overset{u}{\overbrace{x}} \, \overset{dv}{\overbrace{x^{-2} \, dx}} = \overset{u}{\overbrace{(x)}} \overset{v}{\overbrace{(-x^{-1})}} - \int \overset{v}{\overbrace{(-x^{-1})}} \overset{du}{\overbrace{dx}}.$$

Thus $\int x^{-1} \, dx = -1 + \int x^{-1} \, dx$. Subtraction of $\int x^{-1} \, dx$ from both sides yields $0 = -1$.

10. (a) Using the reduction formula of Example 4, prove that

$$\int_0^{\pi/2} \sin^n x \, dx = \frac{n - 1}{n} \int_0^{\pi/2} \sin^{n-2} x \, dx$$

(b) Let $I_n = \int_0^{\pi/2} \sin^n x \, dx$. Show that $I_0 = \pi/2$ and $I_1 = 1$.

(c) With the aid of (a) and (b), show that

$$I_7 = \frac{6}{7} \frac{4}{5} \frac{2}{3} \quad \text{and} \quad I_6 = \frac{5}{6} \frac{3}{4} \frac{1}{2} \frac{\pi}{2}$$

(d) With the aid of (a) and (b), show that

$$I_{2n} = \frac{2n - 1}{2n} \frac{2n - 3}{2n - 2} \cdots \frac{3}{4} \frac{1}{2} \frac{\pi}{2} \qquad I_{2n+1} = \frac{2n}{2n + 1} \frac{2n - 2}{2n - 1} \cdots \frac{4}{5} \frac{2}{3}$$

(e) Show that $\dfrac{I_7}{I_6} = \dfrac{6}{7}\,\dfrac{6}{5}\,\dfrac{4}{5}\,\dfrac{4}{3}\,\dfrac{2}{3}\,\dfrac{2}{1}\,\dfrac{2}{\pi}$

(f) Show that $\dfrac{I_{2n+1}}{I_{2n}} = \dfrac{2n}{2n+1}\,\dfrac{2n}{2n-1}\,\dfrac{2n-2}{2n-1} \cdots \dfrac{2}{3}\,\dfrac{2}{1}\,\dfrac{2}{\pi}$

(g) Show that $\dfrac{2n}{2n+1}\,I_{2n} < \dfrac{2n}{2n+1}\,I_{2n-1} = I_{2n+1} < I_{2n}$, and thus $\displaystyle\lim_{n\to\infty} \dfrac{I_{2n+1}}{I_{2n}} = 1$

(h) From (f) and (g) deduce that

$$\lim_{n\to\infty} \frac{2\cdot 2}{1\cdot 3}\,\frac{4\cdot 4}{3\cdot 5}\,\frac{6\cdot 6}{5\cdot 7} \cdots \frac{(2n)(2n)}{(2n-1)(2n+1)} = \frac{\pi}{2}$$

This is Wallis' formula, usually written in shorthand as

$$\frac{2\cdot 2}{1\cdot 3}\,\frac{4\cdot 4}{3\cdot 5}\,\frac{6\cdot 6}{5\cdot 7} \cdots = \frac{\pi}{2}$$

□ □ □

11. Obtain the reduction formula

$$\int \sec^n x\,dx = \frac{1}{n-1}\left[\sec^{n-2} x \tan x + (n-2)\int \sec^{n-2} x\,dx\right] \qquad n > 1$$

[Hint: $\int \sec^n x\,dx = \int \underbrace{(\sec^{n-2} x)}_{u}\,\underbrace{(\sec^2 x\,dx)}_{dv}]$

12. Compute $\int e^{\sqrt[3]{x}}\,dx$.

13. Obtain a formula relating $\int \cos^n x\,dx$ to $\int \cos^{n-2} x\,dx$.

14. Obtain a formula relating $\int \tan^n x\,dx$ to $\int \tan^{n-2} x\,dx$.
    [Hint: Write $\tan^n x = \tan^{n-2} x\,(\sec^2 x - 1)$.]

15. Compute $\int e^x \sin x\,dx$. (Hint: This requires two integrations by parts.)

16. [See Exercise 10(h).]

    (a) Show that Wallis' formula is equivalent to

    $$\left(1 - \frac{1}{2^2}\right)\left(1 - \frac{1}{4^2}\right)\left(1 - \frac{1}{6^2}\right) \cdots = \frac{2}{\pi}$$

    (b) Show that $\left(1 - \dfrac{1}{2^2}\right)\left(1 - \dfrac{1}{3^2}\right)\left(1 - \dfrac{1}{4^2}\right) \cdots = \dfrac{1}{2}$

    (c) From (a) and (b) deduce that

    $$\left(1 - \frac{1}{3^2}\right)\left(1 - \frac{1}{5^2}\right)\left(1 - \frac{1}{7^2}\right) \cdots \frac{\pi}{4}$$

17. (See Exercise 16.) Find the flaw in this reasoning:

    $$\frac{2}{\pi} = \left(1 - \frac{1}{2^2}\right)\left(1 - \frac{1}{4^2}\right)\left(1 - \frac{1}{6^2}\right) \cdots = \left(\frac{1\cdot 3}{2\cdot 2}\right)\left(\frac{3\cdot 5}{4\cdot 4}\right)\left(\frac{5\cdot 7}{6\cdot 6}\right) \cdots$$

    $$= \left(\frac{3\cdot 3}{2\cdot 2}\right)\left(\frac{5\cdot 5}{4\cdot 4}\right)\left(\frac{7\cdot 7}{6\cdot 6}\right) \cdots$$

    which is clearly larger than 1. Hence $2 > \pi$.

18. When $2n$ coins are tossed, the probability of obtaining exactly n heads is $C_n^{2n} (\frac{1}{2})^{2n}$, where C_n^{2n} is the binomial coefficient $(2n)!/(n!)^2$. Using Exercise 10(f), show that a good estimate of this probability is $1/\sqrt{\pi n}$. How close is it for $n = 4$? Hint: Show that

$$\frac{I_{2n+1}}{I_{2n}} = \left[\frac{(2^{2n})(n!)^2}{(2n)!} \right]^2 \frac{1}{2n+1} \frac{2}{\pi}$$

4. The antidifferentiation of rational functions by partial fractions. We will *not* find

$$\int \frac{x^4 + x^3 - 3x + 5}{x^3 + 2x^2 + 2x + 1} dx$$

in a table of integrals. If we are faced with an integrand that is a rational function— a quotient of two polynomials—then we must use the algebra of partial fractions to rewrite the integrand as the sum of simpler rational functions (which we can integrate by the methods described below or with a table of integrals). We summarize here the technique of partial fractions and discuss it in more detail in Appendix G.

To find $\int (A/B) dx$, where A and B are polynomials, follow these steps:

1. If the degree of A is *not* less than the degree of B, divide B into A to obtain a quotient and a remainder: $A = QB + R$, where the degree of R is less than the degree of B or else $R = 0$. We then have

$$\frac{A}{B} = Q + \frac{R}{B}$$

Apply the remaining steps to R/B.

2. If the degree of A is less than the degree of B, then

   (a) express B as the product of polynomials of degree 1 or 2, where the second-degree factors are irreducible.

   (b) if $ax + b$ appears exactly n times in the factorization of B, then form the sum

   $$\frac{k_1}{ax + b} + \frac{k_2}{(ax + b)^2} + \cdots + \frac{k_n}{(ax + b)^n}$$

   where the constants $k_1, k_2, \ldots, k_n$ are to be determined later.

   (c) if $ax^2 + bx + c$ appears exactly m times in the factorization of B, then form the sum

   $$\frac{c_1 x + d_1}{ax^2 + bx + c} + \frac{c_2 x + d_2}{(ax^2 + bx + c)^2} + \cdots + \frac{c_m x + d_m}{(ax^2 + bx + c)^m}$$

   where the constants $c_1, c_2, \ldots, c_m$ and $d_1, d_2, \ldots, d_m$ are to be determined later.

(d) determine appropriate k's, c's, and d's, described in (b) and (c), such that A/B is equal to the sum of all the terms formed in (b) and (c) for all the factors of B described in (a).

3. After completing the algebra of steps 1 and 2, integrate the various terms whose sum is A/B.

Example 1. Find $\int (4x - 7)/(x^2 - 3x + 2)\,dx$. Since the numerator has degree less than that of the denominator, we do not need step 1. Beginning at 2(a), we factor $x^2 - 3x + 2$ as $(x - 1)(x - 2)$. The B in this case has only first-degree factors; hence 2(c) will not be pertinent. Since both $x - 1$ and $x - 2$ appear only once in the factorization, we have $n = 1$ in each case for 2(b).

According to 2(d) we must find constants such that

(1) $$\frac{4x - 7}{x^2 - 3x + 2} = \frac{a_1}{x - 1} + \frac{a_2}{x - 2}$$

To find a_1 and a_2, we multiply both sides of (1) by $x^2 - 3x + 2$, obtaining

(2) $$4x - 7 = a_1(x - 2) + a_2(x - 1)$$

To find two equations for the two unknowns, we replace the x in (2) by two numbers. Since $x - 1$ vanishes for x equal to 1, and since $x - 2$ vanishes for x equal to 2, we will for convenience replace x by 1 and by 2. This gives

$$4(1) - 7 = a_1(1 - 2) + a_2(0) \qquad \text{[Setting } x = 1 \text{ in (2)]}$$

$$4(2) - 7 = a_1(0) + a_2(2 - 1) \qquad \text{[Setting } x = 2 \text{ in (2)]}$$

which simplify to $-3 = -a_1$ and $1 = a_2$, hence $a_1 = 3$ and $a_2 = 1$.

We are now ready for step 3. Exploiting (1), we have

$$\int \frac{4x - 7}{x^2 - 3x + 2}\,dx = \int \left(\frac{3}{x - 1} + \frac{1}{x - 2} \right) dx$$

which is not difficult to compute:

$$\int \left(\frac{3}{x - 1} + \frac{1}{x - 2} \right) dx = 3\ln|x - 1| + \ln|x - 2|$$

Example 2. We consider $\int [(x^2 + 7x + 1)/(x + 2)^2 (2x + 1)]\,dx$. The degree of the numerator is less than the degree of the denominator (which is 3). Hence step 1 does not apply. Since the denominator is already factored (a common occurrence in practice), 2(a) is done. We shall do 2(b) and 2(d) simultaneously; 2(c) does not apply.

Since $x + 2$ appears twice in the factorization and $2x + 1$ once, we have

(3) $$\frac{x^2 + 7x + 1}{(x + 2)^2 (2x + 1)} = \frac{a_1}{x + 2} + \frac{a_2}{(x + 2)^2} + \frac{a_3}{2x + 1}$$

To find the constants a_1, a_2, a_3 we clear the denominators in (3):

(4) $$x^2 + 7x + 1 = a_1(x + 2)(2x + 1) + a_2(2x + 1) + a_3(x + 2)^2$$

We need three equations for the three unknowns a_1, a_2, and a_3. To obtain them we will replace x in (4) by three different numbers in turn. Since $x + 2 = 0$ when $x = -2$, and

$2x + 1 = 0$ when $x = -\frac{1}{2}$, we will replace x by -2 and then by $-\frac{1}{2}$. To obtain a third equation, let us use $x = 0$. Thus

$$-9 = -3a_2 \qquad \text{[Setting } x = -2 \text{ in (4)]}$$

$$-\tfrac{9}{4} = (\tfrac{9}{4})a_3 \qquad \text{[Setting } x = -\tfrac{1}{2} \text{ in (4)]}$$

$$1 = 2a_1 + a_2 + 4a_3 \qquad \text{[Setting } x = 0 \text{ in (4)]}$$

Thus $a_2 = 3$, $a_3 = -1$, and finally $a_1 = 1$. Replacing a_1, a_2, and a_3 in (3), we obtain

$$\int \frac{x^2 + 7x + 1}{(x + 2)^2 (2x + 1)}\, dx = \int \left[\frac{1}{x + 2} + \frac{3}{(x + 2)^2} - \frac{1}{2x + 1} \right] dx$$

$$= \ln|x + 2| - \frac{3}{x + 2} - \tfrac{1}{2} \ln|2x + 1|$$

Example 3.   We compute

$$\int \frac{x^4 + x^3 - 3x + 5}{(x + 1)(x^2 + x + 1)}\, dx$$

Since the degree of the numerator, 4, is at least as large as the degree of the denominator, 3, step 1 is necessary. We divide by the denominator, $(x + 1)(x^2 + x + 1) = x^3 + 2x^2 + 2x + 1$, as follows:

$$
\begin{array}{r}
x - 1 \qquad \text{quotient} \\
x^3 + 2x^2 + 2x + 1 \,\overline{\big)\, x^4 + x^3 + 0x^2 - 3x + 5} \\
\underline{x^4 + 2x^3 + 2x^2 + x} \\
- x^3 - 2x^2 - 4x + 5 \\
\underline{- x^3 - 2x^2 - 2x - 1} \\
-2x + 6 \qquad \text{remainder}
\end{array}
$$

Hence

(5)
$$\frac{x^4 + x^3 - 3x + 5}{(x + 1)(x^2 + x + 1)} = x - 1 + \frac{-2x + 6}{(x + 1)(x^2 + x + 1)}$$

Next, we represent

$$\frac{-2x + 6}{(x + 1)(x^2 + x + 1)}$$

by 2(*d*). Since $x + 1$ and $x^2 + x + 1$ are irreducible, there are constants a_1, a_2, a_3 such that

(6)
$$\frac{-2x + 6}{(x + 1)(x^2 + x + 1)} = \frac{a_1}{x + 1} + \frac{a_2 x + a_3}{x^2 + x + 1}$$

To find a_1, a_2, and a_3 we multiply (6) by $(x + 1)(x^2 + x + 1)$, obtaining

(7)
$$-2x + 6 = a_1 (x^2 + x + 1) + (a_2 x + a_3)(x + 1)$$

Let us replace x by -1 (the root of $x + 1 = 0$), and then by 0 and 1, which are simple numbers. We arrive at

$$8 = a_1 \qquad \text{[Setting } x = -1 \text{ in (7)]}$$

$$6 = a_1 + a_3 \qquad \text{[Setting } x = 0 \text{ in (7)]}$$

$$4 = 3a_1 + 2a_2 + 2a_3 \qquad \text{[Setting } x = 1 \text{ in (7)]}$$

The first equation yields $a_1 = 8$, the second then gives $a_3 = -2$, and the third $a_2 = -8$.

Thus (6) takes the form

(8) $$\int \frac{-2x + 6}{(x + 1)(x^2 + x + 1)} = \frac{8}{x + 1} + \frac{-8x - 2}{x^2 + x + 1} = \frac{8}{x + 1} - \frac{8x}{x^2 + x + 1} - \frac{2}{x^2 + x + 1}$$

Combining equations (5) and (8), we have

(9) $$\int \frac{x^4 + x^3 - 3x + 5}{(x + 1)(x^2 + x + 1)}\, dx = \int \left(x - 1 + \frac{8}{x + 1} - \frac{8x}{x^2 + x + 1} - \frac{2}{x^2 + x + 1} \right) dx$$

It is not difficult to see that

$$\int \left(x - 1 + \frac{8}{x + 1} \right) dx = \frac{x^2}{2} - x + 8 \ln|x + 1|$$

Examples 4 and 5 to follow (or a table of integrals) will dispose of the integration of the last two terms in (9). We conclude that

$$\int \frac{x^4 + x^3 - 3x + 5}{(x + 1)(x^2 + x + 1)}\, dx = \frac{x^2}{2} - x + 8 \ln|x + 1|$$
$$- 8 \left\{ \tfrac{1}{2} \ln|x^2 + x + 1| - \tfrac{1}{2} \sqrt{\tfrac{4}{3}} \tan^{-1} [\sqrt{\tfrac{4}{3}}(x + \tfrac{1}{2})] \right\} - 2 \left\{ \sqrt{\tfrac{4}{3}} \tan^{-1} [\sqrt{\tfrac{4}{3}}(x + \tfrac{1}{2})] \right\}$$

which can be simplified a little by collecting the two like terms.

Example 4. Consider $\int [1/(x^2 + x + 1)]\, dx$. Let use see what happens when we try *partial fractions*. The degree of the numerator is 0, which is less than the degree of the denominator. Thus step 1 is bypassed. Since $x^2 + x + 1$ cannot be factored, 2(*a*) is done; 2(*b*) does not apply. Step 2(*d*) tells us that there are numbers c_1 and d_1 such that

$$\frac{1}{x^2 + x + 1} = \frac{c_1 x + d_1}{x^2 + x + 1}$$

It is evident that these constants are $c_1 = 0$ and $d_1 = 1$, so step 3 tells us only that

$$\int \frac{1}{x^2 + x + 1}\, dx = \int \frac{1}{x^2 + x + 1}\, dx$$

which is of no help.

As a matter of fact, a table of integrals contains a formula for $\int [1/(ax^2 + bx + c)]\, dx$. We will, however, compute $\int [1/(x^2 + x + 1)]\, dx$ without a table.

Because of the similarity of the integrand to $1/(x^2 + 1)$, we will "complete the square" in $x^2 + x + 1$. We do so as follows:

$$x^2 + x + 1 = [x^2 + x + (\tfrac{1}{2})^2] + 1 - (\tfrac{1}{2})^2 = (x + \tfrac{1}{2})^2 + \tfrac{3}{4}$$

Thus $$\int \frac{1}{x^2 + x + 1}\, dx = \int \frac{1}{(x + \tfrac{1}{2})^2 + \tfrac{3}{4}}\, dx$$

We now make a substitution such that $(x + \tfrac{1}{2})^2 = (\tfrac{3}{4}) u^2$. This is accomplished if $x + \tfrac{1}{2} = \sqrt{\tfrac{3}{4}}\, u$, hence $dx = \sqrt{\tfrac{3}{4}}\, du$ and $u = \sqrt{\tfrac{4}{3}}(x + \tfrac{1}{2})$. Therefore

$$\int \frac{1}{(x + \tfrac{1}{2})^2 + \tfrac{3}{4}}\, dx = \int \frac{1}{\tfrac{3}{4} u^2 + \tfrac{3}{4}} (\sqrt{\tfrac{3}{4}})\, du = \sqrt{\tfrac{4}{3}} \int \frac{du}{u^2 + 1}$$
$$= \sqrt{\tfrac{4}{3}} \tan^{-1} u = \sqrt{\tfrac{4}{3}} \tan^{-1} [\sqrt{\tfrac{4}{3}}(x + \tfrac{1}{2})]$$

Example 5. Consider $\int [x/(x^2 + x + 1)]\, dx$. As in Example 4, partial fractions are of no use. A table of integrals contains a formula for $\int [x/(ax^2 + bx + c)]\, dx$, but we will solve this problem without using a table.

Notice that the numerator, x, is not too far from being $2x + 1$, the derivative of the denominator. We therefore rewrite the integrand as

$$\frac{x}{x^2 + x + 1} = \frac{\tfrac{1}{2}(2x + 1) - \tfrac{1}{2}}{x^2 + x + 1}$$

and obtain

$$\int \frac{x}{x^2 + x + 1}\, dx = \tfrac{1}{2} \int \frac{2x + 1}{x^2 + x + 1}\, dx - \tfrac{1}{2} \int \frac{1}{x^2 + x + 1}$$

Recalling Example 4, and recalling also that $\int [(\text{derivative of } f)/f]\, dx = \ln|f|$, we have

$$\int \frac{x}{x^2 + x + 1}\, dx = \tfrac{1}{2} \ln|x^2 + x + 1| - \tfrac{1}{2}\sqrt{\tfrac{4}{3}} \tan^{-1}[\sqrt{\tfrac{4}{3}}(x + \tfrac{1}{2})]$$

The technique illustrated in Examples 4 and 5 disposes of any integrand of the form $(c_i x + d_i)/(ax^2 + bx + c)$, where $ax^2 + bx + c$ is irreducible. The seldom-encountered $\int [(c_i x + d_i)/(ax^2 + bx + c)^n]\, dx$, with $n \geqslant 2$, is disposed of by the recursion formulas discussed in Exercises 16 and 17 and included in any table of integrals.

We point out that any integrand in the form of a rational function of $\sin x$ and $\cos x$ can be transformed to an integrand that is a rational function of x (see Exercise 8, page 175).

EXERCISES

1. Compute $(a) \int \dfrac{1}{(2x - 1)^2}\, dx$; $(b) \int \dfrac{x + 1}{(2x - 1)^2}\, dx$; $(c) \int \dfrac{x^2}{(2x - 1)^2}\, dx$, and check your answers by differentiating them.

2. Compute by completing the square $(a) \int \dfrac{1}{x^2 + 2x + 3}\, dx$; $(b) \int \dfrac{1}{2x^2 + 4x + 3}\, dx$, and check your answers by differentiating them.

3. Check the answers to Examples 1 and 2 by differentiating them.

4. Compute $(a) \int \dfrac{1}{x^2 + 5x - 6}\, dx$; $(b) \int \dfrac{1}{x^2 + 5x + 6}\, dx$. Check your answers by differentiating them.

5. If $b^2 - 4ac < 0$, then $ax^2 + bx + c$ is an irreducible polynomial. A table of integrals contains this formula:

$$\int \frac{dx}{ax^2 + bx + c} = \frac{2}{\sqrt{4ac - b^2}} \tan^{-1} \frac{2ax + b}{\sqrt{4ac - b^2}} \qquad b^2 < 4ac$$

Check that it is correct by differentiating the right side.

6. Compute $\int \dfrac{1}{2x^2 - 6x + 5}\, dx$ by (a) completing the square; (b) the formula in Exercise 5.

7. (a) Express $\dfrac{1}{(x - 1)(x)(x + 1)}$ as a sum of partial fractions.
   (b) Find an antiderivative for the function in (a).

8. Compute $\int \dfrac{8 - 4x}{(x - 1)^2 (x^2 + 1)} \, dx.$

9. Compute $\int \dfrac{x^4}{(x^2 - 1)(x + 2)} \, dx.$

10. Compute $\int \dfrac{x^2}{x^2 + 4x + 4} \, dx.$

11. Use the formula quoted in Exercise 16 to help compute $\int \dfrac{dx}{(x^2 + x + 1)^2}.$

12. Use the formula quoted in Exercise 17 to help compute $\int \dfrac{x}{(x^2 + x + 1)^2} \, dx.$

13. Compute (a) $\int \dfrac{2x^3 + x}{x^4 + x^2 + 1} \, dx;$ (b) $\int \dfrac{1}{x^4 + x^2 + 1} \, dx.$

   [Hint: For (b) note that $x^4 + x^2 + 1 = (x^2 + x + 1)(x^2 - x + 1)$.]

14. Evaluate the antiderivative displayed in the opening paragraph of this section.

15. Obtain the formula quoted in Exercise 5 by completing the square.

16. Prove that this formula, found in a table of integrals, is correct:

$$\int \frac{dx}{(ax^2 + bx + c)^{n+1}} = \frac{2ax + b}{n(4ac - b^2)(ax^2 + bx + c)^n} + \frac{2(2n - 1)a}{n(4ac - b^2)} \int \frac{dx}{(ax^2 + bx + c)^n}$$

17. Prove that this formula is correct:

$$\int \frac{x \, dx}{(ax^2 + bx + c)^{n+1}} = -\frac{2c + bx}{n(4ac - b^2)(ax^2 + bx + c)^n} - \frac{b(2n - 1)}{n(4ac - b^2)} \int \frac{dx}{(ax^2 + bx + c)^n}$$

5. Some special techniques. The techniques discussed so far in this chapter are of wide applicability. We now present some methods of dealing with certain integrands by special substitutions and identities.

   METHOD 1: *Integration of certain powers of the trigonometric functions.* We illustrate this method, which exploits trigonometric identities, by some examples.

   Example 1. To find $\int \sin^2 \theta \, d\theta$, we use the identity,

$$\sin^2 \theta = \frac{1 - \cos 2\theta}{2}$$

We have

$$\int \sin^2 \theta \, d\theta = \int \frac{1 - \cos 2\theta}{2} \, d\theta = \int \frac{1}{2} \, d\theta - \int \frac{\cos 2\theta}{2} \, d\theta = \frac{\theta}{2} - \frac{\sin 2\theta}{4}$$

$$= \frac{\theta}{2} - \frac{2 \sin \theta \cos \theta}{4} = \frac{\theta}{2} - \frac{\sin \theta \cos \theta}{2}$$

a result to be found in any table of integrals.

Example 2. The equations $\sin \theta \, d\theta = -d(\cos \theta)$ and $\sin^2 \theta = 1 - \cos^2 \theta$ enable us to compute $\int \cos^m \theta \sin^n \theta \, d\theta$, where n is an odd integer and m is any real number. For instance, in the case $m = 0$, $n = 3$, we have

$$\int \sin^3 \theta \, d\theta = \int \sin^2 \theta \sin \theta \, d\theta = \int (1 - \cos^2 \theta) \sin \theta \, d\theta$$

To compute the latter we use the substitution $u = \cos \theta$, hence $du = -\sin \theta \, d\theta$. Thus

$$\int \sin^3 \theta \, d\theta = \int (1 - \cos^2 \theta) \sin \theta \, d\theta$$

$$= \int (1 - u^2)(-du) = \int (u^2 - 1) \, du$$

$$= \frac{u^3}{3} - u = \frac{\cos^3 \theta}{3} - \cos \theta$$

Example 3. The equations $\sec \theta \tan \theta \, d\theta = d(\sec \theta)$ and $\tan^2 \theta = \sec^2 \theta - 1$ enable us to compute $\int \sec^m \theta \tan^n \theta \, d\theta$, where n is an odd integer and m is any real number. For instance, we have

$$\int \sec^4 \theta \tan^3 \theta \, d\theta = \int \sec^3 \theta \tan^2 \theta \sec \theta \tan \theta \, d\theta$$

$$= \int \sec^3 \theta (\sec^2 \theta - 1) \sec \theta \tan \theta \, d\theta$$

Now we introduce the substitution $u = \sec \theta$, hence $du = \sec \theta \tan \theta \, d\theta$, which changes the last antiderivative to

$$\int u^3(u^2 - 1) \, du = \int (u^5 - u^3) \, du = \frac{u^6}{6} - \frac{u^4}{4} = \frac{\sec^6 \theta}{6} - \frac{\sec^4 \theta}{4}$$

Example 4. To find $\int (1/\cos \theta) \, d\theta = \int \sec \theta \, d\theta$, which is not covered by the preceding examples, it is wisest to go to a table of integrals, where we find

$$\int \sec \theta \, d\theta = \ln |\sec \theta + \tan \theta|$$

We verify it by differentiation:

$$\frac{d(\ln |\sec \theta + \tan \theta|)}{d\theta} = \frac{1}{\sec \theta + \tan \theta} (\sec^2 \theta + \sec \theta \tan \theta)$$

$$= \frac{\sec \theta (\sec \theta + \tan \theta)}{\sec \theta + \tan \theta} = \sec \theta$$

METHOD 2: *Trigonometric substitutions.* Recall that $\cos \theta = \sqrt{1 - \sin^2 \theta}$, $\sec \theta = \sqrt{1 + \tan^2 \theta}$, and $\tan \theta = \sqrt{\sec^2 \theta - 1}$ when θ describes an angle in the first quadrant. These facts can be useful in simplifying integrands containing $\sqrt{a^2 - x^2}$, $\sqrt{a^2 + x^2}$, or $\sqrt{x^2 - a^2}$, as the following examples show.

Example 5. Consider $\int (x^3/\sqrt{16 - x^2}) \, dx$. Motivated by the identity $\sqrt{16 - 16 \sin^2 \theta} = 4 \cos \theta$, we introduce the substitution $x = 4 \sin \theta$, hence $du = 4 \cos \theta \, d\theta$. Thus

$$\int \frac{x^3}{\sqrt{16 - x^2}} \, dx = \int \frac{(4 \sin \theta)^3}{\sqrt{16 - 16 \sin^2 \theta}} 4 \cos \theta \, d\theta$$

$$= \int \frac{64 \sin^3 \theta}{4 \cos \theta} 4 \cos \theta \, d\theta$$

$$= 64 \int \sin^3 \theta \, d\theta$$

which by Example 2 is equal to $^{64}\!/_{3} \cos^3 \theta - 64 \cos \theta$.

To express this result in terms of x rather than θ, we make use of the relation $x = 4\sin\theta$, which is shown in the following right triangle:

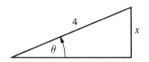

This diagram records that $\sin\theta = x/4$ or $x = 4\sin\theta$

By the Pythagorean theorem, the horizontal side of the triangle is $\sqrt{4^2 - x^2} = \sqrt{16 - x^2}$. Thus $\cos\theta = (\sqrt{16 - x^2})/4$. Hence we conclude that

$$\int \frac{x^3}{\sqrt{16 - x^2}}\, dx = {}^{64}\!/\!_3 \cos^3\theta - 64\cos\theta = \frac{(16 - x^2)^{3/2}}{3} - 16\sqrt{16 - x^2}$$

Example 6. Consider $\int \sqrt{1 + x^2}\, dx$. Motivated by the identity $\sec\theta = \sqrt{1 + \tan^2\theta}$, we make the substitution $x = \tan\theta$, hence $du = \sec^2\theta\, d\theta$. Thus

$$\int \sqrt{1 + x^2}\, dx = \int \sec\theta \sec^2\theta\, d\theta = \int \sec^3\theta\, d\theta$$

which we rewrite as $\int \sec\theta \sec^2\theta\, d\theta$ and subject to an integration by parts with $u = \sec\theta$ and $dv = \sec^2\theta\, d\theta$; hence $du = \sec\theta\tan\theta\, d\theta$, with $v = \tan\theta$. This yields

$$\int \sec^3\theta\, d\theta = \int \overbrace{\sec\theta}^{u} \overbrace{\sec^2\theta\, d\theta}^{dv} = \overbrace{\sec\theta}^{u} \overbrace{\tan\theta}^{v} - \int \overbrace{\tan\theta}^{v} \overbrace{\sec\theta\tan\theta\, d\theta}^{du}$$

$$= \sec\theta\tan\theta - \int \tan^2\theta \sec\theta\, d\theta$$

$$= \sec\theta\tan\theta - \int (\sec^2\theta - 1)\sec\theta\, d\theta$$

$$= \sec\theta\tan\theta - \int \sec^3\theta\, d\theta + \int \sec\theta\, d\theta$$

Collecting $\int \sec^3\theta\, d\theta$, which appears twice, we obtain

$$2\int \sec^3\theta\, d\theta = \sec\theta\tan\theta + \int \sec\theta\, d\theta$$

By Example 4, we have $\int \sec\theta\, d\theta = \ln|\sec\theta + \tan\theta|$; thus

(10) $$\int \sec^3\theta\, d\theta = \frac{\sec\theta\tan\theta}{2} + \tfrac{1}{2}\ln|\sec\theta\tan\theta|$$

To express the antiderivative just obtained in terms of x rather than θ, we must express $\tan\theta$ and $\sec\theta$ in terms of x. Starting with the relation $x = \tan\theta$, we find $\sec\theta$ by means of the relation $\sec\theta = \sqrt{1 + \tan^2\theta} = \sqrt{1 + x^2}$. Expressing (10) in terms of x, we obtain

$$\int \sqrt{1 + x^2}\, dx = \frac{(\sqrt{1 + x^2})(x)}{2} + \tfrac{1}{2}\ln|\sqrt{1 + x^2} + x|$$

a formula listed in a table of integrals.

METHOD 3: *The substitution* $u = \sqrt[n]{ax + b}$. We illustrate this technique by an example.

Example 7. Consider $\int (\sqrt[4]{1 + x}/x^2)\, dx$. Let us try the substitution $u = \sqrt[4]{x + 1}$, hence $u^4 = x + 1$, $x = u^4 - 1$, and $dx = 4u^3\, du$. Thus

$$\int \frac{\sqrt[4]{1 + x}}{x^2}\, dx = \int \frac{u}{(u^4 - 1)^2}\, 4u^3\, du = 4 \int \frac{u^4}{(u^4 - 1)^2}\, du$$

a problem than can be treated by partial fractions.

EXERCISES

1. (a) Compute $\int \sin^4 \theta\, d\theta$ by the method shown in Example 1.
   (Answer: $\tfrac{3}{8}\theta - \tfrac{1}{4}\sin 2\theta - \tfrac{1}{32}\sin 4\theta$)
   (b) Compute $\int \sin^4 \theta\, d\theta$, using the reduction formula of Example 4, page 164.
   (Answer: $-\tfrac{1}{4}\sin^3 \theta \cos \theta - \tfrac{3}{8}\sin \theta \cos \theta + \tfrac{3}{8}\theta$)
   (c) What does your table of integrals say about $\int \sin^4 \theta\, d\theta$?
   (d) The answers to (a) and (b) do not look alike. By how much do the two functions differ?
2. Using the method of Example 2, compute (a) $\int \sin^5 2x\, dx$; (b) $\int \cos^5 2x\, dx$; (c) $\int \cos^2 x \sin^3 x\, dx$.
3. Using the method of Example 3, compute (a) $\int \sec^3 2x \tan^3 2x\, dx$; (b) $\int \sec \theta \tan^5 \theta\, d\theta$.
4. Compute $\int \cot \theta\, d\theta$. (Hint: See $\int \tan \theta\, d\theta$, page 160.)
5. Using trigonometric substitutions, compute (a) $\displaystyle\int \frac{1}{\sqrt{4 - x^2}}\, dx$; (b) $\displaystyle\int \frac{1}{\sqrt{x^2 - 4}}\, dx$;
   (c) $\displaystyle\int \frac{1}{\sqrt{x^2 + 4}}\, dx$.
6. Compute $\int x \sqrt[3]{x + 1}\, dx$, using (a) the the substitution $u = \sqrt[3]{x + 1}$; (b) the substitution $u = x + 1$.
7. Compute $\displaystyle\int \frac{\sqrt[3]{x + 8}}{x}\, dx$, using the substitution $u = \sqrt[3]{x + 8}$ and integrating the resulting rational function by parts.

□ □ □

8. Reduce
$$\int \frac{3 + \sin \theta}{5 + 4 \cos \theta}\, d\theta$$
to the integral of a rational function by the substitution $u = \tan (\theta/2)$. For this type of substitution, show (a) $d\theta = \dfrac{du}{1 + u^2}$; (b) $\sin \theta = \dfrac{2u}{1 + u^2}$; (c) $\cos \theta = \dfrac{1 - u^2}{1 + u^2}$.
   (Do not integrate the resulting rational function.) The formulas in (a), (b), and (c) are usually included in a table of integrals.
9. (a) Prove the trigonometric identity
$$\sin mx \sin nx = \tfrac{1}{2}\left\{\cos \left[(m - n)\, x\right] - \cos \left[(m + n)\, x\right]\right\}$$
   by expanding the right side.
   (b) Use it to compute $\int \sin 2x \sin 3x\, dx$.

6. Summary and practice. We conclude with a variety of problems solvable by one or more of the methods discussed in this chapter. Answers can be checked either by differentiation or by use of a table of integrals.

The purpose of this chapter and these practice problems is threefold: (1) to enable us to compute simple antiderivatives swiftly; (2) to show the role of a table of integrals; (3) to remind us that there are elementary functions that do not possess elementary antiderivatives—and therefore that the fundamental theorem of calculus does not dispose of all important definite integrals. The techniques described are substitution, integration by parts, partial fractions, and some special devices.

EXERCISES

1. Transform $\int \dfrac{\sqrt{x^2+9}}{x^3} dx$ by each of the substitutions (a) $x = 3\tan\theta$, (b) $u = \sqrt{x^2+9}$,

   and (c) solve the easier problem that results.

2. Transform $\int \dfrac{x^2}{\sqrt{1+x}} dx$ by each of the substitutions (a) $u = \sqrt{1+x}$, (b) $u = 1+x$,

   (c) $x = \tan^2\theta$, and solve the easiest of the resulting problems.

3. Compute $\int \dfrac{x}{\sqrt{1+x}} dx$ with the aid of a table of integrals.

In Exercises 4 through 11 compute without integral tables and with integral tables:

4. (a) $\int \dfrac{dx}{2x^2 + 5x + 6}$; (b) $\int \dfrac{x\,dx}{2x^2 + 5x + 6}$.

5. (a) $\int \dfrac{x^2}{x^2 + 1} dx$; (b) $\int \dfrac{x}{x^2 + 1} dx$; (c) $\int \dfrac{x^2}{x^2 - 1} dx$.

6. (a) $\int \dfrac{dx}{x^2 + 5x + 6}$; (b) $\int \dfrac{4x + 10}{x^2 + 5x + 6} dx$.

7. (a) $\int \dfrac{x^2}{x^4 - 1} dx$; (b) $\int \dfrac{x^3}{x^4 - 1} dx$.

8. $\int \dfrac{1}{1 + x^4} dx$.   9. $\int \dfrac{x}{1 + x^4} dx$.

10. $\int \dfrac{x^3}{1 + x^4} dx$.   11. $\int \dfrac{dx}{x^3 + 4x}$.

In Exercises 12 through 18 use a table of integrals to find:

12. (a) $\int \sqrt{4x^2 + 1}\, dx$; (b) $\int \sqrt{-4x^2 + 1}\, dx$.

13. (a) $\int \dfrac{dx}{x\sqrt{2x^2 + 9}}$; (b) $\int \dfrac{dx}{x\sqrt{2x^2 - 9}}$.

14. (a) $\int \dfrac{1}{x\sqrt{3x + 1}} dx$; (b) $\int \dfrac{\sqrt{3x + 1}}{x} dx$.

15. (a) $\int \dfrac{x^2}{3x + 1} dx$; (b) $\int \dfrac{x^2}{(3x + 1)^2} dx$; (c) $\int \dfrac{x^2}{(3x + 1)^3} dx$.

16. (a) $\displaystyle\int \frac{dx}{2x^2 + 5x + 6}$; (b) $\displaystyle\int \frac{dx}{2x^2 + 5x - 6}$.

17. (a) $\displaystyle\int \frac{dx}{2 + 3 \sin x}$; (b) $\displaystyle\int \frac{dx}{3 + 2 \sin x}$. (Hint: See Exercise 8, page 175.)

18. (a) $\displaystyle\int \frac{1}{\sin^2 x}\, dx$; (b) $\displaystyle\int \frac{1}{\sin^4 x}\, dx$; (c) $\displaystyle\int \frac{1}{\sin^6 x}\, dx$.

19. Transform the problem of finding $\displaystyle\int \frac{x^3}{\sqrt{1 + x^2}}\, dx$ to a different problem, using

   (a) integration by parts with $dv = (x\, dx)/\sqrt{1 + x^2}$; (b) the substitution $x = \tan \theta$; (c) the substitution $u = \sqrt{1 + x^2}$.

20. Find $\displaystyle\int \frac{x^3}{\sqrt{1 + x^2}}\, dx$ with the aid of a table of integrals.

21. Compute $\int (e^{6x})^2\, dx$.

22. Compute $\displaystyle\int \frac{\sqrt{4 - x^2}}{x}\, dx$

23. (a) Compute $\displaystyle\int \frac{x^{2/3}}{x + 1}\, dx$; (b) what does a table of integrals say about $\displaystyle\int \frac{x^{2/3}}{x + 1}\, dx$?

24. Compute (a) $\int \sin^7 2x\, dx$; (b) $\int \sin^7 2x \cos 2x\, dx$.

25. Compute (a) $\displaystyle\int \sec^5 x\, dx$; (b) $\displaystyle\int \sec^5 x \tan x\, dx$; (c) $\displaystyle\int \frac{\sin x}{(\cos x)^6}\, dx$.

26. Compute $\displaystyle\int \frac{x^3}{(x - 1)^2}\, dx$ (a) using partial fractions; (b) using the substitution $u = x - 1$.

   (c) Which method is easier?

27. One of the following two antiderivatives is not an elementary function. Decide which is elementary and compute it.

$$\int \frac{\sin x}{x}\, dx \qquad \int x \sin x\, dx$$

28. (a) Explain why $\int x^m e^x\, dx$ is an elementary function for any positive integer m. (b) Explain why $\int x^m (\ln x)^n\, dx$ is an elementary function for any positive integers m and n. (Hint: Make the substitution $u = \ln x$.)

29. Assuming that $\int (e^x/x)\, dx$ is not elementary (a theorem of Liouville), prove that $\int (1/\ln x)\, dx$ is not elementary.

30. Since $\int (e^x/x)\, dx$ is not elementary, the fundamental theorem of calculus is useless in computing $\displaystyle\int_1^2 (e^x/x)\, dx$. Estimate $\displaystyle\int_1^2 (e^x/x)\, dx$, using the partition $x_0 = 1$, $x_1 = 1.4$, $x_2 = 1.7$, $x_3 = 2$ and sampling points $X_1 = 1.2$, $X_2 = 1.5$, $X_3 = 1.8$. (Use a table of values of e^x.) (Answer: 3.01)

31. Compute (a) $\displaystyle\int \frac{1}{x \ln x}\, dx$; (b) $\displaystyle\int \frac{\ln x}{x}\, dx$.

32. It can be proved that $\int \sin x^2\, dx$ is not elementary, and thus the fundamental theo-

rem of calculus is useless in computing $\int_0^{\pi/2} \sin x^2\, dx$. Estimate $\int_0^{\pi/2} \sin x^2\, dx$ with the aid of a partition of $[0, \pi/2]$ and sampling points.

In Exercises 33 through 51 compute the antiderivatives:

33. $\int x \sin^{-1} x\, dx$.

34. $\int \sin^{-1} x\, dx$.

35. $\int \ln (x^2 + 5)\, dx$.

36. $\int \dfrac{x^2}{(x - 1)^3}\, dx$.

37. $\int (2x + 1) \sqrt{3x + 2}\, dx$.

38. $\int \dfrac{2x^3 + 1}{x^3 - 4x^2}\, dx$.

39. $\int e^x \sin x\, dx$.

40. (a) $\int \dfrac{1}{\sqrt{9 + x^2}}\, dx$;   (b) $\int \dfrac{1}{\sqrt{x^2 - 9}}\, dx$.

41. $\int \dfrac{e^x + 1}{e^x - 1}\, dx$.

42. (a) $\int \dfrac{x}{4x^2 + 1}\, dx$;   (b) $\int \dfrac{1}{4x^2 + 1}\, dx$.

43. $\int (1 + 3x^2)^8 x\, dx$.   44. $\int (1 + 3x^2)^2\, dx$.

45. (a) $\int \dfrac{x^2}{x^3 + 1}\, dx$;   (b) $\int \dfrac{x}{x^3 + 1}\, dx$;   (c) $\int \dfrac{x^3}{x^3 + 1}\, dx$.

46. (a) $\int \dfrac{x^2}{\sqrt{2x + 1}}\, dx$;   (b) $\int \dfrac{1}{\sqrt{2x + 1}}\, dx$;   (c) $\int \dfrac{1}{2x + 1}\, dx$.

47. $\int \dfrac{dx}{(\sqrt{x - 2})(\sqrt{3 - x})}$.   48. $\int \sqrt{(1 + 2x)(1 - 2x)}\, dx$.

49. (a) $\int \sin 3x\, dx$;   (b) $\int x \sin 3x\, dx$.

50. (a) $\int \dfrac{2x}{\sqrt{x^2 + 1}}\, dx$;   (b) $\int \dfrac{2}{\sqrt{x^2 + 1}}\, dx$.

51. (a) $\int \dfrac{x}{(5x + 2)^2}\, dx$;   (b) $\int \dfrac{1}{(5x + 2)^2}\, dx$.

□   □   □

52. Compute $\int e^{\sqrt[4]{x}}\, dx$.   53. Compute $\int \csc x\, dx$.

54. Let p and q be positive rational numbers. Prove that $\int x^p (1 - x)^q\, dx$ is an elementary function (a) if p is an integer [Hint: If $q = s/t$, let $1 - x = v^t$.]; (b) if q is an integer; (c) if $p + q$ is an integer. Chebychef proved that these are the only cases for which the antiderivative in question is elementary. In particular, $\int \sqrt{x} \sqrt[3]{1 - x}\, dx$ and $\int \sqrt[3]{x - x^2}\, dx$ are not elementary.

55. This exercise outlines an elementary proof due to Y. Matsuoka [*Amer. Math. Monthly*, **68**:485–487 (1961)] that

$$\lim_{n \to \infty} \left(\frac{1}{1^2} + \frac{1}{2^2} + \cdots + \frac{1}{n^2} \right) = \frac{\pi^2}{6}$$

and depends on Exercise 10, page 165.

(a) Explain why I_n of Exercise 10, page 165, is equal to $\displaystyle\int_0^{\pi/2} \cos^n t\, dt$.

(b) Using integration by parts, prove that $I_{2n} = 2n \displaystyle\int_0^{\pi/2} t \cos^{2n-1} t \sin t\, dt$. (Hint: $I_{2n} = \displaystyle\int_0^{\pi/2} \cos^{2n} t\, dt$, with $u = \cos^{2n} t$, $dv = dt$.)

(c) Using integration by parts again, prove that

$$I_{2n} = -2n^2 \int_0^{\pi/2} t^2 \cos^{2n} t\, dt + n(2n-1) \int_0^{\pi/2} t^2 \cos^{2n-2} t\, dt$$

(d) Letting $J_n = \displaystyle\int_0^{\pi/2} t^2 \cos^n t\, dt$, conclude from (c) that

$$-2n^2 J_{2n} + n(2n-1) J_{2n-2} = \frac{(2n-1)!!}{(2n)!!} \frac{\pi}{2}$$

where the double factorial notation $a!!$ is short for $a(a-2)(a-4)\cdots (4)(2)$ if a is even and $a(a-2)(a-4)\cdots (3)(1)$ if a is odd, and where $0!! = 1$, $(-1)!! = 1$.

(e) Show that $J_0 = \pi^3/24$.

(f) Show that

$$\frac{(2n)!!}{(2n-1)!!} J_{2n} - \frac{(2n-2)!!}{(2n-3)!!} J_{2n-2} = \left(\frac{-1}{n^2}\right)\frac{\pi}{4}$$

(g) From (f) deduce that

$$\frac{(2k)!!}{(2k-1)!!} J_{2k} - \frac{0!!}{(-1)!!} J_0 = -\frac{\pi}{4}\left(\sum_{n=1}^{k} \frac{1}{n^2}\right)$$

and thus

$$\frac{(2k)!!}{(2k-1)!!} J_{2k} = \frac{\pi}{4}\left(\frac{\pi^2}{6} - \sum_{n=1}^{k} \frac{1}{n^2}\right)$$

(h) Recalling Exercise 32(d), page 130, show that

$$J_{2k} < \left(\frac{\pi}{2}\right)^2 \int_0^{\pi/2} \sin^2 t \cos^{2k} t\, dt = \left(\frac{\pi^2}{4}\right)(I_{2k} - I_{2k+2}) = \left(\frac{\pi^3}{8}\right)\frac{(2k-1)!!}{(2k+2)!!}$$

(i) Show that

$$\frac{(2k)!!}{(2k-1)!!} J_{2k} < \frac{\pi^3}{8}\left(\frac{1}{2k+2}\right)$$

and draw the conclusion that $\displaystyle\lim_{n\to\infty} 1/1^2 + 1/2^2 + \cdots + 1/n^2 = \pi^2/6$.

The first proof of this result, due to Euler in 1736, is described in G. Polya, "Mathematics and Plausible Reasoning," vol. 1, pp. 17–21, Princeton, 1954. When Euler obtained this result, John Bernoulli wrote: "And so is satisfied the burning desire of my brother [James Bernoulli], who, realizing that the investigation of the sum was more difficult than anyone would have thought, openly confessed that all his zeal had been mocked. If only my brother were alive now." James Bernoulli died in 1705. Incidentally it is still not known whether $\displaystyle\sum_{n=1}^{\infty} \frac{1}{n^3}$ is a rational multiple of π^3. Of these problems Mengoli said in 1658 "They demand the strength of a most splendid genius."

56. With the aid of Exercise 55, show that $1/1^2 + 1/3^2 + 1/5^2 + \cdots = \pi^2/8$.

8

Computing and applying definite integrals over intervals

THIS is the position in which we now find ourselves: If we can express a certain quantity as a limit of sums which appear in the definition of the definite integral, we can represent that quantity as a definite integral. (We have observed this in dealing with area, mass, distance traveled, and volume.) Then, hopefully, we can compute the relevant definite integral. For this task the fundamental theorem of calculus, which relates the definite integral to antiderivatives, is our main tool. Chapter 7 presented various ways of finding antiderivatives, including using the table of integrals.

This chapter simply applies the technique we have just described to problems in area, volume, arc length, surface area, work, force and probability. We also discuss improper integrals and moments of a function. (More extensive illustrations are given in Part III.) Our purpose is to develop skill in (1) recognizing when a quantity is representable as a definite integral, and (2) evaluating definite integrals by means of the fundamental theorem of calculus. It is pointless to memorize the various formulas that we shall obtain. With understanding of the basic ideas, we should be able to reconstruct any formula when needed.

1. Area. We saw in Chap. 1 that area can be expressed as the definite integral of a cross-sectional length. We will illustrate this by another example and then develop a second way of computing area.

Example 1. We find the area between the curves $y = 4x$ and $y = 2x^2$. First we graph the two curves.

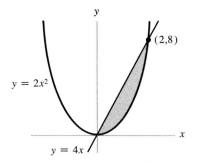

We seek the area of the shaded region

(Observe that they cross when $4x = 2x^2$, that is, when $x = 0$ or $x = 2$.) If we take cross sections parallel to the y axis, then the typical cross section, $c(x)$, is given by

$$c(x) = 4x - 2x^2$$

and the interval over which we integrate is [0,2]. Thus

$$\text{Area} = \int_0^2 (4x - 2x^2)\, dx \underset{\text{FTC}}{=} \left(2x^2 - \frac{2x^3}{3} \right)\Big|_0^2 = \left[2(2^2) - \frac{2(2^3)}{3} \right] - \left[2(0^2) - \frac{2(0^3)}{3} \right] = \frac{8}{3}$$

Let us solve the same problem, using horizontal cross sections:

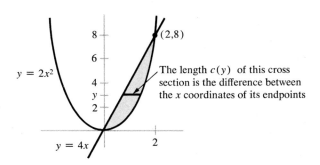

The length $c(y)$ of this cross section is the difference between the x coordinates of its endpoints

To find $c(y)$ we write the equations of the two curves in such a manner that x is given as a function of y. Thus $y = 2x^2$ may be written as $x = \sqrt{y/2}$ (since we are not interested in $x < 0$), and $y = 4x$ as $x = y/4$. So $c(y) = \sqrt{y/2} - (y/4)$. The interval of integration is $[0,8]$. Hence

$$\text{Area} = \int_0^8 \left(\sqrt{\frac{y}{2}} - \frac{y}{4} \right) dy \underset{\text{FTC}}{=} \left(\frac{2y^{3/2}}{3\sqrt{2}} - \frac{y^2}{8} \right) \Bigg|_0^8$$

$$= \left(\frac{2}{3\sqrt{2}} (8)^{3/2} - \frac{8^2}{8} \right) - \left(\frac{2}{3\sqrt{2}} (0)^{3/2} - \frac{0^2}{8} \right)$$

$$= \frac{2}{3\sqrt{2}} (8^{3/2}) - 8 = \frac{\sqrt{2}}{3} (2\sqrt{2})^3 - 8 = 32/3 - 8 = 8/3$$

Observe that the integrand is more complicated here; this suggests that we should generally choose carefully the direction in which we take the cross sections.

Example 2: Area in polar coordinates. We find the area inside the curve $r = 3 + \cos \theta$. First we graph the curve by computing a few points on it:

θ	0	$\dfrac{\pi}{4}$	$\dfrac{\pi}{2}$	π	$\dfrac{3\pi}{2}$	2π
r	4	3.7	3	2	3	4

We note that for all θ, we have $2 \leqslant r \leqslant 4$, and obtain the following graph:

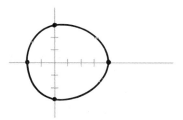

It would be difficult to compute the length of parallel cross sections no matter what fixed direction we choose.

We therefore develop a way for computing area in terms of polar coordinates. To do so, let us recall that in a circle of radius r, a sector of central angle θ has area $(\theta/2) r^2$.

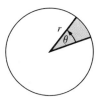

The area of the shaded set is $\frac{\theta}{2} r^2$

(Note that when $\theta = 2\pi$ we obtain $(2\pi/2) r^2 = \pi r^2$, the correct formula for the area of the circle.)

If a curve is given in polar coordinates by the formula $r = f(\theta)$, then we approximate the area bounded by the curve and the rays $\theta = \alpha$, $\theta = \beta$

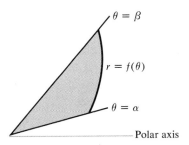

by a family of sectors (not a family of rectangles), as is shown here:

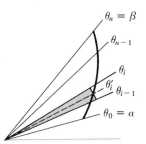

The typical sector has radius $f(\theta_i')$, angle $\theta_i - \theta_{i-1}$, and area $\frac{\theta_i - \theta_{i-1}}{2}[f(\theta_i')]^2$

We partition the interval $[\alpha,\beta]$ and select a number θ_i' in each interval. (We use θ_i' to denote the sampling point because of the similarity of the capital and lowercase θ.)

We make the assumption that the sum of the areas of the sectors approaches the area within the curve as the sectors become narrow. In other words we assume that

$$\lim_{\text{mesh}\to 0} \sum_{i=1}^{n} \tfrac{1}{2}[f(\theta_i')]^2 (\theta_i - \theta_{i-1}) = \text{area in question}$$

But, by the definition of the definite integral, we have

$$\lim_{\text{mesh}\to 0} \sum_{i=1}^{n} \tfrac{1}{2}[f(\theta_i')]^2 (\theta_i - \theta_{i-1}) = \int_{\alpha}^{\beta} \tfrac{1}{2}[f(\theta)]^2 \, d\theta$$

We conclude that area $= \int_{\alpha}^{\beta} \tfrac{1}{2}[f(\theta)]^2 \, d\theta$, which we write simply as

$$\text{Area} = \int_{\alpha}^{\beta} \tfrac{1}{2} r^2 \, d\theta$$

a formula for computing area if a curve is described by polar coordinates.

We apply the formula to the case $r = 3 + \cos\theta$, with $\alpha = 0$ and $\beta = 2\pi$, and obtain

$$\text{Area} = \int_{0}^{2\pi} \tfrac{1}{2}(3 + \cos\theta)^2 \, d\theta = \tfrac{1}{2} \int_{0}^{2\pi} (9 + 6\cos\theta + \cos^2\theta) \, d\theta$$

$$\underset{\text{FTC}}{=} \tfrac{1}{2}\left(9\theta + 6\sin\theta + \frac{\theta}{2} + \frac{\sin 2\theta}{4} \right)\Bigg|_{0}^{2\pi}$$

$$= \tfrac{1}{2}(19\pi) - \tfrac{1}{2}(0) = \frac{19\pi}{2}$$

Observe that any line through the origin intersects the set in Example 2 in a segment of length 6, since $(3 + \cos\theta) + [3 + \cos(\theta + \pi)] = 6$ for any θ. Also, any line through the center of a circle of radius 3 intersects the circle in a segment of length 6. Thus two sets in the plane can have equal corresponding cross sections through a fixed point and yet have different areas: the set in Example 2 has area $19\pi/2$, while the circle of radius 3 has area 9π.

Example 3: Substitution in a definite integral. We find the area of the region below $y = x^2/\sqrt{3x + 4}$, above $y = 0$, right of $x = 0$, and left of $x = 1$.

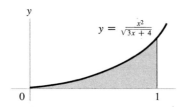

We wish to compute the area of the shaded region

Here we wish to compute $\int_0^1 (x^2/\sqrt{3x + 4})\, dx$. In order to apply the fundamental theorem of calculus, we must find an antiderivative, $\int (x^2/\sqrt{3x + 4})\, dx$. This we do by the substitution $u = 3x + 4$

$$\int \frac{x^2\, dx}{\sqrt{3x + 4}} \underset{\substack{u = 3x+4 \\ du = 3\, dx \\ [x = (u-4)/3]}}{=\!=} \int \frac{[(u - 4)/3]^2\, du}{\sqrt{u}}\frac{1}{3} = \frac{1}{27}\int \frac{u^2 - 8u + 16}{\sqrt{u}}\, du$$

$$= \frac{1}{27}\int (u^{3/2} - 8u^{1/2} + 16u^{-1/2})\, du$$

$$= \frac{1}{27}\left(\frac{u^{5/2}}{5/2} - \frac{8u^{3/2}}{3/2} + \frac{16u^{1/2}}{1/2}\right)$$

Thus

$$\frac{1}{27}\left[\frac{(3x + 4)^{5/2}}{5/2} - \frac{8(3x + 4)^{3/2}}{3/2} + \frac{16(3x + 4)^{1/2}}{1/2}\right]$$

is an antiderivative of $x^2/\sqrt{3x + 4}$.

Watch closely what happens when we evaluate the antiderivative at $x = 1$. When $x = 1$, we have $3x + 4 = 7$, and we obtain

$$\frac{1}{27}\left[\frac{(3 \cdot 1 + 4)^{5/2}}{5/2} - \frac{8(3 \cdot 1 + 4)^{3/2}}{3/2} + \frac{16(3 \cdot 1 + 4)^{1/2}}{1/2}\right]$$

We obtain the same expression as if we had evaluated

$$\frac{1}{27}\left(\frac{u^{5/2}}{5/2} - \frac{8u^{3/2}}{3/2} + \frac{16u^{1/2}}{1/2}\right)$$

at $u = 7$. A similar relation holds when $x = 0$ and $u = 3(0) + 4 = 4$. This observation can save us a good deal of arithmetic. We have shown that

$$\int_0^1 \frac{x^2}{\sqrt{3x + 4}}\, dx = \frac{1}{27}\left(\frac{u^{5/2}}{5/2} - \frac{8u^{3/2}}{3/2} + \frac{16u^{1/2}}{1/2}\right)\Bigg|_4^7$$

We could also observe that the expression on the right in the above equation equals, by the fundamental theorem of calculus,

$$\int_4^7 \frac{u^2 - 8u + 16}{27\sqrt{u}}\,du$$

The observations in Example 3 suggest a general method for cutting down on the arithmetic involved in computing a definite integral: *If we use a substitution $u = h(x)$ to change the form of an integrand, then we should use the same substitution to change the interval of integration.* For instance,

$$\int_0^1 \frac{x^2}{\sqrt{3x+4}}\,dx = \int_4^7 \frac{u^2 - 8u + 16}{27\sqrt{u}}\,du \qquad u = \begin{cases} 4 & \text{when } x = 0 \\ 7 & \text{when } x = 1 \end{cases}$$

Similarly, the substitution $x = \sin\theta$ yields

$$\int_0^1 \sqrt{1 - x^2}\,dx = \int_0^{\pi/2} \cos^2\theta\,d\theta \qquad \theta = \begin{cases} 0 & \text{when } x = 0 \\ \dfrac{\pi}{2} & \text{when } x = 1 \end{cases}$$

We state this formally in a theorem which is an analog of the substitution technique for antiderivatives (page 160).

THEOREM: *Substitution in a definite integral.* If the expression $f(x)\,dx$ takes the form $g(u)\,du$ when we introduce the differentiable increasing (or decreasing) function $u = h(x)$, and if $h(a) = A$ and $h(b) = B$, then

$$\int_a^b f(x)\,dx = \int_A^B g(u)\,du$$

An outline of a proof depending on the law of the mean is sketched in Exercise 19.

EXERCISES

1. (a) Sketch the region in the plane bounded by the curve $y = x^2$ and the line $y = 4$.
   (b) Find its area, using vertical cross sections.
   (c) Find its area, using horizontal cross sections.
   [Answer: (b), (c) $32\frac{2}{3}$]

2. (a) Sketch the region in the plane bounded by the curve $x = y^2$, the y axis, and the lines $y = 1$ and $y = 2$.
   (b) Find its area, using horizontal cross sections.
   (c) Find its area, using vertical cross sections.
   [Answer: (b), (c) $\frac{7}{3}$]

3. (a) Sketch the region bounded by the curve $y = 1/(1 + x^2)$, the x axis, and the lines $x = 1$ and $x = -1$.
   (b) Find the area of this region, using vertical cross sections.
   (c) Find its area, using horizontal cross sections.
   [Answer: (b), (c) $\pi/2$]

4. (*a*) Graph the curve $r = 2 \sin \theta$.
   (*b*) Compute the area inside it.

[Answer: (*b*) π]

5. (*a*) Graph the curve $r = \sqrt{\cos 2\theta}$. (Note that r is not defined for all θ.)
   (*b*) Find the area inside one of its two loops.

[Answer: (*b*) ½]

6. Find the area of the shaded region.

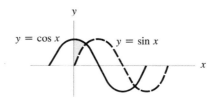

(Answer: $\sqrt{2} - 1$)

7. Find the area of the region inside the cardioid $r = 3 + 3 \sin \theta$ and outside the circle $r = 3$.   [Answer: $18 + 9\pi/4$]

8. (*a*) Graph the spiral $r = e^{\theta}$.
   (*b*) Find the area within the first turn of the spiral, that is, for $0 \leqslant \theta \leqslant 2\pi$.

[Answer: (*b*) $(e^{4\pi} - 1)/4$]

9. Transform the definite integral $\int_{1}^{2} (1 + x^2)^{10}\, 2x\, dx$ into a different integral, using the substitution (*a*) $u = x^2$; (*b*) $u = 1 + x^2$. What are the new limits of integration in each case?

10. Transform the definite integral $\int_{0}^{1/2} [x^3/(1 - x^2)]\, dx$ to another definite integral over a different interval, using the substitution (*a*) $u = x^2$; (*b*) $u = 1 - x^2$; (*c*) $x = \sin \theta$; (*d*) $x = \cos \theta$. Evaluate any one of these five definite integrals.

11. Find the area of the shaded region, (*a*) without the calculus; (*b*) using vertical cross sections; (*c*) using horizontal cross sections.   [Answer: $(\pi + 2)/4$]

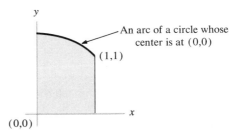

12. Find the area between the curves $y^2 = x$ and $y = x - 2$, using (*a*) horizontal cross sections; (*b*) vertical cross sections.   (Answer: %)

13. Sketch the region common to two circles of radius 1 whose centers are a distance 1 apart. Find the area of this region, using (*a*) vertical cross sections; (*b*) horizontal cross sections; (*c*) only elementary geometry, but no calculus.

(Answer: $2\pi/\sqrt{3} - \sqrt{3}/2$)

14. Compute the area of the region inside the curve $\dfrac{x^2}{a^2} + \dfrac{y^2}{b^2} = 1$, where a and b are fixed positive constants.   (Answer: πab)

15. Compute the area in Example 3.

16. (a) What fraction of the rectangle whose vertices are $(0,0)$, $(a,0)$, (a,a^4), $(0,a^4)$, where a is positive, is occupied by the region under the curve $y = x^4$ and above $[0,a]$?

    (b) Repeat part (a), but with 4 replaced throughout by $\frac{1}{4}$.

17. (a) Show that the area of this triangle is $\displaystyle\int_0^\beta \tfrac{1}{2}\sec^2\theta \, d\theta$.

    (b) From (a) and the fact that the area of a triangle is $(\frac{1}{2})$ (base) (height), show that $\tan\beta = \displaystyle\int_0^\beta \sec^2\theta \, d\theta$. With the aid of this equation, obtain another proof that $D(\tan x) = \sec^2 x$.

18. Prove that if a region in the plane has diameter d, then its area is at most $\pi d^2/4$. (Hint: Use polar coordinates with the pole on the border of the region.)

19. Our observation on the change of limits of integration in a definite integral when we substituted the variable u for x depended on the fundamental theorem of calculus. The law of the mean provides a more direct explanation, as follows:

    (a) Assume that $u = h(x)$ is a differentiable increasing function of x, with $h(a) = A$, $h(b) = B$, and $f(x) = g(h(x))\,h'(x)$ or, in differentials, $f(x)\,dx = g(u)\,du$. Apply the law of the mean to $u_i = u_{i-1}$ in the expression $\displaystyle\sum_{i=1}^n g(U_i)(u_i - u_{i-1})$, an approximating sum to $\displaystyle\int_A^B g(u)\,du$. Show how this operation transforms the sum into a sum approximating $\displaystyle\int_a^b f(x)\,dx$. Choose the specific U_i after applying the law of the mean.

    (b) Proceed as in (a), but let h be decreasing.

20. Show that the area of the shaded crescent between the two circular arcs is equal to the area of square $ABCD$.

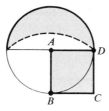

The outer arc has center A
The inner arc has center B

21. Show that the shaded area is $\frac{2}{3}$ the area of the parallelogram *ABCD*.

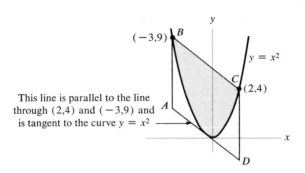

This is an illustration of a theorem of Archimedes concerning sectors of parabolas.

22. Find the error: Using the substitution $u = 1/x$, $du = (-1/x^2)\,dx$, we have

$$\int_{-1}^{1} \frac{1}{1+x^2}\,dx = \int_{-1}^{1} \frac{1}{1+(1/u^2)}\left(-\frac{1}{u^2}\,du\right) = -\int_{-1}^{1} \frac{1}{1+u^2}\,du$$

Thus $\int_{-1}^{1} [1/(1+x^2)]\,dx$, being equal to its negative, is 0.

23. Find the error: Using the identity

$$\sin\frac{x}{2} = \sqrt{\frac{1-\cos x}{2}}$$

we have

$$\int_{0}^{4\pi} \sqrt{1-\cos x}\,dx = \sqrt{2}\int_{0}^{4\pi} \sin\frac{x}{2}\,dx \underset{\text{FTC}}{=} \sqrt{2}\left(-2\cos\frac{x}{2}\right)\Bigg|_{0}^{4\pi} = 0$$

Thus a positive integrand can have a definite integral equal to 0 (even though the interval of integration is not just a point).

24. Find the error: Using the substitution $x = y^2$, $dx = 2y\,dy$, we have

$$\int_{0}^{1} \frac{1}{x}\,dx = \int_{0}^{1} \frac{2y}{y^2}\,dy = \int_{0}^{1} \frac{2}{y}\,dy = 2\int_{0}^{1} \frac{1}{y}\,dy = 2\int_{0}^{1} \frac{1}{x}\,dx$$

Hence $\int_{0}^{1} (1/x)\,dx = 2\int_{0}^{1} (1/x)\,dx$, from which it follows that $\int_{0}^{1} (1/x)\,dx = 0$.

25. A point *P* in a region *R* bounded by a closed curve has the property that each chord through *P* cuts *R* into two regions of equal area. Must *P* bisect each chord through *P*? Explain. (Assume that *R* is convex.)

26. Let *R* be a set in the plane and *P* a point in *R* such that every line in the plane and passing through *P* intersects *R* in an interval of length at least *a*.
(a) Make a conjecture about the area of *R*.
(b) Prove your conjecture.

2. Volume (the cross-section and shell techniques). As we saw in Chap. 1 (page 17), the volume of a solid is the definite integral of the cross-sectional area. We combined this fact with the fundamental theorem of calculus to compute the volume of a sphere (page 136). We present another example and then develop an alternative technique for computing the volumes of a special type of solid.

Example 1. The base of a certain solid is the region bounded by the x axis and the arch of the curve $y = \sin x$ from $x = 0$ to $x = \pi$. Each plane section of the solid is a square whose base lies in the region. Find the volume of this solid, which is depicted in the accompanying diagram:

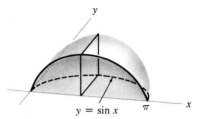

$$y = \sin x \qquad \pi$$

Since the cross section is a square whose side is $\sin x$, its area is $\sin^2 x$. Thus the volume equals $\int_0^\pi \sin^2 x \, dx$. To evaluate this definite integral we use the fundamental theorem of calculus. As Example 1, page 172, shows $x/2 - (\sin x \cos x)/2$ is an antiderivative of $\sin^2 x$. The fundamental theorem of calculus then asserts that

$$\int_0^\pi \sin^2 x \, dx = \left(\frac{x}{2} - \frac{\sin x \cos x}{2} \right) \Big|_0^\pi = \left(\frac{\pi}{2} - \frac{\sin \pi \cos \pi}{2} \right) - \left(\frac{0}{2} - \frac{\sin 0 \cos 0}{2} \right) = \frac{\pi}{2}$$

Hence the volume of the solid is $\pi/2$.

The volumes of certain solids, such as cones, doughnuts, and spheres, that can be formed by revolving a plane region R about a line L in the plane of R, can be computed in another way.

Let us introduce an x axis in the plane of R and perpendicular to L. Assume that L is left of R and cuts this line at $x = k$ and that $[a,b]$ is the portion of the axis that is cut by lines parallel to L and meeting R:

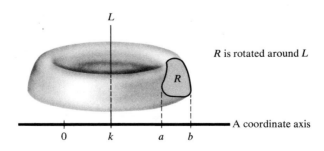

L

R is rotated around L

R

A coordinate axis

$0 \qquad k \qquad a \qquad b$

Instead of approximating the solid by parallel slabs, we can now approximate it by concentric shells (tubes) of which we draw only a typical one:

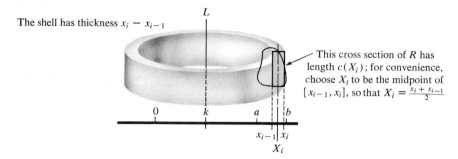

The shell has thickness $x_i - x_{i-1}$

This cross section of R has length $c(X_i)$; for convenience, choose X_i to be the midpoint of $[x_{i-1}, x_i]$, so that $X_i = \frac{x_i + x_{i-1}}{2}$

The volume of the shell is precisely

$$\underbrace{[\pi((x_i - k)^2) - \pi(x_{i-1} - k)^2]}_{\text{area of base}} \underbrace{c(X_i)}_{\text{altitude}}$$

which, after a little arithmetic, reduces to

$$2\pi \left(\frac{x_i + x_{i-1}}{2} - k \right) c(X_i)(x_i - x_{i-1})$$

or

$$2\pi(X_i - k)c(X_i)(x_i - x_{i-1})$$

We now make the assumption that when the shells are thin the total volume of these shells is a good estimate of the volume of the solid of revolution. That is, we assume that

$$\lim_{\text{mesh} \to 0} \sum_{i=1}^{n} 2\pi(X_i - k)c(X_i)(x_i - x_{i-1}) = \text{volume of solid}$$

But this limit is nothing other than a definite integral. Hence we have

$$\text{Volume} = \int_a^b 2\pi(x - k)c(x)\,dx$$

the formula for computing volumes by the shell technique. If we call $x - k$ simply $r(x)$, the radius of the shell, then $V = \int_a^b 2\pi r(x)c(x)\,dx$.

Example 2. We find the volume of this torus (doughnut):

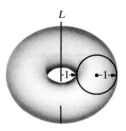

To make the description of the cross section $c(x)$ as simple as possible, we introduce an x axis with its origin 0 below the center of the rotated circle; then the line L has the coordinate -2.

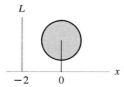

The Pythagorean theorem enables us to compute $c(x)$. Inspection of the triangle in the diagram below shows that $c(x)/2 = \sqrt{1^2 - x^2} = \sqrt{1 - x^2}$, hence $c(x) = 2\sqrt{1 - x^2}$.

Thus volume $= 2\pi \displaystyle\int_{-1}^{1} [x - (-2)]\, 2\sqrt{1 - x^2}\, dx$. All that remain is to compute

$$4\pi \int_{-1}^{1} (x + 2)\sqrt{1 - x^2}\, dx$$

We can do this by using integral tables, looking up

$$\int x\sqrt{1 - x^2}\, dx \qquad \text{and} \qquad \int 2\sqrt{1 - x^2}\, dx$$

but it is faster to make the substitution $x = \sin\theta$, $dx = \cos\theta\, d\theta$. Then

$$4\pi \int_{-1}^{1} (x + 2)\sqrt{1 - x^2}\, dx = 4\pi \int_{-\pi/2}^{\pi/2} (\sin\theta + 2)(\cos\theta)(\cos\theta\, d\theta)$$

$$= 4\pi \int_{-\pi/2}^{\pi/2} \cos^2\theta \sin\theta\, d\theta + 8\pi \int_{-\pi/2}^{\pi/2} \cos^2\theta\, d\theta$$

We evaluate the two summands by the fundamental theorem of calculus:

$$4\pi \int_{-\pi/2}^{\pi/2} \cos^2\theta \sin\theta\, d\theta = 4\pi \left(-\frac{\cos^3\theta}{3} \right)\Bigg|_{-\pi/2}^{\pi/2} = 0$$

and

$$8\pi \int_{-\pi/2}^{\pi/2} \cos^2\theta\, d\theta = 8\pi \int_{-\pi/2}^{\pi/2} \frac{1 + \cos 2\theta}{2}\, d\theta = 8\pi \left(\frac{\theta}{2} + \frac{\sin 2\theta}{4} \right)\Bigg|_{-\pi/2}^{\pi/2} = 8\pi \left(\frac{\pi}{2} \right) = 4\pi^2$$

Thus the volume is $4\pi^2$.

Both the slab and the shell techniques have limitations. It can happen that the desired integrand (such as cross-sectional area) is too complicated, or that even if it is given by a simple formula, its antiderivative is not elementary. In the latter case, the fundamental theorem of calculus cannot be used to evaluate the volume.

EXERCISES

1. Find the volume of a sphere of radius a, using the shell technique.
2. The region in the plane bounded by the curve $y = \sqrt{x}$, $x = 0$, and $y = 2$, is rotated around the y axis.
   (a) Find the volume of the resulting solid by the cross-section method. Draw the typical approximating slab and label its dimensions clearly.
   (b) Find the volume by the shell technique. Draw the typical shell and its dimensions.
   (Answer: $32\pi/5$)
3. Let R be the region in the plane bounded by $y = x^2$, $y = 0$, and $x = 2$. Find the volume of the solid of revolution formed when R is rotated around (a) the x axis; (b) the y axis; (c) the line $y = -1$; (d) the line $x = 3$.
4. Find the volume of one octant of the region common to two right circular cylinders whose axes intersect at right angles.   (Answer: $\frac{2}{3}$)

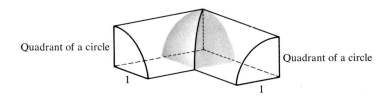

Quadrant of a circle   Quadrant of a circle

1   1

5. Using the shell technique, find the volume of the solid obtained by rotating a 3–4–5 right triangle (a) about its shortest side; (b) about its hypotenuse.
   [Answer: (a) 16π; (b) $48\pi/5$]
6. Find the volume of water in a tilted cylindrical glass (with circular cross section) when the water just covers the bottom and meets the rim of the glass.
   (a) Solve this without calculus.
   (b) Use the calculus.
7. The glass of water described in Exercise 6 is tilted until the water level bisects the base and touches the rim. How much water remains?
8. What fraction of the volume of a sphere is contained between parallel planes that trisect the diameter to which they are perpendicular?   (Answer: $\frac{13}{27}$)
9. Devise and sketch a solid whose volume would be $\displaystyle\int_1^2 e^{x^2}\,dx$.
10. (a) Why is it evident without computation, in Example 2, that $\displaystyle\int_{-1}^1 x\sqrt{1 - x^2}\,dx = 0$?
    (b) Why is it evident that $\displaystyle\int_{-1}^1 \sqrt{1 - x^2}\,dx = \frac{\pi}{2}$? (Hint: Think of the area of a circle.)
    (c) Using (a) and (b), compute $\displaystyle 4\pi\int_{-1}^1 (x + 2)\sqrt{1 - x^2}\,dx$.
11. Find the volume of a torus whose inside radius is 6 and whose outside radius is 8.
12. (a) Show that the volume of the shell in Example 2 is, as we asserted,
$$2\pi (X_i - k)\, c(X_i)\, (x_i - x_{i-1}).$$
    (b) Why did we choose X_i to be the midpoint?

13. A hole is bored all the way through a sphere by a drill whose diameter equals the radius of the sphere and whose point passes through the center of the sphere. Find the volume removed, (*a*) by the shell technique; (*b*) by the slab (parallel-cross-section) technique.   [Answer: $\frac{4}{3}\pi a^3 - (\sqrt{3}/2)\pi a^3$, if sphere has radius *a*]

14. Find the volume of the solid of revolution obtained by revolving the triangle below about *L* (*a*) using the slab technique; (*b*) using the shell technique.

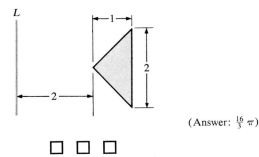

(Answer: $\frac{16}{3}\pi$)

15. Let *a* and *b* be positive numbers and $y = f(x)$ be a decreasing differentiable function of *x*, such that $f(0) = b$ and $f(a) = 0$. Prove that $\displaystyle\int_0^a 2xy\,dx = \int_0^b x^2\,dy$, doing so (*a*) by considering the volume of a certain solid; (*b*) by integration by parts.

16. Let *f* be an increasing function, $f(0) = 0$, and assume that it has an elementary anti-derivative. Then f^{-1} is an increasing function and $f^{-1}(0) = 0$. Prove that if f^{-1} is elementary, then it also has an elementary antiderivative. [Hint: Observe that the sum of the areas of I and II in this figure is $tf(t)$.]

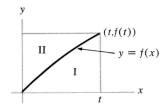

17. Find the volume in Example 2 by the slab technique.

3. The first moment. The definite integral $\displaystyle\int_a^b (x - k)\,f(x)\,dx$, where *f* is a continuous function and *k* is a number, has so many applications that it has been given a name: *the first moment of the function f about k (from a to b)*. The term "first" refers to the power to which $x - k$ is raised in the integrand. (In Sec. 6 we will examine other moments, in which $x - k$ is raised to other powers.) In this section we will discuss several applications of the first moment of the cross-section function of a plane region R, that is, $\int_a^b (x - k)\, c(x)\, dx$, which we call *the moment of R about the line x = k*. Similarly we may consider the function $c(y)$ and its moment about the line $y = k$, $\int_a^b (y - k)\, c(y)\, dy$.

Example 1.   In the preceding section we saw that the volume of a solid of revolution is given by the formula $V = \int_a^b 2\pi(x - k)\, c(x)\, dx$, where k records the position of the axis of rotation. (We place this axis to the left of the region; hence $x - k$ is positive.) Thus under these circumstances

$$V = 2\pi \int_a^b (x - k)\, c(x)\, dx = (2\pi)\ \text{(first moment of cross-section function about } k)$$

Example 2: Work done in emptying a tank.   The work done in lifting an object a certain vertical distance is defined as the product Wx (in foot-pounds), where W is its weight in pounds and x is the number of feet we raise it. Now consider this problem: How much work is done when we pump all the water out of a horizontal right cylindrical tank through an outlet above the tank? Not all the water is lifted the same distance, so the definition does not apply. Let us see how the definite integral and first moment solve this problem. We shall assume that the radius of the cylinder is 1 foot and its length 11 feet, and that the outlet is 1 foot above the top of the tank, as in this diagram:

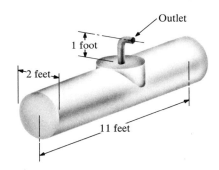

Some water is raised only one foot, some is raised as much as 3 feet. *Notice, however, that all the water in a thin horizontal slab is lifted about the same distance.* This suggests how we can estimate the total work: Cut the cylinder into some horizontal slabs, and estimate the work done in lifting each slab. We do this by introducing an x axis vertically to describe the slabs. Also, we approximate the slabs by flat boxes.

For convenience we place the origin of the axis on a level with the horizontal diameter of one end, and the positive part downward. At the outlet x equals -2. The interval $[-1,1]$ corresponds to the tank. We will, as usual, let $c(x)$ denote the length of cross section of the end corresponding to x in $[-1,1]$. Partitioning $[-1,1]$ and selecting a point X_i in each section, we will obtain an estimate of the work done in emptying the tank. (In our computations we assume that water weighs 62.4 pounds per cubic foot.)

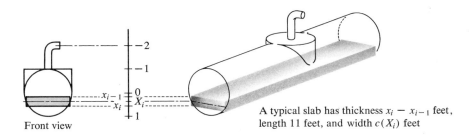

Front view

A typical slab has thickness $x_i - x_{i-1}$ feet, length 11 feet, and width $c(X_i)$ feet

The typical flat box of water is raised about $X_i + 2$ feet (some of it a little less, some a little more, since the box has a nonzero thickness). Thus the work done in lifting this typical box is approximately

$$\underbrace{(X_i + 2)}_{\substack{\text{distance} \\ \text{lifted}}} (62.4) \underbrace{(11)\, c(X_i)\, (x_i - x_{i-1})}_{\substack{\text{volume of box} \\ \text{weight of box}}}$$

and the sum

$$(62.4)\,(11)\sum_{i-1}^{n} (X_i + 2)\, c(X_i)\, (x_i - x_{i-1})$$

is an estimate of the total work. We would expect our sums to approach the total work involved. For this reason a physicist *defines* the total work as

$$\text{Work} = (62.4)\,(11)\int_{-1}^{1} (x + 2)\, c(x)\, dx \qquad \text{foot-pounds}$$

We say "defines" because the definition "work = weight × distance" applies only when all parts of the object are raised the same distance.

To finish our computation, note that $c(x) = 2\sqrt{1 - x^2}$, just as in Example 2 of Sec. 2. In that example we showed that $2\pi \int_{-1}^{1} (x + 2)\, c(x)\, dx = 4\pi^2$, from which we deduce that $\int_{-1}^{1} (x + 2)\, c(x)\, dx = 2\pi$. Thus

$$\text{Work} = (62.4)\,(11)\,(2\pi) \qquad \text{foot-pounds}$$

Notice that the work is equal to $(62.4)\,(11)\int_{-1}^{1} (x - (-2))\, c(x)\, dx$; that is,

Work = density of water × length of tank × first moment of end of tank about a horizontal line through the outlet

The result holds for any homogeneous liquid and any cylindrical tank, even though its base may not be a disk.

If we try to guess the answer to Example 2 by concentrating all the water at an average depth, presumably at the level of the center of the circular base, we will obtain this estimate:

$$(62.4)\;\underbrace{(\pi 1^2)}_{\substack{\text{area of}\\ \text{base of}\\ \text{cylinder}}}\;\underbrace{(11)}_{\substack{\text{height}\\ \text{of}\\ \text{cylinder}}}\;\underbrace{(2)}_{\substack{\text{vertical}\\ \text{distance from}\\ \text{center of}\\ \text{circular}\\ \text{end to outlet}}}\qquad = (62.4)\,(11)\,(2\pi)\qquad \text{foot-pounds}$$

In Example 3 we explain why our guess is right.

Example 3: Centroids. In Chap. 9 we will prove that (1) a homogeneous flat object occupying a region R in the plane balances on exactly one line in a given direction; (2) the lines on which the object balances all pass through a single point, called the *centroid*; (3) the x coordinate of the centroid, which we denote by $\bar{x}$, is given by this formula:

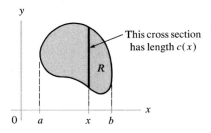

This cross section has length $c(x)$

$$\bar{x} = \frac{\displaystyle\int_a^b xc(x)\,dx}{\text{area of } R}$$

where c is the cross-section function of R. From this we obtain

$$\int_a^b xc(x)\,dx = (\bar{x})\,(\text{area of } R)$$

Now, $\displaystyle\int_a^b xc(x)\,dx = \int_a^b (x - 0)\,c(x)\,dx$, the first moment of R about the y axis. Thus we have

$$\text{Moment of } R \text{ about } y \text{ axis} = (\bar{x})\,(\text{area of } R)$$

a relation between the first moment, the x coordinate of the centroid, and the area, enabling us to compute one of them if we know the other two.

For instance, let us use this observation to compute $\displaystyle\int_{-1}^1 (x + 2)\,c(x)\,dx$, which appeared in Example 2. We have

$$\int_{-1}^1 (x + 2)\,c(x)\,dx = \int_{-1}^1 xc(x)\,dx + 2\int_{-1}^1 c(x)\,dx$$

We have $\int_{-1}^{1} xc(x)\, dx = (\bar{x})$ (area of R), but the symmetry of a circle shows that $\bar{x} = 0$.

Thus $\int_{-1}^{1} xc(x)\, dx = 0$. (Incidentally, the second definite integral can also be easily computed, since it is simply the area of a circle of radius 1, hence π.)

The usefulness of the centroid is shown by the next two theorems.

THEOREM 1.   *The volume of a solid of revolution obtained by revolving, about a line, a plane region R situated on one side of the line is equal to the area of R multiplied by the distance through which the centroid revolves; that is,*

$$V = (area\ of\ R)\,(2\pi\bar{x})$$

where $\bar{x}$ is the distance from the centroid to the axis of revolution.

PROOF.   We know that the volume of a solid of revolution is $2\pi \int_{a}^{b} (x - k)\, c(x)\, dx$. For convenience we may place the origin of the x axis on the axis of revolution; hence we may assume that $k = 0$. Thus the volume is equal to $2\pi \int_{a}^{b} xc(x)\, dx$. On the other hand, $\int_{a}^{b} xc(x)\, dx = (\bar{x})$ (area of R). Thus

$$\text{Volume} = (2\pi\bar{x})\,(\text{area of } R)$$

The proof is completed.

Example 1.   With the aid of Theorem 1, we find that the volume of the torus in Example 2 of Sec. 2 is

$$(2\pi)\,(2)\,[\pi(1^2)] = 4\pi^2$$

Example 5.   With the aid of Theorem 1, we find the centroid of this right triangle:

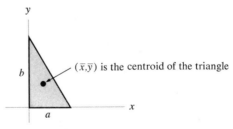

$(\bar{x},\bar{y})$ is the centroid of the triangle

If we rotate the triangle about the y axis, we obtain a cone of volume $\tfrac{1}{3}\pi a^2 b$. Thus, by Theorem 1,

$$\tfrac{1}{3}\pi a^2 b = (2\pi\bar{x})\,(\tfrac{1}{2}\,ab)$$

Solving for $\bar{x}$, we obtain $\bar{x} = a/3$. If we rotate the triangle about the x axis, we obtain, in a similar way, $\bar{y} = b/3$.

Thus the centroid of a right triangle is at the intersection of its three medians. This can be shown to hold for any triangle. The role of the centroid in work problems is shown in the next theorem.

THEOREM 2.   *The work done in pumping the water out of a full horizontal cylindrical tank with vertical base R is equal to weight of the water times distance the water at the centroid is lifted.* In other words, the work is the same as it would be if all the water were located at the centroid.

PROOF.   Let us introduce a vertical coordinate system whose origin is at the level of the outlet and whose positive part is pointed down. We denote the length of the tank by h. (In Example 2, $h = 11$.)

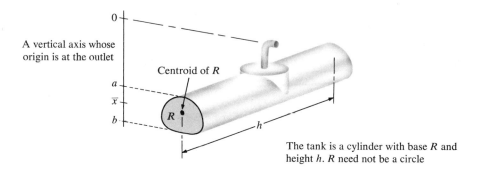

The work done is $(62.4)\,(h) \int_a^b xc(x)\,dx$. [We have the integrand $xc(x)$ instead of $(x + 2)\,c(x)$ because the origin is now at the level of the outlet; the distance a typical slab is raised is simply x, not $x + 2$ as it was in Example 2.] But $\int_a^b xc(x)\,dx = (\bar{x})\,(\text{area of } R)$. Thus

$$\text{Work} = (62.4)\,(h)\,(\bar{x})\,(\text{area of } R) = (62.4)\,\underbrace{\underbrace{(h)\,(\text{area of } R)}_{\text{volume of water}}\,(\bar{x})}_{\text{weight of water}}$$

and the theorem is proved.

Theorem 2 explains why our guess in Example 2 is correct. It holds for any homogeneous liquid.

Example 6: Force against a vertical submerged surface.   The force that a column of water h feet high exerts against its base is its weight. If the column has a cross-sectional area A, then the weight of the water in the column is $62.4\,Ah$ pounds. Since pressure is force per unit area, we see that the pressure at a depth h is $62.4\,Ah/A = 62.4\,h$ pounds per square foot. As the depth h increases, so does the pressure. Moreover, the pressure is the same in all directions (a submerged swimmer does not avoid the pressure against his ear drums by turning his head); at a given depth the same pressure is exerted against the floor of a swimming pool as against its vertical wall.

Let us see how to compute the force against a submerged vertical surface R. Because the pressure varies over R, we will be dealing with a definite integral. To see what it is, we construct a sum which we would expect to be a good estimate of the force. We begin by introducing a vertical x axis whose origin is at the surface of the water and whose positive part is in the water. We define a, b, and the cross-section function for R as usual; and as shown in the diagram below, we focus our attention on the force against a typical narrow strip of R from depth x_{i-1} to depth x_i.

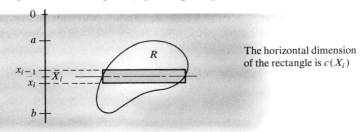

The horizontal dimension of the rectangle is $c(X_i)$

The force against this typical strip is presumably about

$$62.4\,X_i\,c(X_i)\,(x_i - x_{i-1})$$

hence we would expect the sum $\sum_{i=1}^{n} 62.4\,X_i\,c(X_i)\,(x_i - x_{i-1})$ to be a good estimate of the force against R when the mesh is small. For this reason the physicist *defines* the total force against R to be $62.4 \int_a^b xc(x)\,dx$ (pounds). Again we have a first moment; again, as Theorem 3 shows, the centroid is important.

THEOREM 3. *The total force against a vertical submerged surface R is equal to the pressure at the centroid of R times the area of R.*

PROOF. The total force is equal to $(62.4) \int_a^b xc(x)\,dx = 62.4\bar{x}$ (area of R). But $62.4\bar{x}$ is the pressure at the centroid of R. This ends the proof.

Example 7. Let us compute the force against the submerged triangle shown in this diagram:

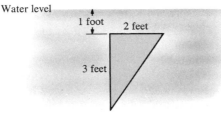

To use Theorem 3 we must find the depth of the centroid and the area of the triangle. Example 5 shows that the centroid has a depth of 2 feet; the area of the triangle is 3 square feet. By Theorem 3, the force against the triangle is $(62.4)(2)(3) = 374.4$ pounds.

It is interesting to observe that we found the force in Example 7 by knowing the centroid of a triangle, a result we obtained in Example 5 from the formula for the volume of a cone. It may seem surprising that a volume problem is related to a force problem. However, if we keep in mind that the volume of a solid of revolution, the force against a submerged surface, and the work done in emptying a tank all involve the first moment, our surprise should vanish; mathematically speaking, the problems are virtually the same, and intimately involved with the centroid, which tends to play the role of an "average point."

EXERCISES

1. Set up a definite integral for the first moment of the triangle whose vertices are $(1,1)$, $(4,1)$, $(4,3)$, if the moment is taken around (a) the x axis; (b) the line $y = -1$; (c) the line $y = 7$. Evaluate these definite integrals directly, without making use of the centroid.

[Answer: (a) 5, (b) 8, (c) -16]

2. Show that the first moment of a region about a line parallel to the y axis and passing through its centroid is 0.

3. We found the centroid of a right triangle by using Theorem 1 and the volume of a cone. Find it directly by the formula $\bar{x} = \int_a^b xc(x) \, dx / \text{area}$.

4. (a) Find the centroid of a semicircular plane region of radius r, whose center is at $(0,0)$ and whose diameter lies on the y axis by the formula

$$\bar{x} = \frac{\int_a^b xc(x) \, dx}{\text{area}}.$$

(b) Find it by Theorem 1.

(c) Using elementary geometry, show why $x < r/2$.   [Answer: (a) $4r/3\pi$]

5. (a) Cut out an irregularly shaped piece of cardboard. Experimentally find three lines on which the piece balances. Are they concurrent?

(b) Introduce a coordinate system on the cardboard and estimate $\int_a^b xc(x) \, dx$ by an approximating sum. [To determine $c(X_i)$, measure the cross section at X_i.]

(c) With the aid of (b), find $\bar{x}$ and compare it to the x coordinate of the center of gravity obtained experimentally.

6. Consider the region bounded by $y = e^{x^2}$, $x = 1$, $x = 2$, and $y = 0$. Set up a definite integral for (a) its area; (b) its moment about the y axis; (c) its moment about the line $x = -1$. (d) The fundamental theorem of calculus can be used to compute one of these three definite integrals. Which one? Compute it.

7. Draw the region bounded by $y = x^2$ and $y = 4$. (It lies in two quadrants.)

(a) Compute its cross section $c(y)$ made by a horizontal line.

(b) Compute its area.

(c) Compute its moment about the x axis.

(d) Compute its centroid.

[Answer: (a) $2\sqrt{y}$; (b) $32\frac{2}{3}$; (c) $128\frac{4}{5}$; (d) $\bar{x} = 0$, $\bar{y} = 1\frac{2}{5}$]

8. Using Exercise 7(d) and the theorems of this section, compute (a) the volume of the solid obtained by revolving the region in Exercise 7 about the line $y = -1$; (b) the force against the region if the surface of the water is at the line $y = 9$; (c) the

work done in emptying a cylindrical water tank whose base is the region in Exercise 7, whose length is 10 feet, and whose outlet is 5 feet above the top of the tank.
[Answer: (*a*) $1088\pi/15$ cubic feet; (*b*) $(62.4)(35\frac{2}{5})$ pounds;
(*c*) $(62.4)(704)$ foot-pounds]

9. Who puts a greater pressure on the ground, a 5-ton elephant each of whose feet is a circle 8 inches in diameter, or a 100-pound woman balancing on her spike heels, each of diameter ½ inch?   (Answer: The woman is about 5 times as dangerous)

10. Compute the cross-section length $c(y)$ for the triangle with each of these three choices of the origin and direction of the y axis·

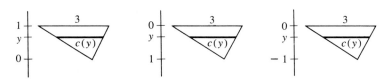

(Hint: Use similar triangles in each case. Note that a wise choice of coordinate system can simplify the cross-section function.)
[Answer: (*a*) $3y$; (*b*) $3 - 3y$; (*c*) $3 + 3y$]

11. Find the volume of the solid obtained by revolving the triangle whose vertices are $(5,0)$, $(6,1)$, $(6,-1)$ about the line $x = 2$ (*a*) by the shell method; (*b*) by Theorem 1.

12. Repeat Exercise 11 about the line $y = 2$.

13. (*a*) Guess what $c(y)$ is in this isosceles trapezoid. [Hint: What is the simplest formula that gives $c(0) = 8$ and $c(2) = 14$?]

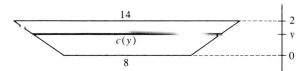

(*b*) Using similar triangles, find $c(y)$.

14. The ends of a 20-foot-long ditch are of the shape shown in Exercise 13.
    (*a*) Find the y coordinate of the centroid of an end.
    (*b*) Find the force of the water against an end.
    (*c*) Find the work done in emptying the ditch if water is pumped out over the side.
[Answer: (*a*) $\bar{y} = \frac{24}{22}$; (*b*) $(62.4)(20)$ pounds; (*c*) $(62.4)(400)$ foot-pounds]

15. Find the centroid of the region bounded by $y = \sin x$ and the x axis and situated between $x = 0$ and $x = \pi$. (Hint: Use Theorem 1.)   (Answer: $\bar{x} = \pi/2$, $\bar{y} = \pi/8$)

16. A water tower has a storage tank in the form of a right circular cone pointed downward. The cone has a radius of 3 feet and an altitude of 8 feet. Its vertex is 20 feet above the ground. How much work is required to fill the tank if water is pumped from ground level directly up to a pipe leading to the vertex of the tank?
    (*a*) Draw a typical horizontal slab of water.
    (*b*) Where will you put the origin of a vertical coordinate axis?
    (*c*) About how much work is required to lift the typical slab of water?
    (*d*) What definite integral is equal to the total work required to fill the tank?
    (*e*) Compute it.
    (*f*) How much work would be required if the intake pipe were at the top of the cone?
[Answer: (*e*) $(62.4)(624\pi)$ foot-pounds; (*f*) $(62.4)(672\pi)$ foot-pounds]

17. Find the force of the water against this rectangle inclined at an angle of 30° to the vertical and whose top base lies on the water surface:

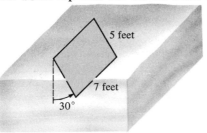

5 feet

7 feet

30°

The uppermost corner of the rectangle touches the surface of the water

Use a definite integral (*a*) in which the interval of integration is vertical; (*b*) in which the interval of integration is inclined at 30° to the vertical; (*c*) in which the interval of integration is horizontal. In each case draw a neat picture that shows the interval [*a*,*b*] of integration, and campute the integrand carefully.

[Answer: $175\sqrt{3}\,(62.4)/4$ pounds]

18. (*a*) Do you think Theorem 3 is true if the surfacc is horizontal rather than vertical? (*b*) Prove that Theorem 3 is true for a flat surface inclined at an angle of $\pi/4\,(=45°)$.

□ □ □

19. Let *R* be the region bounded by the graph of the positive function $y = f(x)$, $x = a$, $x = b$, and $y = 0$. Prove that the moment of *R* about the *x* axis is $\frac{1}{2}\int_a^b [f(x)]^2\,dx$.

20. (See Exercise 19.) Devise a region whose moment about the *y* axis can be computed with the aid of the fundamental theorem of calculus, but whose moment about the *x* axis cannot.

21. Prove that Theorem 3 holds for any submerged flat surface, vertical or not.

22. Repeat Example 2, except that the liquid in the tank is *not* homogeneous; assume that it has a density $50D$ pounds per cubic foot at a depth of *D* feet in the tank. (*a*) Does Theorem 2 hold for (*a*)? (*b*) How would you generalize Theorem 2 so that it would hold for the liquids whose density depends on depth?

23. (*a*) By looking at this square, show that

$$(1 + 2 + 3 + 4)^2 = 1(1)^2 + 2(2)^2 + 3(3)^2 + 4(4)^2 = 1^3 + 2^3 + 3^3 + 4^3$$

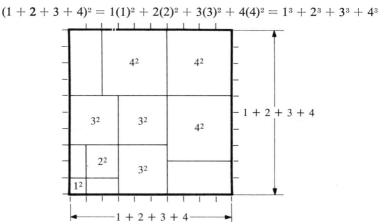

(*b*) Draw a similar diagram for $(1 + 2 + 3 + 4 + 5)^2 = 1^3 + 2^3 + 3^3 + 4^3 + 5^3$.

(*c*) Using this geometric approach, prove that $\left(\sum_{k=1}^{n} k \right)^2 = \sum_{k=1}^{n} k^3$.

(*d*) Prove that $\left(\sum_{k=1}^{n} k \right)^{2w} = \left(\sum_{k=1}^{n} k^3 \right)^{w}$.

24. (*a*) Using an appropriate definite integral, prove that

$$\lim_{n \to \infty} \frac{\sum_{k=1}^{n} k^r}{n^{r+1}} = \frac{1}{r + 1}$$

for any positive integer *r*.

(*b*) With (*a*) in mind, prove that the only identities of the type

$$\left(\sum_{k=1}^{n} k^r \right)^s = \left(\sum_{k=1}^{n} k^t \right)^u$$

valid for all *n* and for fixed positive integers *r*, *s*, *t*, *u* are either the cases given in Exercise 23(*c*) and (*d*) or the obvious case $r = t$, $s = u$. Sketch of a solution:

(1) Prove that $(r + 1)s = (t + 1)u$ and $(r + 1)^s = (t + 1)^u$.

(2) Let $R = r + 1$ and $T = t + 1$ and assume $u > s$. Prove that $u^s = T^{u-s} s^s$.

(3) Prove that *s* divides *u*.

(4) Let $u = ks$; then *k* is an integer $\geqslant 2$. Prove that $k = T^{k-1}$.

(5) Show that if *T* and *k* are integers such that $k \geqslant 2$ and $k = T^{k-1}$, then $k = 2$, $T = 2$.

(6) From (5) deduce the assertion made at the beginning of (*b*).

25. Show that the centroid of any triangle is located at the intersection of its three medians.

4. Arc length.

If we throw a ball horizontally with a speed of 32 feet per second, it falls in a curved path. If we neglect air resistance, its position *t* seconds later is given by

$$x = 32t \qquad y = -16t^2$$

relative to this coordinate system:

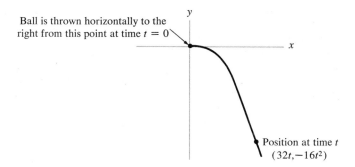

Ball is thrown horizontally to the right from this point at time $t = 0$

Position at time *t*
$(32t, -16t^2)$

Here the curve is completely described, not by expressing y as a function of x, but by expressing both x and y as functions of a third variable t. The third variable is called a *parameter* (para = together, meter = measure). And the equations $x = 32t$, $y = -16t^2$ are called *parametric equations* for the curve.

In this example it is easy to eliminate t and so find a direct relation between x and y:

$$t = \frac{x}{32} \qquad \text{hence } y = -16\left(\frac{x}{32}\right)^2 = -\frac{16}{(32)^2}x^2 = -\frac{1}{64}x^2$$

The path of the falling ball is part of the curve $y = -\frac{1}{64}x^2$.

In this section we shall develop means of computing the speed of the ball and the distance it travels. Before doing this, let us give an example of parametric equations in which the parameter is not time.

Example 1. As a bicycle wheel of radius a rolls along, a tack stuck in its circumference traces out a curve called the cycloid, which consists of a sequence of arches, one arch for each revolution of the wheel.

We find the position of the tack as a function of the angle θ through which the wheel turns.

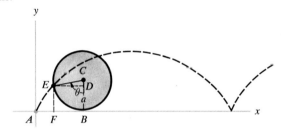

The rolling wheel has radius a

Note that because the wheel doesn't slip, arc $ED = AB$, thus $AB = a\theta$

When $\theta = 0$, the tack is on the ground at $x = 0$, $y = 0$

The x coordinate of the tack, corresponding to θ, is

$$AF = AB - ED = a\theta - a\sin\theta$$

and the y coordinate is

$$EF = BC - CD = a - a\cos\theta$$

Thus the position of the tack, as a function of the parameter θ, is

$$x = a\theta - a\sin\theta$$
$$y = a - a\cos\theta$$

In this case, eliminating θ would lead to a complicated relation between x and y.

In the following theorems we shall call the parameter t and think of it as time, but the results will apply to any parameter, such as the geometric θ in Example 1.

THEOREM 1. *If a moving particle is at the point* $(x,y) = (g(t), h(t))$ *at time* t, *then the length of its path from time* $t = a$ *to time* $t = b$ *is equal to*

$$\int_a^b \sqrt{[g'(t)]^2 + [h'(t)]^2}\, dt$$

(We assume that g and h have continuous derivatives.)

SKETCH OF PROOF. We shall argue for the plausibility of Theorem 1. A complete proof depends on a property of continuous functions which we do not have the space to develop.

We partition the time interval $[a,b]$ and use this partition to inscribe a polygon in the curve of the moving particle.

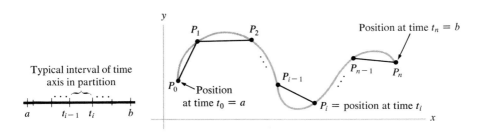

The length of such a polygon approaches the arc length, as the mesh of the partition of $[a,b]$ shrinks toward 0. (See Appendix E.) The length of the typical straight-line segment $P_{i-1}P_i$ is

$$\sqrt{[g(t_i) - g(t_{i-1})]^2 + [h(t_i) - h(t_{i-1})]^2}$$

the length of the polygon is the sum

$$(1) \qquad \sum_{i=1}^{n} \sqrt{[g(t_i) - g(t_{i-1})]^2 + [h(t_i) - h(t_{i-1})]^2}$$

We shall relate this sum to sums of the type appearing in the definition of a definite integral over $[a,b]$.

By the law of the mean, there exist T_i^* and T_i^{**}, both in the interval $[t_{i-1}, t_i]$, such that

$$g(t_i) - g(t_{i-1}) = g'(T_i^*)(t_i - t_{i-1}) \qquad \text{and} \qquad h(t_i) - h(t_{i-1}) = h'(T_i^{**})(t_i - t_{i-1})$$

Thus the sum (1) can be rewritten as

$$(2) \qquad \sum_{i=1}^{n} \sqrt{[g'(T_i^*)]^2 + [h'(T_i^{**})]^2}\,(t_i - t_{i-1})$$

If T_i^{**} were T_i^*, then this sum (2) would be an approximating sum used in defining

$$\int_a^b \sqrt{[g'(t)]^2 + [h'(t)]^2}\,dt$$

We get around this difficulty by noticing that since h' is continuous, $h'(T_i^*)$ is probably near $h'(T_i^{**})$ when the mesh of the partition of $[a,b]$ is small. We would expect that if the sum in (2) were a good approximation to the arc length, then so would be the sum

$$(3) \qquad \sum_{i=1}^{n} \sqrt{[g'(T_i^*)]^2 + [h'(T_i^*)]^2}\,(t_i - t_{i-1})$$

In other words, we would expect that

$$\lim_{\text{mesh} \to 0} \sum_{i=1}^{n} \sqrt{[g'(T_i^*)]^2 + [h'(T_i^*)]^2}\, (t_i - t_{i-1}) = \text{arc length}$$

But that limit is precisely the definition of the definite integral

$$\int_a^b \sqrt{[g'(t)]^2 + [h'(t)]^2}\, dt$$

This shows why the definite integral yields arc length, and ends the sketch of the proof.

Example 2. We find the distance s which the ball described at the beginning of the section travels during the first b seconds. Here $x = 32t$ and $y = -16t^2$. Thus $g'(t) = 32$ and $h'(t) = -32t$. We have

$$s = \int_0^b \sqrt{(32)^2 + (-32t)^2}\, dt = 32 \int_0^b \sqrt{1 + t^2}\, dt$$

a definite integral that can be evaluated with the aid of Example 6 (page 174) or a table of integrals; its value is $16\, b \sqrt{1 + b^2} + 16 \ln (b + \sqrt{1 + b^2})$.

Example 3. We find the length of one arch of the cycloid in Example 1. Here the parameter is θ, and we compute $dx/d\theta$ and $dy/d\theta$. We have

$$\frac{dx}{d\theta} = \frac{d(a\theta - a \sin \theta)}{d\theta} = a - a \cos \theta \quad \text{and} \quad \frac{dy}{d\theta} = \frac{d(a - a \cos \theta)}{d\theta} = a \sin \theta$$

To complete one arch, θ varies from 0 to 2π. By Theorem 1, the length of one arch is $\int_0^{2\pi} \sqrt{(a - a \cos \theta)^2 + (a \sin \theta)^2}\, d\theta$. Now we evaluate this definite integral, first factoring out a:

$$\text{Length of arc} = a \int_0^{2\pi} \sqrt{(1 - \cos \theta)^2 + (\sin \theta)^2}\, d\theta$$

$$= a \int_0^{2\pi} \sqrt{1 - 2 \cos \theta + (\cos^2 \theta + \sin^2 \theta)}\, d\theta$$

$$= a \int_0^{2\pi} \sqrt{2 - 2 \cos \theta}\, d\theta$$

$$= a \sqrt{2} \int_0^{2\pi} \sqrt{1 - \cos \theta}\, d\theta \underset{\text{trig}}{=} a \sqrt{2} \int_0^{2\pi} \sqrt{2} \sin \frac{\theta}{2}\, d\theta$$

$$= 2a \int_0^{2\pi} \sin \frac{\theta}{2}\, d\theta \underset{\text{FTC}}{=} 2a \left(-2 \cos \frac{\theta}{2} \right) \Big|_0^{2\pi}$$

$$= 2a\, [-2(-1) - (-2)(1)] = 8a$$

While the bicycle travels a distance $2\pi a = 6.28a$, the tack travels $8a$.

Theorem 1 also enables us to compute how fast a particle travels along a curved path. Let us consider a particle which at time t is at the point $(x,y) = (g(t), h(t))$. Pick a point B on the curve from which we will measure distance along the curve.

(We assume that the curve has an arc length.) Let $s(t)$ denote the distance from B to $(g(t), h(t))$. *If ds/dt exists, we call it the velocity of the particle.* The velocity, denoted v, can be positive or negative. *We define speed as the absolute value of velocity,* $|v|$; speed is always nonnegative.

THEOREM 2. *If a particle at time t is at the point $(x,y) = (g(t), h(t))$, where g and h are functions having continuous derivatives, then its speed at time t is equal to*

$$\sqrt{[g'(t)]^2 + [h'(t)]^2}$$

PROOF. Let $s(T)$ denote the arc length along the curve from some base point B to the particle at time T. (We use T rather than t because in a moment we will need t for another purpose.) Let us assume that $B = (g(a), h(a))$ is so chosen that the particle is moving away from B; that is, ds/dT is positive.

By Theorem 1, we have $s(T) = \int_a^T \sqrt{[g'(t)]^2 + [h'(t)]^2}\, dt$. Differentiating this relation with respect to T and using Theorem 3, page 146, we have

$$\frac{ds}{dT} = \sqrt{[g'(T)]^2 + [h'(T)]^2}$$

If B were chosen in such a way that $s(T)$ would decrease as T increased, then we would have $ds/dT = -\sqrt{[g'(T)]^2 + [h'(T)]^2}$. In either case, since speed is non-negative, the conclusion of the theorem holds.

Example 4. The speed at time t of the ball described at the beginning of the section is $\sqrt{(32)^2 + (32t)^2} = 32\sqrt{1 + t^2}$.

MEMORY AID. Theorem 2 provides a simple device for recalling the formula for arc length. From Theorem 2 it follows that $(ds/dt)^2 = (dx/dt)^2 + (dy/dt)^2$; or in the notation of differentials, after multiplying both sides by $(dt)^2$, we have $(ds)^2 = (dx)^2 + (dy)^2$. A right triangle helps us to remember this relation:

Example 5. We set up two different definite integrals for the length of curve $y = x^{2/3}$ from $x = 1$ to $x = 8$.

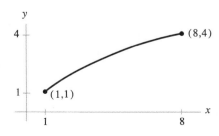

We can take x itself as a parameter, for the point (x,y) is dependent on x. To emphasize this, let us write

$$x = t \qquad y = t^{2/3}$$

We shall measure arc length from the base point $B = (1,1)$, hence ds/dt is positive. Rather than look back to Theorem 1, let us use our memory aid,

$$(ds)^2 = (dx)^2 + (dy)^2$$

Since our parameter is $t = x$, let us divide by $(dt)^2$ to obtain

$$\left(\frac{ds}{dt}\right)^2 = 1 + \left(\frac{dy}{dt}\right)^2$$

and so, since ds/dt is positive and $dt = dx$,

$$\frac{ds}{dx} = \sqrt{\left(\frac{dx}{dt}\right)^2 + \left(\frac{dy}{dt}\right)^2} = \sqrt{1 + \left(\frac{dy}{dx}\right)^2}$$

By the fundamental theorem of calculus, we then have

$$\text{Arc length} = s(8) - s(1) = \int_1^8 \sqrt{1 + (dy/dx)^2}\, dx$$

Now, $dy/dx = \frac{2}{3} x^{-1/3}$. Thus

$$\text{Arc length} = \int_1^8 \sqrt{1 + (\tfrac{2}{3} x^{-1/3})^2}\, dx$$

We can, however, choose y as the parameter. Then, as the memory aid will show, we will have to compute

$$\int_1^4 \sqrt{1 + \left(\frac{dx}{dy}\right)^2}\, dy$$

Now, $y^3 = x^2$, so $x = y^{3/2}$. Hence $dx/dy = \frac{3}{2} y^{1/2}$, and we have the definite integral

$$\text{Arc length} = \int_1^4 \sqrt{1 + \tfrac{9}{4} y}\, dy$$

The second definite integral for the arc length is easier to compute, though neither is very difficult. We use the substitution $u = 1 + \frac{9}{4} y$, hence $du = \frac{9}{4}\, dy$, and $dy = \frac{4}{9}\, du$. Thus

$$\int_1^4 \sqrt{1 + (\tfrac{9}{4}) y}\, dy = \int_{13/4}^{10} \sqrt{u}\,(\tfrac{4}{9})\, du \underset{\text{FTC}}{=} \tfrac{8}{27} u^{3/2}\Big|_{13/4}^{10} = \tfrac{8}{27}\,[10^{3/2} - (\tfrac{13}{4})^{3/2}]$$

THEOREM 3: *Arc length in polar coordinates.* If a particle moves on the curve $r = f(\theta)$, with $\alpha \leqslant \theta \leqslant \beta$, then the distance it travels is $\int_\alpha^\beta \sqrt{r^2 + (r')^2}\, d\theta$, where $r' = dr/d\theta$. (We assume that r' is continuous.)

PROOF. We have $x = f(\theta) \cos \theta$ and $y = f(\theta) \sin \theta$, parametric equations to which we may apply Theorem 1. We have

$$\frac{dx}{d\theta} = f(\theta)\,(-\sin \theta) + f'(\theta)\,(\cos \theta) \qquad \frac{dy}{d\theta} = f(\theta) \cos \theta + f'(\theta) \sin \theta$$

hence

$$\left(\frac{dx}{d\theta}\right)^2 + \left(\frac{dy}{d\theta}\right)^2 = [f(\theta)]^2 \sin^2 \theta - 2f(\theta) f'(\theta) \sin \theta \cos\theta + [f'(\theta)]^2 \cos^2 \theta$$
$$+ [f(\theta)]^2 \cos^2 \theta + 2f(\theta) f'(\theta) \sin \theta \cos \theta + [f'(\theta)]^2 \sin^2 \theta$$

which the identity $\sin^2 \theta + \cos^2 \theta = 1$ simplifies to $[f(\theta)]^2 + [f'(\theta)]^2$. The theorem is proved.

MEMORY AID.   Theorem **3** of this section, together with Theorem **3** of page 146, tells us that $(ds/d\theta)^2 = r^2 + (r')^2$. Rewriting this in the differential notation, we have $(ds)^2 = [r^2 + (r')^2] (d\theta)^2$ or $(ds)^2 = (r\,d\theta)^2 + (r'\,d\theta)^2$. By definition of the differential of r, we have $dr = r'\,d\theta$. Thus we have

$$(ds)^2 = (r\,d\theta)^2 + (dr)^2$$

which is easy to remember if we keep in mind this "almost-right" triangle:

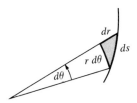

The meat of this section is in Theorem 1, from which Theorems 2 and 3 and the memory aids follow. The important points are that arc length can be expressed as a definite integral and that we can now deal with the velocity of a particle moving along a curve.

EXERCISES

1. Let $y = f(x)$, where f' is continuous. Use our method of obtaining Theorem 1, but not Theorem 1 itself, to show that the arc length of the curve $y = f(x)$ between $x = a$ and $x = b$ is $\int_a^b \sqrt{1 + (dy/dx)^2}\,dx.$

2. Find the speed of the thrown ball referred to at the beginning of this section, at times $t = 0$, $t = 1$, and $t = 2$.

3. Evaluate the definite integral in Example 5 for which the parameter is x.

4. Show that if
$$y = \frac{x^{m+1}}{m+1} + \frac{x^{1-m}}{4(m-1)}$$
where m is an integer other than 1 or -1, then the definite integral for the arc length of this curve can be computed with the aid of the fundamental theorem of calculus. Consider only arcs corresponding to x in $[a,b]$, $0 < a < b$.

5. (a) How far does a bug travel from time $t = 1$ to time $t = 2$, if at time t it is at the point (t^2, t^3)?
    (b) How fast is it moving at time t?

(c) Graph its path relative to an x,y-coordinate system. Where is it at $t = 1$? At $t = 2$?

(d) Eliminate t to find y as a function of x.   [Answer: (a) $\frac{1}{27}(40^{3/2} - 13^{3/2})$]

6. Let $P = (x,y)$ depend on θ as shown in this diagram:

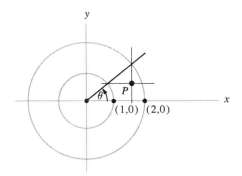

P lies in the horizontal line through $(\cos \theta, \sin \theta)$ and the vertical line through $(2 \cos \theta, 2 \sin \theta)$

(a) Sketch the curve that P sweeps out.

(b) Show that $P = (2 \cos \theta, \sin \theta)$.

(c) Set up a definite integral for the length of the curve described by P. (Do not evaluate it.)

(d) Eliminate θ and show that P is on the curve

$$\frac{x^2}{4} + \frac{y^2}{1} = 1$$

7. At time t a particle is at $P = (\cos t + t \sin t, \sin t - t \cos t)$. Find the distance it travels from time $t = 1$ to time $t = \pi$.   [Answer: $(\pi^2 - 1)/2$]

8. (a) Graph the spiral given in polar coordinates by $r = e^{\theta}$.

(b) Find the length of one turn, from $\theta = 0$ to $\theta = 2\pi$.

(c) Find the length of the turn $\theta = 2\pi$ to $\theta = 4\pi$.

     [Answer: (b) $\sqrt{2}(e^{2\pi} - 1)$; (c) $\sqrt{2}(e^{4\pi} - e^{2\pi})$]

9. (a) Graph the cardioid $r = 1 - \cos \theta$.

(b) Find its perimeter.   [Answer: (b) 8]

10. (a) At time t a bug is at $(\cos^3 t, \sin^3 t)$. Graph its path for time $t = 0$ to time $t = \pi/2$.

(b) How far did it travel in that interval?

(c) Show that it was traveling along the curve $x^{2/3} + y^{2/3} = 1$.

     [Answer: (b) $\frac{3}{2}$]

11. (a) Graph $y = x^3/3$.

(b) Estimate its arc length from $(0,0)$ to $(3,9)$ by an inscribed polygon whose vertices have x coordinates 0, 1, 2, 3. A table of square roots will be useful.

(c) Set up a definite integral for the arc length in question.

(d) Estimate the definite integral in (c) by using a partition of $[0,3]$ into three segments, each of length one, and as sampling X_i, the right end points.

(e) Proceed as in (d), but use left end points.

(f) Do you think that the fundamental theorem of calculus is of use in evaluating the definite integral in (c)?

     [Answer: (b) 10.004; (d) 14.5927; (e) 6.5373]

12. Let R be the region bounded by one arch of a cycloid and the x axis.
    (a) Without using the calculus, show that the area of R is between two and four times the area of the rolling wheel.
    (b) Show that the area of R is three times the area of the wheel. (Hint: Express $\int_0^{2\pi a} y\, dx$ in terms of θ.)

13. At time t a particle is at $r = g(t)$, $\theta = h(t)$, where (r,θ) are polar coordinates. How fast is it moving?

14. (a) Graph $y = (e^x + e^{-x})/2$.
    (b) Find the length of arc along the curve above $[0,b]$.
    (c) Set up a definite integral for the same problem, but use y as the parameter.
    [Answer: (b) $(e^b - e^{-b})/2$]

15. Why would $\left(\int_a^b y\, ds\right)$/length of arc be a reasonable definition of the y coordinate of the centroid of an arc? Use this definition to compute the y coordinate of the centroid of the semicircle $y = \sqrt{a^2 - x^2}$.
    (a) Use rectangular coordinates.
    (b) Use polar coordinates.
    (c) Explain without the calculus why $\bar{y} > a/2$.
    [Answer: (a), (b) $2a/\pi$]

□ □ □

16. (This proof is due to G. D. Chakerian, *Elem. der Math.*, vol. 20, 1965, p. 89.) Assume the isoperimetric theorem: Of all closed curves enclosing a given area, the circle is the shortest. With the aid of the following diagram, which shows four quadrants of an ellipse rearranged, prove that the perimeter of this ellipse is greater than $\pi(a + b)$ if $a > b$. (See Exercise 6.)

17. Sketch a direct proof of Theorem 3. That is, begin by inscribing a polygonal path corresponding to a partition of the θ interval $[\alpha,\beta]$, and compute its length in terms of r and θ rather than x and y.

18. Let Q and P be points on a curve. Prove that the chord length $\overline{PQ}$ is a good approximation to the arc length $\overset{\frown}{PQ}$ along the curve, if Q is near P. That is, prove that $\lim_{Q \to P} (\overset{\frown}{PQ}/\overline{PQ}) = 1$. What assumptions do you use about the curve?

19. (a) Draw the curve defined by $y = \sin(1/x)$ if $x \neq 0$, and $y = 0$, if $x = 0$.
    (b) Show that a snail moving along this curve from $(1, \sin 1)$ to $(0,0)$ must travel an infinite distance.

5. *Area of a surface of revolution*. We now develop a technique for computing the surface area of a solid of revolution, such as a sphere. As Appendix E shows, the definition of the area of a surface is much more complicated than that for the length of arc or the area of a region in the plane. For this reason our approach will be intuitive, and we will only justify defining the area of a surface of revolution as a certain definite integral.

Let us begin by considering the lateral area of a rather simple surface of revolution, a cone whose base has radius r and whose slant height is l. If we cut this cone along a lateral edge and lay it flat, it becomes a sector of a circle of radius l.

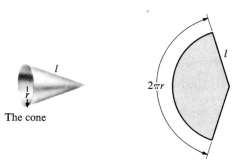

The cone

The cone laid flat is the sector of a circle

Now, the area of a sector of radius l and angle θ (in radians) is $(\pi l^2)(\theta/2\pi) = (\frac{1}{2})l^2\theta$. In our case $\theta = (2\pi r)/l$. For this reason we define the lateral surface area of a cone as $\pi r l$. To remember this definition, keep in mind that the area of a sector is

$$\underbrace{\frac{1}{2}(2\pi r)}_{\text{``base''}} \quad \underbrace{(l)}_{\text{``height''}} \ = \pi r l$$

Next, how shall we define the area of the surface formed when a line segment of length L is rotated about an axis a distance r from its midpoint? This surface is a band, which we may consider as the difference of two cones. (See the diagram below.) We therefore define its area as the difference of the areas of the two cones whose dimensions are shown in this diagram:

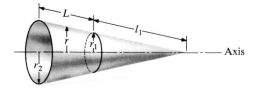

The inner cone has area $\pi r_1 l_1$, and the larger cone has area $\pi r_2(l_1 + L)$

The area of the band is therefore

$$\pi r_2(l_1 + L) - \pi r_1 l_1 = \pi(r_2 l_1 - r_1 l_1 + r_2 L)$$

By similar triangles,

$$\frac{L + l_1}{r_2} = \frac{l_1}{r_1}$$

Therefore, we have

$$r_1 L + r_1 l_1 = r_2 l_1 \qquad \text{or} \qquad r_2 l_1 - r_1 l_1 = r_1 L$$

Thus the area of the band is

$$\pi(r_1 L + r_2 L) = \pi(r_1 + r_2)L = 2\pi \frac{r_1 + r_2}{2} L = 2\pi r L$$

where $r = (r_1 + r_2)/2$. To remember this formula $2\pi r L$, keep in mind a rectangle of length $2\pi r$ and width L.

We have defined the area of a surface formed by revolving a line segment. We use it to justify the definition of the area swept out when we revolve a curve. We give the definition first and its justification afterward.

DEFINITION: *Area of a surface of revolution.*   Consider a curve that has the parametric equations $x = g(t)$, $y = h(t)$, where g and h have continuous derivatives and $h(t) \geqslant 0$. Let C be that portion of the curve corresponding to t in $[a,b]$. Then the area of the surface of revolution formed by revolving C about the x axis is

$$\int_a^b 2\pi h(t) \sqrt{[g'(t)]^2 + [h'(t)]^2}\, dt$$

To show that this is a reasonable definition, we begin by partitioning the interval $[a,b]$ in the t axis, and consider a typical interval $[t_{i-1}, t_i]$. We would expect the surface area of the solid of revolution corresponding to this "small" interval on the t axis to be approximated by the area of the band:

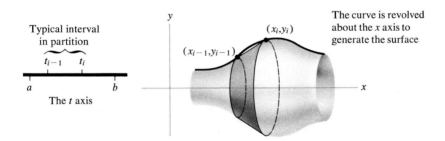

The approximating band swept out by rotating the straight-line segment from (x_{i-1}, y_{i-1}) to (x_i, y_i) has area

$$2\pi \frac{y_{i-1} + y_i}{2} \sqrt{(x_i - x_{i-1})^2 + (y_i - y_{i-1})^2}$$

which should be a good "local approximation" to the area of the curved surface.

This is *not* the typical summand of the type leading to a definite integral over the t axis from a to b, since in particular, no $t_i - t_{i-1}$ appears. But we do the same thing that we did for arc length.

By the law of the mean,

$$x_i - x_{i-1} = g'(T_i^*)(t_i - t_{i-1}) \qquad \text{and} \qquad y_i - y_{i-1} = h'(T_i^{**})(t_i - t_{i-1})$$

and by the intermediate value theorem,

$$\frac{y_{i-1} + y_i}{2} = h(T_i^{***})$$

where $T_i^*, T_i^{**}, T_i^{***}$ are all in $[t_{i-1}, t_i]$. So we now expect

$$2\pi h(T_i^{***}) \sqrt{[g'(T_i^*)]^2 + [h'(T_i^{**})]^2}\,(t_i - t_{i-1})$$

to be a good local approximation.

Since h and h' are continuous, we would also expect $h(T_i^{***})$ to be near $h(T_i^*)$, and $h'(T_i^{**})$ to be near $h'(T_i^*)$, when the mesh of the partition of $[a,b]$ is small. We shall therefore *define the surface area as*

$$\lim_{\text{mesh}\to 0} \sum_{i=1}^{n} 2\pi h(T_i^*) \sqrt{[g'(T_i^*)]^2 + [h'(T_i^*)]^2}\,(t_i - t_{i-1})$$

that is, $$\text{Surface area} = \int_a^b 2\pi h(t) \sqrt{[g'(t)]^2 + [h'(t)]^2}\,dt$$

This shows why we defined the area of a surface of revolution as we did.

If a curve is given as $y = f(x)$, where f has a continuous derivative and $f(x) \geqslant 0$, we may parametrize it by the equations $x = t$ and $y = f(t)$. Hence the surface area swept out by rotating about the x axis that part of the curve above $[a,b]$ is

$$\text{Surface area} = \int_a^b 2\pi y \sqrt{1 + \left(\frac{dy}{dx}\right)^2}\,dx$$

MEMORY AID.   Observe that the definition asserts that surface area is $\int_a^b 2\pi y\,ds$, where $[a,b]$ is the interval of the parameter. The expression $2\pi y\,ds$ should call to mind the area of a band. We have considered only revolution around the x axis, but if we revolve a curve about some other line and let r denote the distance from a typical point on the curve to that line, the surface area will be defined as $\int_a^b 2\pi r\,ds$. For instance, in the case of revolution about the y axis, we have the definition

$$\int_a^b 2\pi x\,ds = \text{surface area}.$$

Example 1.   We compute the surface area of a sphere of radius a. In this case we shall rotate a semicircle of radius a about the x axis. The typical point on this semicircle is given by

$$x = a \cos \theta \qquad y = a \sin \theta$$

where our parameter θ is the angle shown here:

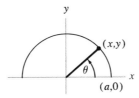

We use the definition of surface area with θ playing the role of t. Since

$$\frac{dx}{d\theta} = -a \sin \theta \qquad \text{and} \qquad \frac{dy}{d\theta} = a \cos \theta$$

we have

$$\text{Surface area} = \int_0^\pi 2\pi(a \sin \theta) \sqrt{(-a \sin \theta)^2 + (a \cos \theta)^2}\, d\theta$$

$$= \int_0^\pi 2\pi a \sin \theta \sqrt{a^2(\sin^2 \theta + \cos^2 \theta)}\, d\theta$$

$$= 2\pi a^2 \int_0^\pi \sin \theta\, d\theta \underset{\text{FTC}}{=} [2\pi a^2(-\cos \theta)] \Big|_0^\pi$$

$$= 2\pi a^2 [-(-1) - (-1)] = 4\pi a^2$$

Thus the surface area of a sphere is four times that of its equatorial cross section.

Example 2. We find the surface area of a sphere of radius a, enclosed between two parallel planes. For convenience, we take the two planes perpendicular to the x axis and passing through $(d_1,0)$ and $(d_2,0)$. We assume that the revolved semicircle has its center at $(0,0)$ and has the equation $y = \sqrt{a^2 - x^2}$. The surface area of the sphere between the two planes is

$$\int_{d_1}^{d_2} 2\pi y \sqrt{1 + \left(\frac{dy}{dx}\right)^2}\, dx$$

Now, $y = \sqrt{a^2 - x^2}$ and $dy/dx = -x/\sqrt{a^2 - x^2}$. Thus

$$\sqrt{1 + \left(\frac{dy}{dx}\right)^2} = \sqrt{1 + \left(\frac{-x}{\sqrt{a^2 - x^2}}\right)^2} = \sqrt{1 + \frac{x^2}{a^2 - x^2}}$$

$$= \sqrt{\frac{(a^2 - x^2) + x^2}{a^2 - x^2}} = \frac{a}{\sqrt{a^2 - x^2}}$$

Our definite integral reduces to

$$\int_{d_1}^{d_2} 2\pi \sqrt{a^2 - x^2}\, \frac{a}{\sqrt{a^2 - x^2}}\, dx = \int_{d_1}^{d_2} 2\pi a\, dx = 2\pi a \int_{d_1}^{d_2} 1\, dx = 2\pi a(d_2 - d_1)$$

We obtain these interesting results: (1) the surface area in question depends only on the distance between the two planes—not on their location; (2) the surface area is proportional to the distance between the two planes.

Example 3.   We find the surface area of the headlight formed by rotating about the *x* axis the part of the curve $y = \sqrt{x}$ that lies to the left of the line $x = 6$ and to the right of the line $x = 1$.

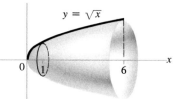

Though we could use the formula $\int_a^b 2\pi y \sqrt{1 + (dy/dx)^2}\, dx$ directly, we will show how the memory aid helps us to recover this formula. If we consider a line segment of length ds, whose midpoint has ordinate y, and rotate it about the x axis, we get a band of area $2\pi y\, ds$. This should remind us of the formula: surface area $= \int_a^b 2\pi y\, ds.$

In our case, where $y = \sqrt{x}$, we have $dy/dx = 1/(2\sqrt{x})$. Thus $ds = \sqrt{1 + [1/(2\sqrt{x})]^2}\, dx$, which simplifies to $\sqrt{1 + (1/4x)}\, dx$. Our definite integral is

$$\int_1^6 2\pi\sqrt{x}\sqrt{1 + \frac{1}{4x}}\, dx$$

or simply,

$$\int_1^6 \pi\sqrt{4x + 1}\, dx$$

Now, the substitution $u = 4x + 1$, hence $du = 4\, dx$ and $dx = (\tfrac{1}{4})\, du$, transforms $\int_1^6 \sqrt{4x + 1}\, dx$ into $\int_5^{25} \pi\sqrt{u}(\tfrac{1}{4})\, du$, which we evaluate by the fundamental theorem of calculus:

$$\int_5^{25} \frac{\pi}{4}\sqrt{u}\, du = \left(\frac{\pi}{4} \cdot \tfrac{2}{3} u^{3/2}\right)\Big|_5^{25} = \frac{\pi}{6}(25^{3/2} - 5^{3/2}) = \frac{\pi}{6}(125 - \sqrt{125})$$

EXERCISES

1. Check that our definition of surface area as a definite integral agrees with our definition of the area of a cone.
2. Show how the polar angle θ could have been used instead of x in Example 2.
3. Check that Example 2 gives the formula $4\pi r^2$ for the surface area of a sphere of radius r.
4. Consider the smallest tin can that contains a given sphere. (The height and diameter of the tin can equal the diameter of the sphere.)
   (*a*) Compare the volume of the sphere to the volume of the tin can. Archimedes, who obtained the solution some 2,200 years ago, considered it his greatest accomplishment. Cicero wrote, some two centuries after Archimedes' death, "I shall call up from the dust [the ancient equivalent of a blackboard] and his measuring-rod an obscure, insignificant person belonging to the same city [Syracuse], who lived many years after, Archimedes. When I was quaestor I tracked out his grave, which

was unknown to the Syracusans (as they totally denied its existence), and found it enclosed all round and covered with brambles and thickets; for I remembered certain doggerel lines inscribed, as I had heard, upon his tomb, which stated that a sphere along with a cylinder had been set up on the top of his grave. Accordingly, after taking a good look all round (for there are a great quantity of graves at the Agrigentine Gate), I noticed a small column rising a little above the bushes, on which there was the figure of a sphere and a cylinder. And so I at once said to the Syracusans (I had their leading men with me) that I believed it was the very thing of which I was in search. Slaves were sent in with sickles who cleared the ground of obstacles, and when a passage to the place was opened we approached the pedestal fronting us; the epigram was traceable with about half the lines legible, as the latter portion was worn away." Archimedes was killed by a Roman soldier in 212 B.C. Cicero was quaestor in 75 B.C. (Cicero, "Tusculan Disputations," v, 23, translated by J. E. King, Loeb Classical Library, Harvard, Cambridge, Mass., 1950.

(*b*) Compare the surface area of the sphere to the area of the curved side of the can.

5. We developed our formulas for rotation relative to the x axis.

(*a*) What would be the corresponding formula for rotation about the y axis?

(*b*) Apply it to the case in which the curve $x = \sqrt[3]{y}$ between $(1,1)$ and $(2,8)$ is rotated about the y axis.

6. What would the surface area be if the curve in Example 3 were rotated about the line $y = -1$, instead of the x axis?

(*a*) Explain, with the aid of a picture, how you would have to change the memory device $2\pi y \, ds$.

(*b*) Set up the appropriate definite integral.

(*c*) Compute it with the aid of a table of integrals.

7. Find the surface area if the curve in Example 3 is rotated about the y axis.

(*a*) Draw a clear picture showing how you obtained the integrand and limits of integration.

(*b*) Set up the definite integral.

(*c*) Compute it with the aid of a table of integrals.

8. Two planes are perpendicular to the axis of the tin can in Exercise 4. Compare the area they intercept on the sphere and on the tin can. What does the comparison tell mapmakers?

9. If the band formed by revolving a line segment is cut along the rotated segment and laid out in the plane, what shape will it be? (Hint: It is *not* a rectangle.) With this approach, compute its area.

10. Find the area of the surface obtained by rotating about the x axis that part of the curve $y = e^x$ that lies above $[0,1]$.
$$\text{(Answer: } \pi[e\sqrt{1+e^2} - \sqrt{2} + \ln(e + \sqrt{1+e^2}) - \ln(1 + \sqrt{2})])$$

11. Find the area of the surface formed by rotating an arch of the curve $y = \sin x$ about the x axis. $\qquad$ (Answer: $2\pi[\sqrt{2} + \ln(\sqrt{2} + 1)])$

12. Find the area of the surface obtained when the cardioid $r = 1 + \cos\theta$ is rotated about the polar axis. $\qquad$ (Answer: $32\pi/5$)

13. Though the fundamental theorem of calculus is of no use to us in computing the perimeter of the ellipse $\dfrac{x^2}{a^2} + \dfrac{y^2}{b^2} = 1$, it is useful in computing the area of the "football" formed when the ellipse is rotated about one of its axes. Find that area. Does your answer give the correct formula for the area of a sphere of radius a, $4\pi a^2$?

14. Prove the following analog of Theorem 1, page 197.

    Theorem. The area of the surface of revolution obtained by revolving about a line a curve situated on one side of the line is equal to (length of curve) times (distance centroid of curve is resolved). Centroid of a curve is defined in Exercise 15, page 211.

15. Using the theorem stated in Exercise 14, compute the surface area of a torus.

16. Using the theorem stated in Exercise 14, compute the lateral surface area of a cone.

17. Using the theorem stated in Exercise 14, find the centroid of a semicircular arc.

18. If $y = f(x)$ is an increasing positive function of x, and $b > a > 0$, $f(a) = A$, $f(b) = B$, interpret geometrically $\displaystyle\int_A^B 2\pi y \sqrt{1 + \left(\frac{dx}{dy}\right)^2}\, dy$, $\displaystyle\int_A^B 2\pi x \sqrt{1 + \left(\frac{dx}{dy}\right)^2}\, dy$,

    $\displaystyle\int_a^b 2\pi y \sqrt{1 + \left(\frac{dy}{dx}\right)^2}\, dx$, and $\displaystyle\int_a^b 2\pi x \sqrt{1 + \left(\frac{dy}{dx}\right)^2}\, dx$.

19. A certain arc of length A is situated above the x axis. When revolved about the x axis, it sweeps out a surface area S. What is the surface area when the curve is rotated around the line $y = -3$?

20. A disk of radius a is covered by a finite number of strips (perhaps overlapping). Prove that the sum of their widths is at least $2a$. (If the strips are parallel, the assertion is clearly true; do not assume that the strips are parallel.)

21. As we saw in Example 2, the surface area of the sphere between two parallel planes depends only on the distance between the two planes, and is proportional to that distance. Prove that the sphere is the only surface of revolution, other than a cylinder, with that property. Specifically, prove that if f is a function such that $y = f(x)$ is positive, dy/dx is continuous, and

    $$\int_a^b 2\pi y \sqrt{1 + \left(\frac{dy}{dx}\right)^2}\, dx = k(b - a)$$

    for a fixed constant k, then the graph of f is part of a circle or a horizontal straight line.

22. We have assumed that such concepts as length, area, and volume have been defined. Of these, surface area is the most difficult. To see why, read the remarks in Appendix E on surface area. In your own words and diagrams, describe the difficulty.

The first five sections of this chapter, devoted to area, volume, the first moment, arc length, and surface area, are primarily geometric. The remaining sections present the definite integral in more varied circumstances. For instance, improper integrals (Sec. 8) are used to determine the present value of future income (Chap. 22), the delay at an intersection (Chap. 24), and the work done in launching a payload to outer space (Chap. 25).

6. The higher moments of a function. We have seen in Sec. 3 that the first moment of the cross-section function is related to volume, work, force, and centroid. We now define all the moments of a function and indicate some of their uses.

DEFINITION: *Moments of a function.* Let n be a nonnegative integer, k some real number, and f a continuous function defined on $[a,b]$. The nth moment of f about k (over $[a,b]$) is $M_n = \int_a^b (x - k)^n f(x)\, dx.$

For $n = 1$ we obtain the first moment of f. For $n = 0$ we obtain the zeroth moment, $M_0 = \int_a^b (x - k)^0 f(x)\, dx$, which is simply $\int_a^b f(x)\, dx$. In particular, if f is the cross-section function of a plane region, then M_0 equals the area of that region. Thus the x coordinate of the centroid of the region can be expressed as M_1/M_0. If f records the density of material in a (perhaps nonhomogeneous) string, then M_0 is the mass of the string. The centroid of the string is defined as M_1/M_0. As we will indicate below, the second moment of the density function is also of physical importance. It should be pointed out that the first four moments are frequently used in statistics. In engineering and physics, where M_0, M_1, and M_2 are used, M_n is called the "nth moment about the line $x = k$."

Example 1. We compute the first three moments of the function $f(x) = e^{-x}$ over $[0,b]$. Using Example 1, page 163, and Example 2, page 164, we have

$$M_0 = \int_0^b e^{-x}\, dx \underset{\text{FTC}}{=} -e^{-x} \Big|_0^b = -e^{-b} - (-e^{-0}) = 1 - e^{-b}$$

$$M_1 = \int_0^b xe^{-x}\, dx \underset{\text{FTC}}{=} (-e^{-x} - xe^{-x}) \Big|_0^b = e^{-x}(-1 - x) \Big|_0^b = 1 - e^{-b}(1 + b)$$

$$M_2 = \int_0^b x^2 e^{-x}\, dx \underset{\text{FTC}}{=} e^{-x}(-x^2 - 2x - 2) \Big|_0^b = 2 - e^{-b}(b^2 + 2b + 2)$$

These results will be needed in our study of traffic in Chap. 24.

Example 2: M_2 and the kinetic energy of a spinning stick. The kinetic energy of an object of mass m all of whose parts are moving with velocity v is defined as $(\tfrac{1}{2})mv^2$. This represents the work required to bring it from a state of rest to that velocity.

How shall we define the kinetic energy of a stick spinning 100 times per second about an end? Since the velocity of its parts varies with the distance from the end, we have to resort to a definite integral. We shall assume that its density is $f(x)$ pounds per linear foot at a distance of x feet from the end around which it spins.

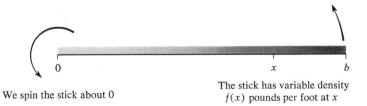

We spin the stick about 0

The stick has variable density
$f(x)$ pounds per foot at x

To arrive at a definition of the kinetic energy of the stick, we cut it into small pieces by a partition $x_0 = 0, x_1, \ldots, x_n = b$ and pick some point X_i in the ith interval.

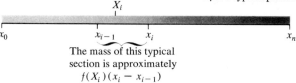

X_i is a typical point in the ith interval

The mass of this typical
section is approximately
$f(X_i)(x_i - x_{i-1})$

The point X_i sweeps out a circle of radius X_i at a rate of 100 times a second. Thus its velocity is $(100)(2\pi X_i)$ feet per second. Hence we would expect the kinetic energy of the typical section to be roughly

$$\tfrac{1}{2} f(X_i)(x_i - x_{i-1}) \quad (200\pi X_i)^2$$

$$\underbrace{\phantom{\tfrac{1}{2} f(X_i)(x_i - x_{i-1})}}_{\text{estimate of its mass}} \quad \underbrace{}_{\substack{\text{square of} \\ \text{velocity of } X_i}}$$

Thus

$$\tfrac{1}{2}(200\pi)^2 \sum_{i=1}^{n} X_i^2 f(X_i)(x_i - x_{i-1})$$

should be an estimate of the kinetic energy of the whirling stick. *We therefore define the kinetic energy of the stick as*

$$\tfrac{1}{2}(200\pi)^2 \int_0^b x^2 f(x)\, dx \qquad \text{foot-pounds}$$

Note that 200π records the rate of change of angle with respect to time (200π radians per second). If we rotate the stick with the angular velocity ω instead of 200π, the kinetic energy is defined as

$$(\tfrac{1}{2})\, \omega^2 \int_0^b x^2 f(x)\, dx$$

Thus the second moment, $\int_0^b x^2 f(x)\, dx$, is important in measuring the energy of a rotating object. It is called its *moment of inertia*.

Just as M_1/M_0 has physical meaning in the case of the stick in Example 2 (it gives its balancing point or *center of gravity*), so does M_2/M_1. If we suspend the stick from its left end and start it oscillating, it will do so at a certain frequency. This frequency is the same as that of a pendulum consisting of a point mass at the end of a "weightless" string of length M_2/M_1. Moreover, if we hold the stick at its left end and use it as a bat, then we should strike the ball at a point a distance M_2/M_1 from our hands in order to avoid "sting." This point is called the *center of percussion*. As Exercise 18, page 226 shows, it is always to the right of the center of gravity.

EXERCISES

1. Compute the first three moments about 0 and over $[-1,1]$ of the function x^2.

   (Answer: $M_0 = \tfrac{2}{3}$; $M_1 = 0$; $M_2 = \tfrac{2}{5}$)

2. Compute the first three moments about $\pi/2$ and over $[0,\pi]$ of the function $\sin x$.

3. Is the kinetic energy of the stick in Example 2 the same as it would be if all its mass were placed at its balancing point? Explain.
4. A homogeneous stick 3 feet long oscillates from one end.
   (a) A pendulum of what length would oscillate at the same frequency?
   (b) If you use the stick as a bat, where should you strike the ball?
   (c) Test (a) and (b) experimentally.
                                    [Answer: (a) 2 feet; (b) 2 feet from the end]
5. Let f be a differentiable function such that $f(b) = 0$. Prove that $n + 1$ times the nth moment of f about 0 and over $[0,b]$ is equal to the negative of the $(n + 1)$st moment of f' about 0 and over $[0,b]$.
6. A flat piece of steel of mass m and covering a region R in the plane is spun around the y axis 100 times per second. The region lies between $x = a$ and $x = b$ and has cross section $c(x)$ at x, and an area A. Explain in detail why its kinetic energy should be defined as $(\frac{1}{2}) (200\pi)^2 (m/A) \int_a^b x^2 c(x)\, dx$. This is a physical application of the second moment of the cross-section function.
7. A homogeneous steel triangle of mass m has vertices $(0,0)$, $(2,0)$, $(0,3)$. Compute its kinetic energy if it is spun with an angular velocity ω about (a) the x axis; (b) the y axis. Why would you expect the answer to (b) to be smaller than the answer to (a)?
8. Compute M_0, M_1, M_2 about 0 and over $[-1,1]$ for the function $y = \sqrt{1 - x^2}$, the cross-section function of a semicircle.   (Answer: $M_0 = \pi/2$, $M_1 = 0$, $M_2 = \pi/8$)
9. Find a polynomial of degree 2 whose first three moments about 0 and over $[0,1]$ are $M_0 = 1$, $M_1 = 1$, $M_2 = 1$.
10. The moment of inertia of a rod situated on the x axis about the point $x = c$ is defined as $\int_a^b (x - c)^2 f(x)\, dx$, where f is its density function. Assume now that we place our coordinate system in such a way that the center of gravity of the rod is at $x = 0$.
    (a) Prove that the moment of inertia of the rod about c is $M_2 + c^2 m$, where M_2 is the moment of inertia about the center of gravity and m is the mass (or zeroth moment M_0 of f).
    (b) In view of (a), about which point is it easiest to spin the rod?
    By virtue of (a), the center of gravity could be defined as the "point relative to which the moment of inertia is least."
11. Find M_0 and M_1 about 0 and over $[0,b]$ for $f(x) = ce^{-cx}$.
                        [Answer: $M_0 = 1 - e^{-cb}$, $M_1 = (1/c) - be^{-cb} - (1/c)e^{-bc}$]

□ □ □

12. Let f be a continuous function defined on $[a,b]$.
    (a) Prove that if $\int_a^b f(x)\, dx = 0$, then f has at least one root in $[a,b]$.
    (b) Prove that if $\int_a^b f(x)\, dx = 0 = \int_a^b xf(x)\, dx$, then f has at least two roots in $[a,b]$.
    (c) State and prove a generalization of (a) and (b).

13. (See Exercise 12.) Prove that if f and g are polynomials such that the nth moment of f and g about 0 and over $[a,b]$ are equal for all integers $n \geqslant 0$, then $f = g$. Thus we may say that "a polynomial is known by its moments."

14. (a) Show that the tendency of the water to rotate a vertical submerged gate about an axis on the surface of the water is related to the second moment of a cross-section function. Do *not* assume that the gate is a rectangle.

(b) If the water is replaced by a fluid whose density is proportional to its depth, then what moment of the cross-section function is related to the tendency of the gate to turn?

7. Average value of a function.

In Chap. 1 we defined the average value of a function $y = f(x)$, for x in $[a,b]$, as $\int_a^b f(x)\,dx / (b - a)$. We are now in a position to compute some of these averages. We begin with two examples which, taken together, convey an important moral.

Example 1. If we travel 30 miles per hour for one hour, and then 50 miles per hour for one hour, what is the average of our velocity with respect to time?

Let us denote our velocity at time t by $f(t)$. The average velocity with respect to time is defined as

$$\frac{\int_0^2 f(t)\,dt}{2 - 0}$$

The simplest way to compute $\int_0^2 f(t)\,dt$ is to interpret it as the area of the shaded region shown in this diagram:

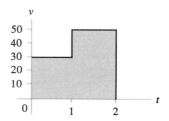

Since the shaded region has area 80, we have $\int_0^2 f(t)\,dt = 80$. Thus

$$\text{Average velocity with respect to time} = \frac{\int_0^2 f(t)\,dt}{2 - 0} = \frac{80}{2} = 40 \text{ miles per hour}$$

Example 2. If we travel 30 miles per hour for 30 miles and then 50 miles per hour for 50 miles, what is the average of our velocity with respect to distance? (Note that this is the same trip as in Example 1.)

We now consider the velocity as a function of distance. The velocity after x miles of travel we denote $g(x)$. The average with respect to distance is therefore

$$\frac{\int_0^{80} g(x)\,dx}{80 - 0}$$

To compute the definite integral we may interpret it as the area of the shaded region in this diagram:

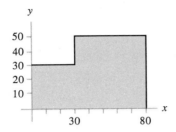

The area is $30 \cdot 30 + 50 \cdot 50 = 3{,}400$. We therefore have

$$\begin{array}{l}\text{Average velocity}\\ \text{with respect to distance}\end{array} = \frac{\int_0^{80} g(x)\,dx}{80 - 0} = \frac{3{,}400}{80} = 42.5 \text{ miles per hour}$$

The reader should pause and explain to his own satisfaction why the average with respect to distance "ought to be" larger than the average with respect to time.

The moral of these two examples is this: When we speak of the average value of a quantity, we must also indicate the variable with respect to which the average is to be computed.

Example 3. We find the average of the radius r for the cardioid $r = 1 - \cos\theta$ as a function of θ. The graph of this cardioid looks like this:

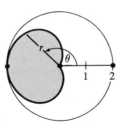

To sweep out this cardioid, θ goes from 0 to 2π. (Note that since $1 - \cos\theta \leqslant 2$, the average is less than 2.)

The average is $\int_0^{2\pi} (1 - \cos\theta)\,d\theta/(2\pi - 0)$. By the fundamental theorem of calculus,

$$\begin{array}{l}\text{Average with}\\ \text{respect to } \theta\end{array} = \frac{\int_0^{2\pi}(1 - \cos\theta)\,d\theta}{2\pi} = \frac{(\theta - \sin\theta)\Big|_0^{2\pi}}{2\pi} = \frac{2\pi}{2\pi} = 1$$

Example 4. We find the average of the radius r for the cardioid of Example 3, this time as a function of s, arc length. We are now considering r as a function of s; that is, $r = f(s)$.

We must first compute the total arc length of this cardioid in order to find the denominator in the definition of average.

$$\text{Arc length} = \int_0^{2\pi} \sqrt{r^2 + (r')^2}\, d\theta = \int_0^{2\pi} \sqrt{(1 - \cos\theta)^2 + (\sin\theta)^2}\, d\theta$$

$$= \int_0^{2\pi} \sqrt{2 - 2\cos\theta}\, d\theta = \sqrt{2} \int_0^{2\pi} \sqrt{1 - \cos\theta}\, d\theta = \sqrt{2} \int_0^{2\pi} \sqrt{2} \sin\frac{\theta}{2}\, d\theta$$

$$= 2 \int_0^{2\pi} \sin\frac{\theta}{2}\, d\theta \underset{\text{FTC}}{=} \left(-4\cos\frac{\theta}{2} \right) \Big|_0^{2\pi} = 8$$

Thus the average of r with respect to s is $\int_0^8 f(s)\, ds/(8 - 0)$. Rather than find r explicitly as a function of s, we change from the variable s to the variable θ in order to compute $\int_0^8 f(s)\, ds$. We may consider r to be a function of θ; that is, $r = g(\theta)$; substitution in the definite integral yields

$$\int_0^8 f(s)\, ds = \int_0^{2\pi} g(\theta) \left(\frac{ds}{d\theta} \right) d\theta$$

Now, $ds/d\theta = \sqrt{r^2 + (r')^2} = \sqrt{2} (\sqrt{1 - \cos\theta})$, as we saw above. Thus

$$\int_0^{2\pi} g(\theta) \frac{ds}{d\theta}\, d\theta = \int_0^{2\pi} (1 - \cos\theta) \sqrt{2} \sqrt{1 - \cos\theta}\, d\theta$$

$$= 2 \int_0^{2\pi} (1 - \cos\theta)^{3/2}\, d\theta$$

$$= \sqrt{2} \int_0^{2\pi} (\sqrt{2})^3 \left(\sin\frac{\theta}{2} \right)^3 d\theta$$

$$= 4 \int_0^{2\pi} \left(\sin\frac{\theta}{2} \right)^3 d\theta$$

which, by the substitution $u = \theta/2$, becomes

$$8 \int_0^{\pi} \sin^3 u\, du = 8 \int_0^{\pi} (1 - \cos^2 u) \sin u\, du$$

$$= 8 \int_0^{\pi} (\sin u - \cos^2 u \sin u)\, du$$

$$\underset{\text{FTC}}{=} 8 [-\cos u + (\cos^3 u)/3] \Big|_0^{\pi} = (8)(4/3) = 32/3$$

Thus the average of r with respect to s is $(32\frac{2}{3})/8 = 4\frac{1}{3}$, which is greater than the average of r with respect to θ, computed in Example 3. Again, the average depends on the choice of the variable with respect to which the average is computed.

EXERCISES

1. In t seconds a falling body drops $16t^2$ feet. Let its position relative to the y axis at time t be $16t^2$. (We aim the positive part of the axis downward.)
   (a) Compute velocity as a function of time. (Note that it is positive.)
   (b) Compute velocity as a function of y.
   (c) Find the average of velocity with respect to time during the first t seconds.
   (d) Find the average of velocity with respect to distance during the first t seconds.
   [Answer: (a) $32t$; (b) $8\sqrt{y}$; (c) $16t$; (d) $(64\frac{4}{3})t$]

2. (a) Find r explicitly as a function of s in Example 4.

   (b) Use (a) to compute $\displaystyle\int_0^8 f(s)\,ds$ directly.
   [Answer: (a) $r = s(1 - s/8)$; (b) $32\frac{2}{3}$]

3. (a) Graph $r = \cos\theta$ in polar coordinates for θ in $[-\pi/2, \pi/2]$.
   (b) Find the average of r as a function of θ.
   (c) Find the average of r as a function of s.
   [Answer: (b) $2/\pi$; (c) $2/\pi$]

4. (a) Show that every line through the origin cuts off a line segment of length 2 within the cardioid of Example 3.
   (b) In view of (a), explain why the average of r with respect to θ is 1.

5. Prove that the average speed with respect to time is equal to the distance traveled divided by the time elapsed.

6. A person travels 20 miles per hour for ½ hour, 30 miles per hour for 2 hours, and 40 miles per hour for ½ hour.
   (a) Compute the average of velocity with respect to time.
   (b) Compute the average of velocity with respect to distance.
   [Answer: (a) 30 miles per hour; (b) $31\frac{1}{9}$ miles per hour]

7. Find the average length of the vertical cross section of the following circle of radius r: (a) as a function of x; (b) as a function of θ; (c) as a function of y.

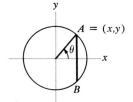

   AB is a typical vertical cross section

   (d) Why would you expect the answer to (b) to be less than the answer to (a)?
   [Answer: (a) $(\pi/2)r$; (b) $(4/\pi)r$; (c) r]

8. The function $r = f(\theta)$ describes, for θ in $[0, 2\pi]$, a curve in polar coordinates. Assume r' is continuous and $f(\theta) > 0$. Prove that the average of r as a function of arc length is at least as large as the quotient $2A/s$, where A is the area swept out by the radius and s is the arc length of the curve. When is the average equal to $2A/s$?

9. Find the average distance from the center of a square of side 2 to the border (*a*) considered as a function of angle; (*b*) considered as a function of arc length *s* around the square. (*c*) Which is larger?

$$\text{[Answer: } (a) \ \frac{4}{\pi} \ln (1 + \sqrt{2}); (b) \frac{\sqrt{2} + \ln (1 + \sqrt{2})}{2}; (c) \text{ the latter]}$$

10. Find the average distance from the intersection of the three altitudes of an equilateral triangle of side 2 to points on the border, (*a*) considered as a function of angle; (*b*) considered as a function of arc length on the border. (*c*) Which is larger?

$$\text{[Answer: } (a) \ (\sqrt{3}/\pi) \ln (2 + \sqrt{3}); (b) \ 1/\sqrt{3} + \tfrac{1}{6} \ln (2 + \sqrt{3}); (c) \text{ the latter]}$$

11. (See Exercises 9 and 10.) Draw a picture of a closed curve enclosing the origin in such a way that the average of *r* with respect to θ is greater than the average with respect to arc length on the curve.

12. Compute $\lim\limits_{b \to a} \int_a^b f(x)\, dx/(b - a)$, where f is a continuous function.

□ □ □

13. Explain carefully why $\int_0^8 f(s)\, ds = \int_0^{2\pi} g(\theta)\, (ds/d\theta)\, d\theta$, as we asserted in Example 4.

14. (*a*) Prove that if the quadratic polynomial $ax^2 + bx + c = 0$ has at most one root, then $b^2 - 4ac \leqslant 0$.

(*b*) Let $a_1, \ldots, a_n$ and $b_1, \ldots, b_n$ be real numbers such that not all a_i are 0. By considering the quadratic polynomial $\sum\limits_{i=1}^{n} (a_i x - b_i)^2$, prove that

$$\sum_{i=1}^{n} a_i b_i \leqslant \left(\sum_{i=1}^{n} a_i^2 \right)^{\!\frac{1}{2}} \left(\sum_{i=1}^{n} b_i^2 \right)^{\!\frac{1}{2}}$$

(*c*) Prove that *equality* holds in (*b*) only if there is a constant *r* such that $b_1 = ra_1$, $b_2 = ra_2, \ldots, b_n = ra_n$.

15. (See Exercise 14.) A person travels at a speed v_i for a period of time t_i, with $i = 1, 2, 3, \ldots, n$.

(*a*) Compute the average speed as a function of time and as a function of distance.

(*b*) Prove that the latter average is larger than the former except when all the v_i's are equal. (Then the two averages are, of course, equal.)

16. (*a*) Using Exercise 14(*b*), prove that if f and g are continuous functions, then

$$\int_a^b f(x)\, g(x)\, dx \leqslant \left\{ \int_a^b [f(x)]^2\, dx \right\}^{\!\frac{1}{2}} \left\{ \int_a^b [g(x)]^2\, dx \right\}^{\!\frac{1}{2}}$$

This is known as Schwarz's inequality.

(*b*) Obtain the inequality in (*a*) by considering the quadratic polynomial in *t*,

$$h(t) = \int_a^b [tf(x) - g(x)]^2\, dx.$$

17. Prove that the average speed as a function of time is never larger than the average of speed as a function of distance. (Hint: See Exercise 16.)

18. Show that the center of gravity of the stick in Example 2, page 219, lies to the left of its center of percussion. (Hint: See Exercise 16.)

19. Let f be a function such that $f(x)$ is always positive. Prove that

$$\int_a^b f(x)\,dx \int_a^b \frac{1}{f(x)}\,dx \geqslant (b-a)^2$$

(Hint: See Exercise 16.)

8. *Improper integrals.* Consider the volume of the solid of revolution formed by rotating about the x axis the region under $y = 1/x$, above the x axis, and to the right of $x = 1$:

What is the volume of this endless solid of revolution?

The typical cross section made by a plane perpendicular to the x axis is a circle of radius $1/x$. We might therefore be tempted to say that the volume is $\int_1^\infty \pi(1/x)^2\,dx$. Unfortunately, the symbol $\int_a^\infty f(x)\,dx$ has not been given any meaning. The definition of the definite integral involves sums of the form $\sum_{i=1}^{n} f(X_i)(x_i - x_{i-1})$. If a section in the partition has infinite length, such a sum is meaningless.

It does make sense, however, to examine the volume of that part of the solid from $x = 1$ to $x = b$ and then see how it behaves when $b \to \infty$. In other words, let us look at $\lim\limits_{b \to \infty} \int_1^b \pi(1/x)^2\,dx$. Now,

$$\int_1^b \pi\left(\frac{1}{x}\right)^2 dx \underset{\text{FTC}}{=} -\left.\frac{\pi}{x}\right|_1^b = -\frac{\pi}{b} - \left(-\frac{\pi}{1}\right) = \pi - \frac{\pi}{b}$$

Thus $\lim\limits_{b \to \infty} \int_1^b (\pi/x^2)\,dx = \pi - 0 = \pi$. The volume of the endless solid is finite.

This approach suggests how we should give meaning to the symbol $\int_a^\infty f(x)\,dx$.

DEFINITION: *Improper integral* $\int_a^\infty f(x)\,dx$. Let f be a continuous function. If $\lim\limits_{b \to \infty} \int_a^b f(x)\,dx$ exists, we call it the improper integral of f from a to ∞. This number is denoted $\int_a^\infty f(x)\,dx$.

Example 1.   We have just shown that $\int_1^\infty \pi(1/x)^2\, dx = \pi$.

Example 2.   We consider the area of the region below $y = 1/x$, above the x axis and to the right of $x = 1$. This is

$$\int_1^\infty \frac{1}{x}\, dx = \lim_{b \to \infty} \int_1^b \frac{1}{x}\, dx \underset{\text{FTC}}{=} \lim_{b \to \infty} (\ln b - \ln 1) = \lim_{b \to \infty} \ln b$$

How does $\ln b$ behave as b increases without bound? First of all, since $D(\ln t) = 1/t$, the function $\ln t$ is increasing. Moreover, since $\ln e = 1$, $\ln e^2 = 2$, . . . , $\ln e^n = n$, we see that $\ln b$ becomes arbitrarily large. Thus $\lim_{b \to \infty} \ln b = \infty$. We may summarize these observations in the statement "the area is infinite" or, in shorthand, $\int_1^\infty (1/x)\, dx = \infty$.

Example 3.   In statistics it is frequently important to compute moments that involve improper integrals. For instance, the nth moment of the function e^{-x} around 0 and over the positive x axis is defined as the improper integral $\int_0^\infty x^n e^{-x}\, dx$. For later reference let us compute its first three moments. We have, making use of Example 1 (page 219),

$$M_0 = \int_0^\infty x^0 e^{-x}\, dx = \lim_{b \to \infty} (1 - e^{-b}). \text{ Thus } M_0 = 1. \text{ Now,}$$

$$M_1 = \int_0^\infty x e^{-x}\, dx = \lim_{b \to \infty} [1 - (1 + b)\, e^{-b}]$$

but, as Example 5 (page 125) shows, $\lim_{b \to \infty} (1 + b)\, e^{-b} = 0$. Thus $M_1 = 1$. Similarly,

$$M_2 = \int_0^\infty x^2 e^{-x}\, dx = \lim_{b \to \infty} [2 - e^{-b} (b^2 + 2b + 2)]$$

By Example 5 (page 125), this limit is 2. Thus $M_2 = 2$.

Sometimes it is necessary to consider improper integrals over the whole x axis. For this purpose we must make two definitions.

DEFINITIONS: *The improper integrals* $\int_{-\infty}^b f(x)\, dx$ *and* $\int_{-\infty}^\infty f(x)\, dx$. Let f be a continuous function. If $\lim_{t \to -\infty} \int_t^b f(x)\, dx$ exists, we call it the improper integral of f from $-\infty$ to b. It is denoted $\int_{-\infty}^b f(x)\, dx$. If both $\int_{-\infty}^0 f(x)\, dx$ and $\int_0^\infty f(x)\, dx$ exist, we call their sum the improper integral of f from $-\infty$ to ∞ and denote it $\int_{-\infty}^\infty f(x)\, dx$.

Example 4.   Let us consider the area of the region bounded by the curve $y = 1/(1 + x^2)$ and the x axis. To do so we will compute $\int_{-\infty}^\infty [1/(1 + x^2)]\, dx$. We have

$$\int_0^\infty \frac{1}{1 + x^2}\, dx = \lim_{b \to \infty} \int_0^b \frac{1}{1 + x^2}\, dx \underset{\text{FTC}}{=} \lim_{b \to \infty} (\tan^{-1} b - \tan^{-1} 0) = \frac{\pi}{2}$$

Similarly, or by symmetry,
$$\int_{-\infty}^{0} \frac{1}{1+x^2}\, dx = \frac{\pi}{2}$$

Hence $\int_{-\infty}^{\infty} \dfrac{1}{1+x^2}\, dx = \dfrac{\pi}{2} + \dfrac{\pi}{2}$ and the area in question is π.

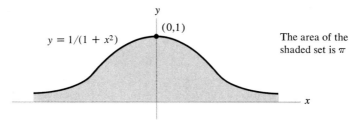

The area of the shaded set is π

Now let us consider the area of the region bounded by $y = 1/\sqrt{x}$, $x = 1$, and the coordinate axes:

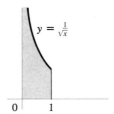

We must resist the temptation to write "area $= \displaystyle\int_{0}^{1} (1/\sqrt{x})\, dx$," for $\displaystyle\int_{0}^{1} (1/\sqrt{x})\, dx$ does not exist, since its integrand is unbounded (see page 88). We must instead consider the behavior of $\displaystyle\int_{t}^{1} (1/\sqrt{x})\, dx$ as t approaches 0 from the right. Since

$$\int_{t}^{1} \frac{1}{\sqrt{x}}\, dx \underset{\text{FTC}}{=} 2\sqrt{x}\,\Big|_{t}^{1} = 2\sqrt{1} - 2\sqrt{t} = 2(1 - \sqrt{t})$$

we see that as t shrinks toward 0 from the right, $\displaystyle\int_{t}^{1} (1/\sqrt{x})\, dx$ approaches 2, and we may say that the area in question is 2. This reasoning justifies our definition of a second t type of improper integral, one in which the function rather than the interval is unbounded.

DEFINITION: *Improper integral* $\displaystyle\int_{a}^{b} f(x)\, dx.$ Let a and b be real numbers, $a < b$, and let f be continuous on $[t,b]$ for each t, with $a < t < b$, but let f be unbounded on (a,b). If $\displaystyle\lim_{t \to a^+} \int_{t}^{b} f(x)\, dx$ exists, we call it the improper integral of f from a to b. It is denoted $\displaystyle\int_{a}^{b} f(x)\, dx.$ (The symbol $t \to a^+$ is read "as t approaches a from the right.")

Example 5. The computations just made show that $\int_0^1 (1/\sqrt{x})\,dx = 2$. Keep in mind that $\int_0^1 (1/\sqrt{x})\,dx$ is not defined as a limit of sums.

In a similar manner, if f is unbounded only "near" b and to the left of b, we define $\int_a^b f(x)\,dx$ as $\lim_{t \to b-} \int_a^b f(x)\,dx$, where $t \to b^-$ is read "as t approaches b from the left."

Example 6. Consider the arc length of a quadrant of a circle of radius 1. We have $y = \sqrt{1 - x^2}$ and $dy/dx = -x/\sqrt{1 - x^2}$. Thus the integrand $\sqrt{1 + (dy/dx)^2}$, in the formula for arc length, is unbounded near $x = 1$. We have the improper integral

$$\int_0^1 \sqrt{1 + \left(\frac{dy}{dx}\right)^2}\,dx = \int_0^1 \sqrt{1 + \frac{x^2}{1 - x^2}}\,dx = \int_0^1 \frac{1}{\sqrt{1 - x^2}}\,dx$$

Now,

$$\int_0^1 \frac{1}{\sqrt{1 - x^2}}\,dx = \lim_{t \to 1} \int_0^t \frac{1}{\sqrt{1 - x^2}}\,dx \underset{\text{FTC } t \to 1}{=} \lim (\sin^{-1} t - \sin^{-1} 0) = \frac{\pi}{2}$$

Example 7: Substitution in an improper integral. The first three moments, about 0 and over the positive x axis, of the function ce^{-cx}, where c is a positive constant, will be useful in our study of traffic in Chap. 24. If c is 1, then we have the moments computed in Example 3. We could compute the moments for arbitrary c in the manner employed in Example 3. We shall, however, reduce the general case to the case $c - 1$ by a "substitution in an improper integral" which is analogous to substitution in a definite integral, described on page 185. We omit its justification (which is similar to that for substitution in the definite integral) and simply illustrate its use.

In the present case we have $M_0 = \int_0^\infty ce^{-cx}\,dx$. The substitution $u = cx$, $du = c\,dx$ yields $M_0 = \int_0^\infty ce^{-u}(1/c)\,du$. (Note that the limits of integration remain the same, because as x sweeps out the positive x axis, so does $u = cx$.) Thus $M_0 = \int_0^\infty e^{-u}\,du$, which (as we saw in Example 3) is 1.

We have $M_1 = \int_0^\infty xce^{-cx}\,dx$. The same substitution yields

$$M_1 = \int_0^\infty \frac{u}{c} ce^{-u} \frac{1}{c}\,du = \frac{1}{c}\int_0^\infty ue^{-u}\,du$$

which, by Example 3, is $1/c$. In a similar manner we can show that

$$M_2 = \int_0^\infty x^2 ce^{-cx}\,dx = 2/c^2$$

It should be emphasized that there are two types of improper integrals, both of which are defined as limits of definite integrals. In one type the *interval* is unbounded, while in the other type the *function* is unbounded.

EXERCISES

1. (a) Show that when the volume we computed at the beginning of this section is computed by the shell method, we are led to a definite integral, not an improper integral.

   (b) Compute the volume by the shell method.

2. Our computation of the area of the region bounded by $y = 1/\sqrt{x}$ and the lines $y = 0$, $x = 0$, $x = 1$ led us to an improper integral having an unbounded function. and a bounded interval of integration. Show that the use of horizontal cross sections leads to an improper integral having a bounded function and an unbounded "interval of integration." Compute this improper integral.

3. Show that the surface area of the solid described at the beginning of the section is infinite. Does this mean that the infinite surface can be painted by filling the solid of finite volume with paint? Explain.

4. Make the substitution $x = t/\sqrt{1 + t^2}$ to show that

$$\int_0^1 \frac{1}{\sqrt{1 - x^2}}\, dx = \int_0^\infty \frac{1}{1 + t^2}\, dt$$

   (Disregard our knowledge that both equal $\pi/2$.)

5. By interpreting these improper integrals as expressions for the area of a certain region, show that

$$\int_0^\infty \frac{1}{1 + x^2}\, dx = \int_0^1 \sqrt{\frac{1 - y}{y}}\, dy$$

6. Define $G(a) = \int_0^\infty \dfrac{a}{1 + a^2 x^2}\, dx$. (a) Compute $G(0)$. (b) Compute $G(a)$ if a is negative.

   (c) Compute $G(a)$ if a is positive. (d) Graph G.

7. Find the area under $y = e^{-x}$, above $y = 0$, and to the right of $x = 1$, by (a) vertical cross sections; (b) horizontal cross sections.   (Answer: $1/e$)

8. Find the error:

$$\int_{-1}^1 \frac{1}{x^2}\, dx \underset{\text{FTC}}{=} \left. \frac{-1}{x} \right|_{-1}^1 = \frac{-1}{1} - \frac{-1}{-1} = -2$$

   (The integrand is positive, yet we have a negative result!)

9. How would you define

$$\int_{-2}^3 \frac{1}{x^{1/3}}\, dx?$$

   [A reasonable definition gives it the value $\frac{3}{2}(\sqrt[3]{9} - \sqrt[3]{4})$].

10. When is $\displaystyle\int_1^\infty x^a\, dx$ finite?

11. When is $\displaystyle\int_0^1 x^a\, dx$ finite?

12. We will show in Chap. 9 that $\int_0^\infty e^{-x^2} dx = \sqrt{\pi}/2$. Using this fact if necessary, find the moments $M_1 = \int_0^\infty xe^{-x^2} dx$ and $M_2 = \int_0^\infty x^2 e^{-x^2} dx$.

(Answer: $M_1 = \frac{1}{2}$, $M_2 = \sqrt{\pi}/4$)

13. (a) Compute M_2 in Example 7 by means of the substitution $u = cx$.
    (b) Compute the three moments of Example 7 without using a substitution (that is, as it was done in Example 3).

14. Show that $\int_{-\infty}^\infty (1/\sqrt{2\pi})\, e^{-x^2/2} dx = 1$. (Hint: See Exercise 12.) This is important in statistics.

15. Show that $\int_0^\infty e^{-x^2} dx$ is finite by comparing it to $\int_0^\infty e^{-x} dx$. (Warning: The fundamental theorem of calculus is useless in computing $\int_a^b e^{-x^2} dx$, since e^{-x^2} does not have an elementary antiderivative.)

16. Show that for a positive b,
$$\int_0^\infty \frac{\sin bx}{x}\, dx$$
is independent of b. (Warning: The fundamental theorem of calculus is useless here too.)

17. The study of rockets makes use of $\int_1^\infty 1/x^2\, dx$. Compute it.

□   □   □

18. Prove that $\int_0^\infty \frac{\sin x^2}{x}\, dx = \frac{1}{2} \int_0^\infty \frac{\sin x}{x}\, dx$.

19. Prove that $\int_1^\infty \frac{e^{-x^2}}{x}\, dx = \frac{1}{2} \int_1^\infty \frac{e^{-x}}{x}\, dx$.

20. Prove that $\int_0^1 \frac{x^n}{\sqrt{1-x^2}}\, dx = \int_0^{\pi/2} \sin^n \theta \, d\theta$.

21. Compute $\int_0^1 x^4 \ln x \, dx$.

22. (a) Let $G(a) = \int_0^\infty \frac{1}{(1+x^a)(1+x^2)}\, dx$. Evaluate $G(0)$, $G(1)$, $G(2)$.

    (b) Show, using the substitution $x = 1/y$, that $G(a) = \int_0^\infty \frac{x^a\, dx}{(1+x^a)(1+x^2)}$

    (c) From (b), show that $G(a) = \pi/4$, independent of a.

23. (a) Graph $f(x) = (\sin x)/x$ if $x > 0$, $f(0) = 1$.
    (b) Show that, if n is an integer, $n \geqslant 1$, then
$$\int_{2n\pi}^{(2n+2)\pi} \frac{\sin x}{x}\, dx < \int_{2n\pi}^{(2n+1)\pi} \frac{\pi}{x(x+\pi)}\, dx < \int_{2n\pi}^{(2n+1)\pi} \frac{\pi}{x^2}\, dx < \frac{1}{4n^2}$$

(c) In view of (a) and (b), show that $\int_0^\infty f(x)\,dx$ is finite.

24. Show that $\int_0^\infty \dfrac{1}{1+x^4}\,dx = \dfrac{\pi\sqrt{2}}{4}$.

25. It can be proved that $\int_0^\infty \dfrac{x^{n-1}}{1+x}\,dx = \dfrac{\pi}{\sin n\pi}$ for $0 < n < 1$.
    Verify that this equation is correct for $n = \frac{1}{2}$.

26. Prove that $\int_0^\infty \left(\dfrac{\sin x}{x}\right)^2 dx = \int_0^\infty \dfrac{\sin x}{x}\,dx$.

27. Define for $n > 0$, $f(n) = \int_0^\infty x^{n-1} e^{-x}\,dx$, the $(n-1)$th moment of the function e^{-x} over the positive part of the x axis. Show that $f(1) = 1$, $f(2) = 1$, and $f(n+1) = nf(n)$.

28. The function $f(x) = (\sin x)/x$ for $x \neq 0$ and $f(0) = 1$ occurs often in communication theory. Show that the energy E of the signal represented by f is finite, where
$$E = \int_{-\infty}^\infty [f(x)]^2\,dx.$$

9. Probability distribution and density.

9. Probability distribution and density. Electronic equipment, ball bearings, and light bulbs, no matter how well designed, eventually fail and are replaced or repaired. The mathematical theory of reliability is devoted to obtaining maximum life and dependability from such equipment. It uses, as its basic tools, probability distribution and density, concepts that will be useful in Chap. 24 and that, as exercises in this section will show, are fundamental in actuarial work.

Consider a complex electronic device manufactured in large numbers. Some of them may function for a long time before failing, and some may fail quickly. Let $F(t)$ be the proportion that fail within the first t hours of use. We have $F(t) \geqslant 0$, $F(0) = 0$, and $\lim_{t \to \infty} F(t) = 1$, since any electronic device eventually requires repair. The values $F(t)$ may be determined experimentally, or sometimes, theoretically. In reliability theory the function F is known as the *failure distribution*. (In actuarial work $F(t)$ is the proportion of people who die before reaching the age t years; F is the *life distribution*. In Chap. 24, $F(x)$ is the proportion of the gaps in a line of traffic that have length at most x; F is the *gap distribution*.) In view of the wide applicability of this concept, we make the following definition.

DEFINITION: *Probability distribution.* A probability distribution (over the nonnegative real numbers) is any function F such that $F(0) = 0$, $x_2 > x_1$ implies $F(x_2) \geqslant F(x_1)$, and $\lim_{x \to \infty} F(x) = 1$.

Example 1. The following data were compiled for 100 transistor radios.

Time interval (hours)	0–10	10–20	20–30	30–40	40–50	50–60
Number that failed during the interval	53	24	11	6	4	2

From the data we conclude that $F(10) = {}^{53}/_{100} = 0.53$, $F(20) = (53 + 24)/100 = 0.77$, $F(30) = 0.88$, $F(40) = 0.94$, $F(50) = 0.98$, and $F(t) = 1$ for $t \geqslant 60$. We sketch a graph of F, passing a smooth curve through the points given by the data.

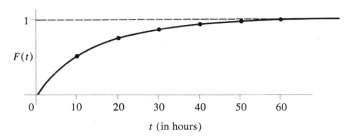

Observe that in Example 1 the breakdowns do not occur with equal frequency in each 10-hour interval of use. These radios are more likely to fail in the first 10 hours than between 50 and 60 hours. This suggests that we examine the proportion of any equipment that fails in a typical interval of time, from t to $t + \Delta t$. This proportion is $F(t + \Delta t) - F(t)$. (For instance, in Example 1, $F(20) - F(10) = {}^{24}/_{100} = 0.24$.) The expression $F(t + \Delta t) - F(t)$ is reminiscent of the derivative of F. For this reason, let us write

$$(1) \qquad F(t + \Delta t) - F(t) = \left[\frac{F(t + \Delta t) - F(t)}{\Delta t} \right] \Delta t$$

Assume that F is differentiable. Then, when Δt is small, $[F(t + \Delta t) - F(t)]/\Delta t$ is approximately $F'(t)$. From (1) we conclude that the proportion that fail in the short interval of time $[t, t + \Delta t]$ of duration Δt is approximately $F'(t) \Delta t$. Thus $F'(t)$ *measures the tendency of the equipment to fail "near time t."* In practice F' is more important than F.

Let F be a probability distribution with a continuous derivative $f = F'$. We have

$$F(x) = F(x) - F(0) = \int_0^x F'(t) \, dt = \int_0^x f(t) \, dt. \text{ Thus we see that } f \text{ determines } F,$$

$$F(x) = \int_0^x f(t) \, dt$$

Since $\lim_{x \to 1} F(x) = 1$, the improper integral $\int_0^\infty f(t) \, dt$ has the value 1. In reliability theory f is called the *failure density.* More generally we make the following definition.

DEFINITION: *Probability density.* A probability density (over the nonnegative real numbers) is any continuous function f such that $f(x) \geqslant 0$ for each $x \geqslant 0$ and also $\int_0^\infty f(x)\,dx = 1$. (The assumption that f is continuous is sometimes relaxed to the assumption that $\int_0^x f(t)\,dt$ exists for each $x \geqslant 0$.)

From a probability density f we may obtain a probability distribution F by defining $F(x) = \int_0^x f(t)\,dt$. If we think of f as the density function of a piece of non-homogeneous string occupying the nonnegative portion of the x axis, then $F(x)$ is the mass of that part of the string in the interval $[0,x]$. The two figures below show the geometric relation between f and F.

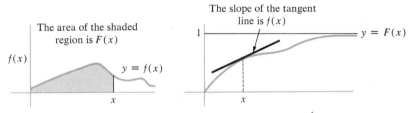

Example 2. Let us graph the probability density f for the data in Example 1. [Note that $f(t)$ would be the slope of the graph of F if the horizontal axis had the same scale as the vertical axis.] For instance, to estimate $f(20)$ we use the quotient $[F(30)-F(20)]/(30-20) = 0.11/10 = 0.011$ (failures per hour). On the other hand, $f(0)$ is approximately $[F(10) - F(0)]/(10-0) = 0.53/10 = 0.053$ (failures per hour), about five times as large as $f(20)$. Similarly $f(10)$ is approximately 0.024, $f(30)$ is approximately 0.006, $f(40)$ is approximately 0.004, $f(50)$ is approximately 0.002, and $f(t) = 0$ for $t \geqslant 60$. With these estimates we sketch a graph of f and indicate the relation of F to this graph. ("Failures per hour" refers to the "proportion of radios" that fail per hour.)

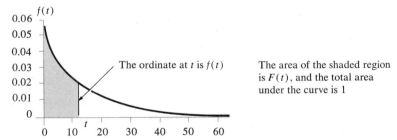

Since $f(t)$ is larger when t is near 0, we may conclude that the defects in construction of the radios tend to show up early in use.

The proportion of the equipment that performs without failure throughout the interval $[0,t]$ is $1 - F(t)$. The proportion of this surviving equipment that then fails in the interval $[t, t + \Delta t]$ is thus approximately

$$\frac{f(t)\,\Delta t}{1 - F(t)} = \frac{f(t)}{1 - F(t)}\,\Delta t$$

The function z such that $z(t) = f(t)/[1 - F(t)]$, defined for those $t \geqslant 0$ such that $F(t) \neq 1$, is known in reliability theory as the *hazard rate* and in actuarial work as the *mortality rate*.

Example 3. Complex machines whose wornout parts are replaced with new ones have the property that an old machine is just as dependable as a new one. We express this mathematically by the assumption that the hazard rate is constant.

$$(2) \qquad \frac{f(t)}{1 - F(t)} = k$$

From this assumption we will determine F and its derivative f. We rewrite (2) as

$$(3) \qquad \frac{d[-\ln(1 - F(t))]}{dt} = \frac{d(kt)}{dt}$$

Since two functions whose derivatives are equal differ by a constant, there is a number A such that

$$-\ln[1 - F(t)] = kt + A$$

or $\ln[1 - F(t)] = -kt - A$, from which we obtain

$$(4) \qquad 1 - F(t) = e^{-kt-A}$$

To determine A, recall that $F(0) = 0$. Replacing t in (4) by 0, we have $1 - 0 = e^{-k0-A} = e^{-A}$; thus $A = 0$. Since $A = 0$, we deduce from (4) that

$$(5) \qquad F(t) = 1 - e^{-kt}$$

which is known as the *exponential distribution*. Observe that the probability density f associated with F is given by $f(t) = d(1 - e^{-kt})/dt = ke^{-kt}$, a decreasing function.

Let us next estimate the average number of hours that the radios in Example 1 perform before their first repair. Of the 100 radios 53 failed in the first 10 hours. For the sake of simplicity, let us say that these 53 radios each worked for 5 hours. Similarly we will say that 24 radios worked for 15 hours, and so on. The average number of hours is therefore

$$(6) \qquad \frac{53 \cdot 5 + 24 \cdot 15 + 11 \cdot 25 + 6 \cdot 35 + 4 \cdot 45 + 2 \cdot 55}{100} = 14$$

To relate this average to the functions F and f, we rewrite (6) as

$$(7) \qquad \frac{53}{100} \cdot 5 + \frac{24}{100} \cdot 15 + \frac{11}{100} \cdot 25 + \frac{6}{100} \cdot 35 + \frac{4}{100} \cdot 45 + \frac{2}{100} \cdot 55$$

Now $53/100 = F(10) = F(10) - F(0)$, which by the law of the mean is $f(T_1) \cdot 10$ for some T_1, with $0 < T_1 < 10$, and hence is approximately $f(5) \cdot 10$. Similarly $24/100$ is approximately $f(15) \cdot 10$, and so on. Letting $t_0 = 0$, $t_1 = 10$, $t_2 = 20$, . . . , $t_6 = 60$, and $T_1 = 5$, $T_2 = 15$, . . . , $T_6 = 55$, we thus have the following approximation to (6) or (7).

$$(8) \qquad \sum_{i=1}^{6} T_i f(T_i)(t_i - t_{i-1})$$

which is an approximating sum to the first moment $\int_0^{60} tf(t)\,dt$. This suggests the following definition.

DEFINITION: *Expectation.* The expectation (average value) for the probability density f is $\int_0^\infty xf(x)\,dx$, and is denoted $E(x)$.

The expectation is analogous to the center of gravity of material distributed on the nonnegative part of the x axis. In reliability theory the expectation is known as *the expected duration to the first repair*; in actuarial work it is *life expectancy at birth*.

Example 4. Let us compute the expectation for the probability density of Example 3, $f(x) = ke^{-kx}$. In this case the expectation is

$$E(x) = \int_0^\infty xke^{-kx}\,dx$$

which by Example 7, page 230, equals $1/k$. Note that the higher the hazard rate k, the shorter the expected duration $1/k$ between repairs.

EXERCISES

1. (a) Show that F defined by $F(t) = t/(1 + t)$ is a probability distribution.
   (b) Find its associated probability density.
2. (a) Show that f defined by $f(x) = 2/[\pi(1 + x^2)]$ is a probability density.
   (b) Find its associated probability distribution.
3. In Chap. 9 it will be proved that $\int_0^\infty e^{-t^2}\,dt = \sqrt{\pi}/2$.
   (a) Show that f defined by $f(t) = (\sqrt{2/\pi})\,e^{-t^2/2}$ is a probability density.
   (b) Find its expectation. [Answer: (b) $\sqrt{2/\pi}$]
4. Let $p_n = F(n) - F(n-1)$ denote the probability that the machine in Example 3 breaks down during the nth interval of time.
   (a) Compute p_n.
   (b) Show that $p_1, p_2, \ldots$ is a geometric progression.
   (c) Compute $\sum_{n=1}^\infty p_n$.
5. Of 1,000 people born alive in the United States in 1960 the following projection has been made.

Age	0	1	5	10	20	30	40	50	60	70	80	90	100
Number surviving to the age	1,000	974	970	968	961	949	931	888	791	609	336	71	0

This tabulates $1,000\,[1 - F(t)]$.
   (a) Tabulate $F(t)$.   (c) Estimate $f(0)$, $f(5)$, $f(10)$, $f(20)$, and so on.
   (b) Graph F.   (d) Graph f.
   (e) Estimate the expected life span.
   (f) Estimate the mortality rate $m(t) = f(t)/[1 - F(t)]$ for $t = 0$, 5, 20, and 60.

6. In reliability theory the Weibull distribution is also used. It is defined as $F(t) = 1 - e^{-t^a/b}$, where a and b are appropriate constants. If $a = 1 = b$, it reduces to the exponential distribution.
   (a) Compute the failure rate f and the hazard rate z.
   (b) Graph f and z for $a = 1$, $b = 1$ and for $a = 3$, $b = 1$.
   (c) In your opinion which case in (b) approximates more closely the failure rate of light bulbs?

7. Using the data in Example 1, estimate or compute (a) $F(35)$; (b) $f(35)$; (c) $\int_{20}^{40} f(t)\, dt$.

8. (a) On the basis of the data in Exercise 5, estimate the average life span of those who do not reach age 50.
   (b) Develop a formula for this average that involves f, F, and a definite integral.

9. (a) On the basis of the data in Exercise 5, estimate the average number of years of life remaining for a person of age 50.
   (b) Develop a formula for this average that involves f, F, and a definite integral.

10. In a study of ball bearings it was found that 10 percent did not perform for more than 20,000,000 revolutions and that 50 percent did not perform for more than 80,000,000 revolutions. Let $F(x)$ denote the proportion that fail before x million revolutions.
    (a) Translate the data into assertions about F.
    (b) It has also been observed that for ball bearings F takes the form $F(x) = 1 - e^{-x^a/b}$. Show that a satisfies the equation $4^a = \ln(0.5)/\ln(0.9)$.

11. In the life distribution F, let us set $F(t) = 1$ if $t \geqslant 100$. The expected life span $\int_0^\infty tf(t)\, dt$ is thus equal to the definite integral $\int_0^{100} tf(t)\, dt$.
    (a) Using an integration by parts, prove that the expected life span equals $\int_0^{100} [1 - F(t)]\, dt$.
    (b) Use the result in (a) and the table below to estimate the expected life span of males in rural India.

Age	0	1	5	15	25	35	45	55	65	75	85	95
Number surviving to the age	1,000	857	738	699	675	647	610	536	385	179	26	1

(c) Apply the same technique to the data in Exercise 5.

12. The contrast of the table below, for male infants born in 1900, with that of Exercise 5 illustrates the impact primarily of improved public health measures and secondly of an increased standard of living in the United States between 1900 and 1960.

Age	0	1	5	10	20	30	40	50	60	70	80	90	100
Number surviving to the age	1,000	867	809	791	763	713	649	572	464	306	140	38	0

(a) Tabulate $F(t)$, where $F(t)$ is the proportion *not* reaching age t.

(b) Graph F in (a).

(c) Estimate $f(0)$, $f(60)$, $f(5)$ for the functions f of this exercise and for Exercise 5.

13. In the examples we considered, the variables are nonnegative. In some experiments, however, the data are both positive and negative. Instances of this are examination scores and errors in measurement. For this reason probability densities and distribution over the whole x axis are also studied. They are defined as follows: A probability density on the x axis is any function f such that $f(x) \geqslant 0$ and $\int_{-\infty}^{\infty} f(x)\,dx = 1$.

[The demand that f be continuous is sometimes too restrictive; but $\int_{a}^{b} f(x)\,dx$ should exist for each a and b.] A probability distribution on the x axis is any function F such that $x_2 > x_1$ implies $F(x_2) \geqslant F(x_1)$, and $\lim_{x \to \infty} F(-x) = 0$ and $\lim_{x \to \infty} F(x) = 1$.

(a) Verify that f given by $f(x) = 0$, if $x < 0$, and $f(x) = e^{-x}$, if $x \geqslant 0$, is a probability density over the x axis.

(b) Define $F(x) = \int_{-\infty}^{x} f(t)\,dt$, where f is given in (a). Show that F is a probability distribution over the x axis.

(c) Graph f and F. Note that f is not continuous.

14. (See Exercise 13.) (a) Show that $f(x) = (1/\sqrt{2\pi})\,e^{-x^2/2}$ defines a probability density over the x axis. (Recall Exercise 3.)

(b) Sketch a graph of f. This particular probability density is known as the "normal curve" or "bell curve." It is the most commonly used probability density in applied statistics.

15. In an experiment it was found that 11 out of 10,000 who were nonsmokers at the age of 40 died before reaching age 41, while 44 out of 10,000 of the same age who smoked more than a pack a day died before reaching the age of 41.

(a) On the basis of these data can you estimate for each group $f(40)$ or $m(40) = f(40)/[1 - F(40)]$?

(b) Compute for smokers and nonsmokers the value in (a) that can be estimated.

16. Show that if the "hazard" function z is known, then (a) $F(x) = 1 - e^{-\int_0^x z(t)\,dt}$ and (b) $f(x) = z(x)\,e^{-\int_0^x z(t)\,dt}$.

17. Let f be a probability density over the positive x axis. Let $M_1 = \int_0^{\infty} x f(x)\,dx$. The second moment about M_1 is denoted M_2, $M_2 = \int_0^{\infty} (x - M_1)^2 f(x)\,dx$. It is called the *variance*. Its square root, $\sqrt{M_2}$, is called the *standard deviation*. Find the standard deviation of the probability density $f(x) = ce^{-cx}$, where c is a constant. (Computations in Example 7, page 230, may be helpful.)

(Answer: $1/c$)

18. A machine that has survived a hours has a "mean residual life," defined as the expected number of hours remaining before it breaks down. A person a years old

has a "life expectancy," the expected number of years of life remaining for persons at age a.

(a) Explain why these quantities are measured by $\int_a^\infty (t - a) f(t) \, dt / [1 - F(a)]$.

(b) Show that $\int_a^b (t - a) f(t) \, dt = (a - b) [1 - F(b)] + \int_a^b [1 - F(t)] \, dt$.

19. Let f be a probability density and F its associated probability distribution. Assuming that $\lim_{t \to \infty} t[1 - F(t)] = 0$, prove that the expectation for f is simply $\int_0^\infty [1 - F(t)] \, dt$. [Hint: See Exercise 18(b).]

20. The design of transmitting satellites, rockets, and other complex mechanisms makes use of redundant components to obtain longer life.
    (a) Assume that the distribution function F for a component is given by $F(t) = 1 - e^{-kt}$. Show that the distribution function G for a device that fails only when two such components fail is given by $G(t) = (1 - e^{-kt})^2$.
    (b) By Example 4, the expected life of a component is $1/k$. Show that the expected life of the device described in (a) is $\frac{3}{2}(1/k)$.

21. A certain device is designed to perform if at least one of its two components is performing. One of these components has an expected life of A years, and the other, of B years. Can the expected life C of the device be arbitrarily large? If not, find some bound on C in terms of A and B. (a) Solve this intuitively; (b) solve with the aid of the calculus.

10. Summary and memory aids. The main object of this chapter is the development of skill in recognizing when a quantity can be expressed as a definite integral. We used the definite integral to compute area, volume, arc length, surface area, work, and force. The moments of a function were introduced, and it was shown that volume (by the shell technique), work, and force all involve the first moment of the cross-section function. Improper integrals, which are limits of definite integrals, were applied to area, volume, and probability.

This table reviews some of the uses of the first three moments.

Function f	M_0	M_1	M_2
Cross section of plane set in fixed direction	Total area	Useful in finding centroid, volume of solid of revolution, force, work	The moment of inertia of plane region about line parallel to cross sections (see Exercise 6, page 221)
Density of mass along a line	Total mass	Useful in finding center of gravity of mass	The moment of inertia; useful in computing energy of rotating stick, center of percussion, length of equivalent pendulum
Probability density	1	Expectation (mean average)	Used in defining standard deviation (see Exercise 17, page 239)

We now present some aids for remembering the ideas and tactics in our application of the definite integral. For instance, consider the formula for finding volume by the slab technique, which we write as

$$V = \int_a^x A(t)\, dt$$

since we shall consider how V varies with respect to the upper limit of integration. By Theorem 3, page 146,

$$\frac{dV}{dx} = A(x)$$

In the notation of differentials,

$$dV = A(x)\, dx$$

The formula $dV = A(x)\, dx$ should remind us of the formula $V = \int_a^b A(x)\, dx$. To remember $dV = A(x)\, dx$, just keep this diagram in mind:

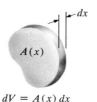

$$dV = A(x)\, dx$$

This picture proves nothing. It merely reminds us of how we estimate volume as the sum of the volumes of thin slabs.

Note that $A(x)\, dx$ resembles the approximation $A(X_i)\,(x_i - x_{i-1})$, which is a typical term in an approximating sum in the slab technique.

Here are pictures that will help us recall some other definite integrals we have met in this chapter.

$$dV = 2\pi r\, c\, dr$$
Length $\uparrow$ Height
Width of
carpet

Imagine the shell unrolled and laid flat like a carpet

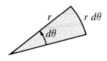

$$dA = \tfrac{1}{2}\, r\,\ (r\, d\theta) = \tfrac{r^2}{2}\, d\theta$$
Height   Base

$$dA = c(x)\, dx$$
Height   Width

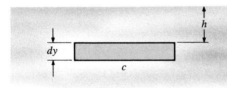

The force due to the water is
$$dF = 62.4\, h\, c\, dy$$
Pressure   Area

The surface area of
the band is
$$dS = 2\pi r\, ds$$

Imagine the band cut and
stretched into a long belt
of length $2\pi r$ and width ds

$$(ds)^2 = (dx)^2 + (dy)^2$$

9

Computing and applying definite integrals over plane and solid sets

In Chap. 1 the definite integrals over plane and solid sets were defined. Now we develop methods for computing them. First, however, to review the concept of a definite integral over a plane set, let us begin with an application which does not require any computation.

1. The center of gravity of a flat object (lamina). In this section the definite integral over a plane set is used to deal with "balancing lines" and the center of gravity. The results obtained would be difficult to derive if our only tool were the definite integral over intervals.

243

A small boy on one side of a seesaw (which we regard as weightless) can balance a bigger boy on the other side. For example, these two boys balance.

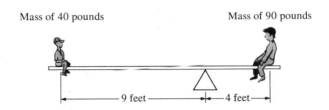

Mass of 40 pounds   Mass of 90 pounds

9 feet   4 feet

The small mass with the long lever arm balances the large mass with the small lever arm. Each contributes the same "tendency to turn"—but in opposite directions. To be more precise, let us introduce on the seesaw an x axis with its origin 0 at the fulcrum.

Mass 40   Mass 90

$x = -9$ 0 $x = 4$

We define the moment, about 0, of a mass m located at the point x on the x axis to be the product mx. Then the bigger boy has a moment $(90)(4)$, while the smaller boy has a moment $(40)(-9)$. The total moment of the lever–mass system is 0, and the boys balance.

If a mass m is located on a line at coordinate x, then we shall define its moment about the point having coordinate a as the product $m(x - a)$.

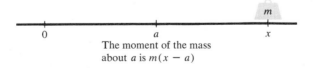

0   a x
The moment of the mass
about a is $m(x - a)$

Let us now consider several masses, $m_1, m_2, \ldots, m_n$. If mass m_i is located at x_i, with $i = 1, 2, \ldots, n$, then $\sum_{i=1}^{n} m_i(x_i - a)$ is the total moment of all the masses about the point a. If we place a fulcrum at a, then the seesaw rotates clockwise if the total moment is greater than 0, counterclockwise if it is less than 0, and is in equilibrium if the total moment is 0.

Example. Where should the fulcrum be placed so that these three masses will be in equilibrium?

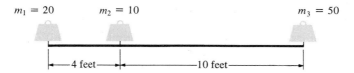

Let us introduce an x axis with origin at mass m_1 and compute the moments about a typical fulcrum having coordinate a; then we shall select a to make the total moment 0.

$m_1 = 20$ $m_2 = 10$ Typical fulcrum $m_3 = 50$

$x_1 = 0$ $x_2 = 4$ a $x_3 = 14$

The total moment about a is

$$20(0 - a) + 10(4 - a) + 50(14 - a)$$

We seek a such that this expression is equal to 0, or equivalently,

$$20 \cdot 0 + 10 \cdot 4 + 50 \cdot 14 = a(20 + 10 + 50)$$

Hence

$$a = \frac{20 \cdot 0 + 10 \cdot 4 + 50 \cdot 14}{80} = 9.25$$

This means the fulcrum is to the right of the midpoint, which was to be expected.

How should we define the moment, about a line L in the plane, of a distribution of matter in the plane, a so-called "lamina"? Let us assume that the lamina occupies the plane region R and has a density $f(P)$ at P, where $f(P) > 0$. We introduce an x axis perpendicular to L in order to measure "lever arm." Let us assume that L passes through the point $x = a$ on this axis.

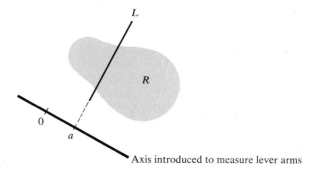

Axis introduced to measure lever arms

Imagine R partitioned into small regions $R_1, R_2, \ldots, R_n$. What would be a reasonable estimate of the moment about L contributed by the mass in R_i? If we choose a point P_i in R_i and denote the area of R_i by A_i, then the mass in R_i is approximately $f(P_i)A_i$. The lever arm of P_i is $(x_i - a)$ if the line through P_i and parallel to L meets the x axis at x_i.

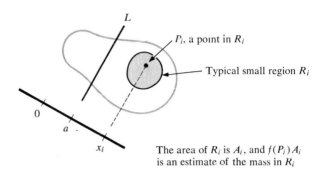

P_i, a point in R_i

Typical small region R_i

The area of R_i is A_i, and $f(P_i)A_i$
is an estimate of the mass in R_i

The typical small region R_i contributes a moment about L roughly equal to lever arm $\times$ mass, or $(x_i - a)f(P_i)A_i$. As we make finer partitions, we expect such estimates to be more accurate. Therefore *we define the moment of the lamina about L as*

$$\int_R (x - a) f(P)\, dA$$

(Note that this is the two-dimensional analog of the first moment defined on page 193.) *If the total moment about L is 0, then L is called a balancing line.*

THEOREM 1.   *There is exactly one balancing line in each direction in the plane of a given lamina.*

PROOF.   Introduce an x axis perpendicular to the given direction. We seek a such that $\int_R (x - a) f(P)\, dA = 0$. Now, just as in definite integrals over intervals,

$$\int_R (x - a) f(P)\, dA = \int_R x f(P)\, dA - a \int_R f(P)\, dA$$

So we want a such that

$$a \int_R f(P)\, dA = \int_R x f(P)\, dA$$

This equation for a has a unique solution,

$$a = \frac{\int_R x f(P)\, dA}{\int_R f(P)\, dA}$$

and the theorem is proved.

COROLLARY 1.   The coordinate of the balancing line of a lamina is given by

$$\bar{x} = \frac{\int_R x f(P)\, dA}{\text{mass of lamina}}$$

PROOF.   The expression $\int_R f(P)\, dA$ in the Theorem 1 proof is the total mass in R.

THEOREM 2. *All the balancing lines for a given lamina pass through a single point.*

PROOF. Let L_1 and L_2 be two perpendicular balancing lines. Let L be any line through the intersection of L_1 and L_2. We will prove that L is a balancing line. (That will be sufficient to establish Theorem 2, since Theorem 1 shows that there is only one balancing line in any direction.)

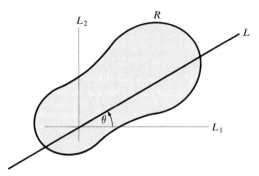

For convenience, let us use L_1 and L_2 as x and y axes. Since L_1 and L_2 are balancing lines, we have

$$\int_R yf(P)\, dA = 0 \qquad \text{and} \qquad \int_R xf(P)\, dA = 0$$

We now examine the lever arm of $P = (x,y)$ around L.

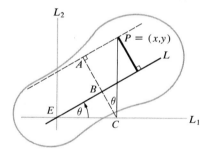

$AC = y \cos \theta$ (by right triangle CAP)
$BC = x \sin \theta$ (by right triangle EBC)

Inspection of the diagram shows that this lever arm is

$$AC - BC = y \cos \theta - x \sin \theta$$

an expression which is positive or negative depending upon the side of L on which the point P lies.

We must show that

(1) $$\int_R (y \cos \theta - x \sin \theta)\, f(P)\, dA = 0$$

Since L is fixed, $\cos \theta$ and $\sin \theta$ are constants; hence the above definite integral is equal to

$$\cos \theta \int_R yf(P)\, dA - \sin \theta \int_R xf(P)\, dA$$

From the information that $\int_R yf(P)\,dA = 0$ and $\int_R xf(P)\,dA = 0$, the relation (1) follows, and the theorem is proved.

We call the point through which all the balancing lines pass the *center of gravity* of the lamina. Observe that two balancing lines suffice to determine the center of gravity. Its y coordinate $\bar{y}$, according to Corollary 1, equals $\int_R yf(P)\,dA$/mass of lamina, and its x coordinate $\bar{x}$ equals $\int_R xf(P)\,dA$/mass of lamina.

EXERCISES

1. (*a*) Cut an irregular shape out of cardboard and find three balancing lines for it experimentally. Are they concurrent? Glue a small piece of cardboard onto it so that its density is not constant, and carry out the same experiment.
   (*b*) In the second case compare $\bar{x}$ with the formula in Corollary 1. (Hint: To estimate the definite integrals in the formula, use approximating sums.)
2. Where should the fulcrum be located in order to have this seesaw in equilibrium?

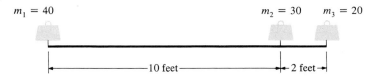

3. What formula for point masses on a line is the analog of the formula in Corollary 1?
4. Show that if the density function f is constant, $f(P) = k$, then the formula in Corollary 1 reduces to

$$\bar{x} = \frac{\int_R x\,dA}{\text{area of } R}$$

   In this case the center of gravity is independent of the particular density. It is determined only by the geometry of R and is called the "centroid" of R.
5. Develop a definition for moments and balancing lines of matter distributed along a curve. Prove that all the balancing lines pass through a single point.
6. (See Exercises 4 and 5.)
   (*a*) Define the centroid of a curve.
   (*b*) Find the centroid of a semicircle of radius a.
         [Answer: (*b*) on the line of symmetry, at a distance of $2a/\pi$ from center]
7. Prove that the area of a surface of revolution is equal to the product of the length of the curve revolved and the distance traveled by the centroid of the curve. [Hint: See Exercise 6(*a*) and the proof of Theorem 1, page 197.]
8. Let R be a rectangle with vertices $(0,0)$, $(3,0)$, $(3,2)$, $(0,2)$. Let $f(P) = f(x,y) = xy$. By partitioning R into six squares and selecting P_i to be the center of R_i, estimate (*a*) the mass in R; (*b*) the moment of the lamina about the x axis; (*c*) the moment about the y axis, and hence (*d*) the coordinates of the center of gravity.
         [Answer: (*a*) 9; (*b*) $45\!/\!4$; (*c*) $35\!/\!2$; (*d*) $(35\!/\!18, 5\!/\!4)$]
9. Repeat Exercise 8 for $f(x,y) = x^2 + y^2$.
         [Answer: (*a*) 25; (*b*) 28; (*c*) $49\tfrac{1}{2}$; (*d*) $(99\!/\!50, 28\!/\!25)$]
10. Repeat Exercise 8 for $f(x,y) = x$.   [Answer: (*a*) 9; (*b*) 9; (*c*) $35\!/\!2$; (*d*) $(35\!/\!18, 1)$]

11. Repeat Exercise 8 for $f(x,y) = 1$.   [Answer: (a) 6; (b) 6; (c) 9; (d) ($\frac{3}{2}$, 1)]

12. A lamina of mass M and center of gravity $(\bar{x},\bar{y})$ is cut into two objects, one of mass M_1 and center of gravity $(\bar{x}_1,\bar{y}_1)$, the other of mass M_2 and center of gravity $(\bar{x}_2,\bar{y}_2)$. (a) Prove that the masses and centers of gravity of the two smaller pieces completely determine the center of gravity of the original lamina.

    (b) Why must the center of gravity of the original lamina lie on the line segment joining $(\bar{x}_1,\bar{y}_1)$ to $(\bar{x}_2,\bar{y}_2)$? [Hint: Do (b) by considering moments about a wisely chosen line.]

13. A lamina is hung on a nail in a wall. Prove that its center of gravity lies on a vertical line through the nail. (Remark: the tendency of a force to turn an object about a fixed point is proportional to the length of its lever arm and to that component of the force which is perpendicular to the lever. Keep in mind the parallelogram of forces.)

14. Explain why the tendency of the water in a dam to rotate a submerged gate about a horizontal hinge on the surface of the water is proportional to $\int_0^b y^2 c(y)\,dy$,

    where $c(y)$ is the length of the horizontal cross section of the gate at depth y and b is the height of the gate. Note that this is a second moment.

15. The kinetic energy of a particle of mass m and speed v is $\frac{1}{2}mv^2$. Now consider a lamina R spinning about an axis perpendicular to its plane. Why would its kinetic energy involve the definite integral, $I = \int_R r^2 f(P)\,dA$, where $f(P)$ is the density at P and r is the distance from P to the axis? This second moment, I, is called the *polar moment of inertia* of the lamina about the axis. Similarly, one can define moment of inertia about a line in the plane of R.

16. (See Exercise 15.) Let L_1 and L_2 be two perpendicular lines in R, and let L_3 be perpendicular to both and pass through their intersection. Prove that the polar moment of inertia (about L_3) is equal to the sum of the moments of inertia about L_1 and L_2.

17. (See Exercise 10, page 221.) Let I_0 be the polar moment of inertia of a lamina about an axis L_0 through its center of gravity, P_0. (The axis L_0 is perpendicular to the lamina.) Let P_1 be another point in the lamina and I_1 be the polar moment of inertia about an axis through P_1, perpendicular to the lamina. Prove that $I_1 = I_0 + Md^2$, where M is the mass of the lamina and $d = \overline{P_0 P_1}$. (Hint: Choose an x,y-coordinate system such that its origin is at the center of gravity. Observe that if $P_1 = (x_1,y_1)$, then we are considering $\int_R [(x - x_1)^2 + (y - y_1)^2] f(x,y)\,dA$, where f is density.)

18. In Exercise 17, where is the polar moment of inertia least? How could the center of gravity be defined relative to rotational motion?

19. (See Exercises 17 and 18.) Where is the most effective place to station a helicopter for fighting fires in a large forest R? Assume that the helicopter travels at a constant speed in a straight line toward a fire, that it goes to the fire as soon as the fire starts, that the fire spreads in a circle whose radius is proportional to the duration of the fire, and that the forest is flat, with the trees uniformly distributed.

          (Answer: the center of gravity of the forest)

20. (See Exercise 19.) Devise a simple practical procedure for finding the center of gravity of a forest. Assume that the forest is shown accurately on a map. What would you do if certain parts of the forest were denser or had more valuable wood?

2. Computing $\int_R f(P)\,dA$ by introducing rectangular coordinates in R. We will give an intuitive development of formulas for the rapid computation of a plane integral. We will not concern ourselves with questions such as "what properties of f and R assure the existence of $\int_R f(P)\,dA$?" Just as our reasoning on pages 132 and 133 made the fundamental theorem of calculus plausible, our reasoning in this chapter will be more persuasive than rigorous. We will not include proofs for the assertions we make. We were able to do so for the fundamental theorem of calculus (see the proof on page 139) because the law of the mean was available, and because an interval $[a,b]$ offers little complication. Suffice it to say that if R is convex and f is "continuous" [in the sense that if Q is near P, then $f(Q)$ is near $f(P)$], then the various formulas we present are valid. (A set R is convex if for every pair of points in R the line segment joining them is also in R.)

If $f(P) \geqslant 0$ for all P in R, then we can interpret $\int_R f(P)\,dA$ as the volume V of the solid whose base is R and which has at P a vertical cross section of length $f(P)$.

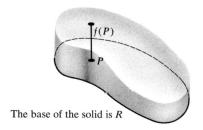

The vertical cross section of the solid at P has length $f(P)$

The base of the solid is R

Now, we introduce an x,y-coordinate system in the plane of R. Let $A(x)$ be the area of the cross section made by a plane perpendicular to the x axis and having abscissa x. Let us assume that each line parallel to the y axis meets the border of R at most twice, at the points $(x,y_1(x))$ and $(x,y_2(x))$, where $y_1(x) \leqslant y_2(x)$.

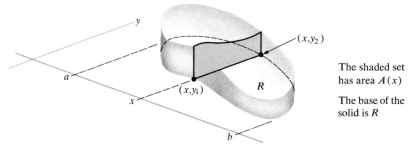

The shaded set has area $A(x)$

The base of the solid is R

Then, as we saw in Chap. 1,

$$V = \int_a^b A(x)\,dx$$

where a and b are defined in the diagram above.

But the area $A(x)$ is easily computed. We have

$$A(x) = \int_{y_1(x)}^{y_2(x)} f(x,y)\,dy$$

Hence we have a *repeated integral* whose value is V or $\int_R f(P)\,dR$, namely

$$\int_a^b \left[\int_{y_1(x)}^{y_2(x)} f(x,y)\,dy \right] dx$$

A repeated integral is also called an iterated integral. Of course, we could take cross sections perpendicular to the y axis. Then

$$\int_R f(P)\,dA = \int_c^d \left[\int_{x_1(y)}^{x_2(y)} f(x,y)\,dx \right] dy$$

where $c, d, x_1(y), x_2(y)$ are determined by R in a similar manner:

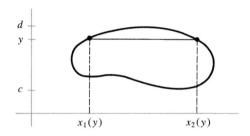

Example 1. Let us compute the definite integral $\int_R f(P)\,dA$ when R is the following rectangle and the function f is defined by $f(P) = (\overline{AP})^2$.

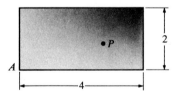

(We estimated this integral in Chap. 1, page 30.)

We introduce x,y coordinates in the expected manner.

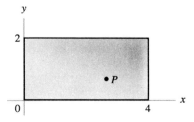

Then f has this description in rectangular coordinates: $f(x,y) = (\overline{AP})^2 = x^2 + y^2$.

To describe R, we observe that x takes all values from 0 to 4 and that for each x, y takes all values between 0 and 2. Thus $y_1(x) = 0$ and $y_2(x) = 2$, and we have

$$\int_R f(P)\,dA = \int_0^4 \left[\int_0^2 (x^2 + y^2)\,dy\right]dx$$

We must first compute

$$\int_0^2 (x^2 + y^2)\,dy$$

where x is *fixed* in $[0,4]$. To apply the fundamental theorem of calculus, we find a function $F(y)$ such that

$$\frac{dF}{dy} = x^2 + y^2$$

Keeping in mind that x is constant relative to this first integration, we see that

$$F(y) = x^2 y + \frac{y^3}{3}$$

is such a function. The appearance of x in its formula should not disturb us, since we have fixed x for the time being. By the fundamental theorem of calculus,

$$\int_0^2 (x^2 + y^2)\,dy = \left(x^2 y + \frac{y^3}{3}\right)\Bigg|_{y=0}^{y=2}$$

Thus $$\int_0^2 (x^2 + y^2)\,dy = \left[x^2(2) + \frac{2^3}{3}\right] - \left[x^2(0) + \frac{0^3}{3}\right] = 2x^2 + \tfrac{8}{3}$$

which, as might be anticipated, depends on x. We then compute

$$\int_0^4 (2x^2 + \tfrac{8}{3})\,dx$$

By the fundamental theorem of calculus,

$$\int_0^4 (2x^2 + \tfrac{8}{3})\,dx = \left(\frac{2x^3}{3} + \frac{8x}{3}\right)\Bigg|_0^4 = 160\tfrac{}{3}$$

Hence the two-dimensional definite integral has the value $160\tfrac{}{3}$.

Example 2. A triangular lamina is located as in this diagram.

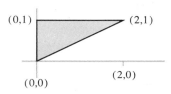

Its density at (x,y) is e^{y^2}. We find its mass. Now, this mass is

$$\int_R f(P)\,dA = \int_0^2 \left(\int_{y_1(x)}^{y_2(x)} e^{y^2}\,dy\right)dx$$

Observe that $y_2(x) = 1$, independently of x. However, $y_1(x)$ increases with x, and in fact, $y_1(x) = x/2$. So we face the repeated integral

$$\int_0^2 \left(\int_{x/2}^1 e^{y^2}\,dy \right) dx$$

Unfortunately, we can't use the fundamental theorem of calculus to compute $\int_{x/2}^1 e^{y^2}\,dy$, since e^{y^2} does not have an elementary antiderivative.

Let us try taking horizontal sections first; that is, let us use the equation

$$\int_R f(P)\,dA = \int_0^1 \left(\int_{x_1(y)}^{x_2(y)} e^{y^2}\,dx \right) dy$$

We must determine $x_1(y)$ and $x_2(y)$. For each y, we have $x_1(y) = 0$; also, since $(x_2(y),y)$ lies on the line $y = x/2$, we have $x_2(y) = 2y$.

Thus
$$\int_R f(P)\,dA = \int_0^1 \left(\int_0^{2y} e^{y^2}\,dx \right) dy$$

The first integration, $\int_0^{2y} e^{y^2}\,dx$, is easy, since we have a fixed y; the integrand is constant.

Thus
$$\int_0^{2y} e^{y^2}\,dx = e^{y^2} \int_0^{2y} 1\,dx = e^{y^2} x \Big|_{x=0}^{x=2y} = 2y\,e^{y^2}$$

The second definite integral is thus $\int_0^1 e^{y^2}\,2y\,dy$, which luckily can be evaluated by the

fundamental theorem of calculus, since $d(e^{y^2})/dy = e^{y^2}\,2y$:

$$\int_0^1 e^{y^2}\,2y\,dy = e^{y^2} \Big|_0^1 = e^{1^2} - e^{0^2} = e - 1$$

The total mass is $e - 1$.

Notice that computing a definite integral over R by this technique involves first, a wise choice of an x,y-coordinate system; second, a description of R and f relative to this coordinate system; and finally, the computation of *two* successive definite integrals over intervals. The order of these integrations should be considered carefully, since the computation may be much simpler in one than in the other.

Example 3. Let R be the region in the plane bounded by $y = x^2$, $x = 2$, and $y = 0$. At each point $P = (x,y)$ we erect an ordinate of height $3xy$. What is the volume of the resulting solid?

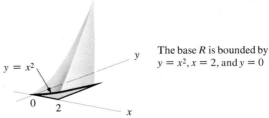

$y = x^2$

The base R is bounded by $y = x^2, x = 2,$ and $y = 0$

We know that the volume is $\int_R f(P)\, dA$, where $f(P)$ is the length of the interval cut off by the solid on a vertical line through P. We wish to compute $\int_R 3xy\, dA$. If we use cross sections parallel to the y axis first in forming our repeated integral, then R is described by

$$0 \leqslant y \leqslant x^2 \text{ for each } x \text{ in } [0,2].$$

Thus

$$\int_R 3xy\, dA = \int_0^2 \left(\int_0^{x^2} 3xy\, dy \right) dx$$

which is easy to compute: first, with x fixed,

$$\int_0^{x^2} 3xy\, dy \underset{\text{FTC}}{=} 3x\, \frac{y^2}{2}\bigg|_{y=0}^{y=x^2} = 3x\, \frac{(x^2)^2}{2} - 3x\, \frac{(0)^2}{2} = \frac{3x^5}{2}$$

and then

$$\int_0^2 \frac{3x^5}{2}\, dx \underset{\text{FTC}}{=} \frac{3x^6}{12}\bigg|_0^2 = 16$$

Alternatively, we can describe R in terms of cross sections parallel to the x axis:

$$\sqrt{y} \leqslant x \leqslant 2 \text{ for each } y \text{ in } [0,4]$$

Then

$$\int_R 3xy\, dA = \int_0^4 \left(\int_{\sqrt{y}}^2 3xy\, dx \right) dy$$

which, as the reader may verify, equals 16.

Example 4. Assume that a lamina occupies R of the preceding example and that its density at (x,y) is $3xy$. We will find the balancing line parallel to the y axis, that is, the abscissa, $\bar{x}$, of its center of gravity.

By the preceding section,

$$\bar{x} = \frac{\int_R x f(P)\, dA}{\int_R f(P)\, dA} = \frac{\int_R 3x^2y\, dA}{\int_R 3xy\, dA}$$

where f is the density function, $f(x,y) = 3xy$.

The total mass, $\int_R 3xy\, dA$, involves the same definite integral we computed in Example 3. Thus $\int_R 3xy\, dA = 16$.

To compute $\int_R 3x^2y\, dA$, we use a repeated integral. Since R is the same as in Example 3, we have

$$\int_R 3x^2y\, dA = \int_0^2 \left(\int_0^{x^2} 3x^2y\, dy \right) dx$$

which, as a routine computation shows, equals $\int_0^2 \frac{3x^6}{2}\, dx = \frac{192}{7}$

Thus

$$\bar{x} = \frac{192/7}{16} = \frac{12}{7}$$

a reasonable answer, since $\bar{x}$ must be between 0 and 2.

EXERCISES

1. Compute $\displaystyle\int_0^4 \left(\int_{\sqrt{y}}^2 3xy\, dx \right) dy$.   (Answer: 16)

2. (a) Draw the region R whose description is "$x^2 \leqslant y \leqslant x$ for each x in $[0,1]$."

(b) Obtain a description of R by vertical cross sections.

3. (a) Draw the region R whose description is "$-\sqrt{4-y^2} \leqslant x \leqslant \sqrt{4-y^2}$ for each y in $[-2,2]$."

   (b) Obtain a description of R by vertical cross sections.

4. (a) Draw the set R that is bounded by the four lines $y = 1$, $y = 2$, $y = x$, $y = x/3$.

   (b) Describe R in terms of cross sections. (Choose the direction that is most convenient.)

5. Compute $\displaystyle\int_0^3\left(\int_x^3 \frac{\sin y}{y}\,dy\right)dx$. [Warning: $\dfrac{\sin y}{y}$ does not have an elementary anti-

   derivative.]   (Answer: $1 - \cos 3$)

6. Compute (a) $\displaystyle\int_0^1 x^2 y\,dy$; (b) $\displaystyle\int_0^1 x^2 y\,dx$.   [Answer: (a) $x^2/2$; (b) $y/3$]

7. Compute (a) $\displaystyle\int_1^{x^2}(x+y)\,dy$; (b) $\displaystyle\int_y^{y^2}(x+y)\,dx$.

   [Answer: (a) $x^3 + x^4/2 - x - \frac{1}{2}$; (b) $y^4/2 + y^3 - 3y^2/2$]

8. Compute the easier of (a) $\displaystyle\int_0^1 \sin(x^2 y)\,dy$; (b) $\displaystyle\int_0^1 \sin(x^2 y)\,dx$.

9. The density at $P = (x,y)$ in a square is $\sqrt{xy}$, where the vertices of the square are $(0,0)$, $(0,2)$ $(2,0)$, $(2,2)$. Find its (a) mass; (b) moment about the x axis; (c) moment of inertia about the x axis; (d) moment of inertia about $y = 1$; and (e) moment of inertia about a line through the center of gravity parallel to the x axis.

10. Compute $\displaystyle\int_0^1\left(\int_0^x \frac{1}{1+x^2}\,dy\right)dx$ and the repeated integral with the order of integration

    reversed.   (Answer: $\ln\sqrt{2}$)

11. Let $f(x,y) = y^2 e^{xy^2}$ and R be the triangle bounded by $y = a$, $y = x/2$, $y = x$.

    (a) Set up two repeated integrals for $\int_R f(P)\,dA$ using cross sections parallel to the axes.

    (b) Evaluate the easier one.

    [Answer: (b) $(\frac{1}{2})e^{a^2}(a^2 - 1) + \frac{1}{2}$]

12. Repeat Exercise 9, but replace the square with the region bounded by the curve $y = x^2$ and by the lines $y = 0$ and $x = 1$.

13. Let $f(P) = f(x,y) = e^{y^3}$.

    (a) Devise a region R in the plane such that $\int_R f(p)\,dA$ can be evaluated with the aid of a repeated integral.

    (b) Devise a region R in the plane such that $\int_R f(p)\,dA$ cannot be evaluated with the aid of a repeated integral, and describe the difficulty.

□ □ □

14. Let R be the rectangle with vertices $(0,0)$, $(3,0)$, $(3,2)$, $(0,2)$. Let f, defined on R, have the property that $|f(P) - f(Q)| \leqslant 2\,\overline{PQ}$.

    (a) Why does $\displaystyle\int_0^2 f(x,y)\,dy$ exist?

    (b) Let $G(x) = \displaystyle\int_0^2 f(x,y)\,dy$. Show that G is continuous.

15. (See Exercise 14, which we continue.) Cut R into n^2 congruent small rectangles by partitioning $[0,3]$ by $x_0, x_1, \ldots, x_n$ and $[0,2]$ by $y_0, y_1, \ldots, y_n$.

(a) Why is $\sum\limits_{i,j=1}^{n} f(x_i, y_j)(x_i - x_{i-1})(y_j - y_{j-1})$ an approximation to $\int_R f(P)\,dA$?

(b) Why would you expect (without thinking of volumes) that the sum in (a) would

be close to $\displaystyle\int_0^3 \left(\int_0^2 f(x,y)\,dy \right) dx$?

16. Let R be the set bounded by the curve $y = \sqrt{x}$ and the line $y = x$. Let f be defined as follows: $f(x,y) = (\sin y)/y$ if $y \neq 0$ and $f(x,0) = 1$. Compute $\int_R f(P)\,dA$.

(Answer: $1 - \sin 1$)

3. Computing $\int_R f(P)\,dA$ by introducing polar coordinates in R.

In Sec. 2 we showed how a repeated integral depending on rectangular coordinates can be used to evaluate $\int_R f(P)\,dA$. It could happen that f or R has a more convenient description in polar coordinates (r,θ) than in rectangular coordinates. Let us see which repeated integral relative to polar coordinates yields $\int_R f(P)\,dA$.

Again let us assume that $f(P) \geqslant 0$ and interpret $\int_R f(P)\,dA$ as the volume of a solid. Let us compute the volume by considering cross sections of the solid for fixed r, letting θ vary from $\theta_1(r)$ to $\theta_2(r)$.

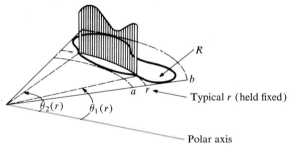

The area of this cross section, whose base is an arc of a circle, is

$$A = \int_{\theta_1(r)}^{\theta_2(r)} f(r,\theta)\, r\, d\theta$$

To see this, partition $[\theta_1(r), \theta_2(r)]$ by $\theta_0, \theta_1, \ldots, \theta_n$ and select θ_i^* in $[\theta_{i-1}, \theta_i]$ for each i; we obtain, as a local approximation to the area of the cross section,

$$f(r, \theta_i^*)\, r(\theta_i - \theta_{i-1})$$

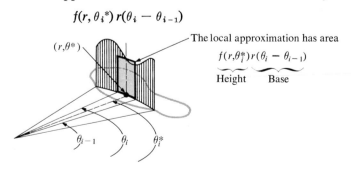

If we denote by $A(r)$ the area of the typical cross section,

$$A(r) = \int_{\theta_1(r)}^{\theta_2(r)} f(r,\theta)\, r\, d\theta$$

then it seems reasonable that the volume is

$$\text{Volume} = \int_a^b A(r)\, dr$$

just as $\int_a^b A(x)\, dx$ = volume (page 17), where $A(x)$ denotes the area of a cross section made by a plane. [We could think of straightening the curved cross sections, just as we did in the shell technique (see the first illustration, page 242).]

We thus suspect that

Note the r

$$\int_R f(P)\, dA = \int_a^b \left[\int_{\theta_1(r)}^{\theta_2(r)} f(r,\theta)\, r\, d\theta \right] dr$$

Example 1.   Let R be a disk of radius 3. Let $f(P)$ be the square of the distance from P to a certain fixed diameter of the disk. We compute $\int_R f(P)\, dA$. Since R is a disk, it has a simple description in polar coordinates if we place the pole at the center of the disk:

For each r in $[0,3]$,
θ goes from 0 to 2π

(r,θ)

Polar axis

We have $\theta_1(r) = 0$, $\theta_2(r) = 2\pi$.

We now describe f. It is easiest to place the fixed diameter along the polar axis. Then $f(r,\theta) = |r \sin\theta|^2 = (r \sin\theta)^2$.

$P = (r, \theta)$

The fixed diameter
lies on the polar axis

$PQ = |r \sin\theta|$

Note this r; it comes
from the use of
polar coordinates,
not from f

Thus

$$\int_R f(P)\, dA = \int_0^3 \left[\int_0^{2\pi} (r \sin\theta)^2\, r\, d\theta \right] dr$$

$$= \int_0^3 \left[\int_0^{2\pi} r^3 \sin^2\theta\, d\theta \right] dr$$

First we compute the inner definite integral:

$$\int_0^{2\pi} r^3 \sin^2\theta\, d\theta = r^3 \int_0^{2\pi} \sin^2\theta\, d\theta = r^3 \int_0^{2\pi} \frac{1 - \cos 2\theta}{2}\, d\theta$$

$$\underset{\text{FTC}}{=} r^3 \left(\frac{\theta}{2} - \frac{\sin 2\theta}{4} \right) \Big|_0^{2\pi} = \pi r^3$$

Then we compute

$$\int_0^3 \pi r^3 \, dr \underset{\text{FTC}}{=} \frac{\pi r^4}{4} \Big|_0^3 = \frac{81\pi}{4}$$

Just as it is sometimes more convenient to consider the repeated integral in which cross sections are taken for fixed x rather than for fixed y, it is also convenient to consider, in polar coordinates, cross sections for fixed θ. As a matter of fact, the latter are more commonly used.

Holding θ fixed gives us a cross section above a ray on which r varies from $r_1(\theta)$ to $r_2(\theta)$:

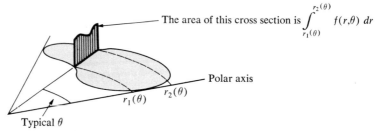

The area of this cross section is $\int_{r_1(\theta)}^{r_2(\theta)} f(r,\theta) \, dr$

Polar axis

$r_1(\theta)$ $r_2(\theta)$

Typical θ

This cross section, determined by fixed θ, is simpler than that determined by a fixed r (for it is flat, not curved), and its area is

$$A(\theta) = \int_{r_1(\theta)}^{r_2(\theta)} f(r,\theta) \, dr$$

But these cross sections for various θ are not parallel. Knowing $A(\theta)$ for each θ is not enough to enable us to determine the volume of the solid. For example, these two simple solids have the same $A(\theta)$ for each θ, yet they clearly have different volumes:

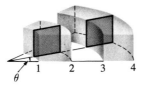

The area of each rectangle is 1

1   2   3   4

θ

Nevertheless, there is a repeated integral for $\int_R f(P) \, dA$ in which cross sections are taken along rays. We will obtain it and show later, in Example 2, that it is quite useful.

Let us now consider the simplest type of set R relative to polar coordinates, a section of a ring:

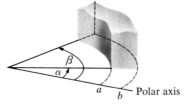

The base R is described by: r goes from a to b for each θ in $[\alpha, \beta]$

β

α

a b Polar axis

Let us approximate $\int_R f(P)\,dA$ by an approximating sum using a convenient choice for the partition. If we partition $[\alpha,\beta]$ by $\theta_0, \theta_1, \ldots, \theta_n$ and $[a,b]$ by $r_0, r_1, \ldots, r_n$, then these two partitions induce a partition of R into n^2 little regions, of which only one is shown, the shaded region in this figure:

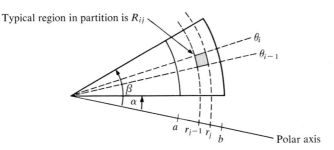

A little arithmetic and geometry show that the area A_{ij} of this typical region R_{ij} is precisely

$$\frac{r_j + r_{j-1}}{2}(r_j - r_{j-1})(\theta_i - \theta_{i-1})$$

To form an approximating sum we must select for each i and each j a point P_{ij} in R_{ij}. For convenience, we use

$$P_{ij} = \left(\frac{r_j + r_{j-1}}{2}, \theta_i\right)$$

P_{ij} appears this way in the typical R_{ij}:

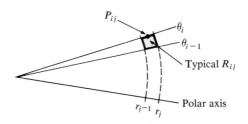

Thus

$$\sum_{i=1}^{n}\left[\sum_{j=1}^{n} f(P_{ij})\,A_{ij}\right]$$

is an approximation to $\int_R f(P)\,dA$. Now

$$\sum_{i=1}^{n}\sum_{j=1}^{n} f(P_{ij})\,A_{ij} = \sum_{i=1}^{n}\sum_{j=1}^{n}\left[f\left(\frac{r_j + r_{j-1}}{2}, \theta_i\right)\frac{r_j + r_{j-1}}{2}\left(r_j - r_{j-1}\right)\left(\theta_i - \theta_{i-1}\right)\right]$$

$$= \sum_{i=1}^{n}\left[\sum_{j=1}^{n} f\left(\frac{r_j + r_{j-1}}{2}, \theta_i\right)\frac{r_j + r_{j-1}}{2}\left(r_j - r_{j-1}\right)\right](\theta_i - \theta_{i-1})$$

Let us denote $(r_j + r_{j-1})/2$ by r_j^*. Then the bracketed sum in the preceding repeated summation is

$$\sum_{j=1}^{n} f(r_j^*, \theta_i)\,(r_j^*)\,(r_j - r_{j-1})$$

(*Notice the factor r_j^* in this sum.*) Such a sum is an approximation to

$$\int_a^b f(r, \theta_i)\,r\,dr$$

(*Notice the factor r in the integrand.*) Letting $g(\theta) = \int_a^b f(r, \theta)\,r\,dr$, we expect that, for fine partitions, $\sum_{j=1}^{n} f(r_j^*, \theta_i)\,(r_j^*)\,(r_j - r_{j-1})$ is close to $g(\theta_i)$. Therefore, when the partitions are fine, we expect the repeated sum

$$\sum_{i=1}^{n} \left[\sum_{j=1}^{n} f(r_j^*, \theta_i)\,(r_j^*)\,(r_j - r_{j-1}) \right] (\theta_i - \theta_{i-1})$$

to be close to $\sum_{i=1}^{n} g(\theta_i)\,(\theta_i - \theta_{i-1})$. But in turn, the latter sum would be close to

$$\int_\alpha^\beta g(\theta)\,d\theta$$

Therefore it seems reasonable that

$$\int_R f(P)\,dA = \int_\alpha^\beta g(\theta)\,d\theta = \int_\alpha^\beta \left[\int_a^b f(r, \theta)\,r\,dr \right] d\theta$$

and we have obtained a second repeated integral for $\int_R f(P)\,dA$. *Notice the factor r in the repeated integral.* If the region R is more complicated, and for each θ in $[a,b]$, r runs from $r_1(\theta)$ to $r_2(\theta)$, we expect

$$\int_R f(P)\,dA = \int_\alpha^\beta \left[\int_{r_1(\theta)}^{r_2(\theta)} f(r, \theta)\,r\,dr \right] d\theta$$

To remember the presence of the extra r keep this little picture in mind.

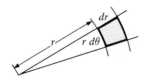

The area is roughly "height" times "width": $(r\,d\theta)(dr)$ or $r\,dr\,d\theta$

Contrast this with rectangular coordinates:

The area is $dx\,dy$; no extra coefficient is needed

The presence of the factor r in the expression $r\,dr\,d\theta$ made the *derivation* of the appropriate repeated integral in polar coordinates more difficult than that in rectangular coordinates. However, the *computation* of the repeated integral in polar coordinates is not any more difficult. For certain f and R, polar coordinates may be more convenient, as the next example shows.

Example 2. A sphere of radius a has its center at the pole of a polar coordinate system. Find the volume of the part of the sphere that lies above the plane region bounded by the curve $r = a \cos \theta$.

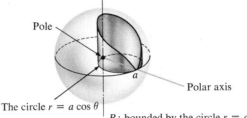

Pole

a

Polar axis

The circle $r = a \cos \theta$

R : bounded by the circle $r = a \cos \theta$

Observe that the lateral surface of the solid in question is part of the surface of a right circular cylinder. Its top surface is part of the surface of a sphere, and its base is the region R. It is not a solid of revolution; its cross sections by parallel planes—no matter how we choose the direction—are difficult to compute. It will, however, be easy to compute the volume by an appropriate repeated integral in polar coordinates.

We must describe f and R in polar coordinates, where $f(P)$ is the length of a cross section of the solid made by a vertical line through P. R is described by: r takes on values from 0 to $a \cos \theta$ for each θ in $[-\pi/2, \pi/2]$. To obtain $f(r,\theta)$ we use the Pythagorean theorem and deduce that $f(r,\theta) = \sqrt{a^2 - r^2}$.

a $f(r,\theta)$

r (r,θ)

$r^2 + [f(r,\theta)]^2 = a^2$

Thus $$\text{Volume} = \int_R f(P)\,dA = \int_{-\pi/2}^{\pi/2} \left(\int_0^{a \cos \theta} \sqrt{a^2 - r^2}\, r\,dr \right) d\theta$$

(*Notice the factor r in the integrand.*) Exploiting symmetry, we will compute half the volume, keeping θ in $[0, \pi/2]$, and then we will double the result.

$$\int_0^{a \cos \theta} \sqrt{a^2 - r^2}\, r\,dr \underset{\text{FTC}}{=} \left. \frac{-(a^2 - r^2)^{3/2}}{3} \right|_0^{a \cos \theta}$$

$$= -\left[\frac{(a^2 - a^2 \cos^2 \theta)^{3/2}}{3} - \frac{(a^2)^{3/2}}{3} \right]$$

$$= \frac{a^3}{3} - \frac{(a^2 - a^2 \cos^2 \theta)^{3/2}}{3}$$

$$= \frac{a^3}{3} - \frac{a^3(1 - \cos^2 \theta)^{3/2}}{3} = \frac{a^3}{3}(1 - \sin^3 \theta)$$

The second integration is then carried out:

$$\int_0^{\pi/2} \frac{a^3}{3}(1 - \sin^3 \theta)\, d\theta = \int_0^{\pi/2} \left[\frac{a^3}{3} - \left(\frac{a^3}{3}\right)(1 - \cos^2 \theta)\sin \theta\right] d\theta$$

$$\underset{\text{FTC}}{=} \left[\frac{a^3}{3}\theta + \frac{a^3}{3}\cos \theta - \frac{a^3}{3}\frac{\cos^3 \theta}{3}\right]_0^{\pi/2}$$

$$= \frac{a^3}{3}\frac{\pi}{2} - \left(\frac{a^3}{3} - \frac{a^3}{9}\right) = a^3\left(\frac{\pi}{6} - \frac{1}{3} + \frac{1}{9}\right)$$

$$= a^3\frac{3\pi - 6 + 2}{18} = a^3\frac{3\pi - 4}{18}$$

The total volume is twice as large, $a^3\dfrac{3\pi - 4}{9}$.

EXERCISES

1. Consider this region R, whose vertices are given in rectangular coordinates.

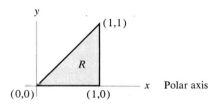

Describe R, using (a) rectangular coordinates and horizontal sections; (b) polar coordinates and cross sections by rays.

(Answer: (a) x goes from y to 1 for each y in $[0,1]$; (b) r goes from 0 to sec θ for each θ in $[0, \pi/4]$)

2. Describe R of Exercise 1 in polar coordinates by indicating how θ varies for each r. (Hint: The formula for θ depends on whether $r \leqslant 1$ or $r \geqslant 1$.)

3. Describe the disk of radius a relative to rectangular- and polar-coordinate systems whose origin is at the center of the disk, using (a) cross sections parallel to the y axis; (b) cross sections by rays; (c) cross sections by circles (that is, fixed r).

4. Describe f in rectangular and in polar coordinates if $f(P)$ is (a) the square of the distance from P to the polar axis (which is placed to coincide with the x axis); (b) the square of the distance from P to the origin.

5. Describe f in polar coordinates if (a) $f(x,y) = x$; (b) $f(x,y) = \sqrt{x^2 + y^2}$.

6. Let F be the constant function, $F(P) = 1$ for all P in R. Let R be bounded by the curve $r = f(\theta)$ and the rays $\theta = \alpha$ and $\theta = \beta$. Show by direct computations that (a) $\int_\alpha^\beta \left(\int_0^{f(\theta)} F(r,\theta)\, r\, dr\right) d\theta$ is the area of R, and (b) $\int_R F(P)\, dA$ is the area of R.

7. (a) Devise and draw a solid whose volume would be represented by the definite integral in Example 1.

(b) Relate the definite integral in Example 1 to the moment of inertia of a suitable lamina with appropriate density function.

8. Show that the formula for the area of R_{ij} on page 259 is correct.

9. Give an intuitive derivation of the formula

$$\int_R f(P)\,dA = \int_a^b \left(\int_{\theta_1(r)}^{\theta_2(r)} f(r,\theta)\, r\, d\theta \right) dr$$

by using the technique we used to obtain the formula for the opposite order of integration.

10. Why did we choose P_{ij} to have the r coordinate $(r_j + r_{j-1})/2$?

11. Show that the moment about the y axis of a region R whose description in polar coordinates is "for each θ in $[\alpha,\beta]$, r goes from 0 to $f(\theta)$" is equal to

$$\int_\alpha^\beta [f(\theta)]^3 (\cos \theta)/3 \, d\theta.$$

(The density at each P is 1.)

12. Compute $\displaystyle\int_0^{\pi/4} \left(\int_{\sin\theta}^{\cos\theta} r\,dr \right) d\theta.$ (Answer: ½)

13. Compute the mass of the lamina inside one loop of the curve $r = \sin 2\theta$ if the density at (r,θ) is r^2.   (Answer: $3\pi/128$)

14. Compute $\displaystyle\int_0^{\pi/2} \left(\int_0^{\cos\theta} r\sin\theta\,dr \right) d\theta.$ (Answer: ⅙)

15. (a) Compute $\displaystyle\int_0^{\pi/2} \left(\int_0^{\cos\theta} r^2\sin\theta\,dr \right) d\theta$; (b) compute $\displaystyle\int_0^{\pi/2} \left(\int_0^{\cos\theta} r^3\sin\theta\,dr \right) d\theta.$

16. Let R_1, R_2, R_3 be the three regions indicated in the diagram below, and $f(P) = e^{-r^2}$, where r is the distance from P to the origin. Hence $f(r,\theta) = e^{-r^2}$ and $f(x,y) = e^{-x^2-y^2}$.

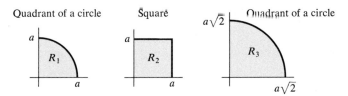

Quadrant of a circle   Square   Quadrant of a circle

(Observe that R_1 is inside R_2, and R_2 is inside R_3.)

(a) Show that $\displaystyle\int_{R_1} f(P)\,dA = \frac{\pi}{4(1-e^{-a^2})}$ and $\displaystyle\int_{R_3} f(P)\,dA = \frac{\pi}{4(1-e^{-2a^2})}.$

(b) By considering $\int_{R_2} f(P)\,dA$, and the results in (a), show that

$$\frac{\pi}{4(1-e^{-a^2})} < \left(\int_0^a e^{-x^2}\,dx \right)^2 < \frac{\pi}{4(1-e^{-2a^2})}$$

(c) Show that $\displaystyle\int_0^\infty e^{-x^2}\,dx = \frac{\sqrt{\pi}}{2}$

"Once when lecturing to a class he [the physicist Lord Kelvin] used the word 'mathematician' and then interrupting himself asked his class: 'Do you know what a mathematician is?' Stepping to his blackboard he wrote upon it: $\int_{-\infty}^{\infty} e^{-x^2}\,dx = \sqrt{\pi}.$ Then putting his finger on what he had written, he turned to his class and said, 'A mathematician is one to whom that is as obvious as that twice two makes four is to you.'" From S. P. Thompson, "Life of Lord Kelvin," Macmillan & Co., Ltd., London, 1910.

The mathematician Littlewood wrote, "Many things are not accessible to intuition at all, the value of $\int_0^\infty e^{-x^2}\,dx$ for instance." From J. E. Littlewood, Newton and the Attraction of the Sphere, *Math. Gaz.*, **32** (1948).

17. Find the moment of inertia of a homogeneous square lamina of mass M and side a about its center, using (*a*) rectangular coordinates; (*b*) polar coordinates.

(Answer: $Ma^2/6$)

18. Describe the following figure in terms of (*a*) rectangular coordinates and vertical cross sections; (*b*) rectangular coordinates and horizontal cross sections; (*c*) polar coordinates and ray cross sections; (*d*) polar coordinates and circular cross sections.

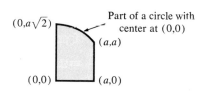

19. In the theory of the spread of epidemics it is assumed that the probability that a contagious individual infects an individual D miles away depends only on D. Consider a population that is uniformly distributed in a circular city R whose radius is 1 mile. Assume that the probability we mentioned is proportional to $2 - D$. For a fixed point Q let $f(P) = 2 - $ (distance from P to Q).

(*a*) Why is $\int_R f(P)\,dA$ a reasonable measure of the exposure of a person residing at Q?

(*b*) Compute this definite integral when Q is the center of town and when Q is on the edge of town.

(*c*) In view of (*b*), which is the safer place?

□ □ □

20. Compute the volume in Example 2 by the repeated integral in polar coordinates in the order opposite to the one used in Example 2.

21. Let f be a continuous function defined for all θ in $[0,\pi]$, with $f(0) = f(\pi)$. Assume that $\int_0^\pi f(\theta)\,d\theta = 0 = \int_0^\pi f(\theta)\cos\theta\,d\theta = \int_0^\pi f(\theta)\sin\theta\,d\theta$. Prove that there are at least two numbers a and b such that $0 < a < b < \pi$ and $f(a) = 0$ and $f(b) = 0$. [Hint: Why is there at least one a such that $f(a) = 0$? If there is only one root a, such that $0 < a < \pi$, then consider $\int_0^\pi f(x)\sin(x - a)\,dx$.]

22. (See Exercises 11 and 21.) Prove that the centroid of a region R bounded by a curve which has the equation $r = g(\theta)$ in polar coordinates (where g is continuous) bisects at least three chords.

23. Let f be a continuous nonconstant function such that $f(\theta + 2\pi) = f(\theta)$, and $f(0) \neq 0$.

Show that if $\int_0^{2\pi} f(\theta)\, d\theta = 0$, then there are at least two numbers, a_1, a_2, such that $0 < a_1 < a_2 < 2\pi$, $f(a_1) = 0 = f(a_2)$, and f "changes sign" at each of the roots.

24. (See Exercise 23.) Assume that f satisfies the hypotheses in Exercise 23 and that

$$\int_0^{2\pi} f(\theta) \sin \theta\, d\theta = 0 = \int_0^{2\pi} f(\theta) \cos \theta\, d\theta$$

Show that there are at least four numbers $0 < a_1 < a_2 < a_3 < a_4 < 2\pi$ where $f(\theta) = 0$ and f changes sign. Suggestions: Why can't there be exactly three such numbers? If a_1 and a_2 are the only places between 0 and 2π where f changes sign, consider

$$\int_0^{2\pi} f(\theta) \sin \frac{\theta - a_1}{2} \sin \frac{\theta - a_2}{2}\, d\theta$$

and argue as in Exercise 21, or as in Exercise 12 of page 221. Recall that $\sin A \sin B = \frac{1}{2}[\cos (A - B) - \cos (A + B)]$.

25. (See Exercises 11 and 24.) Let P be the centroid of a plane region R bounded by a "smooth" curve that doesn't pass through P. Show that there are at least four rays from P that cut the curve at a right angle. (Hint: Let $r = g(\theta)$ describe the curve in polar coordinates with P as the pole, and apply Exercise 24 to the function $f(\theta) = g^2(\theta)\, g'(\theta)$. (This implies that the lamina can be balanced on at least four points of its border. Experiments with models suggest that any homogeneous solid can be balanced on at least four points of its surface, but this has not been proved.)

26. (See Exercise 25.) With the same hypothesis as in Exercise 25, prove that there are at least four different θ, with $0 \leqslant \theta < 2\pi$, such that $g(\theta) = g\left(\theta + \dfrac{\pi}{2}\right)$.

27. In Example 2 we computed half the volume and doubled the result. Evaluate the repeated integral

$$\int_{-\pi/2}^{-\pi/2} \left(\int_0^{a \cos \theta} \sqrt{a^2 - r^2}\, r\, dr \right) d\theta$$

directly. The result should still be $a^3 (3\pi - 4)/9$.

28. Using the fact that $\int_0^\infty e^{-x^2}\, dx = \sqrt{\pi}/2$, show that (a) $\int_0^\infty e^{-4x^2}\, dx = \sqrt{\pi}/4$; (b) $\int_0^\infty (e^{-x}/\sqrt{x})\, dx = \sqrt{\pi}$; (c) $\int_0^\infty x^2 e^{-x^2}\, dx = \sqrt{\pi}/4$; (d) $\int_0^\infty \sqrt{x}\, e^{-x}\, dx = \sqrt{\pi}/2$.

29. Using the equality of repeated integrals in rectangular coordinates in both orders, deduce the equality of the two repeated integrals in polar coordinates. From this obtain an alternative argument for the validity of the equation

$$\int_R f(P)\, dA = \int_\alpha^\beta \int_{r_1(\theta)}^{r_2(\theta)} f(r,\theta)\, r\, dr\, d\theta$$

4. Coordinate systems in three dimensions and their volume elements.

In Sec. 3 we used coordinate systems and repeated integrals to evaluate definite integrals over plane sets. In Sec. 5 we shall do the same for definite integrals over solid sets. In this section we examine the geometry of the most useful coordinate systems in three dimensions.

Rectangular coordinates (in three dimensions) are a natural extension of rectangular coordinates in the plane. A point P is described by three numbers (x,y,z), where z records the distance from P to the xy plane (positive if P is above the xy plane, negative if P is below).

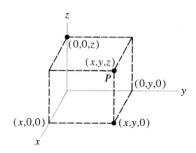

If we consider all points $P = (x,y,z)$ for which $x = 2$, we obtain a plane parallel to the yz plane. Rectangular coordinates are especially suitable for describing planes or the cross sections of solids bounded by planes.

Example 1.   We describe the cross sections of the tetrahedron bounded by the planes $x = 0$, $y = 0$, $z = 0$, and $x + y + z = 1$. (That $x + y + z = 1$ is the equation of a plane is shown on page 388.)

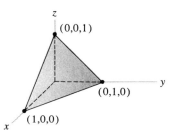

For any x in [0,1] the cross section of the tetrahedron made by a plane parallel to the yz plane and passing through $(x,0,0)$ is a triangle, such as the one shaded in this diagram.

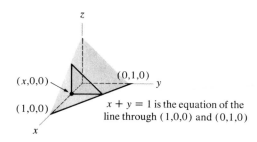

$x + y = 1$ is the equation of the
line through $(1,0,0)$ and $(0,1,0)$

On this typical triangle, y varies from 0 until $x + y = 1$, that is, until $y = 1 - x$.

Finally, z varies from 0 until $x + y + z = 1$ for each such x and y, that is, until $z = 1 - x - y$. Briefly, this is our description of the tetrahedron:

$$0 \leqslant x \leqslant 1 \qquad 0 \leqslant y \leqslant 1 - x \qquad 0 \leqslant z \leqslant 1 - x - y$$

In order to develop the appropriate repeated integral in Sec. 5, we will need the volume of the solid R_{ijk}, consisting of all points $P = (x,y,z)$ such that we have

$$x \text{ in } [x_{i-1}, x_i] \qquad y \text{ in } [y_{j-1}, y_j] \qquad z \text{ in } [z_{k-1}, z_k]$$

where $x_{i-1}, x_i, y_{j-1}, y_j, z_{k-1}, z_k$ are fixed numbers. R_{ijk} is a rectangular box of volume

$$(x_i - x_{i-1})(y_j - y_{j-1})(z_k - z_{k-1})$$

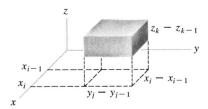

If we call the lengths of three perpendicular edges of the box dx, dy, dz, then the volume is

$$dx\, dy\, dz$$

Cylindrical coordinates combine polar coordinates in the plane with the z of rectangular coordinates in space. Each point P in space receives the name (r, θ, z) as in this diagram:

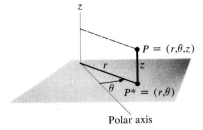

Polar axis

We are free to choose the direction of the polar axis; usually it will coincide with the x axis of an (x, y, z) system. Note that (r, θ, z) is directly above (or below) $P^* = (r,\theta)$ in the (r,θ) plane. Since the set of all points $P = (r, \theta, z)$ for which $r = k$, some constant, is a circular cylinder, this coordinate system is especially convenient for describing such cylinders.

Example 2. We describe by cross section the solid inside the cylinder $r = 3$ and inside the sphere $x^2 + y^2 + z^2 = 5^2$. It consists of a solid cylinder and two rounded caps. We place the polar axis along the x axis.

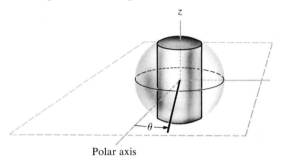

The sphere has radius 5; the cylinder has radius 3

Polar axis

It would be awkward to examine the behavior of r and θ for fixed z, since for some z (such as $z = \frac{9}{2}$) the cross section involves the sphere, while for other z (such as $z = 0$) the cross section involves only the cylinder. It is best to take cross sections with either fixed θ or fixed r. We take cross sections with fixed r. Now, r varies from 0 to 3 and θ varies from 0 to 2π for each r. So far, we have obtained the polar-coordinate description of the "shadow" or projection, on the (r,θ) plane, of the solid. For each r and θ considered, z varies in a manner determined by the sphere. The sphere $x^2 + y^2 + z^2 = 5^2$ has the equation

$$r^2 + z^2 = 5^2$$

in cylindrical coordinates, since $x^2 + y^2 = r^2$. Thus for each r and θ, we see that z varies from

$$-\sqrt{5^2 - r^2} \quad \text{to} \quad \sqrt{5^2 - r^2}$$

The solid is therefore described by

$$0 \leqslant r \leqslant 3 \qquad 0 \leqslant \theta \leqslant 2\pi \qquad -\sqrt{5^2 - r^2} \leqslant z \leqslant \sqrt{5^2 - r^2}$$

In Sec. 5 we will need the volume of the solid consisting of all points $P = (r, \theta, z)$ such that we have

$$r \text{ in } [r_{i-1}, r_i] \qquad \theta \text{ in } [\theta_{j-1}, \theta_j] \qquad z \text{ in } [z_{k-1}, z_k]$$

This solid, which has four flat surfaces and two curved surfaces, has volume

$$\frac{r_i + r_{i-1}}{2}(r_i - r_{i-1})(\theta_j - (\theta_j - \theta_{j-1})(z_k - z_{k-1})$$

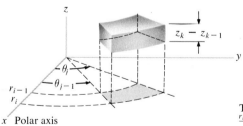

The volume of the shaded set is
$$\frac{r_i + r_{i-1}}{2}(r_i - r_{i-1})(\theta_j - \theta_{j-1})(z_k - z_{k-1})$$

If we let $r = (r_i + r_{i-1})/2$, and $dr, d\theta, dz$ denote the differences, $r_i - r_{i-1}, \theta_j - \theta_{j-1}$, and $z_k - z_{k-1}$, respectively, then the volume is simply

$$r \, dr \, d\theta \, dz$$

Note, once again, the appearance of the extra r. (It will appear in the repeated integral based on cylindrical coordinates, just as r appears in the repeated integral based on polar coordinates.)

Spherical coordinates are designed for the concise description of cones and spheres. A point P is described by three numbers (ρ, ϕ, θ):

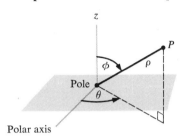

θ is the same as in cylindrical coordinates; ϕ is the indicated angle from the z axis $(0 \leqslant \phi \leqslant \pi)$; and ρ is the distance from P to the pole

Observe that the sphere $x^2 + y^2 + z^2 = 5^2$ now has the simpler equation $\rho = 5$. Note also that the set of points for which ϕ is fixed is the surface of a cone whose axis is the z axis, and the set of points for which θ is prescribed is a half-plane bordered by the z axis. Thus the set of points for which both ϕ and θ are fixed is a ray emanating from the origin, namely the intersection of the surface of a cone and a half-plane whose edge is the axis of the cone.

We can obtain the rectangular coordinates of (ρ, ϕ, θ) by inspection of this diagram:

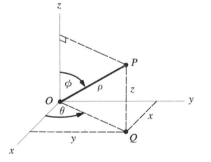

$z = OP \cos \phi = \rho \cos \phi$
$y = OQ \sin \theta = \rho \sin \phi \sin \theta$
$x = OQ \cos \theta = \rho \sin \phi \cos \theta$

Example 3. We describe by spherical-coordinate cross sections the indicated solid cone:

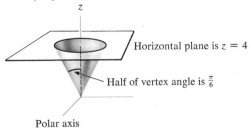

Horizontal plane is $z = 4$

Half of vertex angle is $\frac{\pi}{6}$

Polar axis

It is usually most convenient to let θ and ϕ vary first, and ρ last.

Now, ϕ varies from 0 to $\pi/6$. For each fixed ϕ, we see that θ varies from 0 to 2π (since the cone is a solid of revolution about the z axis). We now examine the behavior of ρ for points in the cone and on this ray of given ϕ and θ. Since the cone has its vertex at the origin, ρ varies from 0 until $z = 4$, that is, until $\rho \cos \phi = 4$, hence $\rho = 4 \sec \phi$. This is the description of the cone:

$$0 \leqslant \phi \leqslant \frac{\pi}{6} \qquad 0 \leqslant \theta \leqslant 2\pi \qquad 0 \leqslant \rho \leqslant 4 \sec \phi$$

In Sec. 5 we will need the volume of the solid consisting of all points $P = (\rho, \phi, \theta)$ satisfying

$$\rho \text{ in } [\rho_{i-1}, \rho_i] \qquad \phi \text{ in } [\phi_{j-1}, \phi_j] \qquad \theta \text{ in } [\theta_{k-1}, \theta_k]$$

We will *estimate* this volume for small $\rho_i - \rho_{i-1}$, $\phi_j - \phi_{j-1}$, and $\theta_k - \theta_{k-1}$.

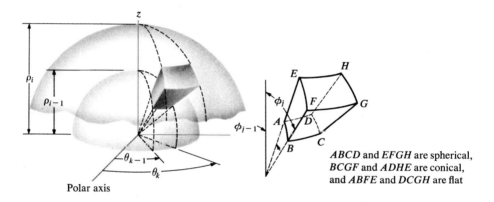

ABCD and EFGH are spherical,
BCGF and ADHE are conical,
and ABFE and DCGH are flat

Since the small solid resembles a rectangular box, we will estimate its volume by the product $AB \cdot BC \cdot CD$. Now, $AB = (EB)(\theta_k - \theta_{k-1}) = \rho_{i-1}(\sin \phi_{j-1})(\theta_k - \theta_{k-1})$, while $BC = (\rho_{i-1})(\phi_j - \phi_{j-1})$ and $CD = \rho_i - \rho_{i-1}$.

Thus an estimate is

$$(\rho_{i-1})^2 (\sin \phi_{j-1}) (\rho_i - \rho_{i-1}) (\phi_j - \phi_{j-1}) (\theta_k - \theta_{k-1})$$

which we state briefly as

$$\rho^2 \sin \phi \, d\rho \, d\phi \, d\theta$$

EXERCISES

1. Describe the tetrahedron in Example 1 in rectangular coordinates by taking, first, cross sections for fixed z, then letting y vary for each z, and then letting x vary for each y and z.

2. Describe in rectangular-coordinate cross sections the tetrahedron bounded by the three coordinate planes and the plane $(x/2) + (y/3) + (z/4) = 1$.

3. Describe in rectangular-coordinate cross sections the sphere whose surface is $x^2 + y^2 + z^2 = 25$.
4. (a) What are the cylindrical coordinates of the typical point $P = (x,y,z)$?
   (b) What are the rectangular coordinates of the typical point $P = (r,\theta,z)$?
5. Describe in cylindrical-coordinate cross sections the sphere whose surface is $x^2 + y^2 + z^2 = 25$.
6. (a) What are the spherical coordinates of $P = (x,y,z)$?
   (b) What are the cylindrical coordinates of $P = (\rho,\phi,\theta)$?
7. Describe the solid in Example 2 by cross sections in rectangular coordinates.
8. Describe the solid in Example 3 by cross sections in rectangular coordinates.
9. Describe the solid in Example 3 by cross sections in cylindrical coordinates.
10. Describe in cylindrical coordinates the surface of the right circular cylinder given by
    the equation $x^2 - x + y^2 - 3 = 0$.   (Answer: $r = \cos\theta$)
11. Describe in spherical coordinates (a) the xy plane; (b) the positive z axis; (c) the
    positive x axis.
12. Describe in cylindrical coordinates (a) the xy plane; (b) the plane $x = y$; (c) the
    positive x axis.

□   □   □

13. A solid has this description in cylindrical coordinates: $0 \leqslant \theta \leqslant \pi/2$, $1 \leqslant z \leqslant 2$, and
    $1 \leqslant r \leqslant z$. Sketch the solid, and describe it (a) in cylindrical coordinates, letting r
    vary first; (b) in spherical coordinates; (c) in rectangular coordinates.
14. Fill in the blanks and explain with the aid of a sketch: Rectangular coordinates
    describe a point by specifying three planes on which it lies. Spherical coordinates de-
    scribe a point by specifying _____, _____, and _____ on which it lies.
    Cylindrical coordinates describe a point by specifying _____, _____, and
    _____ on which it lies.

5. Computing $\int_R f(P)\, dV$ by introducing coordinates in R. In the case of func-

tions that take only positive values, we may interpret $\displaystyle\int_a^b f(x)\,dx$ as the area of a set
in the plane, and $\int_R f(P)\, dA$, where R is a set in the plane, as the volume of a solid.
In other words, integration over a one-dimensional set gives the area of a two-
dimensional set, and integration over a two-dimensional set gives the volume of a
three-dimensional set. Such interpretations suggest that certain repeated integrals
can be used to compute definite integrals over sets in the plane. Our visual intuition
is of little use, however, if we try to interpret $\int_R f(P)\, dV$, a definite integral over a
three-dimensional set, as the measure of some four-dimensional set. In order to develop the appropriate repeated integrals for each coordinate system in space, we are
forced to use the same method we needed for cross sections made by rays in polar
coordinates.

For example, let us introduce cylindrical coordinates into R and see what repeated integral results. For convenience, we assume that R has the simplest possible
description in cylindrical coordinates:

$$a \leqslant r \leqslant b \qquad \alpha \leqslant \theta \leqslant \beta \qquad c \leqslant z \leqslant d$$

This region is a solid with four flat surfaces and two curved surfaces:

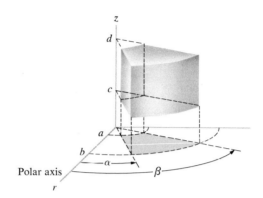

We partition $[a,b]$, $[\alpha,\beta]$, and $[c,d]$ by $r_0, \ldots, r_i, \ldots, r_n; \theta_0, \ldots, \theta_j, \ldots, \theta_n;$ and $z_0, \ldots, z_k, \ldots, z_n$, respectively. These partitions of intervals induce a partition of R into n^3 little solids R_{ijk} (shaped like R) whose volume we denote by V_{ijk}. In R_{ijk} we pick

$$P_{ijk} = \left(\frac{r_i + r_{i-1}}{2}, \theta_j, z_k\right)$$

as the point at which to evaluate f. This sketch shows the typical little region R_{ijk} in our partition of R and the point P_{ijk}:

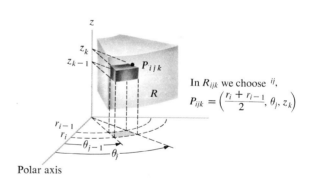

In R_{ijk} we choose ^{ij},
$$P_{ijk} = \left(\frac{r_i + r_{i-1}}{2}, \theta_j, z_k\right)$$

Then
$$\sum_{ijk=1}^{n} f(P_{ijk})(V_{ijk})$$

is an approximation of $\int_R f(P)\, dV$. Using the formula for V_{ijk} from page 268, we have

(1) $\displaystyle\sum_{ijk=1}^{n} f\left(\frac{r_i + r_{i-1}}{2}, \theta_j, z_k\right)\frac{r_i + r_{i-1}}{2}(r_i - r_{i-1})(\theta_j - \theta_{j-1})(z_k - z_{k-1}) \cong \int_R f(P)\, dV$

(We use "$\cong$" as an abbreviation of "is an approximation to.")

The sum (1), consisting of n^3 terms, can be written in six different orders. We pick one of them and rewrite (1) as

(2) $$\sum_{i=1}^{n}\left\{\sum_{j=1}^{n}\left[\sum_{k=1}^{n} f\left(\frac{r_i+r_{i-1}}{2},\theta_j,z_k\right)(z_k-z_{k-1})\right](\theta_j-\theta_{j-1})\right\}\frac{r_i+r_{i-1}}{2}(r_i-r_{i-1})$$

We examine the innermost sum in (2) (j and i are fixed):

(3) $$\sum_{k=1}^{n} f\left(\frac{r_i+r_{i-1}}{2},\theta_j,z_k\right)(z_k-z_{k-1})$$

By the definition of the definite integral over an interval, (3) is an approximation to

$$\int_c^d f\left(\frac{r_i+r_{i-1}}{2},\theta_j,z\right)dz$$

Thus, in view of (2),

(4)

$$\sum_{i=1}^{n}\left\{\sum_{j=1}^{n}\left[\int_c^d f\left(\frac{r_i+r_{i-1}}{2},\theta_j,z\right)dz\right](\theta_j-\theta_{j-1})\right\}\frac{r_i+r_{i-1}}{2}(r_i-r_{i-1})\cong\int_R f(P)dV$$

But

$$\sum_{j=1}^{n}\left[\int_c^d f\left(\frac{r_i+r_{i-1}}{2},\theta_j,z\right)dz\right](\theta_j-\theta_{j-1})$$

is an approximation to

(5) $$\int_\alpha^\beta\left[\int_c^d f\left(\frac{r_i+r_{i-1}}{2},\theta,z\right)dz\right]d\theta$$

To see this, let us abbreviate $\int_c^d f[(r_i+r_{i-1})/2,\theta,z]\,dz$ as $h(\theta)$, since we will keep i fixed, and z is integrated out. Therefore

$$\sum_{j=1}^{n}\left[\int_c^d f\left(\frac{r_i+r_{i-1}}{2},\theta_j,z\right)dz\right](\theta_j-\theta_{j-1})=\sum_{i=1}^{n} h(\theta_j)(\theta_j-\theta_{j-1})\cong\int_\alpha^\beta h(\theta)\,d\theta$$

Replacing $h(\theta)$ in $\int_\alpha^\beta h(\theta)\,d\theta$ by $\int_c^d f[(r_i+r_{i-1})/2,\theta,z]\,dz$, we obtain (5).

Finally, let

$$g(r)=\left\{\int_\alpha^\beta\left[\int_c^d f(r,\theta,z)\,dz\right]d\theta\right\}r$$

Then, in view of (4) and (5), we see that

(6) $$\sum_{i=1}^{n} g\left(\frac{r_i+r_{i-1}}{2}\right)(r_i-r_{i-1})\cong\int_R f(P)\,dV$$

But (6) is an approximation to $\int_a^b g(r)\,dr$; therefore we suspect that

$$\int_R f(P)\,dV=\int_a^b\left\{\int_\alpha^\beta\left[\int_c^d f(r,\theta,z)\,dz\right]d\theta\right\}r\,dr$$

(Note the factor r in the integrand.)

If R is more complicated, then instead of

$$\int_a^b \int_\alpha^\beta \int_c^d$$

we will have

$$\int_a^b \int_{\theta_1(r)}^{\theta_2(r)} \int_{z_1(\theta, r)}^{z_2(\theta, r)}$$

where the limits of integration describe the region R in cylindrical coordinates. Similar formulas, each containing the extra r in the integrand, hold for the five other orders of integration.

Example 1. The moment of a solid about the xy plane is defined as $\int_R z g(P)\, dV$, where $g(P)$ is the density function. We find this moment for the top half of the solid described in Example 2, page 268, and assume that $g(P) = 1$. Then the moment is

$$\int_R z\, dV = \int_0^3 \left[\int_0^{2\pi} \left(\int_0^{\sqrt{25 - r^2}} z\, dz \right) d\theta \right] r\, dr$$

Now,

$$\int_0^{\sqrt{25 - r^2}} z\, dz \underset{\text{FTC}}{=} \frac{z^2}{2} \Big|_0^{\sqrt{25 - r^2}} = \frac{25 - r^2}{2}$$

Then

$$\int_0^{2\pi} \frac{25 - r^2}{2}\, d\theta \underset{\text{FTC}}{=} \left(\frac{25 - r^2}{2}\, \theta \right) \Big|_0^{2\pi} = \pi(25 - r^2)$$

Lastly,

$$\int_0^3 \pi(25 - r^2)\, r\, dr = \int_0^3 (25\pi r - \pi r^3)\, dr \underset{\text{FTC}}{=} \left(\frac{25\pi r^2}{2} - \frac{\pi r^4}{4} \right) \Big|_0^3$$

$$= \frac{(25)\,\pi\,(9)}{2} - \frac{\pi(81)}{4} = \frac{369\pi}{4}$$

In the same manner one can obtain repeated integrals in rectangular or spherical coordinates. In rectangular coordinates, one of the six formulas is

$$\int_R f(P)\, dV = \int_a^b \left\{ \int_{y_1(x)}^{y_2(x)} \left[\int_{z_1(x, y)}^{z_2(x, y)} f(x, y, z)\, dz \right] dy \right\} dx$$

In spherical coordinates we have

$$\int_R f(P)\, dV = \int_\alpha^\beta \left\{ \int_{\phi_1(\theta)}^{\phi_2(\theta)} \left[\int_{\rho_1(\phi, \theta)}^{\rho_2(\phi, \theta)} f(r, \phi, \theta)\, \rho^2 \sin\phi\, d\rho \right] d\phi \right\} d\theta$$

where the limits of integration, as usual, depend on R (not on f). Note the expression $\rho^2 \sin\phi$ in the integrand for spherical coordinates.

Example 2. We find the moment of the tetrahedron in Example 1, page 266, about the yz plane, that is, $\int_R x\, dV$. (We assume that the density is 1 throughout R.) Then

$$\int_R x\, dV = \int_0^1 \left[\int_0^{1-x} \left(\int_0^{1-x-y} x\, dz \right) dy \right] dx$$

We evaluate the inner one-dimensional definite integral:

$$\int_0^{1-x-y} x\, dz \underset{\text{FTC}}{=} xz \Big|_{z=0}^{z=1-x-y} = x(1 - x - y) = x - x^2 - xy$$

Next we have

$$\int_0^{1-x} (x - x^2 - xy)\, dy \underset{\text{FTC}}{=} \left(xy - x^2 y - \frac{xy^2}{2} \right)\Bigg|_{y=0}^{y=1-x}$$

$$= x(1-x) - x^2(1-x) - \frac{x(1-x)^2}{2}$$

$$= \frac{x}{2} - x^2 + \frac{x^3}{2}$$

Finally, $\displaystyle \int_0^1 \left(\frac{x}{2} - x^2 - \frac{x^3}{2} \right) dx \underset{\text{FTC}}{=} \left(\frac{x^2}{4} - \frac{x^3}{3} + \frac{x^4}{8} \right)\Bigg|_0^1 = \frac{1}{4} - \frac{1}{3} + \frac{1}{8} = \frac{1}{24}$.

Example 3. We compute $\int_R z\, dV$, where R is the cone in Example 3, page 269. We express the function z and the region R in spherical coordinates. Now, $z = \rho \cos\phi$, and R is already described on page 270. Thus

$$\int_R z\, dV = \int_0^{\pi/6} \left(\int_0^{2\pi} \left[\int_0^{4\sec\phi} (\rho\cos\phi)\, \rho^2 \sin\phi\, d\rho \right] d\theta \right) d\phi$$

Our computations begin:

$$\int_0^{4\sec\phi} \rho^3 \cos\phi \sin\phi\, d\rho \underset{\text{FTC}}{=} \cos\phi \sin\phi \left(\frac{\rho^4}{4} \right)\Bigg|_{\rho=0}^{\rho=4\sec\phi} = \cos\phi \sin\phi \frac{(4\sec\phi)^4}{4}$$

$$= 64\sec^3\phi \sin\phi$$

Then,

$$\int_0^{2\pi} 64\sec^3\phi \sin\phi\, d\theta = 128\pi \sec^3\phi \sin\phi$$

(since the integrand is simply a constant). Finally,

$$\int_0^{\pi/6} 128\pi \sec^3\phi \sin\phi\, d\phi = 128\pi \int_0^{\pi/6} \frac{\sin\phi}{\cos^3\phi}\, d\phi$$

which the substitution $u = \cos\phi$ changes to

$$128\pi \int_1^{\sqrt{3}/2} \frac{-du}{u^3} = 128\pi \int_{\sqrt{3}/2}^1 \frac{du}{u^3} \underset{\text{FTC}}{=} 128\pi \left[\frac{-1}{2u^2} \right]_{\sqrt{3}/2}^1 = \frac{64\pi}{3}$$

Another example, of great importance in the theory of gravity, is to be found in Chap. 26, pages 539–542.

EXERCISES

1. Explain the appearance of the extra factor r in the integrand in any repeated integral in cylindrical coordinates (no matter which of the six possible orders of integration we use).
2. Explain the appearance of the extra $\rho^2 \sin\phi$ in any repeated integral using spherical coordinates.
3. Why is there no "extra factor" for repeated integrals in rectangular coordinates?
4. Show by using a repeated integral that the volume of the little solid we estimated on page 270 is $[(\rho_i{}^3 - \rho_{i-1}{}^3)/3](\theta_k - \theta_{k-1})(\cos\phi_{j-1} - \cos\phi_j)$. (Hint: Recall that the volume of R is $\int_R 1\, dV$.)

5. How does the formula in Exercise 4 compare to our estimate when the three dimensions are small? (Hint: The law of the mean is useful here.)

6. The moment of inertia I of a solid about a line L is defined as $\int_R D(P)\, f(P)\, dV$, where $D(P)$ is the *square* of the distance from P to L, and $f(P)$ is the density of mass at P. If $f(P) = 1$ for all P, find the moment of inertia of R, described in Example 1, about the z axis. A table of integrals would be useful.
(Answer: $2644\pi/15$)

7. Repeat Exercise 6 but assume that the density at $P = (r,\theta,z)$ is r. Use a table of integrals.   (Answer: $\pi[-6,708 + 15,625 \sin^{-1}(\frac{3}{5})]/8$)

8. Do Example 1 in rectangular coordinates.

9. Find the volume of the solid in Example 1 by a repeated integral in cylindrical coordinates.

10. Compute the moment in Example 2 but use a different order of x, y, z integrations.

11. (See Exercise 6.) Express as a repeated integral the moment of inertia of the tetrahedron of Example 2 about the y axis, if the density f is given by $f(x,y,z) = x$.

12. Find the mass of the solid described in Exercise 11.

13. The x coordinate $\bar{x}$ of the center of gravity of a solid is defined as

$$\frac{\int_R xf(P)\, dV}{\int_R f(P)\, dV}$$

(If $f(P) = 1$ for all P in R, this is simply the "average value of x over R" (page 38). Find $\bar{x}$ for the tetrahedron of Example 2.   (Answer: $\frac{1}{4}$)

14. Find the average value of z over the cone of Example 3.   (Answer: 3)

15. Do Example 3 in cylindrical coordinates.

16. A right circular cone has altitude h, radius a, constant density, and mass M.
    (a) Why is its moment of inertia about its axis less than Ma^2?
    (b) Find its moment of inertia about its axis.
    (c) Find its moment of inertia about an axis through its vertex and parallel to its base. (Why is it less than $M(a^2 + h^2)$?)
[Answer: (b) $3Ma^2/10$; (c) $3M(a^2/20 + h^2/5)$]

17. Let $z = g(y)$ be a decreasing function of y such that $g(1) = 0$. Let R be the solid of revolution formed by rotating, about the z axis, the region in the yz plane bounded by $y = 0$, $z = 0$, and $z = g(y)$. Using appropriate repeated integrals in cylindrical coordinates, show that $\displaystyle\int_R z\, dV = \int_0^1 \pi y[g(y)]^2\, dy$ or $\displaystyle\int_0^{g(0)} \pi[g^{-1}(z)]^2\, z\, dz$.

18. Find the average shadow on the xy plane of all line segments whose length is at most a and one of whose ends is the origin. Assume that the light is parallel to the z axis.   (Answer: $3\pi a/16$)

19. Consider the moment of inertia of a sphere of mass M and radius a about a diameter.
    (a) Set up a repeated integral for this moment in the three types of coordinate systems.
    (b) Evaluate the easiest.
(Answer: (b) $2Ma^2/5$)

20. (See Exercise 19.) Evaluate all three repeated integrals in Exercise 19(a).

21. Find the average distance from the center of a sphere of radius a to other points of the sphere by setting up appropriate repeated integrals in the three types of coordinate systems and evaluating the two easiest.   (Answer: $3a/4$)

22. Let R be the solid sphere of radius a with center at the origin of coordinates.
    (a) Explain why $\int_R x^2\,dV = (\frac{1}{3}) \int_R (x^2 + y^2 + z^2)\,dV$.
    (b) Evaluate the second integral by spherical coordinates.
    (c) Without using paper and pencil, evaluate $\int_R x\,dV$.
23. Compute the volume of a sphere of radius a by each of the three methods.

□ □ □

24. Combining the fact that the volume of R equals $\int_R 1\,dV$ with a repeated integral in

    rectangular coordinates, (a) obtain $V = \displaystyle\int_a^b A(x)\,dx$ (page 17); (b) obtain the formula

    for volume as a definite integral over a plane set (see the table on page 40).
25. Combining the fact that the volume of R equals $\int_R 1\,dV$ with a repeated integral in
    cylindrical coordinates, obtain the shell technique, page 213.
26. A point Q is located at a distance q from the center of a solid sphere of radius
    $a(q > a)$. Find the average of the reciprocal of the distance from Q to points of
    the sphere.   (Answer: $1/q$)
27. (See Exercises 13 and 17.) (a) Show that the y coordinate of the center of gravity of

    the solid of revolution described in Exercise 17 is $\displaystyle\int_0^1 \{x[g(x)]^2/2\}\,dx \Big/ \int_0^1 xg(x)\,dx$,

    while the y coordinate of the center of gravity of the plane region that was revolved

    is $\displaystyle\int_0^1 \{[g(x)]^2/2\}\,dx \Big/ \int_0^1 g(x)\,dx$.

    (b) By considering $\displaystyle\int_0^1 \left(\int_0^1 g(x)\,g(y)\,(x-y)\,[g(x) - g(y)]\,dx \right) dy$, show that the cen-

    troid of the solid of revolution is below that of the plane region. (Hint: Why is the
    repeated integral less than or equal to 0?)
28. Is the analog of Exercise 26 for a disk true? Explain.
29. The set of points (x,y) such that $0 \leqslant x \leqslant 1$ and $0 \leqslant y \leqslant 1$ is called a square or
    "2-cell." The set of points (x,y,z) such that $0 \leqslant x \leqslant 1$, $0 \leqslant y \leqslant 1$, and $0 \leqslant z \leqslant 1$
    is called a cube or "3-cell."
    (a) Devise an example of a "4-cell."
    (b) What definite integral over a three-dimensional set do you think equals its
    "measure"?
    (c) Compute the definite integral in (b).
30. The set of points (x,y) such that $0 \leqslant x \leqslant 1$, $0 \leqslant y \leqslant 1$, and $x + y \leqslant 1$ is called a
    triangle or "2-simplex." The set of points (x,y,z) such that $0 \leqslant x \leqslant 1$, $0 \leqslant y \leqslant 1$,
    $0 \leqslant z \leqslant 1$, and $x + y + z \leqslant 1$ is called a tetrahedron or "3-simplex."
    (a) Devise an analogous example of a "4-simplex."
    (b) What definite integral over a three-dimensional set do you think equals the
    "measure" of the 4-simplex in (a)?
    (c) What repeated integral equals the definite integral in (b)?
    (d) Evaluate the repeated integral in (c). Does the result seem analogous to the tri-
    angle mentioned, having area $\frac{1}{2}$, and the tetrahedron mentioned, having volume $\frac{1}{6}$?

31. The disk of radius 1 and center at $(0,0)$ consists of all points (x,y) such that $x^2 + y^2 \leqslant 1$. It is also called a "2-ball." The sphere of radius 1 and center at $(0,0,0)$ consists of all points (x,y,z) such that $x^2 + y^2 + z^2 \leqslant 1$. It is also called a "3-ball."
(*a*) Define the "4-ball" with center $(0,0,0,0)$.
(*b*) What definite integral over a three-dimensional set do you think equals the measure of the 4-ball in (*a*)?
(*c*) What repeated integral equals the definite integral in (*b*)?
(*d*) What definite integral over a two-dimensional set equals the "measure" of the 4-ball in (*a*)?
(*e*) Using polar coordinates, evaluate the definite integral in (*d*).

[Answer: (*e*) $\pi^2/2$]

6. Summary. In this chapter we reduced the computation of definite integrals over plane and solid sets to the computation of definite integrals over intervals. The repeated integrals that arise depend on the coordinate we choose to introduce. This choice is influenced by both the integrand f and the set R on which the definite integral $\int_R f(P)\,dA$ or $\int_R f(P)\,dV$ depends. When we use polar or cylindrical coordinates we must insert an extra r in the integrand of the repeated integral; in spherical coordinates we insert an extra $\rho^2 \sin \phi$. It is not hard to remember these extra factors; they arise from the formulas $r\,dr\,d\theta$, $r\,dr\,d\theta\,dz$, and $\rho^2 \sin \phi\,d\rho\,d\phi\,d\theta$, for the areas or volumes of the small sets that correspond to small changes in the coordinates.

With this chapter, Part I comes to an end. Many definite integrals that we could only estimate in Chap. 1 can now be computed exactly—without forming a single approximating sum. The basic tool is the fundamental theorem of calculus, even for evaluating definite integrals over plane and solid sets. It must be kept in mind that the fundamental theorem has its limitations: if the integrand does not have an elementary antiderivative, the fundamental theorem does not give useful information. (Chap. 14 presents several ways of estimating definite integrals.)

A glance at each of the chapter introductions and summaries will recall the route that we have traveled. From a mathematical point of view, there is only one major theorem in Part I, the fundamental theorem of calculus, which is the substance of Chap. 6. Each of the remaining eight chapters in Part I is best understood by examining its relation to Chap. 6.

PART II

Topics
in the calculus

*In Part I, in which
we centered our attention on the fundamental theorem of calculus, we introduced
two basic concepts: the definite integral and the derivative. Once they and their
relationship are mastered, we are free to explore the calculus in various directions.*

*For instance, we may examine the role of the derivative outside the fundamental
theorem. This we do in Chaps. 10 through 13, where we consider the derivative of
a derivative, the maximum value of a function, and certain functions that can be
thought of as* polynomials of infinite degree. *This concept provides an efficient
means of estimating such a definite integral as* $\int_0^1 e^{x^2}\,dx$, *a task for which the fundamental theorem cannot be directly used. This and other methods of estimating definite integrals are discussed in Chap. 14. Chapter 15 presents a type of derivative
known as a* partial derivative, *a derivative of a function of two or more variables
with respect to one of them. Chapters 16 and 17 extend the idea of derivative to
vector functions.*

*Chapters 18 and 19 develop an analog in the plane of the fundamental theorem,
which refers only to an interval. Chapter 20 examines the interchange of limits;
it looks two ways, for in it we study certain problems implicit in Parts I and II and
raise questions that will be answered in advanced calculus.*

*The first six chapters in Part II are somewhat closely linked, as are the next four,
which depend on parts of Chaps. 10, 11, and 15.*

279

10

The higher derivatives

SINCE the derivative of a function is itself a function, we can speak of "the derivative of a derivative" and "the derivative of the derivative of a derivative," and so on. For instance, the derivative of the derivative of x^3 is $6x$. This chapter applies these higher derivatives to certain topics in geometry and algebra.

1. The geometric significance of the sign of the second derivative. The derivative of the derivative of a function f is called the *second derivative* of f. If $y = f(x)$, then the second derivative, $d(dy/dx)/dx$, is commonly denoted

$$\frac{d^2y}{dx^2} \qquad D^2y \qquad f'' \qquad y'' \qquad f^{(2)} \qquad \text{or} \qquad D^2f$$

Example 1. Let $y = (x - 2)^2 + e^{-x}$. Then $dy/dx = 2(x - 2) - e^{-x}$, and the second derivative of y is $2 + e^{-x}$. If we had used different letters, say $x = (t - 2)^2 + e^{-t}$, then we would write

$$\frac{d^2x}{dt^2} = 2 + e^{-t} = D^2x$$

281

In this section we examine the significance of the sign of the second derivative in the graph of the function. First, we recall the significance of the sign of the function and of its derivative.

The sign of $f(x_0)$—the function evaluated at x_0—tells us whether the point $(x_0, f(x_0))$ is above or below the x axis. As we saw on page 125, the sign of $f'(x_0)$—the derivative of f evaluated at x_0—tells us whether the graph is rising or falling at $(x_0, f(x_0))$. These diagrams show the various possible combinations:

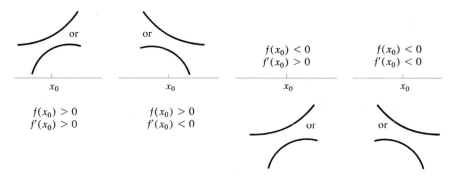

What is the geometric significance of the sign of $f''(x_0)$? Let us consider the case $f''(x_0) > 0$ and for simplicity assume that $f''(x_0)$ is positive in some open interval around x_0.

Now the second derivative, f'', is the derivative of f'. Thus we are assuming that the function f' has a positive derivative, and thus that the derivative is an increasing function (see Corollary 3, page 125). *In other words, as x increases, the slope of the graph of $y = f(x)$ increases.* In an interval around x_0, the graph resembles these curves:

In each case the second derivative f'' is positive; the derivative increases

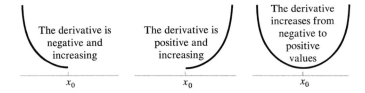

The curve is shaped like the inside of a cup and is called *concave upward*. More precisely, *a curve is concave upward over an interval if it lies above its tangent lines in the interval.* We prove (without referring to any pictures) the following theorem.

THEOREM 1.   *If the second derivative of f is positive throughout some interval, then the graph of $y = f(x)$ is concave upward in that interval.*

PROOF.   The tangent line at a typical point $(x_0, f(x_0))$ has the equation $y = f'(x_0)(x - x_0) + f(x_0)$, for it is the line through $(x_0, f(x_0))$ of slope $f'(x_0)$. We wish therefore to show that $f'(x_0)(x - x_0) + f(x_0)$ is less than $f(x)$ for any x in the interval about x_0 (other than at x_0 itself). We do this for the case $x > x_0$.

The assertion $f'(x_0)(x - x_0) + f(x_0) < f(x)$ is equivalent (for $x - x_0 > 0$) to

$$f'(x_0) < \frac{f(x) - f(x_0)}{x - x_0}$$

By the law of the mean, $[f(x) - f(x_0)]/(x - x_0) = f'(X)$ for some X between x_0 and x. It suffices then to prove that $f'(x_0)$ is less than $f'(X)$, but this follows from our assumption that f' has a positive derivative and hence increases. (The case $x < x_0$ is similar.)

A *curve that lies below its tangent lines* (throughout an interval) *is called concave downward* (over the interval). The analog of Theorem 1 asserts that if the second derivative is negative, then the curve is concave downward. In the lower curve of each pair in the figure on page 282, the second derivative is negative; in the upper curve it is positive. A curve can be concave upward in part and concave downward in part, as the next example illustrates.

Example 2. We examine the concavity of the graph of $y = \frac{1}{6}(x^3 - 3x^2 + 9x + 3)$. Here $dy/dx = \frac{1}{2}x^2 - x + \frac{3}{2}$ and $d^2y/dx^2 = x - 1$. If x is greater than 1, the second derivative is positive, while if x is less than 1, the second derivative is negative. At $x = 1$, therefore, the concavity changes. Since $y = \frac{10}{6}$ and $y' = 1$ when $x = 1$, we can make this rough sketch of the graph near $(1, \frac{10}{6})$:

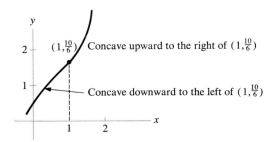

A point—such as $(1, \frac{10}{6})$ in Example 2—at which the sense of concavity changes is called an *inflection point.* In Example 2, we find that $f''(x)$ equals 0 at the inflection point, but in the next example $f''(x)$ isn't even defined at the inflection point.

Example 3. We examine the concavity of $y = \sqrt[3]{x}$ and check the graph for inflection points. In this case $y = x^{1/3}$, $y' = \frac{1}{3}x^{-2/3}$, and $y'' = \frac{1}{3}(-\frac{2}{3})x^{-5/3} = -\frac{2}{9}(\sqrt[3]{x})^{-5}$; hence $y'' > 0$ if $x < 0$, and $y'' < 0$ if $x > 0$. At $x = 0$, y'' is not defined, even though the sense of concavity changes as we pass through $(0,0)$. We sketch the graph:

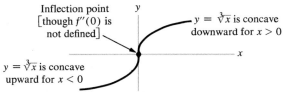

If the first derivative of a function is zero at the point x_0, then the graph of the function has a horizontal tangent line at $(x_0, f(x_0))$. The graph may resemble one of these curves:

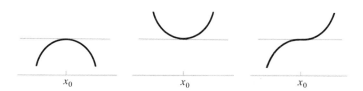

In the left curve, f has a *relative* (local) *maximum* at x_0; *there is an open interval around x such that* $f(x_0)$ *is the maximum value of* $f(x)$ *for x in that interval.* In the middle curve, f has a *relative minimum* at x_0. In the right curve, it has neither. The next theorem shows how the second derivative can be used to distinguish between relative maxima and minima.

THEOREM 2.   *Let f have a derivative and a second derivative in an open interval around* x_0. *If* $f'(x_0) = 0$, *and if* $f''(x)$ *is negative in the interval, then f has a relative maximum at* x_0. *If* $f'(x_0) = 0$, *and if* $f''(x)$ *is positive in the interval, then f has a relative minimum at* x_0.

PROOF.   (For simplicity, we phrase the proof geometrically.) The tangent line at $(x_0, f(x_0))$ is horizontal. If the second derivative is negative, then according to Theorem 1, the graph lies below this tangent line. Hence the function has a relative maximum at x_0. A similar argument yields the second assertion.

There is a somewhat stronger theorem which refers to the behavior of the derivative rather than of the second derivative. This is Theorem 3, which the preceding diagram will make plausible.

THEOREM 3.   *If the derivative of f changes continuously from positive to negative values at* x_0 *as x increases, then f has a relative maximum at* x_0. *If the derivative changes from negative to positive, then f has a relative minimum there.*

PROOF.   We prove the first assertion by showing that when x is near x_0 we have $f(x) \leqslant f(x_0)$. To do so we will examine the sign of $f(x) - f(x_0)$. By the law of the mean, $f(x) - f(x_0)$ equals $f'(X)(x - x_0)$ for some X between x and x_0. If $x > x_0$, we have $x - x_0 > 0$ and $f'(X) < 0$; hence $f(x) - f(x_0) < 0$. If $x < x_0$ we have $x - x_0 < 0$ and $f'(X) > 0$; hence $f(x) - f(x_0) < 0$, and again $f(x) \leqslant f(x_0)$. A similar argument proves the second assertion.

The accompanying table contrasts the geometric interpretations of the sign of a function, its derivative, and its second derivative. It also serves as a concise summary of this section.

	Is positive	*Is negative*	*Changes sign continuously*
Where $f(x)$	The graph is above the x axis	The graph is below the x axis	The graph crosses the x axis
Where $f'(x)$	The graph slopes upward	The graph slopes downward	The graph has a horizontal tangent and a relative maximum or minimum
Where $f''(x)$	The graph is concave upward (like a cup)	The graph is concave downward	The graph has an inflection point

Keep in mind that the graph can have an inflection point at x_0, even though the second derivative is not defined at x_0 (Example 2); and a graph can have a maximum or minimum at x_0 even though the first derivative is not defined at x_0 (for the latter consider $f(x) = |x|$ at $x_0 = 0$).

EXERCISES

1. Compute the second derivative of (a) $17x^2$; (b) e^{2x}; (c) $\sin 2x$; (d) $1/x$; (e) $\ln x$.
    [Answer: (a) 34; (b) $4e^{2x}$; (c) $-4\sin 2x$; (d) $2/x^3$; (e) $-1/x^2$]
2. Let $f(x) = 2x^4 - 4x^3$.
    (a) Where does the graph slope upward?
    (b) Where is the graph concave upward?
    (c) Where does the ordinate change sign?
    (d) Where does the slope change sign?
    (e) Where are the inflection points, if any?
    (f) Sketch the curve with the aid of (a) through (e).
3. Show that the second derivative of each of these functions is proportional to the function: (a) $5e^{3x} + 7e^{-3x}$; (b) $6\sin 4x + 9\cos 4x$.
4. At $x = 1$ the derivative of $f(x) = 2x^2 - 4x + 5$ is zero. Show that f has a relative minimum at $x = 1$, using (a) the behavior of f', and (b) the behavior of f''.
5. Let $f(x) = \sin x$. For which values of x is $f(x) > 0$? $f'(x) > 0$? $f''(x) > 0$? Where do f, f', and f'' change sign? Show these on a graph of $y = \sin x$.
6. Does $y = e^x$ have any inflection points? Explain.
7. Let $y = 1/(1 + x^2)$. Where do y' and y'' change sign? Make a freehand graph showing these data.
8. Find d^2y/dx^2 if $y = f(x) = \int_0^x (1 + t^2)\, dt$.
9. (a) Using the second derivative, show that if f is a positive function and concave upward, then so is its square, g, the function defined by $g(x) = [f(x)]^2$.
    (b) By considering $f(x) = x^{2/3}$ for $x > 0$, show that the analog of (a) for "concave downward" is not valid.
10. Sketch the graph of a hypothetical f such that for all x in some interval
    (a) $f(x) > 0$, $f'(x) < 0$, $f''(x) < 0$; (b) $f(x) < 0$, $f'(x) < 0$, $f''(x) > 0$.

11. The diagram below is the graph of a certain function f.
    (a) Where does f change sign?   (b) Where is $f(x) \geqslant 0$?
    (c) Where does f' change sign?   (d) Where is $f'(x) \geqslant 0$?
    (e) Where does f'' change sign?   (f) Where is $f''(x) \geqslant 0$?

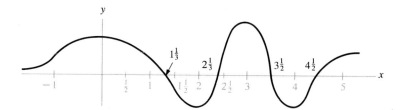

12. Let $y = x^4$.
    (a) Is y'' ever 0?
    (b) Does the graph have any inflection points? Explain.
    (c) Does the graph have any relative maxima or minima? Explain.
13. Sketch the graph of a function such that for all x: (a) $f(x) > 0$, $f'(x) > 0$, $f''(x) > 0$;
    (b) $f'(x) < 0$, $f''(x) < 0$. (c) Can there be a function such that $f(x) > 0$, $f'(x) < 0$,
    $f''(x) < 0$ for all x? Explain.
14. Let $f(x) = x^3 - 6x^2 - 15x$.
    (a) Where does f change sign?
    (b) Where does f' change sign?
    (c) Where does f'' change sign?
    (d) Compute $f(x)$ at these points and make a rough sketch of f.
             [Answer: (a) 0, $3 + 2\sqrt{6}$, and $3 - 2\sqrt{6}$; (b) -1 and 5; (c) 2]
15. (a) Graph $y = 1/(1 + x^2)$ and show its inflection points.
    (b) Graph $y = e^{-x^2}$ and show its inflection points.

□ □ □

16. Let f be a function such that it has an inverse function, which we denote by g. Com-
    plete and explain the following two statements.
    (a) If the graph of f slopes upward, then the graph of g .
    (b) If the graph of f slopes upward and is concave upward, then the graph of g

    _____.
17. Let f be a function such that $f(0) = 0 = f(1)$ and $f''(x) \leqslant 0$ for all x in [0,1].
    (a) Using a sketch, explain why $f(x) \geqslant 0$ for all x in [0,1].
    (b) Without a sketch prove that $f(x) \geqslant 0$ for all x in [0,1].
18. (See Exercise 17.) Prove that if f is a function such that $f''(x) < 0$ for all x, then
    the graph of $y = f(x)$ lies above its chords; that is, $f(ax_1 + (1 - a)x_2) > af(x_1) +
    (1 - a)f(x_2)$ for any a between 0 and 1, and for any x_1 and x_2.
19. Prove (without referring to a picture) that if the graph of f lies above its tangent
    lines for all x in [a,b], then $f''(x) \geqslant 0$ for all x in [a,b]. [This is almost the converse
    of Theorem 1. The case $y = x^4$ shows that we should not try to prove that $f''(x) > 0$.]
20. In Appendix F a function is described that is continuous throughout [0,1] but dif-
    ferentiable nowhere. Devise a function that has a derivative throughout [0,1] but
    a second derivative nowhere.

2. The significance in motion of the second derivative.   Let t represent time, and $x = f(t)$ the location of an object moving on a line. As we saw in Chap. 2, the derivative with respect to time, dx/dt, represents the velocity of the object.

The rate at which velocity changes (the derivative of velocity with respect to time) is the *acceleration*. In other words,

$$\text{Acceleration} = \frac{d(dx/dt)}{dt} = \frac{d^2x}{dt^2}$$

Sometimes velocity is written $\dot{x}$ and acceleration $\ddot{x}$. Just as a physicist uses mainly the first and second moments, he uses mainly the first and second derivatives. We will see how these two derivatives are exploited in the study of motion.

Before we discuss an example, we should remark on the terms "speed" and "velocity," which in daily life are synonymous. In the detailed study of motion, *velocity* will always be dx/dt, while *speed* will be $|dx/dt|$. Velocity can be positive or negative, depending on how we choose the fixed coordinate system. Speed is never negative; it is simply the absolute value of the velocity.

Example.   A ball is thrown straight up with a speed of 64 feet per second, from a cliff 96 feet above the ground. Where is the ball t seconds later? Assume that there is no air resistance and that the acceleration due to gravity is constant.

We introduce a vertical coordinate system to describe the position of the ball. It is more natural to call it the y axis, and so velocity is dy/dt and acceleration is d^2y/dt^2. We place the origin at ground level and let the positive part of the y axis be above the ground.

At time $t = 0$, the velocity $dy/dt = 64$, since the ball is thrown *up* at a speed of 64 feet per second. (If it had been thrown down, dy/dt would be -64.) As time increases, dy/dt decreases from 64 to 0 (when the ball reaches the top of its path and begins its descent) and continues to decrease through negative values as the ball falls down to the ground. Since v is decreasing, the acceleration dv/dt is negative. The (constant) value of dv/dt, obtained from experiments, is approximately -32 (feet per second per second).

From the equation

$$\frac{dv}{dt} = -32$$

we conclude that

$$v = -32t + C$$

where C is some constant. To find C, we recall that $v = 64$ when $t = 0$. Thus

$$64 = -32(0) + C$$

and $C = 64$. Hence $v = -32t + 64$ for any time t until the ball hits the ground. Now, $v = dy/dt$, so we have

$$\frac{dy}{dt} = -32t + 64$$

From this equation we deduce that

$$y = -16t^2 + 64t + K$$

where K is a constant. To find K we make use of the fact that $y = 96$ when $t = 0$. Thus

$$96 = -16(0)^2 + 64(0) + K$$

and $K = 96$.

We have obtained a complete description of the position of the ball at any time t while it is in the air:

$$y = -16t^2 + 64t + 96$$

This, together with $v = -32t + 64$, enables us to answer many questions about the ball's flight.

When does it reach its maximum height? When $v = 0$; that is, when $-32t + 64 = 0$, or when $t = 2$ seconds.

How high above the ground does the ball rise? We simply compute y when $t = 2$. This gives $-16(2)^2 + 64(2) + 96 = 160$ feet.

When does the ball land on the ground? When $y = 0$. We must find t such that

$$y = -16t^2 + 64t + 96 = 0$$

Dividing by -16, we obtain

$$t^2 - 4t - 6 = 0$$

which has the two roots

$$t = \frac{4 \pm \sqrt{16 + 24}}{2}$$

or simply

$$t = 2 \pm \sqrt{10}$$

Since $2 - \sqrt{10}$ is negative, and the ball cannot land on the ground *before* it is thrown, the physically meaningful root is $2 + \sqrt{10}$. The ball lands $2 + \sqrt{10}$ seconds after it is thrown; it is in the air for about 5.2 seconds.

The graphs of y, v, and speed, as functions of time, give us another perspective on the motion of the ball:

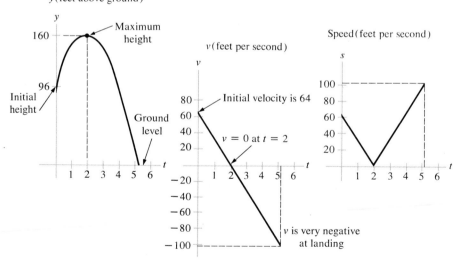

Of course, the actual path of the ball is restricted to a vertical line and looks like this:

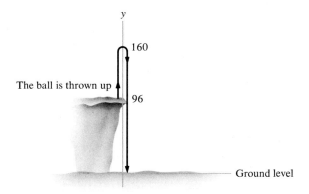

In Chaps. 17 and 24 we will examine the orbits of balls, planets, and satellites that are not restricted to a straight line.

EXERCISES

(Exercises 1 through 6 refer to the example in this section.)
1. We placed the origin of the y axis at ground level. If we had placed it on top of the cliff, what would be the formulas for y and v as functions of t?
2. (a) How long after the ball is thrown does it pass by the top of the cliff?
   (b) What are its speed and velocity then?
                [Answer: (a) 4 seconds; (b) 64 feet per second, -64 feet per second]
3. If the ball was simply dropped from the cliff, what would y be as a function of time? How long would the ball fall?
4. In view of the result of Exercise 3, interpret each of the three terms in the right side of the formula $y = -16t^2 + 64t + 96$.
5. What would be a possible physical interpretation of the root $2 - \sqrt{10}$?
6. Suppose that the ball is thrown with an initial velocity v_0 from a cliff of height y_0 and is subject to the constant acceleration $-a$ (where a is positive).
   (a) Show with the aid of the calculus that its position at any time t is $y = -at^2/2 + v_0 t + y_0$.
   (b) Give a physical interpretation of y_0, $v_0 t$, and $-at^2/2$ in the formula in (a).
   (c) Could you have guessed that $y = -at^2/2 + v_0 t + y_0$?
7. A car can accelerate from 0 (rest) to 60 miles per hour in 15 seconds. How far does it travel in this period? Be sure to do all your computations in seconds or all in hours; for instance, 60 miles per hour is 88 feet per second.   (Answer: ⅛ mile)
8. The reaction time of a driver is about 0.6 second. If a car can decelerate at 16 feet per second, find the total distance covered if the car is braked at (a) 60 miles per hour; (b) 30 miles per hour; (c) 20 miles per hour.
                [Answer: To nearest foot, (a) 295 feet; (b) 87 feet; (c) 44 feet]

9. (*a*) In order to propel an object 100 miles up, what must the launching velocity be? (*b*) How long will the object remain up? (Assume that its acceleration is the same as that of the ball in the example and that there is no air resistance.)

[Answer: (*a*) 5,813 feet per second; (*b*) 363 seconds]

10. Show that a ball thrown straight up from the ground takes as long to rise as to fall back to its initial position. How does the velocity with which it strikes the ground compare with its initial velocity? Consider the same question for its speed.

11. What is the physical significance of $\int_{t_1}^{t_2} v(t)\,dt$ and $\int_{t_1}^{t_2} |v(t)|\,dt$, where $v(t)$ is the velocity of an object at time t?

12. If you graph $v(t)$ as a function of time, from t_1 to t_2, what is the physical significance of the area under the graph and above the t axis? [Assume $v(t) \geqslant 0$.] What is the physical significance of the slope of the graph?

13. A mass at the end of a spring oscillates up and down. At time t seconds its position (relative to its position at rest) is $y = 6 \sin t$ inches.
(*a*) Graph y as a function of t.
(*b*) What is the maximum displacement of the mass?
(*c*) Show that its acceleration is proportional to its displacement, y.
(*d*) Where is it when its speed is maximum?
(*e*) Where is it when the absolute value of its acceleration is maximum? (This type of motion is called *harmonic*.)

14. An express subway train starts with a constant acceleration, then travels at its maximum speed, and finally slows down at a constant (negative) deceleration. It requires 120 seconds to go nonstop from 42nd Street to 72nd Street and 96 seconds to go from 72nd Street to 96th Street.
(*a*) Sketch the graph of speed as a function of time in each case.
(*b*) What is the train's maximum speed? Assume that there are 20 blocks in a mile.

[Answer: (*b*) 45 miles per hour]

15. In a certain race, a car starts from rest and ends at rest, having traveled 1 mile in 1 minute. Let $v(t)$ be its velocity at time t, and $a(t)$ be its acceleration at time t.

Show that (*a*) $\int_0^1 v(t)\,dt = 1$; (*b*) $\int_0^1 a(t)\,dt = 0$; (*c*) $\int_0^1 ta(t)\,dt = -1$.

16. (Continuation of Exercise 15; see also Exercise 12.)
(*a*) Show that at some time t we have $|a(t)| > 4$.
(*b*) Show graphically [drawing $v(t)$ as a function of time] that a race can be driven as in Exercise 15, but with $|a(t)| \leqslant 4.1$ for all t.

3. The second derivative and the curvature of a curve.

The rate of change of y with respect to x measures the steepness of a curve at a point on the curve. What is a reasonable measure of its curvature? Since a circle with a large radius is locally not very curvy, we would want a criterion that showed the curvature to be small for large circles and large for small circles. We would also like the curvature to be 0 for straight lines.

Observe that when we walk around a small circle our direction changes much more rapidly than when we walk around a large circle. To make this more precise, and to obtain a measure of the curvature of a circle, consider this diagram of a circle of radius a and a line tangent to it:

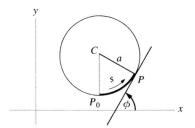

The tangent line turns as P moves counterclockwise and s increases

We start at the bottom of the circle, P_0, and walk counterclockwise. Let us say that after we have traveled a distance s along the curve, our direction is given by the angle ϕ from the positive x axis to the tangent line at P; the angle ϕ depends on s. Let us define *the curvature of a circle* as the rate at which ϕ changes with respect to s, that is, $d\phi/ds$.

The next theorem shows that $d\phi/ds$ is small for a large circle and large for a small circle, as we had hoped; in fact, it is simply the reciprocal of the radius.

THEOREM 1.   *For a circle of radius a, the curvature $d\phi/ds$ is constant and equals $1/a$, the reciprocal of the radius.*

PROOF.   A little geometry shows that ϕ equals the angle P_0CP in the preceding diagram. By the definition of radian measure, angle P_0CP has the measure s/a. Thus we have

$$\phi = \frac{s}{a} \quad \text{and} \quad \frac{d\phi}{ds} = \frac{1}{a}$$

The theorem is proved.

Since $d\phi/ds$ gives a reasonable measure of curvature for a circle—the larger the circle, the less its curvature—let us use it for other curves.

DEFINITION: *Curvature.*   The *curvature* of a curve at a point P is the value of $d\phi/ds$ at P, where ϕ and s are as shown in this diagram:

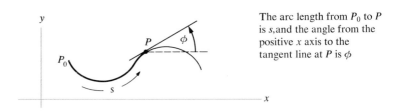

The arc length from P_0 to P is s, and the angle from the positive x axis to the tangent line at P is ϕ

Observe that a straight line has 0 curvature everywhere. Note also that in the above diagram the curvature is negative at the indicated point P, but positive at P_0. If we traversed the curve in the opposite direction, however, the curvature would be negative at P and positive at P_0. (Why?) Inspection of the diagram shows that the curvature changes sign at the inflection point. Therefore we should not be surprised that the curvature, though defined as a derivative, is intimately connected with the second derivative, d^2y/dx^2, as Theorem 2 shows.

THEOREM 2.   *If, as we move along the curve $y = f(x)$ to a point P, arc length s from a point P_0 increases as x increases, then*

$$\text{Curvature at } P = \frac{d^2y/dx^2}{[1 + (dy/dx)^2]^{3/2}}$$

PROOF.   By the chain rule, $d\phi/ds = (d\phi/dx)/(ds/dx)$. As was shown on page 208, we have $ds/dx = \sqrt{1 + (dy/dx)^2}$ (the positive square root, since we are assuming that $ds/dx \geqslant 0$). Also, we can easily compute $d\phi/dx$. Since

$$\phi = \tan^{-1} \frac{dy}{dx}$$

we have

$$\frac{d\phi}{dx} = \frac{\dfrac{d(dy/dx)}{dx}}{1 + (dy/dx)^2} = \frac{d^2y/dx^2}{1 + (dy/dx)^2}$$

From this information, we obtain

$$\frac{d\phi}{ds} = \frac{d\phi/dx}{ds/dx} = \frac{d^2y/dx^2}{[1 + (dy/dx)^2][\sqrt{1 + (dy/dx)^2}]}$$

and the theorem is proved.

Observe that where the curve is horizontal, curvature coincides with the second derivative, d^2y/dx^2. Note that while dy/dx, which records the steepness of a curve relative to certain axes, depends on the tilt of these axes, and d^2y/dx^2 also depends indirectly on this tilt, the quotient $(d^2y/dx^2)/[1 + (dy/dx)^2]^{3/2}$ does not. It records something about the shape of the curve itself, and not about its relation to any particular axes.

Example 1.   We examine the curvature at a typical point P on the curve $y = x^2$. We have $dy/dx = 2x$ and $d^2y/dx^2 = 2$. Thus the curvature at (x,y) is $2/[1 + (2x)^2]^{3/2}$. For instance, at $(0,0)$ the curvature is 2 and the curve near there resembles a circle of radius ½. As x^2 increases, the curvature approaches 0 and the curve gets straighter.

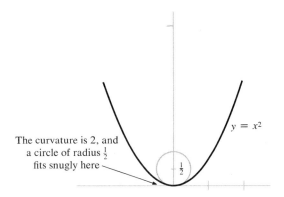

The curvature is 2, and a circle of radius $\frac{1}{2}$ fits snugly here

$y = x^2$

$\frac{1}{2}$

Let us define the *radius of curvature* at a point P on a curve to be $|1/\text{curvature}|$. Theorem 3 tells us that the radius of curvature of a circle is its radius. In Example 1 the radius of curvature is ½ at $(0,0)$ but becomes arbitrarily large as $x \to \infty$.

Example 2.   Let us find the curvature of the cycloid given parametrically by

$$x = \theta - \sin \theta \qquad y = 1 - \cos \theta$$

It would be tedious to solve for y explicitly in terms of x, so let us see how to evaluate d^2y/dx^2 and dy/dx if y and x are given parametrically, in this case in terms of the parameter θ. (Usually time t is the parameter.)

We note by the chain rule that, generally, dy/dx equals $(dy/d\theta)/(dx/d\theta)$. To compute d^2y/dx^2 we again use the chain rule, for

$$\frac{d^2y}{dx^2} = \frac{d(dy/dx)}{dx} = \frac{\dfrac{d(dy/dx)}{d\theta}}{dx/d\theta}$$

Let us apply this technique in our case. First, we have

$$\frac{dx}{d\theta} = 1 - \cos \theta \qquad \text{and} \qquad \frac{dy}{d\theta} = \sin \theta$$

Thus
$$\frac{dy}{dx} = \frac{\sin \theta}{1 - \cos \theta}$$

Next,
$$\frac{d(dy/dx)}{d\theta} = \frac{(1 - \cos \theta)(\cos \theta) - (\sin \theta)(\sin \theta)}{(1 - \cos \theta)^2}$$

$$= \frac{\cos \theta - 1}{(1 - \cos \theta)^2} = \frac{-1}{1 - \cos \theta}$$

Thus
$$\frac{d^2y}{dx^2} = \frac{\dfrac{-1}{1 - \cos \theta}}{dx/d\theta} = \frac{\dfrac{-1}{1 - \cos \theta}}{1 - \cos \theta} = \frac{-1}{(1 - \cos \theta)^2}$$

Therefore the curvature is

$$\frac{\dfrac{-1}{(1 - \cos \theta)^2}}{\left[1 + \left(\dfrac{\sin \theta}{1 - \cos \theta}\right)^2\right]^{3/2}}$$

which simplifies to $(-1)/(\sqrt{8}\sqrt{1 - \cos \theta})$. Note that since $\sqrt{1 - \cos \theta} = \sqrt{y}$, the curvature is simply $-1/\sqrt{8y}$.

REMARK. The curvature of the cycloid in Example 2 is negative. This means that $d\phi/ds$ is negative, or ϕ decreases as we move along an arc of the cycloid with increasing s. This is plausible, for as θ increases we move to the right on the arc and our direction turns clockwise: ϕ decreases as a function of s. In general, the sign of the curvature depends on the base point from which we choose to measure arc length and on the direction in which we choose to traverse the curve.

EXERCISES

1. Find the radius of curvature of the curve in Example 1 (a) at (1,1), and (b) at (2,4).
   [Answer: (a) $\sqrt{125}/2$; (b) $\sqrt{4913/2}$]
2. (a) Compute the curvature and radius of curvature for the curve $y = (e^x + e^{-x})/2$.
   (b) Show that the radius of curvature is y^2 at (x,y).
3. Find the radius of curvature along the curve $y = \sqrt{a^2 - x^2}$, where a is a constant.
   (Answer: a)
4. Show that $|d^2y/dx^2|$ at P is never larger than $|$curvature at $P|$.
5. Find the radius of curvature along the curve $y = \ln|\cos x|$.
   [Answer: $|\sec x|$ at (x,y)]
6. Having sketched a curve $y = f(x)$, draw as well as you can a line tangent to it at (1,1) and a circle through (1,1), fitting the curve snugly. The slope of the line is m and the radius of the circle is R. With the aid of m and R, how can you estimate d^2y/dx^2?
7. Find the curvature at the point (x,y) on the ellipse $x^2/a^2 + y^2/b^2 = 1$.
8. Find the curvature at the point (x,y) of the curve given parametrically by $x = a \cos t$, $y = b \sin t$. Incidentally, this is the same ellipse as in Exercise 7, but use the technique demonstrated in Example 2.
9. (a) Show that at $\theta = \pi$ the radius of curvature of the cycloid in Example 2 is 4.
   (b) Review the definition of the cycloid on page 204. In terms of the rolling wheel, would you have guessed that the radius of curvature would be 4 at $\theta = \pi$? Discuss.
10. A set R in the plane bounded by a curve is *convex* if whenever P and Q are points in R, the line segment PQ also lies in R. A *curve is convex* if it is the border of a convex set.
    (a) Show why the average radius of curvature with respect to angle ϕ as you traverse a convex curve is (length of curve)/2π.
    (b) Deduce from (a) that a convex curve of length L has a radius of curvature equal to $L/2\pi$ somewhere on the curve.

11. Prove that the average value of the curvature as a function of arc length s as you sweep out a convex curve in the counterclockwise direction is $2\pi/$(length of curve).

12. The flexure formula in the theory of beams asserts that the bending moment, M, required to bend a beam is proportional to the desired curvature, $M = k/R$, where k is a constant depending on the beam and R is the radius of curvature. A beam is bent to form the parabola $y = x^2$. What is the ratio between the moments required at $(0,0)$ and at $(2,4)$?   (Answer: 1 to $17\tfrac{3}{4}$)

13. Railroad curves are banked to reduce wear on the rails and flanges. The greater the radius of curvature, the less the curve must be banked. The best bank angle A satisfies the equation $\tan A = v^2/(32R)$, where v is speed in feet per second and R is radius of curvature in feet. A train travels in the elliptical track $x^2/1000^2 + y^2/500^2 = 1$ (where x and y are measured in feet) at 60 miles per hour ($= 88$ feet per second). Find the best angle A at the points $(1000, 0)$ and $(0, 500)$.

(Answer: $44°4'$ and $6°54'$)

14. The larger the radius of curvature of a turn, the faster a given car can travel around that turn. The radius of curvature required is proportional to the square of the maximum speed. Or conversely, the maximum speed around a turn is proportional to the square root of the radius of curvature. If a car moving on the path $y = x^3$ (x and y measured in miles) can go 30 miles per hour at $(1,1)$ without sliding off, how fast can it go at $(2,8)$?   [Answer: $30(^{145}\!/_{10})^{3\!/4}/\sqrt{2} = 158$ miles per hour]

15. Let s denote arc length along a curve. Show that the curvature at a point is equal to $x'y'' - y'x''$ evaluated at that point, where differentiation is with respect to arc length s.

16. (See Exercise 15.) Show (a) that $(x')^2 + (y')^2 = 1$; (b) that $x'x'' + y'y'' = 0$; (c) that $x'y'' - y'x'' = y''(x' + (y')^2/x') = y''/x'$.

17. In Theorem 2 we obtained a formula for curvature if the curve is given in rectangular form, $y = f(x)$. If the curve is given in polar form, $r = f(\theta)$, show that curvature equals $[r^2 + 2(r')^2 - rr'']/[r^2 + (r')^2]^{3\!/2}$. (Hint: Consider the parametric representation of the curve as $x = r\cos\theta$, $y = r\sin\theta$, where $r = f(\theta)$, and use the technique shown in Example 2.)

18. Use the formula in Exercise 17 to show that the cardioid $r = 1 + \cos\theta$ has curvature $3\sqrt{2}/(4\sqrt{r})$ at (r,θ).

4. Information supplied by the higher derivatives.   The derivative of the second derivative (if it exists) is called the third derivative. Similarly, we define the fourth derivative as the derivative of the third derivative, and so on. These higher derivatives are not easy to interpret geometrically, but as we shall see in Chaps. 13

and 14, they are useful for evaluating certain functions and for estimating errors in computational procedures. In this section we apply the higher derivatives in the study of polynomials.

The third derivative of a function $y = f(x)$ is denoted in many ways, including

$$D^3(f(x)) \qquad D^3 f \qquad f^{(3)}(x) \qquad \text{and} \qquad \frac{d^3 y}{dx^3}$$

Similar notations are used for the fourth derivative, and so on. (We should keep in mind, of course, that a function need not possess these higher derivatives.) Sometimes the derivative of f is denoted $f^{(1)}$; sometimes the function f is called *the zeroth derivative of f* and is denoted $D^0 f$ or $f^{(0)}$.

Example 1. Let us compute the various derivatives of $f(x) = x^3$. We have $D^0(x^3) = x^3$, $D(x^3) = 3x^2$, $D^2(x^3) = 6x$, $D^3(x^3) = 6$, $D^4(x^3) = 0$, and $D^n(x^3) = 0$ for $n > 4$.

Example 2. $D(e^{3x}) = 3e^{3x}$, $D^2(e^{3x}) = 3^2 e^{3x}$, and more generally, $D^n(e^{3x}) = 3^n e^{3x}$.

Example 3. The higher derivatives of $(x - a)^n$, where a is a fixed real number and n is a positive integer, will be useful. Let us compute them for $(x - 3)^5$. We have

$$\begin{aligned} D((x - 3)^5) &= 5(x - 3)^4 & D^4((x - 3)^5) &= 5 \cdot 4 \cdot 3 \cdot 2(x - 3) \\ D^2((x - 3)^5) &= D(5(x - 3)^4) = 5 \cdot 4(x - 3)^3 & D^5((x - 3)^5) &= 5 \cdot 4 \cdot 3 \cdot 2 \cdot 1 = 5! \\ D^3((x - 3)^5) &= 5 \cdot 4 \cdot 3(x - 3)^2 \end{aligned}$$

Since $D^5((x - 3)^5)$ is constant, it follows that $D^6((x - 3)^5)$ and all subsequent derivatives of $(x - 3)^5$ are 0. If we evaluate the derivatives of $(x - 3)^5$ at the point $x = 3$, we obtain the value 0 for all but one: the fifth derivative, which has the value 5! at any x, does not vanish at $x = 3$. This phenomenon will be useful in the proof of Theorem 2.

Example 4. $D(\sin x) = \cos x$, $D^2(\sin x) = -\sin x$, $D^3(\sin x) = -\cos x$, $D^4(\sin x) = \sin x$. Since the fourth derivative of $\sin x$ equals $\sin x$, we see that the higher derivatives repeat in groups of four,

$$\ldots, \sin x, \cos x, -\sin x, -\cos x, \ldots$$

an observation that will be useful in Chap. 13.

Now let us see how the higher derivatives are used in the study of polynomials. A little algebra shows that

$$x^2 + x + 2 = (x - 1)^2 + 3(x - 1) + 4$$

and hence that "$x^2 + x + 2$" and "$(x - 1)^2 + 3(x - 1) + 4$" are different formulas for the same function f. Though "$x^2 + x + 2$" may look simpler, for some purposes the formula "$(x - 1)^2 + 3(x - 1) + 4$" is more convenient. For instance, if we wish to compute or estimate $f(1.01)$, the first formula gives $f(1.01) = (1.01)^2 + (1.01) + 2$, while the second formula gives $f(1.01) = (0.01)^2 + 3(0.01) + 4$. From the second formula we see at a glance that $f(1.01)$ is approximately 4.03, and it is precisely $(0.01)^2 + (4.03) = 4.0301$. Clearly, if we are interested in the behavior of the function $x^2 + x + 2$ near $x = 1$, the formula we should use is $(x - 1)^2 + 3(x - 1) + 4$.

If we are interested in the values of $f(x) = x^2 + x + 2$ for x near 5, it is useful to express $f(x)$ as a polynomial in $x - 5$. That is, it is useful to find constants a_0, a_1, and a_2, such that

$$x^2 + x + 2 = a_2(x - 5)^2 + a_1(x - 5) + a_0$$

A tedious way to go about finding a_0, a_1, and a_2 (if they exist) is to expand $a_2(x - 5)^2 + a_1(x - 5) + a_0$, collect coefficients, and obtain equations for a_0, a_1, and a_2 by comparing the coefficients with the three coefficients, 1, 1, and 2 in $x^2 + x + 2$. This cumbersome technique leaves us with three equations for the three unknowns a_0, a_1, and a_2, which must then be solved.

Let us show how the higher derivatives can be used to find a_0, a_1, and a_2 rapidly. Assume that there are numbers a_0, a_1, and a_2, such that

(1) $\qquad f(x) = x^2 + x + 2 = a_2(x - 5)^2 + a_1(x - 5) + a_0$

Differentiation of (1) yields

(2) $\qquad f^{(1)}(x) = 2x + 1 = 2a_2(x - 5) + a_1$

Replace x in (2) with 5. We obtain a simple equation for a_1:

$$(2)(5) + 1 = 2a_2(5 - 5) + a_1 = a_1$$

Thus $a_1 = 11$. To obtain a_2, differentiate (2) to obtain

(3) $\qquad f^{(2)}(x) = 2 = 2a_2$

from which it follows that $a_2 = \frac{2}{2} = 1$.

We have found a_2 and a_1. To find the constant term a_0, we evaluate $f(=f^{(0)})$ at 5. From (1) it follows that

$$5^2 + 5 + 2 = a_2(5 - 5)^2 + a_1(5 - 5) + a_0 = a_0$$

Thus $a_0 = 32$. We have shown that for (1) to hold we must have $a_0 = 32$, $a_1 = 11$, and $a_2 = 1$. Thus

(4) $\qquad x^2 + x + 2 = (x - 5)^2 + 11(x - 5) + 32$

which can be verified by expanding the right-hand side.

The fact that this technique works for every polynomial is the substance of the next two theorems, one involving only algebra, the other involving the higher derivatives.

THEOREM 1.   *Any polynomial can be expressed as a polynomial in powers of $(x - a)$, where a is any fixed number.*

PROOF.   Let $f(x) = a_0 + a_1x + a_2x^2 + \cdots + a_nx^n$ be a polynomial. Then

$$f(x + a) = a_0 + a_1(x + a) + a_2(x + a)^2 + \cdots + a_n(x + a)^n$$

which after being expanded becomes a polynomial in powers of x:

(5) $\qquad f(x + a) = b_0 + b_1x + b_2x^2 + \cdots + b_nx^n$

Now, replace x with $x - a$ throughout (5). This gives

(6) $f((x - a) + a) = b_0 + b_1(x - a) + b_2(x - a)^2 + \cdots + b_n(x - a)^n$

Since $(x - a) + a = x$, Equation (6) provides the desired expansion of $f(x)$, and the proof is completed.

Example 5. We use Theorem 1 to express $f(x) = x^2 + x + 2$ as a polynomial in powers of $x - 5$. In this case $a = 5$. Following the procedure described, we first consider

$$f(x + 5) = (x + 5)^2 + (x + 5) + 2 = x^2 + 11x + 32$$

Then we replace x with $x - 5$ in the equation for $f(x + 5)$. This gives

$$f(x) = f((x - 5) + 5) = (x - 5)^2 + 11(x - 5) + 32$$

in agreement with our previous result.

Theorem 1 assures us that a polynomial in x can be written as a polynomial in $x - a$. The next theorem tells us how to find this representation efficiently with the aid of the higher derivatives of the polynomial.

THEOREM 2. *Let f be a polynomial in $(x - a)$,*

$$f(x) = a_0 + a_1(x - a) + a_2(x - a)^2 + \cdots + a_n(x - a)^n$$

Assume that we know $f(a), f^{(1)}(a), f^{(2)}(a), \ldots, f^{(n)}(a)$. Then the a_j's are completely determined and are given by the formula

(7) $$a_j = \frac{f^{(j)}(a)}{j!}$$

PROOF.   We begin by replacing x with a throughout:

(8) $f(a) = a_0 + a_1(a - a) + a_2(a - a)^2 + a_3(a - a)^3 + \cdots + a_n(a - a)^n$

This yields $f(a) = a_0$. To show that this agrees with (7), which asserts that $a_0 = f^{(0)}(a)/0!$, recall that $f^{(0)} = f$ and $0! = 1$.

To obtain a_1 we differentiate the original polynomial and obtain

(9) $f'(x) = a_1 + 2a_2(x - a) + 3a_3(x - a)^2 + \cdots + na_n(x - a)^{n-1}$

Replacing x with a throughout (9) yields

$$f'(a) = a_1$$

which agrees with (7).

To obtain a_2 we differentiate (9). This yields

(10) $f^{(2)}(x) = 2a_2 + 3 \cdot 2a_3(x - a) + \cdots + (n)(n - 1)a_n(x - a)^{n-2}$

Replacing x with a throughout (10) produces $f^{(2)}(a) = 2a_2$, hence $a_2 = f^{(2)}(a)/2$, in agreement with (7).

Another differentiation yields

(11) $f^{(3)}(x) = 3 \cdot 2a_3 + \cdots + (n)(n - 1)(n - 2)a_n(x - a)^{n-3}$

From (11) it follows that $a_3 = f^{(3)}(a)/3!$. Continuing in this fashion proves the theorem for any particular n.

The next example shows how these techniques are used in estimating roots of a polynomial.

Example 6. Consider the polynomial $f(x) = 2x^3 - 10x^2 + 19x - 10$. Since $f(1) = 1$ and $f(0) = -10$, the equation $f(x) = 0$ has a root between 0 and 1, probably nearer 1, since $f(1)$ is closer to 0 than $f(0)$ is. For this reason we are interested in the behavior of $f(x)$ for x near 1, and will express $f(x)$ as a polynomial in $x - 1$.

In view of Theorem 2, we compute the first three derivatives of f at $x = 1$. We have

$$f(x) = 2x^3 - 10x^2 + 19x - 10 \qquad \text{[hence } f^{(0)}(1) = 1]$$

$$f^{(1)}(x) = 6x^2 - 20x + 19 \qquad \text{[hence } f^{(1)}(1) = 5]$$

$$f^{(2)}(x) = 12x - 20 \qquad \text{[hence } f^{(2)}(1) = -8]$$

$$f^{(3)}(x) = 12 \qquad \text{[hence } f^{(3)}(1) = 12]$$

Then, according to Theorem 2,

$$f(x) = \frac{1}{0!} + \frac{5}{1!}(x - 1) + \frac{(-8)}{2!}(x - 1)^2 + \frac{12}{3!}(x - 1)^3$$

which is simply

$$f(x) = 1 + 5(x - 1) - 4(x - 1)^2 + 2(x - 1)^3$$

When x is near 1, we find that $f(x)$ is approximately $1 + 5(x - 1)$. This suggests that we solve $1 + 5(x - 1) = 0$ to obtain an estimate of a root of $f(x) = 0$. The equation $1 + 5(x - 1) = 0$ is equivalent to $x - 1 = -0.2$ or $x = 0.8$. To check, we note that

$$f(0.8) = 1 + 5(0.8 - 1) - 4(0.8 - 1)^2 + 2(0.8 - 1)^3$$

$$= 1 + 5(-0.2) - 4(-0.2)^2 + 2(-0.2)^3$$

$$= 1 - 1 - 0.16 - 0.016 = -0.176$$

which is close to 0.

A polynomial is completely determined by its value and the values of its higher derivatives at a single number. We shall meet the important formula $a_j = f^{(j)}(a)/j!$ again, in Chap. 13, where f may be such a function as e^x or $\sin x$.

EXERCISES

1. Verify that (a) $d^3(\cos x)/dx^3 = \sin x$; (b) $D^4(5e^x) = 5e^x$; (c) $D^4(5e^{-x}) = 5e^{-x}$; (d) $d^3(e^{-4x})/dx^3 = -64e^{-4x}$.
2. Verify that (a) $D^3(x^5) = 5 \cdot 4 \cdot 3x^2$; (b) $D^4(x^5) = (5!)x$; (c) $D^5(x^5) = 5!$.
3. Verify that (a) $D^3(\tan x) = 2 \sec^4 x + 4 \tan^2 x \sec^2 x$; (b) $D^2(\ln x) = -1/x^2$.
4. Find $D^{31}(f(x))$ if $f(x)$ is (a) $x^{16} + 11x^4 - 9$; (b) e^x; (c) e^{-x}; (d) $\sin(\pi x)$.
5. Find $D^{30}(f(x))$ if $f(x)$ is (a) x^{30}; (b) x^{31}; (c) x^{29}; (d) e^{-x}; (e) $\sin(\pi x)$.
6. Compute for arbitrary x and evaluate at $x = 4$ the following: (a) $[D^3(x - 4)^5]$; (b) $D^4[(x - 4)^5]$; (c) $D^5[(x - 4)^5]$; (d) $D^5[(2x - 4)^5]$; (e) $D^6[(2x - 4)^5]$.
7. (a) Show that $D^j[(x - a)^n]$, evaluated at a, is 0 if $j \neq n$.
   (b) Show that $D^n[(x - a)^n] = n!$.

8. (a) Use the technique shown in the proof of Theorem 1 to express $x^3 - 6x^2 + 7x - 1$ as a polynomial in $x - 2$.
   (b) Use Theorem 2 instead.
9. Using Theorem 2, express $2x^2 - 4x + 1$ as a polynomial in (a) $x - 1$; (b) $x + 2$. (c) Verify your answers in (a) and (b) by expanding them.
10. In the proof of Theorem 2 we stopped at a_3. Continue the argument for a_4 and a_5.
11. A certain function f has derivatives of all orders; furthermore $f(i) = 0$, $i = 1, 2, 3, 4$. What can we say about $f^{(1)}$? $f^{(2)}$? $f^{(3)}$? $f^{(4)}$? $f^{(5)}$? Explain.
12. Verify that $x^2 + x + 2 = (x - 1)^2 + 3(x - 1) + 4 = (x + 3)^2 - 5(x + 3) + 8$.
13. (a) Using Theorem 2, write $f(x) = 4x^3 + 6x^2 - 5x + 2$ in powers of $x - 2$ and verify your result by expanding it.
    (b) Use the expansion in (a) to estimate $f(2.1)$ and $f(1.9)$.
14. (a) Repeat Exercise 13(a), but in powers of $x + 2$.
    (b) Use (a) to estimate $f(-1.9)$.
15. The higher derivatives are occasionally useful in computing an antiderivative. Verify that if f is a polynomial, then

$$\int e^x f(x)\, dx = e^x[f(x) - f^{(1)}(x) + f^{(2)}(x) - f^{(3)}(x) + \cdots + (-1)^n f^{(n)}(x) + \cdots].$$

Note that the number of terms on the right is finite, since f is a polynomial.
16. Use Exercise 15 to compute (a) $\int e^x x^5\, dx$; (b) $\int e^x x^8\, dx$.
17. (See Exercise 16.) Let f be a polynomial. Develop a formula for $\int e^{-x} f(x)\, dx$ involving the higher derivatives of f.
18. (a) Show that $D[F'(x)\sin(\pi x) - \pi F(x)\cos(\pi x)] = [F''(x) + n^2 F(x)]\sin(\pi x)$.
    (b) Now let f be a polynomial of degree $2n$ (or less) and

$$F(x) = \pi^{2n} f(x) - \pi^{2n-2} f^{(2)}(x) + \pi^{2n-4} f^{(4)}(x) - \cdots + \pi^0 f^{(2n)}(x)$$

Show that $F''(x) + \pi^2 F(x) = \pi^{2n+2} f(x)$.
    (c) In view of (a) and (b), show that we have obtained a formula for $\int f(x)\sin(\pi x)\, dx$, where f is a polynomial.
    (d) Apply the formula in the case $f(x) = x^4$.
19. Prove that $\sin x$ cannot be written as a polynomial $P(x)$, even if we demand that $\sin x = P(x)$ only throughout a small interval $[a,b]$.
20. It is proved in trigonometry that $\cos^3 x = (\cos 3x + 3\cos x)/4$. Which is easier, to compute $D^{20}(\cos^3 x)$ or $D^{20}[(\cos 3x + 3\cos x)/4]$? Why? Compute the easier of the two.
21. Show that if a polynomial is constant over some interval, then it is constant everywhere.

22. We proved on page 124 that if $D(f(x)) = 0$ for all x, then f is constant.
    (a) Prove that if $D^2(f(x)) = 0$ for all x, then f is a polynomial of degree at most one.
    (b) Prove that if $D^3(f(x)) = 0$ for all x, then f is a polynomial of degree at most two.
23. Generalize Exercise 22.
24. Let us write the (valid) equation $e^x - D(e^x) = 0$ as $(1 - D)(e^x) = 0$. This suggests that we let a "polynomial in D" operate on a function. For instance, $(2 + 3D - 4D^2) f(x)$ will be short for $2f(x) + 3D(f(x)) - 4D^2(f(x))$. Verify that (a) $(1 + D) e^{-x} = 0$; (b) $(1 + D^2)(\sin x) = 0$; (c) $(1 - D^4)(\sin x) = 0$.
25. A number r is algebraic if it is a root of a nonzero polynomial with rational coefficients. Show that this definition is equivalent to the following: A number r is alge-

braic if it is a root of some function f (not identically zero), such that $D^n(f) = 0$ for some n and $f^{(j)}(0)$ is rational for all j.

26. (See Exercises 24 and 25.) Define r as *quasialgebraic* if it is a root of some function f (not identically zero), such that $f^{(j)}(0)$ is rational for all j, and there is some polynomial in D with integer coefficients, $P(D)$ (not identically zero), such that $[P(D)]f = 0$.
    (a) Show that if r is algebraic, then it is quasialgebraic.
    (b) Show that π is quasialgebraic.

27. Define $f(x) = x^n(1 - x)^n/n!$ for any fixed positive integer n. Show that (a) $f(x) = f(1 - x)$; (b) $f'(x) = -f'(1 - x)$; (c) $f^{(2)}(x) = f^{(2)}(1 - x)$; (d) $f^{(j)}(x) = (-1)^j f^{(j)}(1 - x)$.

28. (See Exercise 27.)
    (a) Show that $f^{(j)}(0) = 0$ for $j < n$ and that $f^{(j)}(0)$ is an integer for $j \geqslant n$.
    (b) Combining (a) with Exercise 27, show that $f^{(j)}(1)$ is an integer.

29. We now use the function f of Exercise 27 to prove that π^2 is irrational. Assuming that $\pi^2 = a/b$, where a and b are positive integers, we will obtain a contradiction in this exercise and Exercise 30 by showing that $\pi a^n \int_0^1 f(x) \sin(\pi x)\, dx$ is a *positive integer* for any n (recall that $f(x)$ depends on n), but that for large n it is *less than 1*.
    (a) Show that if x is in [0,1] then $0 \leqslant f(x) \leqslant 1/n!$.
    (b) Show that $0 < \pi a^n \int_0^1 f(x) \sin(\pi x)\, dx < \pi a^n/n!$.
    (c) Show that $\pi a^n/n!$ is less than 1 if n is large.

30. (See Exercises 18 and 29.) Now we show that $\pi a^n \int_0^1 f(x) \sin(\pi x)\, dx$ is an integer. This will contradict Exercise 29(b) and (c). Let F be defined as in Exercise 18, and let $G(x) = b^n F(x)$.
    (a) Show that $G(0)$ and $G(1)$ are integers. (See Exercise 28.)
    (b) Show that
    $$D[G'(x) \sin(\pi x) - \pi G(x) \cos(\pi x)] = b^n \pi^{2n+2} f(x) \sin(\pi x) = \pi^2 a^n f(x) \sin(\pi x).$$
    (c) Show that
    $$\pi a^n \int_0^1 f(x) \sin(\pi x)\, dx = [G'(x) \sin(\pi x)/\pi - G(x) \cos(\pi x)]_0^1 = G(1) - G(0).$$
    (d) From (c) and Exercise 29, conclude that π^2 is irrational. This proof, based on a method of I. Niven, is due to J. D. Dixon, π Is Not Algebraic, of Degree One or Two, *Amer. Math. Monthly*, **69**:636 (1962).

31. Which is a stronger statement: "π is irrational" or "π^2 is irrational"? Explain.

32. A certain function f has $f(0) = 3$, $f^{(1)}(0) = 2$, $f^{(2)}(0) = 5$, $f^{(3)}(0) = \frac{1}{2}$, and $f^{(j)}(0) = 0$ if $j > 3$. Give an explicit formula for $f(x)$.

5. Summary. In this chapter we defined and applied the higher derivatives of a function. The second derivative is related to concavity, curvature, and acceleration. The higher derivatives, while not as significant geometrically, do convey a great deal of information. In particular, the values at a single number of the higher derivatives of a polynomial completely determine the polynomial as Theorem 2, page 298, shows.

11

The maximum and minimum of a function

In this chapter we present ways of finding the maximum or minimum value of a function (if such a value exists). The function may be defined on part or all of the x axis (Sec. 1), or it may be defined on part or all of the xy plane (Sec. 2). Among our tools for finding these "extreme" values is the derivative, which has its limitations in this task, as we shall emphasize in Sec. 3.

1. Maximum and minimum of $f(x)$*.* If $f(x)$ takes on a largest value M for values of x in a given set, then let us call M the *global maximum* of $f(x)$ on the set. A continuous function defined on a closed interval has a global maximum (see page 84).

302

A function f defined on $[a,b]$ has a *relative maximum* (or *local maximum*) at x_0 if $f(x_0) \geqslant f(x)$ for all x in $[a,b]$ sufficiently near x_0. (As the following graph illustrates, a function may have several relative maxima.) We shall be interested primarily in finding the global maximum of a function.

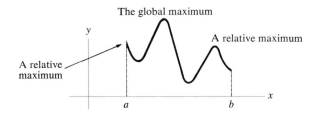

If the global maximum of a differentiable function occurs at a point X which is not an end point of the interval, then $f'(X) = 0$ (see page 120). This is the basis of the following procedure for finding a global maximum of a differentiable function:

Flow Diagram of Procedure for Finding M, the Global Maximum of $f(x)$ for x in $[a,b]$

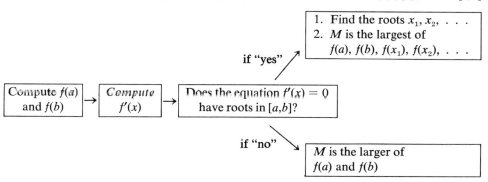

A few examples will illustrate how the technique is carried out.

Example 1. Consider the function $f(x) = x^3 - 3x^2 + 3x + 2$ for x in $[0,2]$. Since the function is continuous, it takes on a maximum value at some point in $[0,2]$. First we compute $f(0) = 2$ and $f(2) = 4$. Next we compute $f'(x) = 3x^2 - 6x + 3$ and find the roots of the equation

$$3x^2 - 6x + 3 = 0$$

This equation simplifies to $3(x^2 - 2x + 1) = 0$ or $3(x - 1)^2 = 0$, and its only root is $x = 1$. Since there is a root in $[0,2]$ we follow the path in the flow diagram labeled "if yes." We find that $f(1) = 3$ and lastly determine the largest of $f(0)$, $f(1)$, and $f(2)$. Since $f(0) = 2$, $f(2) = 4$, and $f(1) = 3$, we conclude that the global maximum is 4 and occurs when $x = 2$.

Though the problem is completely solved, it may be valuable to graph $y = x^3 - 3x^2 + 3x + 2$ for x in $[0,2]$. Since $y' = 3(x - 1)^2$ is never negative, the graph never descends as we move to the right. Since $y'' = 6(x - 1)$ the graph is concave upward for $x > 1$ and concave downard for $x < 1$; there is an inflection point at $x = 1$.

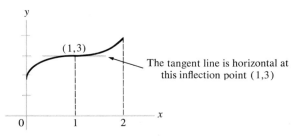

Example 2. If we cut four congruent squares out of the corners of a square piece of cardboard of side 12 inches, we can fold up the four remaining flaps to obtain a tray without a top. What size squares should be cut in order to maximize the volume of the tray?

Let us remove squares of side x, as shown in these two diagrams:

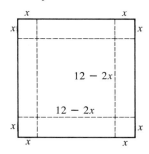

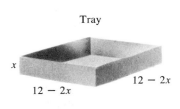

Folding on the dotted lines, we obtain a tray of volume

$$V(x) = (12 - 2x)^2 (x) = 4x^3 - 48x^2 + 144x$$

Since each side of the square is 12 inches, we wish to find the x in $[0,6]$ that maximizes $V(x)$.

Notice that $V(x) = (12 - 2x)^2 (x)$ is small when x is near 0 (that is, when we try to economize on the sides) and small when x is near 6 (that is, when we try to economize on the base). We have a "two-influence" problem; to find the best balance between them we use the calculus.

Since we wish to maximize $V(x)$ for x in $[0,6]$, we follow the flow diagram, and compute $V(0) = 0$ and $V(6) = 0$. Next we compute $V'(x) = D(4x^3 - 48x^2 + 144x) = 12x^2 - 96x + 144 = 12(x^2 - 8x + 12) = 12(x - 6)(x - 2)$. Then we ask whether $12(x - 6)(x - 2) = 0$ has any roots in $[0,6]$. We find that there are two roots, 2 and 6, and since the answer to our question is yes, we see by the flow diagram that the maximum of $V(x)$ for x in $[0,6]$ is simply the largest of $V(0) = 0$, $V(2) = 128$, and $V(6) = 0$. In this case, the global maximum does occur where the derivative is 0. The largest tray is obtained when $x = 2$.

In the next example we will minimize a function defined for all positive numbers. We will analyze the derivative, but will not develop a "flow chart" for this case.

Example 3. Of all the tin cans that enclose a volume of 100 cubic inches, which requires the least metal? The most metal?

We denote the radius of the typical can of volume 100 cubic inches by r; we denote its height by h. The can may be flat or tall.

A typical tin can of volume 100 cubic inches; $\pi r^2 h = 100$. The can may be flat or long

In the typical tin can under consideration the radius and height are related by the equation

(1) $$\pi r^2 h = 100$$

The surface area S of the can is given by

(2) $$S = 2\pi r^2 + 2\pi rh$$

in which we account for the two circular bases and the side. Since the amount of metal in the can is proportional to S, it suffices to minimize S. We use (1) to express S as a function of a single variable. Solving (1) for, say, h, we obtain $h = 100/\pi r^2$.

Thus S has the form

(3) $$S = f(r) = 2\pi r^2 + 2\pi r \left(\frac{100}{\pi r^2}\right) = 2\pi \left(r^2 + \frac{100}{\pi r}\right)$$

Inspection of (3), and in particular of $r^2 + (100/\pi r)$, shows that $S = f(r)$ becomes arbitrarily large when r increases (and the can becomes very flat) or when r approaches 0 (and the can becomes very tall and narrow). Though S has no maximum value, we will show that it has a minimum value. To do so, we examine the behavior of dS/dr.

From Equation (3) we find that

(4) $$\frac{dS}{dr} = 2\pi \left(2r - \frac{100}{\pi r^2}\right) = \frac{2(2\pi r^3 - 100)}{r^2}$$

Observe that when $2\pi r^3 < 100$ we have $dS/dr < 0$, but when $2\pi r^3 > 100$ we have $dS/dr > 0$. Thus S shrinks as we increase r from small values until r satisfies the equation $2\pi r^3 = 100$; that is, $r = \sqrt[3]{100/2\pi}$. When r is greater than $\sqrt[3]{100/2\pi}$, we see that S increases.

In order for the can to have minimal surface area, r must be $\sqrt[3]{100/2\pi}$. From (1) we find that $h = 100/[\pi(\sqrt[3]{100/2\pi})^2]$.

Example 4. We solve the preceding problem in a manner that requires less algebra and yields a more revealing solution.

In our previous equations

(1) $\pi r^2 h = 100$ and   (2) $S = 2\pi r^2 + 2\pi rh$

let us consider h, and hence S, as functions of r. However, we will not find these functions explicitly.

Differentiating (1) and (2) with respect to r, we obtain

(5)
$$\pi\left(r^2\frac{dh}{dr}+2rh\right)=\frac{d(100)}{dr}=0$$

and

(6)
$$\frac{dS}{dr}=4\pi r+2\pi\left(r\frac{dh}{dr}+h\right)$$

Since we are interested in h and r only when $dS/dr = 0$, we consider (6) only in the form

(7)
$$0=4\pi r+2\pi\left(r\frac{dh}{dr}+h\right)$$

From (5) and (7) we obtain, with a little algebra, a relation between h and r, as follows: Factoring πr out of (5) and 2π out of (7), we obtain

(8)
$$r\frac{dh}{dr}+2h=0 \qquad \text{and} \qquad 2r+r\frac{dh}{dr}+h=0$$

Elimination of dh/dr from (8) yields

(9)
$$2r+r\frac{-2h}{r}+h=0$$

which simplifies to

(10)
$$2r=h$$

Equation (10) tells us that the height of the ideal can is the same as its diameter; this fact was concealed by the solution in Example 3. Moreover, this is the ideal shape no matter what the prescribed volume happens to be. (To obtain (5) from (1) all we need to know about "100" is that it is fixed.)

Once we know that $h = 2r$, we use (1) to find the dimensions. Equation (1) becomes $\pi r^2(2r) = 100$; hence $r = \sqrt[3]{100/2\pi}$, and $h = 2r = 2\sqrt[3]{100/2\pi}$, which agrees with our previous solution, as a little algebra will show.

EXERCISES

1. (a) A tray is constructed, as in Example 2, by cutting four congruent squares of side x out of a piece of cardboard whose dimensions are 6 inches by 12 inches. Show that the volume of the tray is $V = f(x) = 4x^3 - 36x^2 + 72x$ cubic inches.
   (b) Graph V as a function of x for all x, not just for the x significant to our problem.
   (c) Why do we wish to examine $f(x)$ only for x in $[0,3]$?
   (d) By inspection of the graph, estimate the x in $[0,3]$ that maximizes $f(x)$.
2. (See Exercise 1.) Using $f'(x)$, find the x in $[0,3]$ that yields the maximum value of $f(x)$. (Answer: $3 - \sqrt{3}$)
3. Find the maximum and minimum values of $y = (x - 1)^3$ for x in $[-1,2]$. (Answer: 1 and -8)
4. (a) Suppose that in Example 3 the top and bottom are each half as thick as the side. Find r that minimizes S.
   (b) Suppose that in Example 3 the can has no top. Find r.
   (c) Is it a coincidence that (a) and (b) have the same answer? Explain.
   [Answer: (a) $r = 3\sqrt{100/\pi}$; (b) $r = 3\sqrt{100/\pi}$]
5. Graph S as a function of r in Example 3.
6. (a) Solve Example 3 by eliminating r instead of h. (b) Graph S as a function of h.
7. Solve Example 4, but consider S and r to be functions of h.

8. Check that the height h of the ideal can in Example 3 coincides with the height in Example 4.

9. If you have 100 feet of fence to enclose a rectangular garden, show that the garden should be laid out as a square to enclose the maximum area (*a*) by the method of Example 3, and (*b*) by the method of Example 4.

10. If you have 100 feet of fence to enclose a rectangular play yard of maximum area, one side of which is to be the bank of a stream, show that to maximize its area you should make its length 50 feet and its width 25 feet, (*a*) using the method of Example 3, and (*b*) using the method of Example 4.

11. An architect wishes to incorporate 100 feet of existing stone wall, laid in a straight line, into a boundary around a rectangular garden. He has an additional 200 feet of fence. How should he lay out the remaining fence in order to maximize the area of the garden? Be careful.

12. The "information content" or "entropy" of a binary source (such as a telegraph that transmits dots and dashes) whose two values occur with probabilities p and $1 - p$ is defined as $H(p) = -p \ln p - (1 - p) \ln (1 - p)$, where $0 < p < 1$. Show that H has a maximum at $p = \frac{1}{2}$. The practical significance of this result is that for maximum flow of information per unit time, dots and dashes should, in the long run, appear in equal proportions.

13. (See Exercise 12.) Let p be fixed so that $0 < p < 1$. Define $M(q) = -p \ln q - (1 - p) \ln (1 - q)$. Show that $H(p) \geqslant M(q)$ for $0 < q < 1$ and that equality holds if and only if $p = q$.

14. An irrigation channel made of concrete is to have a cross section in the form of an isosceles trapezoid, three of whose sides are 4 feet long.

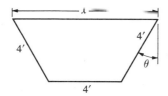

How should the trapezoid be shaped if it is to have the maximum possible area?
(*a*) Consider the area as a function of x and solve as in Example 1.
(*b*) Consider the area as a function of θ and solve as in Example 1.
(*c*) Do the two solutions agree? Explain.

[Answer: (*a*) $x = 8$; (*b*) $\theta = \pi/6$]

15. Find the point on the curve $y^2 = 4x$ closest to $(1,0)$.   [Answer: $(0,0)$]

16. Find the maximum and minimum value of $2x^3 - 9x^2 + 12x + 1$ for x in $[-5,5]$.

(Answer: 86 and -534)

17. The cost of operating a certain truck (for gasoline, oil, and depreciation) is $(5 + s/10)$ cents per mile when it travels at a speed of s miles per hour. A truck driver earns $3.60 per hour. What is the most economical speed at which to operate the truck during a 600-mile trip?
(*a*) If you considered only the truck, would you want s to be small or large?
(*b*) If you considered only the expense of the driver's wages, would you want s to be small or large?
(*c*) Express cost as a function of s and solve.

[Answer: (*c*) 60 miles per hour]

18. Let $y = x^3$. Where does $y' = 0$? Does y have a maximum or a minimum there?
19. Raking up leaves on a large lawn is a typical "collection" problem. Should we make many small piles or a few large ones? This depends on the effort involved in raking as compared with that needed to remove a pile. Unloading gravel in order to pave a large parking lot—a "distribution" problem—raises the same question. So does the distribution of manufactured products.
    (a) Explain why the time required to rake all the leaves in a region R to a point P_0 may be proportional to $\int_R r \, dA$, where r denotes distance to P_0.
    (b) Using (a), show that the time required to rake the leaves in a square to its center is proportional to the cube of its side.
    (c) Assume that it takes 10 seconds to rake a square whose side is 1 yard, and 5 seconds to collect any pile of leaves. A gardener is going to rake a square lawn whose side is 100 yards by dividing it into congruent squares, raking the leaves in each square to its center, and collecting the piles. What should the side of each small square be?

    [Answer (c) 1 yard]
20. At a certain x_0 where y' and y'' are continuous, we have $y' = 0$ and $y'' = 2$. Must $y = f(x)$ have a relative maximum or relative minimum at x_0? What if $y'' = 0$? What if $y'' = -2$? Explain. (Assume that y, y', and y'' are continuous at x_0.)
21. (a) What is the maximum value of $e^{-x} \sin x$ for positive x? What is its minimum value?
    (b) On the same axes, graph the curves $y = e^{-x} \sin x$, $y = e^{-x}$, and $y = -e^{-x}$ for positive x.

□ □ □

22. Find the shape of the right circular cone of largest volume inscribed in a sphere of radius a.
23. A ray of light travels from P to Q in such a way as to minimize the elapsed time.

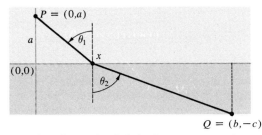

The speed of light is V_1 in the material above the x axis and V_2 in the material below it

Show that the path of light from P to Q therefore has

$$\frac{\sin \theta_1}{\sin \theta_2} = \frac{V_1}{V_2}$$

We outline one approach to the problem.
(a) Show that $b = a \cot \theta_1 + c \cot \theta_2$.
(b) Show that the time required to traverse the general path is

$$T = \frac{a \sec \theta_1}{V_1} + \frac{c \sec \theta_2}{V_2}$$

(c) Use the method of Example 4 to complete the problem.

24. A swimmer stands at a point A on the bank of a circular pond of diameter 200 feet. He wishes to reach the diametrically opposite point B by swimming to some point P on the bank and walking the arc PB along the bank. If he swims 100 feet per minute and walks 200 feet per minute, to what point P should he swim in order to reach B in the shortest possible time? (Quoted with permission from J. L. Walsh, "A Rigorous Treatment of Maximum-Minimum Problems in the Calculus," p. 10, Heath, Boston, 1962.)

25. A spider wishes to descend from P to Q on the lateral surface of this right cylinder and simultaneously wind n times around it.

Assuming that the perimeter of the base is L, show that his shortest possible path has length $\sqrt{h^2 + n^2L^2}$.

26. Show that $\sin 5x/\sin x$ is less than 5 for all x in $(0,\pi)$. How does $\sin 5x/\sin x$ behave when x is near 0? When x is near π?

27. On one side of a river 1 mile wide is an electric power station; on the other side, s miles upstream, is a factory. It costs 3 dollars per foot to run cable over land, and 5 dollars per foot under water. What is the most economical way to run cable from the station to the factory?

(a) Using no calculus, what do you think would be (approximately) the best route if s were very small? if s were very large?

(b) Solve with the aid of the calculus, and draw the routes, for $s = \frac{1}{2}, \frac{3}{4}, 1$, and 2.

(c) Solve for arbitrary s.

28. (a) The crew from the power station of Exercise 27 has to inspect the connection at the factory. Their boat travels 9 miles per hour and their truck 15 miles per hour. What route should they take to reach the factory in least time if they first cross the river?

(b) Compare the answer to (a) with the answer to Exercise 27.

(c) Assume now that the factory is at some distance from the river. Show that in this case the problems of providing electricity to it most economically or reaching it in minimal time are mathematically the same as Exercise 23.

29. A straight highway passes through a dense forest. A hiker parks his car along the highway and walks 1 mile in a direction perpendicular to it. He camps overnight and awakens the next morning, forgetting the direction from which he came but remembering that the car is 1 mile away.

(a) What route should he take to minimize the distance he would have to walk to return to his car?

(b) If he merely wants to return to the highway, is there a shorter route that he could follow?

(c) How short a route can you find in (b)?

30. Graph $y = \ln x/x$ for $x > 0$. In particular, show its maximum value, inflection point, and behavior for large x and x near 0.

2. *Maximum and minimum of* $f(x,y)$. In the preceding section we examined the maximum of a function defined on part of all of the x axis, that is, a function of a single variable. But sometimes we wish to maximize a quantity that depends on two or more variables. For instance, a manufacturer may wish to maximize a profit which may depend on how much he spends on advertising, research, expansion, and production.

Let us then consider a function of two variables, $z = f(x,y)$, which assigns a number to each point (x,y) in a certain set R in the plane. We graph such a function by erecting an ordinate equal to $f(x,y)$ at (x,y). The graph of a well-behaved f is a surface (that lies above R if f is positive and below if f is negative):

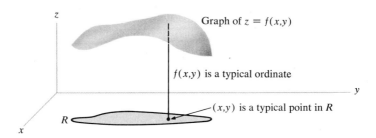

Just as with a function of a single variable, we may speak of a "continuous" function of two variables, its "global maximum" and "relative maxima." Informally, a function f, which assigns to the point (x,y) the number $z = f(x,y)$, is continuous at (a,b) if as (x,y) approaches (a,b), the function $f(x,y)$ comes and remains as close as we please to $f(a,b)$. (A formal definition can be found in Appendix F, page 593.) We define M as the *global maximum* of f over a set R in the plane, if it is the largest value of $f(x,y)$ for (x,y) in R. A *relative maximum* of f occurs at (a,b) if there is a circle around (a,b) such that $f(a,b)$ is the maximum value of $f(x,y)$ for (x,y) within the circle. (Each relative maximum can be pictured as the summit of a hill; the global maximum can be pictured as the highest point in a mountain range.)

Let us look at a point (a,b) where $f(x,y)$ has a relative maximum. The function $g(x) = f(x,b)$ also has a relative maximum at a. We imagine f defined for all (x,y) but sketch its graph only near (a,b):

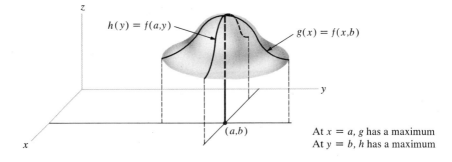

Thus dg/dx must equal 0 when $x = a$. Similar reasoning with $h(y) = f(a,y)$ shows that $dh/dy = 0$ when $y = b$.

These observations suggest that the derivative of z with respect to x (holding y fixed) and the derivative of z with respect to y (holding x fixed) will be of use. We have met these derivatives before, when we were computing repeated integrals. On page 252, for instance, we said, "We find a function $F(y)$ such that $dF/dy = x^2 + y^2$. Keeping in mind that x is constant, we see that $F(y) = x^2y + y^3/3 \ldots$."

If $z = f(x,y)$, we shall denote the derivative of z with respect to x (holding y fixed) by

$$\frac{\partial z}{\partial x} \qquad \frac{\partial f}{\partial x} \qquad z_x \qquad \text{or} \qquad f_x$$

Similarly, $\partial z/\partial y$, and so on, will denote the derivative of z with respect to y (holding x fixed). The derivatives z_x and z_y are called *partial derivatives* (the term "partial" may remind us that the derivative is "partial to" or "favors" one of the variables.) As an illustration, we have

$$\frac{\partial(x^2 \sin y)}{\partial x} = 2x \sin y \qquad \text{and} \qquad \frac{\partial(x^2 \sin y)}{\partial y} = x^2 \cos y$$

In the next two examples we shall make use of the following assumption: If $z = f(x,y)$ is a continuous function such that $f(x,y)$ becomes and remains arbitrarily large when $|x|$ and $|y|$ become large, then z takes on a minimum value (though, of course, no maximum value).

Example 1. We discuss the maximum and minimum values of
$$z = 6x^2 + 2y^2 - 24x + 36y + 2$$
for points (x,y) in the plane. First of all, when $|x|$ and $|y|$ are large, z is large, for the expression $6x^2 + 2y^2$ is then the major influence. Though z has no maximum, it does by our assumption have a minimum value. At that minimum value both $z_x = 0$ and $z_y = 0$. Therefore we should look at all the points where both z_x and z_y are 0.

We want
$$z_x = 12x - 24 = 0 \qquad \text{and} \qquad z_y = 4y + 36 = 0$$
The solution to these simultaneous equations is $x = 2$ and $y = -9$. Since there is only the one solution $(2,-9)$, z reaches its minimum there; inasmuch as $f(2,-9) = -184$, the minimum value of z is -184.

Example 2. What straight line is the "best fit" to these six points which record the results of six experiments concerning amount of advertising (x) and corresponding sales (y)?

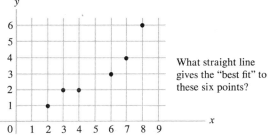

What straight line gives the "best fit" to these six points?

Statisticians frequently must find such a line and use the following definition of best fit: Say that an experiment provides us the points (x_1, y_1), (x_2, y_2), . . . , (x_n, y_n). Let $y = mx + b$ be a typical line; it cuts the y axis at $(0, b)$, and it has slope m. At x_i the line has ordinate $mx_i + b$. Ideally we would like $mx_i + b$ to equal y_i for each i. (This would be possible only if the n points were colinear.) We instead look for the line that *minimizes* the sum of the squares of the differences between y_i and the ordinate of the line at x_i; that is, we seek to minimize

$$[y_1 - (mx_1 + b)]^2 + [y_2 - (mx_2 + b)]^2 + \cdots + [y_n - (mx_n + b)]^2$$

(The differences are squared in order to avoid negative numbers.)

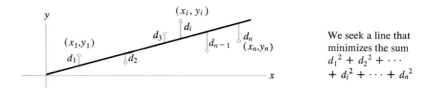

We seek a line that minimizes the sum
$d_1^2 + d_2^2 + \cdots$
$+ d_i^2 + \cdots + d_n^2$

We therefore seek an m and a b that minimize

$$f(m, b) = \sum_{i=1}^{n} [y_i - (mx_i + b)]^2$$

[Such a minimum exists, since when $|m|$ is large (when the line is steep), $f(m, b)$ is large.]

To find the desired m and b, let us compute f_m and f_b, as in Example 1, and set them equal to 0:

(1)
$$f_m = \sum_{i=1}^{n} 2[y_i - (mx_i + b)](-x_i) = 0$$

(2)
$$f_b = \sum_{i=1}^{n} 2[y_i - (mx_i + b)](-1) = 0$$

From (1) we obtain

(3)
$$m \sum_{i=1}^{n} x_i^2 + b \sum_{i=1}^{n} x_i = \sum_{i=1}^{n} x_i y_i$$

and from (2) we obtain

(4)
$$m \sum_{i=1}^{n} x_i + nb = \sum_{i=1}^{n} y_i$$

The simultaneous equations (3) and (4) can in general be solved uniquely for the unknowns m and b. Hence there is a unique line of best fit. It is called the *line of regression*. Formulas (3) and (4) provide a practical procedure for finding the line of regression; when applied to the data cited above, they provide the line $y = \frac{5}{7}x - \frac{4}{7}$, as may be verified. The reader might sketch this line to see whether it is a reasonable fit. The line of regression is used to analyze a psychological experiment on page 493.

EXERCISES

1. Compute z_x and z_y if (a) $z = \ln(x/y)$; (b) $z = (x^2 + 1)/y$; (c) $z = x \tan^{-1} y$.
   [Answer: (a) $z_x = 1/x$, $z_y = -1/y$]
2. Compute $\partial z / \partial x$ and $\partial z / \partial y$ if (a) $z = \sin(x^2 y)$; (b) $z = x^y$; (c) $z = x/y$.

3. Let $z = -3x^2 - 5y^2 + 6x - 9y$.

(a) Why does z have no minimum value?

(b) Find the point (x,y) at which z is a maximum.   [Answer: (b) $(1,-\%_{10})$]

4. The derivative dy/dx represents the slope of a certain line. What line has a slope equal to z_x? Draw a good picture. (Better still, make a model out of wire, soap, or clay.)

5. Let $(z_x)_y$ denote the partial derivative of z_x with respect to y; $(z_y)_x$ is defined similarly. Verify that $(z_x)_y = (z_y)_x$ if z is (a) $x^3 y^4$; (b) $\cos(x^2 y)$; (c) xe^{xy}.

6. Let $z = xy$.

(a) Show that $z_x = 0$ and $z_y = 0$ simultaneously only at $(0,0)$.

(b) Does this mean that z necessarily has a maximum or a minimum at $(0,0)$?

(c) How does z behave on the line $x = 0$? On the line $y = 0$? On the line $y = -x$? On the line $y = x$?

(d) Make a drawing or model of this surface, especially in the vicinity of $(0,0)$.

7. Find the maximum value of $f(x,y) = xy$ for points in the triangular region whose vertices are $(0,0)$, $(1,0)$, and $(0,1)$.   (Answer: $\frac{1}{4}$)

8. Find the maximum value of $f(x,y) = 3x^2 - 4y^2 + 2xy$ for points (x,y) in the square region whose vertices are $(0,0)$, $(0,1)$, $(1,0)$, and $(1,1)$.   (Answer: $1\frac{3}{4}$)

9. To apply equations (3) and (4) it is necessary to compute $\sum\limits_{i=1}^{n} x_i$, $\sum\limits_{i=1}^{n} y_i$, $\sum\limits_{i=1}^{n} x_i y_i$, and $\sum\limits_{i=1}^{n} x_i^2$. Do so for the data quoted at the beginning of Example 2.

(Answer: 30, 18, 110, 178)

10. (See Exercise 9.) Equations (3) and (4) for the data in Example 2 become $178m + 30b = 110$ and $30m + 6b = 18$. Solve these to obtain the line of regression, and draw it on a graph together with the six points. Does it look like a best fit?

11. Prove that if we place a 1-pound mass at each of the points (x_i, y_i), then the center of gravity of these n masses lies on the line of regression. [Hint: Consider Equation (4).]

12. Show that if $y = mx + b$ is the line of regression, then $\sum\limits_{i=1}^{n} [y_i - (mx_i + b)] = 0$. What does this mean geometrically?

13. (a) Show that $z = x^2 - y^2 + 2xy + 2$ has no maximum and no minimum.

(b) Find the minimum and maximum of z if we consider only (x,y) on the circle of radius 1 and center $(0,0)$, that is, all (x,y) such that $x^2 + y^2 = 1$. (Hint: To deal with this, use $x = \cos\theta$, $y = \sin\theta$.)

(c) Find the minimum and maximum of z if we consider all (x,y) in the disk of radius 1 and center $(0,0)$, that is, all (x,y) such that $x^2 + y^2 \leqslant 1$.

[Answer: (b) $2 + \sqrt{2}$, $2 - \sqrt{2}$; (c) $2 + \sqrt{2}$, $2 - \sqrt{2}$]

14. Show that of all rectangular boxes having a volume of 1 cubic inch, the cube has minimal surface area.

15. Show that of all rectangular boxes having a surface area of six square inches, the cube has maximal volume.

□ □ □

16. The line of regression minimizes the sum of squares of *vertical* differences. Determine the equation of the line that minimizes the sum of squares of *horizontal* differences.

17. Solve Example 1 without the aid of the calculus.
18. (a) Give a precise definition of a continuous function $y = f(x)$.
    (b) Devise a precise definition of a continuous function $z = f(x,y)$.
19. If u is a function of three variables, $u = f(x,y,z)$, there are three partial derivatives u_x, u_y, u_z. Compute these, where u is (a) $\sqrt{x^2 + y^2 + z^2}$; (b) $\sin(xy - 3z)$. [One example of such a function is the temperature u in the air at a certain instant; u depends on the position (x,y,z).]

3. Maximum and minimum of $ax + by + c$; linear programming. The maximum of a function $y = f(x)$, considered on $[a,b]$, can occur at a or b; similarly the maximum of a function $z = f(x,y)$, considered in some region bounded by a simple closed curve (or polygon), can occur on the border. In such cases the derivative or partial derivatives may give little useful information. To emphasize this, we present a general and important type of problem in which the *maximum always occurs on the border*. The technique for finding the maximum is known as *linear programming*. This section offers a brief glimpse into this branch of algebra, which has wide application in manufacturing, warehousing, transportation, and business management. We illustrate it by an example.

Example. An appliance dealer has room for 40 washers, stoves, or refrigerators. To please certain customers he will order at least five washers; but he knows he can't sell more than 15. He wants no more than 30 stoves, but at least as many stoves as washers. If his profit is 40 dollars per stove, 20 dollars per refrigerator, and 10 dollars per washer, how many of each should he order to maximize his profit?

Let us say that he orders w washers, s stoves, and r refrigerators. Then his conditions read thus: $w + s + r = 40$, $w \geqslant 5$, $s \leqslant 30$, $s \geqslant w$. If he determines w and s, then $r = 40 - w - s$, so let us examine only w and s, keeping in mind that $w + s \leqslant 40$. The set of points (s,w) in the sw plane, that satisfy

$$w \geqslant 5 \qquad w \leqslant 15 \qquad s \leqslant 30 \qquad s \geqslant w \qquad s + w \leqslant 40$$

is the pentagon R shown here:

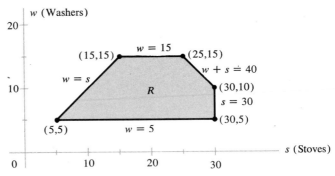

We wish to maximize the profit, which is $40s + 20r + 10w$. Since $r = 40 - w - s$, we see that the profit, P, when he orders s stoves and w washers is $40s + 20(40 - w - s) + 10w$. Now, $P = 20s - 10w + 800$, hence $P = 10(2s - w) + 800$. To maximize P it suffices to maximize the function $z = 2s - w$, which we denote f.

The graph of $z = 2s - w$ is a plane. (This is discussed on page 388.) We draw the part of the plane situated above the pentagon R:

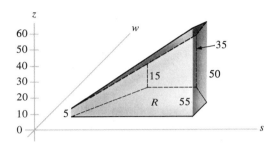

The part of the graph that interests us is the tilted pentagon above R. It seems reasonable that its maximum height occurs at one of its five vertices, and we will assume that it does. To find the maximum of z for points in R we therefore evaluate z at each of the five vertices of R. Now, $f(5,5) = 5$, $f(30,5) = 55$, $f(30,10) = 50$, $f(25,15) = 35$, and $f(15,15) = 15$. Thus the maximum z is 55 and is reached at (30,5). Therefore the profit is maximized by the sale of 30 stoves, 5 washers, and 5 refrigerators.

It should be pointed out that partial derivatives do give a little information. We have

$$\frac{\partial z}{\partial s} = 2 \quad \text{and} \quad \frac{\partial z}{\partial w} = -1$$

Hence, since the partial derivatives are never zero, neither the maximum nor the minimum can occur off the border. This is far from indicating where they do occur.

In this example there are only two independent variables, s and w. In practice, the number of variables may reach 20 or more. Techniques for dealing with the mathematical problems that arise are presented in G. B. Dantzig: "Linear Programming and Extensions," Princeton University Press, Princeton, N. J., 1963, or Dean, Sasieni, and Gupta: "Mathematics for Modern Management," Wiley, New York, 1963. These are only two of the many texts available.

EXERCISES

1. Find the maximum and minimum values over the pentagon R, in the text example, of (a) $2y - x$; (b) $y - x$; (c) $2y + x$; (d) $2y + 3x$.
   [Answer: (a) 15, -20; (b) 0, -25; (c) 55, 15; (d) 110, 25]
2. (a) Draw the triangular region R bounded by the three lines $x + 2y = 5$, $y = 2x$, and $y + 3x = 10$.
   (b) Find its vertices.
   (c) Find the maximum and minimum values of $z = 3y + 4x$ for (x,y) in R.
   [Answer: (c) 20, 10]

3. Draw the set of points (x,y) such that (a) $x + 2y = 5$; (b) $x + 2y \leqslant 5$; (c) $x + 2y \geqslant 5$.

4. If instead of maximizing his profit the merchant prefers to minimize his investment, how many of each appliance should he order? Assume that he still orders 40 appliances, and that a stove costs him 100 dollars, a washer 200 dollars, and a refrigerator 150 dollars.   (Answer: The solution is not unique; $5 \leqslant w = s \leqslant 15$; $r = 40 - 2w$)

5. Maximize the function $-x + 3y + 6$ on the convex polygon whose vertices are $(1,1)$, $(4,2)$, $(3,0)$, $(5,6)$.

6. (a) Draw the region R described by these conditions: $y + 4x \leqslant 22$, $3x \geqslant 2y$, $4y \geqslant x + 3$, $y \leqslant 2x - 1$.
   (b) Find its vertices.
   (c) Maximize $2x - 3y$ for points of R.

7. In our example we chose s and w as the independent variables. Solve the same problem, using w and r as independent variables.

8. A warehouse stores three types of machines, A, B, and C. There is storage space for 100 machines. Type A weighs 200 pounds, Type B 400 pounds, and Type C 100 pounds. The floor can hold only 30,000 pounds. The profit from Type A is 30 dollars, from Type B is 20 dollars, and from Type C is 10 dollars. At least 20 of Type B must be available. How many of each type should be stored in order to maximize profit?
   (Answer: 50 of Type A, 50 of Type B, none of Type C)

□ □ □

9. (a) Show that if c_1 and c_2 are constants, then the maximum value of $f(t) = c_1 t + c_2$ over a closed interval occurs at one of the end points.
   (b) Use (a) to show that if a, b, and c are constants, then the maximum value of $f(x,y) = ax + by + c$ over a convex polygon R occurs at a vertex of R.

4. Summary.   In this chapter we showed how the derivative and partial derivative can be used in the search for the maximum or minimum of a function. In finding the maximum or minimum of a differentiable function over a set, we examine the values of the function on the border of the set and at places where the derivative is zero. The derivative is especially helpful when the maximum does not occur at the ends of the interval or on the border of the region under consideration. In many cases, the maximum does occur on the border; in particular this happens for functions of the type $ax + by + c$ over polygons.

We have examined the maximum and minimum of functions of only one or two variables; similar techniques, involving partial derivatives with respect to each variable, apply to functions of more variables.

12

Series

In this chapter we investigate the behavior of the sequence u_1, $u_1 + u_2$, $u_1 + u_2 + u_3$, . . . formed by adding together more and more elements of a given sequence, $u_1, u_2, u_3, \ldots$. For instance, the sequence

$$p, p + 2p^2, p + 2p^2 + 3p^3, \ldots$$

where $0 < p < 1$, arises in traffic theory (see Chap. 24). In Chap. 13 we prove that the terms of the sequence

$$1, 1 + x^2, 1 + x^2 + \frac{x^4}{2!}, 1 + x^2 + \frac{x^4}{2!} + \frac{x^6}{3!}, \ldots$$

approach e^{x^2}. This provides a practical way of estimating $\int_0^1 e^{x^2}\, dx$, a definite integral which we cannot evaluate by the fundamental theorem of calculus since the antiderivative of e^{x^2} is not elementary.

317

If $|r| < 1$, the numbers in the geometric series

$$1, 1 + r, 1 + r + r^2, \ldots$$

approach $1/(1 - r)$. This fact has been used in machine computations to avoid the time-consuming process of division. As a final example, the terms of the sequence

$$x, x - \frac{x^3}{3!}, x - \frac{x^3}{3!} + \frac{x^5}{5!}, \ldots$$

obtained by adding terms in the sequence $x, -x^3/3!, x^5/5!, -x^7/7!, \ldots$ approach $\sin x$ (proved in Chap. 13). It requires much less of an electronic computer's memory to store the formula for this sequence than to store a table of values of $\sin x$.

1. The nth term test, the integral test, and the alternating series test.

Let $u_1, u_2, u_3, \ldots, u_n, \ldots$ be a sequence. From this sequence we obtain a new sequence $S_1, S_2, S_3, \ldots, S_n, \ldots$ by defining

$$S_1 = u_1$$

$$S_2 = u_1 + u_2$$

$$S_3 = u_1 + u_2 + u_3$$

$$\cdots \cdots \cdots \cdots \cdots \cdots$$

$$S_n = u_1 + u_2 + u_3 + \cdots + u_n$$

The sequence of sums $S_1, S_2, \ldots$ is called the *series* obtained from the sequence $u_1, u_2, \ldots$. Traditionally, though imprecisely, it is referred to as *the series whose nth term is u_n.*

We frequently start with a sequence $u_1, u_2, \ldots$ and have to decide whether the corresponding series converges. Before we present a few of the simpler tests useful in making this decision, it will be helpful to review two of our earlier examples.

Example 1. Let $u_n = (0.8)^{n-1}$. Then $u_1 = 1$, $u_2 = 0.8$, $u_3 = (0.8)^2$, ..., and

$$S_n = 1 + 0.8 + (0.8)^2 + \cdots + (0.8)^{n-1}$$

We showed that $S_1, S_2, \ldots$ converges to 5; that is, $\lim_{n \to \infty} S_n = 5$ (see Example 1, page 67).

Example 2. Let $u_n = 1/\sqrt{n}$. Then $u_1 = 1/\sqrt{1}$, $u_2 = 1/\sqrt{2}$, ..., and

$$S_n = \frac{1}{\sqrt{1}} + \frac{1}{\sqrt{2}} + \cdots + \frac{1}{\sqrt{n}}$$

We showed in Example 2, page 67, that S_n is larger than $\sqrt{n}$ and so becomes arbitrarily large. Thus the series $S_1, S_2, \ldots$ does not converge.

DEFINITION: *Divergent series.* If a series does not converge, then we say that it diverges, or is divergent.

It is customary to use the symbol $u_1 + u_2 + u_3 + \cdots + u_n + \cdots$ to denote the series whose *n*th term is u_n. The number S_n is called *the nth partial sum of the series*. When the sequence $S_1, S_2, \ldots$ has a limit S, it is customary to express this by writing either $u_1 + u_2 + u_3 + \cdots + u_n + \cdots = S$ or $\sum_{n=1}^{\infty} u_n = S$. We then say the series $u_1 + u_2 + u_3 + \cdots + u_n + \cdots$ is *convergent*, and call S *the sum* of the series.

There are then two basic questions concerning any series: Does it converge? If it converges, what is its sum? The next three theorems provide ways of answering the first question, which is usually the easier of the two.

THEOREM 1: *The nth term test.* If the series $u_1 + u_2 + \cdots + u_n + \cdots$ converges, then $\lim_{n \to \infty} u_n = 0$.

PROOF. Since S_n is the sum $u_1 + u_2 + \cdots + u_n$, while S_{n-1} is the sum of the first $n - 1$ terms, $u_1 + u_2 + \cdots + u_{n-1}$, we have $S_n = S_{n-1} + u_n$, or $u_n = S_n - S_{n-1}$. Let $S = \lim_{n \to \infty} S_n$. Then we also have $S = \lim_{n \to \infty} S_{n-1}$, since $S_{2-1}, S_{3-1}, S_{4-1}, \ldots$ run through the same numbers as $S_1, S_2, S_3, \ldots$. Thus

$$\lim_{n \to \infty} u_n = \lim_{n \to \infty} (S_n - S_{n-1}) = \lim_{n \to \infty} S_n - \lim_{n \to \infty} S_{n-1} = S - S = 0$$

and the theorem is proved.

As Example 2 shows, the fact that $u_n \to 0$ as $n \to \infty$ is not enough to make the series $u_1 + u_2 + u_3 + \cdots$ converge. Theorem 1 is, however, a useful test for divergence. For instance, it shows that the series

$$\tfrac{1}{2} + \tfrac{2}{3} + \tfrac{3}{4} + \cdots + \frac{n}{n+1} + \cdots$$

diverges, since the *n*th term, $n/(n+1)$, does not approach 0 as n becomes arbitrarily large. (The terms increase and have the limit 1.)

The next two tests depend on the following fundamental property of the real numbers: if $a_1, a_2, \ldots, a_n, \ldots$ is a sequence such that

$$a_1 \leqslant a_2 \leqslant \cdots \leqslant a_n \leqslant \cdots$$

and there is a number B such that $a_n \leqslant B$ for all n, then the sequence is convergent. (This is related to the completeness of the real number system, discussed in Appendix B.)

THEOREM 2: *The integral test.* Let f be a decreasing positive function, for $x \geqslant 1$, such that the improper integral $\int_1^{\infty} f(x)\,dx$ exists. Then $f(1) + f(2) + \cdots + f(n) + \cdots$ converges. If $\int_1^{\infty} f(x)\,dx$ does not exist, then $f(1) + f(2) + \cdots + f(n) + \cdots$ diverges.

PROOF.   The proof is suggested by comparing the areas of the two shaded regions in the diagram below with the area of the region under the curve $y = f(x)$ and above the interval $[1, n]$. However, we will not refer to the diagram in the proof.

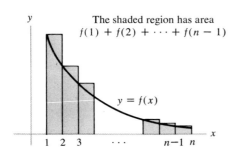

The shaded region has area
$$f(1) + f(2) + \cdots + f(n - 1)$$
$$y = f(x)$$

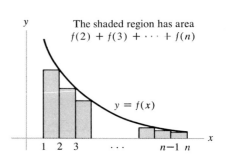

The shaded region has area
$$f(2) + f(3) + \cdots + f(n)$$
$$y = f(x)$$

We have $\int_1^n f(x)\, dx = \int_1^2 f(x)\, dx + \int_2^3 f(x)\, dx + \cdots + \int_{n-1}^n f(x)\, dx$. Since f is decreasing, this sum is less than or equal to $[f(1)]\,(1) + [f(2)]\,(1) + \cdots + [f(n) - 1)]\,(1)$ (see Lemma 2, page 143). Therefore if $\int_1^\infty f(x)\, dx$ does not exist, that is, if $\int_1^n f(x)\, dx$ becomes arbitrarily large as $n \to \infty$, then it follows that $f(1) + f(2) + \cdots + f(n - 1)$ becomes arbitrarily large as $n \to \infty$. Therefore if $\int_1^\infty f(x)\, dx$ does not exist, $f(1) + f(2) + \cdots$ diverges.

In a similar manner, it follows that $\int_1^n f(x)\, dx \geqslant f(2) + f(3) + \cdots + f(n)$; hence

$$f(1) + f(2) + \cdots + f(n) \leqslant f(1) + \int_1^n f(x)\, dx$$

If $\int_1^\infty f(x)\, dx$ exists, then

$$f(1) + f(2) + \cdots + f(n) \leqslant f(1) + \int_1^\infty f(x)\, dx$$

for all n. Thus the series $f(1) + f(2) + \cdots$ converges to a number less than or equal to $f(1) + \int_1^\infty f(x)\, dx$. This proves the theorem.

Example 3.   Let $f(x) = 1/x^2$. Since this is a decreasing positive function, Theorem 1 may be used to determine whether

$$\frac{1}{1^2} + \frac{1}{2^2} + \cdots + \frac{1}{n^2} + \cdots$$

converges. We examine $\int_1^\infty 1/x^2\,dx = \lim_{b\to\infty} \int_1^b 1/x^2\,dx$. By the fundamental theorem of

calculus we have $\int_1^b 1/x^2\,dx = (-1/x)\Big|_1^b = 1 - (1/b)$. Thus $\int_1^\infty 1/x^2\,dx = 1$, and the

series $1/1^2 + 1/2^2 + \cdots + 1/n^2 + \cdots$ is convergent. As the proof of Theorem 2

shows, $\sum_{n=1}^\infty 1/n^2 \leqslant (1/1^2) + \int_1^\infty 1/x^2\,dx = 2$. (The sum of the series is $\pi^2/6$, as is shown

in Exercise 55, page 178.)

Example 4. We apply the integral test to the *harmonic* series

$$\frac{1}{1} + \frac{1}{2} + \cdots + \frac{1}{n} + \cdots$$

Here $f(x) = 1/x$, and we examine $\int_1^\infty 1/x\,dx = \lim_{b\to\infty} \int_1^b 1/x\,dx$, which by the funda-

mental theorem of calculus equals $\lim_{b\to\infty} (\ln b - \ln 1)$. Since $\ln 1 = 0$, we have $\int_1^b 1/x\,dx =$

$\ln b$. Thus $\int_1^\infty 1/x\,dx$ does not exist and the harmonic series diverges.

The integral test shows that the "nearby" series $\frac{1}{1}^{1.01} + \frac{1}{2}^{1.01} + \cdots + 1/n^{1.01} +$
$\cdots$ is convergent.

THEOREM 3: *The alternating series test.* If $p_1, p_2, \ldots, p_n, \ldots$ is a decreasing sequence of positive numbers such that $\lim_{n\to\infty} p_n = 0$, then the series whose
*n*th term is $(-1)^{n+1} p_n$,

$$p_1 - p_2 + p_3 - \cdots + (-1)^{n+1} p_n + \cdots$$

converges.

PROOF. Let us first examine only the sums $S_2, S_4, S_6, \ldots, S_{2n}, \ldots$. We
have $S_2 = p_1 - p_2$, $S_4 = p_1 - p_2 + p_3 - p_4 = S_2 + (p_3 - p_4)$, and so on. Since
$p_3 > p_4$, we have $S_4 > S_2$. Similarly $S_6 = S_4 + (p_5 - p_6)$; hence $S_6 > S_4$. Thus

$$S_2 < S_4 < S_6 < \cdots < S_{2n} < \cdots$$

To show that the sequence $S_2, S_4, S_6, \ldots, S_{2n}, \ldots$ converges, it suffices to find
a fixed number B such that $S_{2n} \leqslant B$ for all n. We assert that $S_1 (= p_1)$ is such a
number.

To see this, rewrite S_2 as $S_1 - p_2$, S_4 as $S_1 - (p_2 - p_3) - p_4$, S_6 as $S_1 - (p_2 - p_3) -$
$(p_4 - p_5) - p_6$, and generally,

$$S_{2n} = S_1 - (p_2 - p_3) - (p_4 - p_5) - \cdots - (p_{2n-2} - p_{2n-1}) - p_{2n}$$

Since $p_2 - p_3 > 0$, $p_4 - p_5 > 0$, $\ldots, p_{2n} > 0$, we see that S_{2n} is obtained from
S_1 by the subtraction of positive numbers. Thus $S_{2n} < S_1$ for all n, and we conclude
that $\lim_{n\to\infty} S_{2n}$ exists.

Let S denote $\lim_{n\to\infty} S_{2n}$. We must show that $S_1, S_3, S_5, \ldots, S_{2n+1}, \ldots$ also has the limit S. This is not difficult, for

$$\lim_{n \to \infty} S_{2n+1} = \lim_{n \to \infty} (S_{2n} + p_{2n+1}) = S + 0 = S$$

The proof is complete.

REMARK. The same style of proof shows that $S_1 > S_3 > S_5 > \cdots$. Thus the "even" sums S_{2n} approach S from the left while the "odd" sums S_{2n-1} approach S from the right. This diagram shows the manner in which S_n approaches S:

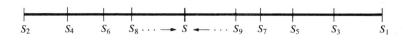

Example 5. By the alternating series test, $1 - \frac{1}{2} + \frac{1}{3} - \frac{1}{4} + \cdots + (-1)^{n+1} 1/n + \cdots$ converges (even though the related series of positive terms diverges). Since any even sum is less than S, the limit of the series, and any odd sum is greater than S, we have, for instance,

$$0.583 = 1 - \tfrac{1}{2} + \tfrac{1}{3} - \tfrac{1}{4} < S < 1 - \tfrac{1}{2} + \tfrac{1}{3} - \tfrac{1}{4} + \tfrac{1}{5} = 0.783$$

It is shown in Exercise 5, page 333, that $S = \ln 2 = 0.693$.

EXERCISES

1. (a) Prove that the series $1/1^{1.01} + 1/2^{1.01} + \cdots + 1/n^{1.01} + \cdots$ converges.
   (b) Using the integral test, find a number that is larger than its sum.

2. (a) Show that the series $1 - \frac{1}{4} + \frac{1}{27} - \frac{1}{256} + \cdots + (-1)^{n+1} 1/n^n + \cdots$ converges.
   (b) Show that the sum of the series is between 0.783 and 0.784. (Most handbooks contain a table of the decimal representations of the reciprocals of the integers from 1 to 999.)

3. Prove that the series $\sum_{n=1}^{\infty} 1/n^k$ diverges if $k \leqslant 1$ and converges if $k > 1$. (This series is of great importance in number theory. The function f defined by $f(k) = \sum_{n=1}^{\infty} 1/n^k$ is called the Riemann zeta function. For a simple illustration of its use, see Exercise 15.)

4. Which of the following series converge? Diverge? Explain.
   (a) $\sum_{n=1}^{\infty} (-1)^n$; (b) $\sum_{n=1}^{\infty} 1/(n \ln n)$; (c) $\sum_{n=1}^{\infty} 1/(1 + n^2)$; (d) $\sum_{n=1}^{\infty} n/(1 + n^2)$;
   (e) $\sum_{n=1}^{\infty} \cos(n\pi)/n!$.   [Answer: (c) and (e) converge; the others diverge]

5. Study the proof of Theorem 3 and prove that $S_1 > S_3 > S_5 > \cdots$.

6. Which of the following series converge? Diverge? Explain.
   (a) $\sum_{n=1}^{\infty} (-1)^{n+1} n/(n + 1)$; (b) $\sum_{n=1}^{\infty} (-1)^{n+1} 1/(n^2 + 1)$; (c) $\sum_{n=1}^{\infty} 1/(n^2 + 1)$;
   (d) $\sum_{n=1}^{\infty} n^2/(n^3 + 1)$; (e) $\sum_{n=1}^{\infty} 1/\sqrt[3]{n}$; (f) $\sum_{n=1}^{\infty} (-1)^{n+1} 1/\sqrt[3]{n}$.

7. By considering $\int_1^{1,000,000} (1/x)\,dx$, estimate the sum of the first million terms of the harmonic series.   (Answer: between 13.8 and 14.8)

8. For which x does the series $\sum_{n=1}^{\infty} x^n$ converge? Diverge? Explain.

    (Answer: it converges for $-1 < x < 1$)

9. (a) Show that $\sum_{n=1}^{\infty} 1/n^3$ is convergent.

    (b) Show that its sum S is less than $\frac{1}{1^3} + \frac{1}{2^3} + \frac{1}{3^3} + \frac{1}{4^3} + \int_4^{\infty} (1/x^3)\,dx$.

    (c) Deduce that $1.17 < S < 1.21$. It is not known whether S is a rational multiple of π^3 (see Exercise 55, page 178).

10. In the next chapter we prove that

$$\sin 1 = 1 - \frac{1}{3!} + \frac{1}{5!} - \frac{1}{7!} + \cdots + (-1)^{n+1}\frac{1}{(2n-1)!} + \cdots$$

    Find two numbers, a and b, such that $a < \sin 1 < b$ and $b - a < 0.001$.

11. For which x does the series $\sum_{n=1}^{\infty} x^n/n$ converge? Diverge? Explain.

    (Answer: If $-1 \leqslant x < 1$, it converges; otherwise, it does not)

12. Test for convergence (a) $\sum_{n=1}^{\infty} \cos n$; (b) $\sum_{n=1}^{\infty} n \sin(\pi/n)$; (c) $\sum_{n=1}^{\infty} \cos(n\pi)/n$.

13. Show that $\sum_{n=1}^{\infty} (-1)^{n+1}(1/n!)$ is between 0.62 and 0.64. (See the advice offered in Exercise 2.)

□ □ □

14. Devise a divergent alternating series $p_1 - p_2 + \cdots$ such that p_n is positive, and $\lim_{n \to \infty} p_n = 0$.

15. We will use the zeta function, defined in Exercise 3, to prove that there is no end to the primes. Assume that there are only a finite number of primes, $p_1, p_2, \ldots, p_m$.
    (a) Show why, under this assumption, we would have

$$\frac{1}{1 - 1/p_1^2} \frac{1}{1 - 1/p_2^2} \cdots \frac{1}{1 - 1/p_m^2} = \sum_{n=1}^{\infty} \frac{1}{n^2}$$

    (b) Recalling that $\sum_{n=1}^{\infty} 1/n^2 = \pi^2/6$ (Exercise 55, page 178) and that π^2 is irrational (Exercise 30, page 301), obtain a contradiction from (a).

16. (See Exercise 15.) Sketch a graph of the zeta function.

17. Rearrange the terms in the series $1 - \frac{1}{2} + \frac{1}{3} - \frac{1}{4} + \cdots$ in such a way that the resulting series diverges.

2. The comparison test, the ratio test, and the absolute convergence test.

The three tests we shall discuss in this section are additional tools for determining whether a series converges. For instance, with their aid we will show that no matter how we distribute the plus and minus signs, term by term, the series

$$\pm \frac{1}{2} \pm \frac{2}{4} \pm \frac{3}{8} \pm \frac{4}{16} \pm \cdots \pm \frac{n}{2^n} \pm \cdots$$

converges.

THEOREM 4: *The comparison test.* If the series $c_1 + c_2 + \cdots + c_n + \cdots$ converges, where each c_n is positive, and if $0 \leqslant p_n \leqslant c_n$ for each n, then the series $p_1 + p_2 + \cdots + p_n + \cdots$ also converges. On the other hand, if $c_1 + c_2 + \cdots + c_n + \cdots$ diverges, and if $p_n \geqslant c_n$ for each n, then the series $p_1 + p_2 + \cdots + p_n + \cdots$ also diverges.

PROOF. We prove only the first assertion. Observe that

$$S_n = p_1 + p_2 + \cdots + p_n \leqslant c_1 + c_2 + \cdots + c_n \leqslant \sum_{n=1}^{\infty} c_n$$

Since $S_1 \leqslant S_2 \leqslant S_3 \leqslant \cdots \leqslant S_n \leqslant \cdots$ and each S_n is less than or equal to the fixed number $\sum_{n=0}^{\infty} c_n$, we know that $\lim_{n \to \infty} S_n$ exists. This ends the proof of the first assertion.

To apply the comparison test we "compare" a series to a series whose behavior is known. For instance, a standard series to keep in mind is $\sum_{n=1}^{\infty} n^k$, which converges if $k > 1$ and diverges if $k \leqslant 1$. (This is easily shown by the integral test.)

Example 1. Does

$$\sum_{n=1}^{\infty} \frac{n+1}{n+2} \frac{1}{n^2}$$

converge or diverge? Let us compare it to $\sum_{n=1}^{\infty} 1/n^2$, which it resembles. Since $(n+1)/(n+2)$ is less than 1, we have

$$\frac{n+1}{n+2} \frac{1}{n^2} < \frac{1}{n^2}$$

The comparison test tells us that since $\sum_{n=1}^{\infty} 1/n^2$ converges, $\sum_{n=1}^{\infty} [(n+1)/(n+2)] (1/n^2)$ does also. Note that the test does not determine the sum of the series.

On the other hand, $$\sum_{n=1}^{\infty} \frac{n+2}{n+1} \frac{1}{n}$$

diverges since its terms are larger than the terms of the harmonic series, $\sum_{n=1}^{\infty} 1/n$, which diverges.

The next theorem is suggested by the geometric series $1 + r + r^2 + \cdots + r^{n-1} + \cdots$, in which the ratio of successive terms is r and which converges when $-1 < r < 1$. [Note that $1 + r + \cdots + r^{n-1} = (1 - r^n)/(1 - r)$; as $n \to \infty$, $r^n \to 0$. Hence $1 + r + r^2 + \cdots + r^{n-1} + \cdots = 1/(1 - r)$.]

THEOREM 5: *The ratio test.* Let $p_1 + p_2 + \cdots + p_n + \cdots$ be a series with positive terms. If $\lim\limits_{n \to \infty} (p_{n+1}/p_n)$ exists and is less than 1, then the series converges. If the limit is greater than 1, the series diverges; its nth term does not approach 0.

PROOF. Let $\lim\limits_{n \to \infty} (p_{n+1}/p_n) = s < 1$. Select a number r such that $s < r < 1$. Then there is an integer N such that $p_{n+1}/p_n < r$ whenever $n \geqslant N$. Thus $p_{n+1} < rp_n$ for $n \geqslant N$. We have

(1)
$$p_{N+1} < rp_N;\ p_{N+2} < rp_{N+1} < r^2 p_N;\ p_{N+3} < rp_{N+2} < r^3 p_N;\ \ldots\ ;\ p_{N+i} < r^i p_N;\ \ldots$$

Now, the series

$$rp_N + r^2 p_N + r^3 p_N + \cdots$$

is a geometric series with ratio of successive terms less than 1; hence it converges. By (1) and the comparison test, $p_{N+1} + p_{N+2} + \cdots$ converges. If we add to this the finite sum $p_1 + p_2 + \cdots + p_N$, we still have a convergent series.

If $\lim\limits_{n \to \infty} p_{n+1}/p_n$ is greater than 1, we have $p_{n+1} > p_n$ for all n sufficiently large. Thus the nth term cannot approach 0, and the series diverges. The theorem is proved.

The ratio test is especially convenient when the nth term involves a factorial or the nth power of a fixed number, as we see in the next two examples.

Example 2. The series

$$p + 2p^2 + 3p^3 + \cdots + np^n + \cdots \qquad 0 < p < 1$$

is important in probability theory. Because of the appearance of p^n in the nth term, it is natural to try the ratio test. We have $p_n = np^n$ and $p_{n+1} = (n + 1) p^{n+1}$. Hence

$$\frac{p_{n+1}}{p_n} = \frac{(n + 1) p^{n+1}}{np^n} = \left(1 + \frac{1}{n}\right) p$$

Since $\lim\limits_{n \to \infty} (1/n) = 0$, we see that $\lim\limits_{n \to \infty} (p_{n+1}/p_n) = p$. The ratio test assures us that the series converges.

To find its sum S, let us use a device employed in summing a geometric series. We have

(2)
$$S = p + 2p^2 + 3p^3 + 4p^4 + \cdots$$

and therefore

(3)
$$pS = p^2 + 2p^3 + 3p^4 + \cdots$$

Subtraction of (3) term by term from (2) yields

$$S - pS = p + p^2 + p^3 + p^4 + \cdots$$

a geometric series whose sum is $p/(1 - p)$. Thus

$$S - pS = (1 - p) S = \frac{p}{1 - p}$$

from which we conclude that $S = p/(1 - p)^2$.

Example 3. Does the series

$$\frac{10}{1!} + \frac{10^2}{2!} + \frac{10^3}{3!} + \cdots + \frac{10^n}{n!} + \cdots$$

converge or diverge? In spite of the large size of its early terms, this series converges, for

$$\frac{p_{n+1}}{p_n} = \frac{10^{n+1}/(n + 1)!}{10^n/n!} = \frac{10^{n+1}}{(n + 1)!} \frac{n!}{10^n} = \frac{10}{n + 1}$$

Thus $\lim_{n \to \infty} (p_{n+1}/p_n) = 0$. By the ratio test the series converges. It follows, by the nth term test, that $\lim_{n \to \infty} p_n = 0$. *In other words, $n!$ grows much more rapidly than 10^n.* The same argument shows that $\lim_{n \to \infty} x^n/n! = 0$ for any fixed positive x, a result that will be useful in Chap. 13.

Example 4. If we try the ratio test on $\sum_{n=1}^{\infty} 1/n^2$, we compute

$$\lim_{n \to \infty} \frac{1/(n + 1)^2}{1/n^2} = \lim_{n \to \infty} \frac{n^2}{(n + 1)^2} = \lim_{n \to \infty} \frac{1}{(1 + 1/n)^2} = 1$$

which is not less than 1. The ratio test gives no information. The integral test is of use, however, and shows that the series converges.

We now present a test that applies to series whose terms need not be positive. Let $u_1 + u_2 + \cdots + u_n + \cdots$ be a series whose individual terms, u_n, may be positive or negative in any order whatsoever. We expect it to behave at least as nicely as $|u_1| + |u_2| + \cdots + |u_n| + \cdots$ since, by "making all the terms positive," we encourage the series to diverge. The next theorem confirms our expectation.

THEOREM 6: *The absolute convergence test.* If $|u_1| + |u_2| + \cdots + |u_n| + \cdots$ converges, then so does $u_1 + u_2 + \cdots + u_n + \cdots$.

PROOF. Since the series whose nth term is $|u_n|$ converges, the series whose nth term is $|u_n| + |u_n|$ also converges (and incidentally has a sum equal to $2 \sum_{n=1}^{\infty} |u_n|$).

Next, consider the series whose nth term is $u_n + |u_n|$. Note that $u_n + |u_n|$ is equal to 0 if u_n is negative, and to $|u_n| + |u_n|$ if u_n is positive. Therefore if we let $p_n = u_n + |u_n|$ and $c_n = |u_n| + |u_n|$, we have

$$0 \leqslant p_n \leqslant c_n$$

By the comparison test, $\sum_{n=1}^{\infty} (u_n + |u_n|)$ converges. Now let $\sum_{n=1}^{\infty} (u_n + |u_n|) = A$ and

$\sum_{n=1}^{\infty} |u_n| = B$. Since $u_1 = (u_1 + |u_1|) - |u_1|$, $u_2 = (u_2 + |u_2|) - |u_2|$, . . . , we have

$$\sum_{i=1}^{n} u_i = \sum_{i=1}^{n} [(u_i + |u_i|) - u_i] = \sum_{i=1}^{n} (u_i + |u_i|) - \sum_{i=1}^{n} |u_i|$$

Thus $\sum_{i=1}^{n} u_i$ approaches $A - B$ as $n \to \infty$, and the theorem is proved.

Example 5. We return to the series discussed at the beginning of the section,

$$\pm \frac{1}{2} \pm \frac{2}{4} \pm \frac{3}{8} \pm \frac{4}{16} \pm \cdots \pm \frac{n}{2^n} \pm \cdots$$

where the pluses and minuses are chosen in any order whatsoever. If all the signs are pluses, then we have

$$\frac{1}{2} + \frac{2}{4} + \frac{3}{8} + \frac{4}{16} + \cdots + \frac{n}{2^n} + \cdots$$

which, as we saw in Example 2, converges. Theorem 6 tells us that, no matter what the choice of signs, the series still converges.

A series $u_1 + u_2 + \cdots$ is said to converge absolutely if the series $|u_1| + |u_2| + \cdots$ converges. A series that converges absolutely, converges (Theorem 6). But the converse does not necessarily hold: $1 - \frac{1}{2} + \frac{1}{3} - \frac{1}{4} + \cdots$ converges, but not absolutely.

EXERCISES

1. Test for convergence or divergence:

   (a) $\sum_{n=1}^{\infty} \dfrac{(-1)^n n/(1 + n^2)}{1 + n^2}$; (b) $\sum_{n=1}^{\infty} \dfrac{(-1)^n n^2}{2^n}$; (c) $\sum_{n=1}^{\infty} \dfrac{n + 2}{(n + 1)\sqrt{n}}$; (d) $\sum_{n=1}^{\infty} \dfrac{(-1)^n}{\sqrt[3]{n}}$

   [Answer: All except (c) converge]

2. Prove that each of these series converges: (a) $\sum_{n=1}^{\infty} \left(\dfrac{n+1}{2n+1}\right)^n$; (b) $1 - \frac{1}{4} - \frac{1}{9} + \frac{1}{16} - \frac{1}{25} - \frac{1}{36} + \cdots$ (one plus sign alternating with two minus signs); (c) $\sum_{n=1}^{\infty} \dfrac{n^3}{2^n}$.

3. (a) Give an example of a series of positive terms such that the limit of the ratio between successive terms is 1, and the series converges.

   (b) Repeat (a), this time constructing a series that diverges.

   (c) Why is there no "ratio test" when the limit of the ratio is 1?

4. Prove this theorem: Let $p_1 + p_2 + \cdots + p_n + \cdots$ be a series with positive terms. If $\lim_{n \to \infty} p_{n+1}/p_n$ exists and is greater than 1, then p_n gets arbitrarily large.

5. Prove that $\sum_{n=1}^{\infty} (1/n^3) \sin(n\sqrt{2})$ converges.

6. For which values of x does $x - x^2/2^2 + x^3/3^2 - x^4/4^2 + \cdots + (-1)^{n+1} x^n/n^2 + \cdots$ converge? Diverge?

7. Prove that if $\sum\limits_{n=1}^{\infty} |a_n| r^n$ converges, where r is some positive number, then $\sum\limits_{n=1}^{\infty} a_n x^n$ converges if $|x| \leqslant r$.

8. Prove that $\lim\limits_{n \to \infty} nx^n = 0$ if $|x| < 1$. (Hint: Prove first that the series $\sum\limits_{n=1}^{\infty} nx^n$ is convergent.)

9. (a) Differentiate both sides of the identity

$$1 + x + x^2 + \cdots + x^n = \frac{x^{n+1} - 1}{x - 1} \qquad x \neq 1$$

to obtain the identity

$$1 + 2x + 3x^2 + \cdots + nx^{n-1} = \frac{nx^{n+1} - (n+1)x^n + 1}{(x-1)^2}$$

(b) From (a) deduce that for $|x| < 1$

$$\sum_{n=1}^{\infty} nx^{n-1} = \frac{1}{(1-x)^2}$$

(c) From (b) obtain an alternative development of the formula for the sum of the series in Example 2.

10. Prove the second assertion in Theorem 4.

11. Let $a_n = 4^n/n!$
   (a) Compute a_1, a_2, a_3, a_4, a_5, a_6, and a_7 and express them decimally.
   (b) Prove that $\lim\limits_{n \to \infty} a_n = 0$.
   (c) Prove that $\lim\limits_{n \to \infty} (x^n/n!) = 0$ for any fixed x.

12. Throw a coin until it turns up heads. Record the number of throws in your experiment. This number can be any integer from 1 upward.
   (a) Average the numbers obtained from 20 experiments.
   (b) How does the average compare with $\sum\limits_{n=1}^{\infty} n(1/2)^n$?
   (c) Why should the average be "close" to the sum in (b)? (See Exercise 32, page 74.)

13. Show that $\sum\limits_{n=1}^{\infty} (-1)^{n+1} 1/n^3$ converges, and exhibit a number (in decimal form) which is larger than the sum and a number which is smaller.

14. (a) Prove that if $\lim\limits_{n \to \infty} u_{n+1}/u_n = -\frac{1}{2}$, then $\sum\limits_{n=1}^{\infty} u_n$ converges.
   (b) Devise an example illustrating (a), other than a geometric series.

15. (a) Graph $3^n/n!$ as a function of n. In particular, compute it for $n = 1, 2, 3, 4, 5, 6$.
   (b) What is the largest value of $3^n/n!$?
   (c) How does $3^n/n!$ behave for large n?

□ □ □

16. In Chap. 13 we will prove that e is equal to $1/0! + 1/1! + 1/2! + \cdots + 1/n! + \cdots$. Prove that e is irrational. (Hint: Assume $e = a/b$, where a and b are positive integers, and multiply the relation $a/b = 1/0! + 1/1! + 1/2! + \cdots + 1/n! + \cdots$ by $b!$.)

17. By considering

$$\tfrac{1}{2} + \tfrac{1}{4} + \tfrac{1}{8} + \tfrac{1}{16} + \cdots = 1$$

$$\tfrac{1}{4} + \tfrac{1}{8} + \tfrac{1}{16} + \cdots = \tfrac{1}{2}$$

$$\tfrac{1}{8} + \tfrac{1}{16} + \cdots = \tfrac{1}{4}$$

$$\cdots \cdots \cdots \cdots \cdots$$

show that $\sum\limits_{n=1}^{\infty} n(\tfrac{1}{2})^n = 2$.

18. The following result is frequently used in the theory of stochastic process in statistics: Let a_n and c_n, $n = 1, 2, 3, \ldots$, be two sequences of nonnegative numbers such that $\sum\limits_{n=1}^{\infty} a_n c_n$ converges and $\lim\limits_{n \to \infty} c_n = 0$. Prove that $\sum\limits_{n=1}^{\infty} a_n c_n^2$ converges.

19. (See Exercise 9.) Prove that $\sum\limits_{n=1}^{\infty} n^2 x^n = x(1 + x)/(1 - x)^3$ for $|x| < 1$.

20. Throw a die until it shows an ace (one). Count the number of throws in your experiment.

(a) Average these numbers of throws obtained from 10 experiments.

(b) Compute $\sum\limits_{n=1}^{\infty} n(\tfrac{5}{6})^{n-1} (\tfrac{1}{6})$.

(c) Why should the average in (a) be "close" to the sum in (b)?

21. A ball dropped from a height of h feet rebounds to a height of $4h/9$ feet. Suppose it is dropped from a height of 16 feet. Compute (a) the total distance it travels as it bounces, and (b) the total time it bounces. (c) When is it at rest?

3. The truncation error E_n.

In this section we examine the difference between the nth partial sum S_n of a convergent series $u_1 + u_2 + \cdots$ and S, which we may think of as "the sum of all its terms." This is of special importance in computations which use S_n as an approximation to S. The difference $S - S_n$ is denoted E_n and is called *the remainder after n terms, the truncation error*, or simply *the error*. Note that E_n is the "tail-end" sum, $u_{n+1} + u_{n+2} + \cdots$.

In the case of an *alternating series* satisfying the conditions of Theorem 3, page 321, we see that $|E_n|$ is less than p_{n+1}, the first omitted term. (This is implicit in our proof of Theorem 3.) Any "even" sum is less than S, while any "odd" sum is larger than S. For instance,

$$S_4 < S < S_5$$

Hence $E_4 = S - S_4 < S_5 - S_4 = p_5$.

Example 1. The alternating series test shows that $1 - 1/2! + 1/3! - 1/4! + \cdots + (-1)^{n+1} 1/n! + \cdots$ converges; $|E_3|$ is less than $p_4 = 1/4!$. In fact, the sum S of the series satisfies

$$0.625 = 1 - \tfrac{1}{2} + \tfrac{1}{6} - \tfrac{1}{24} < S < 1 - \tfrac{1}{2} + \tfrac{1}{6} = 0.667$$

The error E_n can be computed explicitly for a geometric series,

$$a + ar + ar^2 + \cdots + ar^{n-1} + \cdots \qquad |r| < 1$$

In this case the nth term is ar^{n-1}, and the "tail end" is itself a geometric series whose first term is ar^n and whose ratio is r:

$$E_n = ar^n + ar^{n+1} + ar^{n+2} + \cdots = \frac{ar^n}{1-r}$$

Example 2. A computing machine uses $1 + r + r^2 + r^3 + r^4$ as an estimate of $1/(1-r)$. What can we say about the error E_5 if $|r| \leqslant \frac{1}{3}$? The error is precisely $r^5/(1-r)$. Therefore we have

$$|E_5| = \frac{|r|^5}{1-r} \leqslant \frac{(\frac{1}{3})^5}{1-r} \leqslant \frac{(\frac{1}{3})^5}{\frac{2}{3}} = \frac{1}{2}\frac{1}{3^4} = \frac{1}{162} < 0.01$$

The integral test, comparison test, and absolute convergence test also can be used to yield estimates of E_n, as the next two examples show.

Example 3. The alternating series test shows that

$$\frac{1}{1!} - \frac{1}{2!} + \cdots + (-1)^{n+1}\frac{1}{n!} + \cdots$$

is convergent and that $|E_3|$ is less than $1/4! = \frac{1}{24}$. The ratio test shows that the series converges absolutely. Thus

$$|E_3| \leqslant \frac{1}{4!} + \frac{1}{5!} + \frac{1}{6!} + \cdots$$

which is less than the sum of a geometric series whose first term is $1/4!$ and whose ratio is $\frac{1}{5}$:

$$\frac{1}{4!} + \left(\frac{1}{5}\right)\left(\frac{1}{4!}\right) + \left(\frac{1}{5}\right)^2\left(\frac{1}{4!}\right) + \cdots = \frac{\frac{1}{4!}}{1-\frac{1}{5}} = \left(\frac{5}{4}\right)\left(\frac{1}{4!}\right)$$

and thus $|E_3| < \frac{5}{96}$. This bound on $|E_3|$ is somewhat weaker than that given in Example 1.

Example 4. Consider the series

$$\frac{1}{1+1} + \frac{1}{1+8} + \cdots + \frac{1}{1+n^3} + \cdots$$

Since all the terms have the same sign, we cannot use results that apply to the alternating series. However, comparing it to

$$\frac{1}{1} + \frac{1}{8} + \cdots + \frac{1}{n^3} + \cdots$$

shows that it converges. We have, for instance,

$$E_5 = \frac{1}{1+6^3} + \frac{1}{1+7^3} + \cdots < \frac{1}{6^3} + \frac{1}{7^3} + \cdots < \int_5^\infty \left(\frac{1}{x^3}\right) dx$$

Evaluation of the improper integral shows that E_5 is less than $\frac{1}{50} = 0.02$.

EXERCISES

1. Discuss the truncation error for the series

$$\left(\frac{1}{2}\right)\left(\frac{1}{2}\right) - \left(\frac{2}{3}\right)\left(\frac{1}{2}\right)^2 + \cdots + (-1)^{n+1}\left(\frac{n}{n+1}\right)\left(\frac{1}{2}\right)^n + \cdots$$

by (a) comparing it to the sum of a geometric progression, (b) noting that it is an alternating series.   [Answer: (a) $|E_n| < 2^{-n}$; (b) $|E_n| < [(n+1)/(n+2)] 2^{-n-1}]$

2. (a) Show that $f(x) = xe^{-x}$ decreases if $x > 1$.

(b) Prove that $\sum\limits_{n=1}^{\infty} ne^{-n}$ converges, using the ratio test and the integral test.

(c) Discuss the size of E_n by comparing it to the sum of a geometric series and also by comparing it to an improper integral.

3. If we want to use $1 + r + \cdots + r^n$ as an estimate of $1/(1-r)$ with an error less than 0.001 for $|r| < 0.6$, how large should we choose n?

4. Consider $S = \frac{1}{1} + \frac{1}{4} + \cdots + 1/n^2 + \cdots$.

(a) Using improper integrals, show that $\frac{1}{6} < E_5 < \frac{1}{5}$.

(b) With the aid of (a), show that $1.630 < S < 1.664$.

5. How many terms of $\frac{1}{1} + \frac{1}{4} + \frac{1}{9} + \cdots + 1/n^2 + \cdots$ should we take to be sure that E_n is less than 0.001? Explain.

6. We will prove in Chap. 13 that $e - 1 = \sum\limits_{n=1}^{\infty} 1/n!$ Use this fact to estimate $e - 1$ with an error less than 0.001.

$$\square \quad \square \quad \square$$

7. Let $u_n = f(n)$, where f satisfies the hypothesis of the integral test. Prove that

$$\int_{n+1}^{\infty} f(x)\,dx \leqslant E_n \leqslant \int_{n}^{\infty} f(x)\,dx.$$

4. Power series.   A series of the form $\sum\limits_{n=0}^{\infty} a_n x^n = a_0 + a_1 x + a_2 x^2 + \cdots$ is called a *power series* in x (since it involves the powers of x). For $x = 0$ it surely converges; in fact, its sum is a_0. Otherwise, it may converge for all x, or just for some x or no other x. In this section we study the particular power series

(1) $$x - \frac{x^3}{3} + \frac{x^5}{5} - \frac{x^7}{7} + \cdots + (-1)^{n+1}\frac{x^{2n-1}}{2n-1} + \cdots$$

to illustrate some of the properties and applications of power series in general.

First of all, for which x does (1) converge or diverge? Because of the appearance of a power of x in each term, we turn to the ratio test to examine (1) for absolute convergence. The ratio between the absolute value of the nth term and the absolute value of its successor is

$$\left| \frac{(-1)^{n+2} \dfrac{x^{2n+1}}{2n+1}}{(-1)^{n+1} \dfrac{x^{2n-1}}{2n-1}} \right| = \left| \frac{x^{2n+1}}{2n+1} \frac{2n-1}{x^{2n-1}} \right| = x^2 \frac{2n-1}{2n+1} = x^2 \frac{1-1/2n}{1+1/2n}$$

Thus the ratio approaches x^2 as $n \to \infty$. For $x^2 < 1$, the ratio approaches a number less than 1. Hence for $-1 < x < 1$ series (1) converges absolutely; thus it converges for $-1 < x < 1$.

If $x^2 > 1$, the ratio approaches a number larger than 1. By the ratio test, the nth term of (1) does not approach 0, hence (1) diverges. All that remains is to test $x = 1$ and $x = -1$. For $x = 1$, series (1) becomes $1 - \frac{1}{3} + \frac{1}{5} - \frac{1}{7} + \cdots$, which converges by the alternating series test. If $x = -1$ it converges for the same reason. Thus (1) converges for x in $[-1,1]$ and diverges for any other x.

Let $f(x)$ be the sum of the series (1) for x in $[-1,1]$. We will show that $f(x) = \tan^{-1} x$. This means that we may think of $\tan^{-1} x$ as a "polynomial of infinite degree."

We begin with the identity

(2) $$\frac{1}{1+t} = 1 - t + t^2 - \cdots + (-1)^{n-1} t^{n-1} + (-1)^n \frac{t^n}{1+t}$$

which holds when t is not -1. (The easiest way to verify (2) is to multiply both sides by $1 + t$.) Replacing t by t^2 throughout (2) yields

(3) $$\frac{1}{1+t^2} = 1 - t^2 + t^4 - \cdots + (-1)^{n-1} t^{2n-2} + (-1)^n \frac{t^{2n}}{1+t^2}$$

Therefore

(4)
$$\int_0^x \frac{1}{1+t^2} \, dt = \int_0^x [1 - t^2 + t^4 - \cdots + (-1)^{n-1} t^{2n-2}] \, dt + (-1)^n \int_0^x \frac{t^{2n}}{1+t^2} \, dt$$

Evaluation of the left two definite integrals in (4) by the fundamental theorem of calculus produces

(5) $$\tan^{-1} x = x - \frac{x^3}{3} + \frac{x^5}{5} - \cdots + (-1)^{n-1} \frac{x^{2n-1}}{2n-1} + (-1)^n \int_0^x \frac{t^{2n}}{1+t^2} \, dt$$

All that remains is to show that if $-1 \leqslant x \leqslant 1$, then

$$\lim_{n \to \infty} \int_0^x \frac{t^{2n}}{1+t^2} \, dt = 0$$

We do this for x in $[0,1]$. In that case, since $t^{2n}/(1+t^2) \leqslant t^{2n}$,

$$\int_0^x \frac{t^{2n}}{1+t^2} \, dt \leqslant \int_0^x t^{2n} \, dt \underset{\text{FTC}}{=} \frac{t^{2n+1}}{2n+1} \Big|_0^x = \frac{x^{2n+1}}{2n+1} - \frac{0^{2n+1}}{2n+1} = \frac{x^{2n+1}}{2n+1} \leqslant \frac{1}{2n+1}$$

which approaches 0 as $n \to \infty$; hence the positive number $\int_0^x t^{2n}/(1+t^2)$ approaches 0 as $n \to \infty$. Similar reasoning applies when x is in $[-1,0]$. Hence for x in $[-1,1]$,

(6) $$\tan^{-1} x = x - \frac{x^3}{3} + \frac{x^5}{5} - \cdots + (-1)^{n-1}\frac{x^{2n-1}}{2n-1} + \cdots$$

When $x = 1$ we have $\tan^{-1} x = \tan^{-1}(1) = \pi/4$. Thus

(7) $$\frac{\pi}{4} = 1 - \frac{1}{3} + \frac{1}{5} - \cdots + (-1)^{n+1}\frac{1}{2n-1} + \cdots$$

an equation which relates π to all the odd numbers.

EXERCISES

1. Using (6), show that
$$\frac{\pi\sqrt{3}}{6} = 1 - \left(\frac{1}{3}\right)\left(\frac{1}{3}\right) + \left(\frac{1}{5}\right)\left(\frac{1}{3}\right)^2 - \left(\frac{1}{7}\right)\left(\frac{1}{3}\right)^3$$
$$+ \cdots + (-1)^{n+1}\frac{1}{2n-1}\left(\frac{1}{3}\right)^{n-1} + \cdots$$
   (Hint: Replace x in (6) by $1/\sqrt{3}$.)
2. (a) Verify (3) by multiplying both sides by $(1 + t)$.
   (b) Verify (3) by noticing that $1 - t + t^2 - \cdots + (-1)^{n-1}t^{n-1}$ is a geometric series with ratio $-t$. [Recall that $1 + r + r^2 + \cdots + r^{n-1} = (1 - r^n)/(1 - r)$.]

3. We showed that for x in $[0,1]$, the definite integral $\int_0^x t^{2n}/(1+t^2)\,dt$ approaches 0 as $n \to \infty$. Prove the same for x in $[-1,0]$.
4. Using the series (7) we obtained for $\pi/4$, show that $3.01 < \pi < 3.28$. It suffices to use the first seven terms.
5. (a) Using (2), show that, for $x > -1$,
$$\ln(1 + x) = x - \frac{x^2}{2} + \frac{x^3}{3} - \cdots + (-1)^{n-1}\frac{x^n}{n} + (-1)^n\int_0^x \frac{t^n}{1+t}\,dt$$
   (b) Show that if x is in $[0,1]$, then $\int_0^x [t^n/(1+t)]\,dt$ approaches 0 as $n \to \infty$.

   (c) Show that if $-1 < x \leqslant 0$, then $\int_0^x [t^n/(1+t)]\,dt$ approaches 0 as $n \to \infty$.

   (d) Conclude that if $-1 < x \leqslant 1$, then
$$\ln(1 + x) = x - \frac{x^2}{2} + \frac{x^3}{3} - \frac{x^4}{4} + \cdots + (-1)^{n-1}\frac{x^n}{n} + \cdots$$

6. [See Exercise 5(d).] Show that (a) $\ln 2 = 1 - \frac{1}{2} + \frac{1}{3} - \frac{1}{4} + \cdots$; (b) $\ln 1.5 = \frac{1}{2} - (\frac{1}{2})(\frac{1}{2})^2 + (\frac{1}{3})(\frac{1}{2})^3 - \cdots + (-1)^{n-1}(1/n)(\frac{1}{2})^n + \cdots$.
7. (See Exercise 6.)
   (a) Using at most the first seven terms of each of the series in Exercise 6(a) and (b), show that $0.616 < \ln 2 < 0.760$ and $0.404 < \ln 1.5 < 0.406$.
   (b) From (a), deduce immediately that $1.020 < \ln 3 < 1.166$.

8. (a) Using at most the first six terms of $1 - \frac{1}{2} + \frac{1}{3} - \cdots$, show that $0.616 < \ln 2 < 0.784$.

(b) Using at most three terms of $\ln \frac{3}{2} = \frac{1}{2} - (\frac{1}{2})(\frac{1}{2})^2 + (\frac{1}{3})(\frac{1}{2})^3 - \cdots$, show that $0.375 < \ln \frac{3}{2} < 0.417$.

(c) Using at most three terms of $\ln \frac{4}{3} = \frac{1}{3} - (\frac{1}{2})(\frac{1}{3})^2 + (\frac{1}{3})(\frac{1}{3})^3 + \cdots$, show that $0.277 < \ln \frac{4}{3} < 0.291$.

(d) Using (b) and (c), deduce that $0.652 < \ln 2 < 0.708$.

(e) Which is a more efficient way of estimating $\ln 2$, method (d) or method (a)? Observe that each uses the same number of terms.

9. (a) Using the series for $\ln (1 + x)$ in Exercise 5(d), with $x = -\frac{1}{2}$, show that $\ln \frac{1}{2} = -[\frac{1}{2} + (\frac{1}{2})(\frac{1}{2})^2 + (\frac{1}{3})(\frac{1}{2})^3 + (\frac{1}{4})(\frac{1}{2})^4 + \cdots]$.

(b) Deduce that $\ln 2 = \frac{1}{2} + (\frac{1}{2})(\frac{1}{2})^2 + (\frac{1}{3})(\frac{1}{2})^3 + (\frac{1}{4})(\frac{1}{2})^4 + \cdots$.

(c) Show that $(\frac{1}{5})(\frac{1}{2})^5 + (\frac{1}{6})(\frac{1}{2})^6 + (\frac{1}{7})(\frac{1}{2})^7 + \cdots$ is less than the sum of the geometric progression whose first term is $(\frac{1}{5})(\frac{1}{2})^5$ and whose ratio is $\frac{1}{2}$, and hence less than $(\frac{1}{5})(\frac{1}{2})^4$.

(d) Show that $\frac{1}{2} + \frac{1}{8} + \frac{1}{24} + \frac{1}{64} < \ln 2 < \frac{1}{2} + \frac{1}{8} + \frac{1}{24} + \frac{1}{64} + \frac{1}{80}$, and hence that $\ln 2$ is between 0.682 and 0.695.

10. Using the relation $\ln 5 = \ln \frac{5}{3} + \ln \frac{3}{2} + \ln 2$, obtain some bounds in decimal form on $\ln 5$.

11. (a) Prove that $\displaystyle\int_0^1 1/(1 + t^3)\, dt = 1 - \frac{1}{4} + \frac{1}{7} - \cdots + (-1)^{n-1}\, 1/(3n - 2) + (-1)^n \int_0^1 t^{3n}/(1 + t^3)\, dt$. [Hint: First replace t with t^3 in (2)].

(b) Prove that $\displaystyle\lim_{n \to \infty} \int_0^1 [t^{3n}/(1 + t^3)]\, dt = 0$.

(c) By partial fractions (or integral tables if you wish), show that $\displaystyle\int_0^1 [1/(1 + t^3)]\, dt = \frac{1}{3}[(\pi/\sqrt{3}) + \ln 2]$.

(d) Deduce that $1 - \frac{1}{4} + \frac{1}{7} - \frac{1}{10} + \cdots = \frac{1}{3}[(\pi \sqrt{3}) + \ln 2]$.

12. (See Exercise 11.) By considering $\displaystyle\int_0^1 t/(1 + t^3)\, dt$, prove that $\frac{1}{2} - \frac{1}{5} + \frac{1}{8} - \frac{1}{11} + \cdots = \frac{1}{3}(\pi/\sqrt{3} - \ln 2)$.

□ □ □

13. From Exercise 5 it follows that

$$\ln 2 = 1 - \frac{1}{2} + \frac{1}{3} - \frac{1}{4} + \cdots$$

and thus the nth partial sum of the series $1 - \frac{1}{2} + \frac{1}{3} - \frac{1}{4} + \cdots$ is an estimate of $\ln 2$ with a truncation error less than $1/(n + 1)$, the first omitted term. Here is a method for obtaining much closer estimates of $\ln 2$ with the same amount of arithmetic: "Add n terms of the above series, omit the next n terms, then add the next term with *sign opposite* to that of the nth term." In other words, use $t_n = 1 - \frac{1}{2} + \frac{1}{3} - \cdots + (-1)^{n+1}(1/n) + (-1)^n[1/(2n + 1)]$. For instance, $t_3 = 1 - \frac{1}{2} + \frac{1}{3} - \frac{1}{7} = 0.691$, and $t_4 = 1 - \frac{1}{2} + \frac{1}{3} - \frac{1}{4} + \frac{1}{9} = 0.694$. (Note how close t_3 is to t_4.)

(a) Prove that $t_{n+1} - t_n = (-1)^{n-1}/[(n + 1)(2n + 3)(2n + 1)]$.

(b) From (a) deduce that the difference between $\ln 2$ and t_n is less than $1/4n^3$. From (b) we see that t_n is a much better approximation to $\ln 2$ than $S_n = 1 - \frac{1}{2} + \frac{1}{3} - \cdots + (-1)^{n+1}(1/n)$.

14. Show that the method of Exercise 13 also works for the series $1 - \frac{1}{3} + \frac{1}{5} - \frac{1}{7} + \cdots$. Use the method to obtain estimates for $\pi/4$ and hence for π.

15. Since the nth term in (7) approaches zero "slowly," (7) does not provide convenient estimates of $\pi/4$. The following provides better estimates with the same amount of arithmetic.

    (a) Let $A = \tan^{-1} \frac{1}{2}$ and $B = \tan^{-1} \frac{1}{3}$. Using the identity $\tan(x + y) = (\tan x + \tan y)/(1 - \tan x \tan y)$, prove that $A + B = \pi/4$.

    (b) Use Equation (5) and (a) to obtain an estimate of $\pi/4$ and hence of π.

5. Summary. There are three questions we ask about an infinite series: Does it converge? If it does, what is its sum? By how much does a partial sum S_n differ from the sum of S of the series?

In order to answer the first question we developed six tests: the nth term test (for divergence), the integral test (for convergence or divergence), the alternating series test (for convergence), the comparison test (for convergence or divergence), the ratio test (for convergence or divergence), and the absolute convergence test (for convergence).

The second question is usually more difficult to answer. We did, however, find the sums $p + 2p^2 + 3p^3 + \cdots$ and $x - x^3/3 + x^5/5 - \cdots$.

The third question concerns the truncation error E_n. We presented several ways of finding a bound for E_n. These are based on the alternating series test, comparison test, integral test, and absolute convergence test. In a geometric series, the error can be calculated easily, since the "tail end" is itself a geometric series.

It should be emphasized that the theory of infinite series is both extensive and deep. This chapter and the next only scratch the surface.

13

Taylor's series

In Chap. 12 we saw that $\tan^{-1} x = x - x^3/3 + x^5/5 - \cdots$ for x in $[-1,1]$. This suggests that other familiar functions may be described by power series in x. In this chapter we develop machinery for deciding whether a function is representable by a power series and for finding the representation if there is one. In particular we will show that

$$(1) \qquad \sin x = x - \frac{x^3}{3!} + \frac{x^5}{5!} - \frac{x^7}{7!} + \cdots$$

$$(2) \qquad \cos x = 1 - \frac{x^2}{2!} + \frac{x^4}{4!} - \frac{x^6}{6!} + \cdots$$

and

$$(3) \qquad e^x = 1 + x + \frac{x^2}{2!} + \frac{x^3}{3!} + \cdots$$

But we need not restrict ourselves to power series in x. For instance, we will show that

$$(4) \quad \sin x = \frac{\sqrt{2}}{2} + \frac{\sqrt{2}}{2}\left(x - \frac{\pi}{4}\right) - \frac{\sqrt{2}}{2}\frac{1}{2!}\left(x - \frac{\pi}{4}\right)^2 - \frac{\sqrt{2}}{2}\frac{1}{3!}\left(x - \frac{\pi}{4}\right)^3 + \cdots$$

The formula

$$a_n = \frac{f^{(n)}(a)}{n!}$$

which we met while determining a polynomial f from the values of its derivatives, will play a large role in our work with other functions.

1. Taylor's series in powers of x and in powers of $x - a$. Let f be a function having derivatives of all orders at $x = a$. Recalling our experience with polynomials, we may suspect that

$$f(x) = f(a) + \frac{f^{(1)}(a)}{1!}(x - a) + \frac{f^{(2)}(a)}{2!}(x - a)^2 + \frac{f^{(3)}(a)}{3!}(x - a)^3 + \cdots$$

(If f is a polynomial, this series terminates.)

Let us consider the special case $a = 0$. We suspect that under some suitable assumptions

(5) $$f(x) = f(0) + \frac{f^{(1)}(0)}{1!}x + \frac{f^{(2)}(0)}{2!}x^2 + \frac{f^{(3)}(0)}{3!}x^3 + \cdots$$

Let us therefore introduce

(6) $$R_n(x) = f(x) - \left[f(0) + \frac{f^{(1)}(0)}{1!}x + \frac{f^{(2)}(0)}{2!}x^2 + \cdots + \frac{f^{(n)}(0)}{n!}x^n \right]$$

which is the difference between $f(x)$ and the sum of the first $n + 1$ terms of the power series. In proving (5), our burden is to show that if the $f^{(j)}(x)$ satisfy suitable hypotheses for x near 0, then

$$\lim_{n \to \infty} R_n(x) = 0$$

In this case (5) holds. [$R_n(x)$ is then a truncation error, E_{n+1}.] The next theorem is the main tool for accomplishing this mission. It provides a formula for $R_n(x)$ that involves only the $(n + 1)$st derivative of f and is more convenient than the defining formula (6).

THEOREM 1: *Integral formula for $R_n(x)$.* Let f be defined in the interval from 0 to x for some number x. Assume that the first $n + 1$ derivatives of f exist and are continuous in that interval. If $R_n(x)$ is defined by

(7) $$f(x) = f(0) + \frac{f^{(1)}(0)}{1!}x + \frac{f^{(2)}(0)}{2!}x^2 + \cdots + \frac{f^{(n)}(0)}{n!}x^n + R_n(x)$$

then $$R_n(x) = \int_0^x \frac{(x - t)^n}{n!} f^{(n+1)}(t)\, dt$$

PROOF. Let us begin with the case $n = 0$. Theorem 1 asserts that

$$f(x) = f(0) + \int_0^x \frac{(x - t)^0}{0!} f^{(0+1)}(t)\, dt$$

that is,

(8)
$$f(x) = f(0) + \int_0^x f'(t) \, dt$$

But (8) is just a restatement of the fundamental theorem of calculus. We have thus proved Theorem 1 for $n = 0$.

For $n = 1$, Theorem 1 asserts that

(9)
$$f(x) = f(0) + f'(0)x + \int_0^x (x - t) f''(t) \, dt$$

We will obtain (9) from (8) through an integration by parts as follows:

(10)
$$\int_0^x \overbrace{f'(t)}^{u} \overbrace{dt}^{dv} = uv \Big|_0^x - \int_0^x v \, du$$

Setting $u = f'(t)$, we have $du = f''(t) \, dt$. Setting $dv = dt$, we will choose for v, *not* the expected t, but $-(x - t)$. Then (10) becomes

(11)
$$\int_0^x f'(t) \, dt = f'(t) [-(x - t)] \Big|_{t=0}^{t=x} + \int_0^x (x - t) f''(t) \, dt$$

Now,

(12)
$$f'(t) [-(x - t)] \Big|_{t=0}^{t=x} = f'(x) [-(x - x)] - f'(0) [-(x - 0)] = f'(0)(x)$$

Combining (8), (11), and (12), we obtain (9). Theorem 1 is proved for $n - 1$.

To prove Theorem 1 for $n = 2$ we use (9) and apply integration by parts to its last term, which we write for convenience as

$$\int_0^t f''(t)(x - t) \, dt$$

Let $u = f''(t)$ and $dv = (x - t) \, dt$. Then $du = f^{(3)}(t) \, dt$ and for v use $-(x - t)^2/2$. Hence

(13)
$$\int_0^t \underbrace{f''(t)}_{u} \underbrace{(x - t) \, dt}_{dv} = \underbrace{f''(t)}_{u} \underbrace{[-(x - t)^2/2]}_{v} \Big|_{t=0}^{t=x} - \int_0^x \underbrace{\frac{-(x - t)^2}{2}}_{v} \underbrace{f^{(3)}(t) \, dt}_{du}$$

Carrying out the evaluations at $t = 0$ and $t = x$ in (13), we obtain

(14)
$$\int_0^t f''(t)(x - t) \, dt = \frac{f''(0) x^2}{2} + \int_0^x \frac{(x - t)^2}{2} f^{(3)}(t) \, dt$$

Combining (9) and (14), we arrive at

(15)
$$f(x) = f(0) + f'(0)x + \frac{f''(0)}{2} x^2 + \int_0^x \frac{(x - t)^2}{2} f^{(3)}(t) \, dt$$

which establishes Theorem 1 for $n = 2$.

To establish Theorem 1 for $n = 3$, just integrate by parts again. In this manner Theorem 1 can be proved for $n = 4, 5, \ldots$ (Mathematical induction will establish it for all n.)

We should not be astonished if Theorem 1, which includes the fundamental theorem of calculus as a special case, gives us a good deal of information about a function. The next example illustrates its use.

Example 1. Let $f(x) = e^x$. Then $f^{(n)}(x) = e^x$ for all n and is continuous. The hypotheses of Theorem 1 hold for this function. Hence the difference between e^x and the first n terms of the power series on the right side of (5) is

(16) $$R_n(x) = \int_0^x \frac{(x-t)^n}{n!} e^t \, dt$$

For convenience, let us assume $x > 0$. Does $R_n(x)$ approach 0 as $n \to \infty$? We have $0 \leqslant x - t \leqslant x$ for t in $[0,x]$; hence

$$R_n(x) \leqslant \int_0^x \frac{x^n}{n!} e^t \, dt = \frac{x^n}{n!} \int_0^x e^t \, dt$$

Now, $\int_0^x e^t \, dt$ is a fixed number (actually, its value is $e^x - 1$), while $x^n/n! \to 0$ as $n \to \infty$ (Example 3, page 326). Hence $R_n(x)$ approaches 0 as $n \to \infty$. Similar reasoning disposes of the case $x < 0$.

Since $R_n \to 0$ as $n \to \infty$ in this case, Theorem 1 gives us a power series for e^x, valid for any x. Moreover, we have $f^{(n)}(0) = e^0 = 1$, and therefore

$$e^x = 1 + x + \frac{1}{2!} x^2 + \frac{1}{3!} x^3 + \cdots + \frac{1}{n!} x^n + R_n(x)$$

Since $R_n(x) \to 0$ as $n \to \infty$, we may write

$$e^x = 1 + x + \frac{x^2}{2!} + \frac{x^3}{3!} + \cdots + \frac{x^n}{n!} + \cdots$$

which is (3). Similar reasoning establishes (1) and (2).

Taylor's formula is a formula for $R_n(x)$. The power series that results for $f(x)$ if $R_n(x) \to 0$ as $n \to \infty$ is called *Taylor's series around 0 for* $f(x)$ or *Taylor's series in powers of x for* $f(x)$. The next theorem generalizes Theorem 1 to powers of $(x - a)$; if $a = 0$, it reduces to Theorem 1.

THEOREM 2: *Integral formula for* $R_n(x)$. Let f be defined in the closed interval from a to x for some x. Assume that the first $n + 1$ derivatives of f exist and are continuous in that interval. Then if $R_n(x)$ is defined by

$$f(x) = f(a) + f'(a)(x-a) + \frac{f''(a)}{2!}(x-a)^2 + \cdots + \frac{f^{(n)}(a)}{n!}(x-a)^n + R_n(x)$$

we have $$R_n(x) = \int_a^x \frac{(x-t)^n}{n!} f^{(n+1)}(t) \, dt$$

We omit the proof, which is similar to that of Theorem 1.

In applying Theorem 2 (or the special case, Theorem 1), it is sometimes more convenient to show that $|R_n(x)|$ approaches 0 as $n \to \infty$, than to show directly that R_n approaches 0 as $n \to \infty$. For this task the following lemma is frequently of use. It asserts that one doesn't decrease the size of a definite integral by making its integrand positive.

LEMMA.   If $\displaystyle\int_a^b f(x)\,dx$ and $\displaystyle\int_a^b |f(x)|\,dx$ exist, for $a < b$, then

$$\left|\int_a^b f(x)\,dx\right| \leqslant \int_a^b |f(x)|\,dx.$$

PROOF.   We have $-|f(x)| \leqslant f(x) \leqslant |f(x)|$ for all x in $[a,b]$. Thus

$$\int_a^b -|f(x)|\,dx \leqslant \int_a^b f(x)\,dx \leqslant \int_a^b |f(x)|\,dx$$

Hence $\displaystyle\int_a^b f(x)\,dx$ is between the nonnegative number $\displaystyle\int_a^b |f(x)|\,dx$ and $-\displaystyle\int_a^b |f(x)|\,dx$.
Thus $\left|\displaystyle\int_a^b f(x)\,dx\right| \leqslant \displaystyle\int_a^b |f(x)|\,dx$, and the proof is done.

Example 2.   Let us see what Theorem 2 gives us in the case $f(x) = \sin x$ and $a = \pi/4$.
We first examine $R_n(x)$, which equals

$$\int_{\pi/4}^x \frac{(x-t)^n D^{n+1} \sin t}{n!}\,dt$$

Since $R_n(x)$ may be negative (either because the integrand is negative or because x is
less than $\pi/4$), let us examine $|R_n(x)|$. We do so only in the case $x > \pi/4$. Keeping in
mind that $D^{n+1} \sin t$ is either $\pm\sin t$ or $\pm\cos t$, we have

$$|R_n(x)| \leqslant \int_{\pi/4}^x \frac{|(x-t)^n D^{n+1}\sin t|}{n!}\,dt \leqslant \int_{\pi/4}^x \frac{(x-\pi/4)^n (1)}{n!}\,dt = \frac{(x-\pi/4)^n}{n!}\int_{\pi/4}^n 1\,dt$$

$$= \frac{(x-\pi/4)^{n+1}}{n!}$$

which, just as in Example 1, approaches 0 as $n \to \infty$. Since $R_n(x)$ approaches 0 as $n \to \infty$,
we know that $\sin x$ has a power-series expansion in powers of $(x - \pi/4)$, valid for all x.
The coefficient of $(x - \pi/4)^n$ in this expansion is $\sin^{(n)}(\pi/4)/n!$. Now, since the higher
derivatives of $\sin x$ repeat in blocks of four ($\sin x$, $\cos x$, $-\sin x$, $-\cos x$), their values
at $\pi/4$ also repeat in blocks of four ($\sqrt{2}/2$, $\sqrt{2}/2$, $-\sqrt{2}/2$, $-\sqrt{2}/2$). This justifies (4).

The next example illustrates the use of Taylor's series in solving differential equations, and will be useful in Chap. 26, where we show that the orbit of a planet is an
ellipse.

Example 3.   Let $y = f(x)$ satisfy the differential equation

(17)
$$\frac{d^2y}{dx^2} = -y$$

[For instance, $y = \sin x$ and $y = \cos x$ satisfy (17).] *We will show that any solution of*
(17) *must be of the form*

(18)
$$y = c_1 \cos x + c_2 \sin x$$

where c_1 and c_2 are constants.

Let $y = f(x)$ be a solution of (17). Then y has derivatives of all orders, for

$$f^{(3)} = \frac{d^3y}{dx^3} = \frac{d(d^2y/dx^2)}{dx} = \frac{d(-y)}{dx} = -\frac{dy}{dx} = -f^{(1)}$$

$$f^{(4)} = \frac{d^4y}{dx^4} = \frac{d^2(d^2y/dx^2)}{dx^2} = \frac{d^2(-y)}{dx^2} = -\frac{d^2y}{dx^2} = -f^{(2)}$$

and so on. We have

(19) $f = -f^{(2)} = f^{(4)} = -f^{(6)} = \cdots$ and $f^{(1)} = -f^{(3)} = f^{(5)} = -f^{(7)} = \cdots$

In particular, if $f(0) = c_1$ and $f'(0) = c_2$, then $f^{(2)}(0) = -c_1$, $f^{(4)}(0) = c_1, \ldots$, and $f^{(3)}(0) = -c_2$, $f^{(5)}(0) = c_2, \ldots$. Thus, if $R_n(x)$ approaches 0 as $n \to \infty$, we have

$$f(x) = c_1 + c_2 x - \frac{c_1}{2!}x^2 - \frac{c_2}{3!}x^3 + \frac{c_1}{4!}x^4 + \frac{c_2 x^5}{5!} - \cdots$$

Now, the sum of the first $2n$ terms of this series, rearranged, is

$$c_1 \left[1 - \frac{x^2}{2!} + \frac{x^4}{4!} - \cdots + (-1)^{n-1}\frac{x^{2n-2}}{(2n-2)!} \right]$$

$$+ c_2 \left[x - \frac{x^3}{3!} + \frac{x^5}{5!} - \cdots + (-1)^{n+1}\frac{x^{2n-1}}{(2n-1)!} \right]$$

But the expressions in brackets are parts of the expansions of $\cos x$ and $\sin x$, from which it follows that $f(x) = c_1 \cos x + c_2 \sin x$.

To show that $R_n(x) \to 0$ as $n \to \infty$, observe that f and f' are bounded in $[0,x]$, since they are continuous (maximum value theorem, page 84). Hence, in view of (19) there is a number B such that

$$|f^{(n)}(X)| \leq B$$

for all X in $[0,x]$ and all n. As in Example 2, this implies that $R_n(x) \to 0$ as $n \to \infty$. Hence any solution of (17) is of the form (18).

Incidentally Taylor, who discussed the relation between a function f and the values of its higher derivatives, published his result in 1715, but did not apply it. MacLaurin in 1742, giving credit to Taylor, discussed power series around $a = 0$. For this reason, a Taylor's series in powers of x is frequently called a MacLaurin's series.

EXERCISES

1. (a) Use Eq. (1) to find $\sin(1)$ to five decimal places.
   (b) Recalling that 1 radian is $180/\pi$ degrees, compare your answer with that given in a table of $\sin x$.
2. We proved Theorem 1 for $n = 0$, 1, and 2. Prove it for $n = 3$ and for $n = 4$.
3. Assuming that Theorem 1 is true for $n = 15$, prove it for $n = 16$.
4. In obtaining (11) we chose $v = -(x - t)$, not the obvious choice $v = t$. Show that if we had chosen $v = t$, we would have obtained

$$f(x) = f(0) + xf'(x) - \int_0^x tf''(t)\, dt$$

Would this have been useful?

5. Carry out this alternative proof that $\lim\limits_{n \to \infty} (x^n/n!) = 0$.

   (a) Let $F(x) = (1 + x + x^2/2! + \cdots + x^n/n!) e^{-x}$ and show that $F'(x) = -e^{-x}(x^n/n!)$.

   (b) Deduce that for $x \geqslant 0$, we have $F(x) \leqslant 1$.

   (c) From (b) conclude that $1 + x + \cdots + x^n/n! < e^x$ if $x > 0$, and therefore that $x^n/n! \to 0$ as $n \to \infty$.

6. Apply Theorem 1, as we did in Example 1, to obtain (1).

7. Apply Theorem 1, as we did in Example 1, to obtain (2).

8. Let $f(x) = \tan^{-1} x$.

   (a) Compute $f(0)$, $f'(0)$, $f''(0)$, and $f^{(3)}(0)$.

   (b) Does the expansion $\tan^{-1} x = x - x^3/3 + x^5/5 - \cdots$ seem to agree with Taylor's formula? Explain.

9. By replacing x with 1 in the power series for e^x in Example 1, we obtain $e^1 = e = 1 + 1 + 1/2! + 1/3! + \cdots$.

   (a) Show that $R_6(1) = \displaystyle\int_0^1 [(1 - t)^6/6!] e^t \, dt < (e/6!) \int_0^1 (1 - t)^6 \, dt = e/(7!) < 3/(7!)$, since $e < 3$.

   (b) Deduce that $2.718 < e < 2.719$.

10. The power series (1) for $\sin x$ is an alternating series.

   (a) Show that if $x^2 < 6$, the terms decrease in size.

   (b) Using the first three terms of (1), show that $0.84 < \sin (1) < 0.85$.

   (c) Estimate $\sin (2)$.

11. Why would you expect (1) to have only odd powers and (2) to have only even powers?

12. (a) Prove that $\cos x = 1 - x^2/2! + \displaystyle\int_0^{} [(x - t)^2/2] \sin t \, dt$, with the aid of Theorem 1.

   (b) With the aid of (a), show that $\lim\limits_{x \to 0} [(1 - \cos x)/x^2] = \frac{1}{2}$, a result we obtained in Exercise 3, page 79.

13. Apply Theorem 1 to the function $f(x) = (1 + x)^6$ to obtain the "binomial" expansion

$$(1 + x)^6 = \sum_{k=0}^{6} \binom{6}{k} x^k$$

where $\dbinom{6}{k} = 6!/[k! (6 - k)!]$.

14. As (1) indicates, $x - x^3/6$ is a good approximation to $\sin x$ when x is small (and when radian measure of angle is used).

   (a) If θ measures an angle in degrees, show that $\pi\theta/180 - (\pi\theta/180)^3/6$ is an approximation of $\sin \theta$.

   (b) Use (a) to estimate $\sin 10°$, taking 0.0174 for $\pi/180$.

                                     [Answer: (b) about 0.173]

15. Use the formula in Exercise 14 to estimate $\sin 20°$, and compare your result with $\sin 20°$ as listed in a table of sines.

16. Expand $\sin x$ in powers of $x - \pi/2$. Write out the first six terms.

17. Expand $\cos x$ in powers of $x - \pi/3$. Write out the first six terms.

18. Use Theorem 1 to obtain the power series $\ln (1 + x) = x - x^2/2 + x^3/3 - \cdots$ if $-1 < x \leqslant 1$.

(a) First show that $R_n(x) = (-1)^{n+1} \int_0^x (x - t)^n/(1 + t)^{n+1}\, dt$.

(b) Show that if $0 \leqslant x \leqslant 1$, then $R_n(x) \to 0$ as $n \to \infty$.

(c) Show that if $-1 < x \leqslant 0$, then $R_n(x) \to 0$ as $n \to \infty$.

19. Prove Theorem 2 for (a) $n = 0$ and 1; (b) $n = 2$ and 3.

20. Prove that if Theorem 2 is valid for $n = 25$, then it is valid for $n = 26$.

21. (See Example 3.)

(a) Show that $y = c_1 \cos \sqrt{k}x + c_2 \sin \sqrt{k}x$ is a solution of the differential equation $d^2y/dx^2 = -ky$, where k is a fixed positive number.

(b) Show that $c_1 \cos \sqrt{k}x + c_2 \sin \sqrt{k}x$ is the most general solution to the equation in (a).

22. (See Example 3.) Show that the most general solution of the differential equation $d^2y/dx^2 = ky$, where k is a fixed positive number, is $y = c_1 e^{\sqrt{k}x} + c_2 e^{-\sqrt{k}x}$.

23. Using the method of Example 3, show that the most general solution of the differential equation $dy/dx = ky$ is $y = Ae^{kx}$. (This was proved in Chap. 5, page 125.)

24. (a) Draw, relative to the same axes, the curves $y = e^x$; $y = 1 + x$; $y = 1 + x + x^2/2$; $y = 1 + x + x^2/2 + x^3/6$.

(b) Are the polynomials in (a) close to e^x when x is large?

25. (a) Draw, relative to the same axes, the curves $y = \tan^{-1} x$; $y = x$; $y = x - x^3/3$; $y = x - x^3/3 + x^5/5$.

(b) Are the polynomials in (a) close to $\tan^{-1} x$ when x is near 1?

26. Compute $\sqrt{e}$ to two decimals, using (1).   (Answer: 1.65)

□ □ □

27. Theorem 2 is a consequence of Theorem 1. To prove Theorem 2, apply Theorem 1 to the function g, where $g(x) = f(x + a)$.

28. Assume that $e^x = a_0 + a_1 x + a_2 x^2 + \cdots + a_n x^n + \cdots$. Set $x = 0$ and get $e^0 = a_0$. Thus $a_0 = 1$. Differentiation yields $e^x = a_1 + 2a_2 x + 3a_3 x^2 + \cdots + na_n x^{n-1} + \cdots$; set $x = 0$, and get $a_1 = 1$. Differentiate again and obtain $a_2 = \frac{1}{2}$.

Continuing, obtain $a_n = 1/n!$. Hence $e^x = \sum_{n=0}^{\infty} (1/n!)\, x^n$. The conclusion of the reasoning is correct, but there is a hole in the argument. What is it?

29. We might suspect that if f has derivatives of all orders at 0, then it has a Taylor's series expansion around 0. This is not true. Indeed, a function *can have all its derivatives* at 0 equal to 0 and yet not be the constant function 0. Consider, for example, f defined by $f(0) = 0$, $f(x) = e^{-1/x^2}$, for $x \neq 0$. Compute $f'(0)$, $f''(0)$, and $f'''(0)$, for instance.

30. An engineer wants to simulate the behavior of the function $\cos x$ for x in $[-\pi/2, \pi/2]$. He has available any polynomial of degree 2 or less.

(a) Which available polynomial g minimizes $\int_{-\pi/2}^{\pi/2} [g(x) - \cos x]^2\, dx$?

(b) If he has available any polynomial of degree 3 can he do better?

31. Repeat Exercise 30 for the function $\sin x$ instead of $\cos x$.

32. Show that $\pi + \pi^5/5! + \pi^9/9! + \cdots = \pi^3/3! + \pi^7/7! + \pi^{11}/11! + \cdots$.

2. $R_n(x)$ expressed in terms of a derivative; Newton's method. In Sec. 1 we expressed $R_n(x)$ as a definite integral. In this section we will express it in terms of a derivative. Consider $R_n(x)$, for instance, in the case $n = 0$. $R_0(x)$ is defined in Sec. 1 by the equation

$$(1) \qquad\qquad f(x) = f(a) + R_0(x)$$

The law of the mean (page 123) tells us that if f is differentiable, then

$$(2) \qquad\qquad f(x) - f(a) = f'(X)(x - a)$$

for some X between a and x. Rewriting (2) in the form resembling (1),

$$f(x) = f(a) + f'(X)(x - a)$$

we see that $R_0(x)$ equals $f'(X)(x - a)$ for some X. The next theorem is therefore a generalization of the law of the mean to higher derivatives. It was published in 1772 by Lagrange, who was the first to realize the theoretical importance of Taylor's series. In fact, he used the series to *define* the derivatives of f. [He defined $f^{(n)}(a)$ as $n!$ times the coefficient of $(x - a)^n$ in the power series for f around $x = a$.] He hoped to bypass the notion of limit and to found calculus on algebra. But there are differentiable functions that lack a Taylor's series, so that his goal cannot be realized.

THEOREM 3: *Derivative formula for $R_n(x)$.* Let f be defined at least from a to x. Assume that the first $n + 1$ derivatives of f exist and are continuous in that interval. If $R_n(x)$ is defined by

$$f(x) = f(a) + f'(a)(x - a) + \frac{f''(a)}{2!}(x - a)^2 + \cdots + \frac{f^{(n)}(a)}{n!}(x - a)^n + R_n(x)$$

then
$$R_n(x) = \frac{(x - a)^{n+1}}{(n + 1)!} f^{(n+1)}(X)$$

for some X between a and x.

PROOF. We consider only the case $x > a$. By Theorem 2, we have $R_n(x) = \int_a^x [(x - t)^n/n!] f^{(n+1)}(t)\, dt$. Let M be the maximum value, and m be the minimum value, of $f^{(n+1)}(t)$ for t in $[a,x]$. Then $m \leqslant f^{(n+1)}(t) \leqslant M$ for t in $[a,x]$ and we have

$$(3) \qquad m\int_a^x \frac{(x - t)^n}{n!}\, dt = \int_a^x m\frac{(x - t)^n}{n!}\, dt \leqslant R_n(x) \leqslant \int_a^x M\frac{(x - t)^n}{n!}\, dt$$

$$= M\int_a^x \frac{(x - t)^n}{n!}\, dt$$

Now, $$\int_a^x \frac{(x - t)^n}{n!}\, dt \underset{\text{FTC}}{=} \frac{-(x - t)^{n+1}}{(n + 1)!}\Bigg|_{t=a}^{t=x} = \frac{(x - a)^{n+1}}{(n + 1)!}$$

Thus, by (3), $$\frac{m(x - a)^{n+1}}{(n + 1)!} \leqslant R_n(x) \leqslant \frac{M(x - a)^{n+1}}{(n+ 1)!}$$

or
$$m \leqslant R_n(x) \frac{(n+1)!}{(x-a)^{n+1}} \leqslant M$$

By the intermediate value theorem, $f^{(n+1)}(t)$ assumes all values between m and M, hence there is an X in $[a,x]$ such that $f^{(n+1)}(X) = R_n(x)(n+1)!/(x-a)^{n+1}$ or

$$f^{(n+1)}(X) \frac{(x-a)^{n+1}}{(n+1)!} = R_n(x)$$

The theorem is proved. (The case $x \leqslant a$ is left to the reader.)

Example 1. Let $f(x) = \sin x$ and $a = 0$. Then $R_n(x) = f^{(n+1)}(X) x^{n+1}/(n+1)!$ for some X between 0 and x. Since the higher derivatives of $\sin x$ are either $\pm \cos x$ or $\pm \sin x$, we have $|f^{(n+1)}(x)| \leqslant 1$. Hence $|R_n(x)| \leqslant |x|^{n+1}/(n+1)!$, which approaches 0 as $n \to \infty$, and $R_n(x) \to 0$ as $n \to \infty$. Of course, we could obtain this result with the aid of the integral form of $R_n(x)$.

The derivative formula for $R_n(x)$ is frequently useful in estimating the accuracy of certain computational procedures. By way of illustration, we apply it to Newton's method for estimating a root of an equation, which we now describe.

Suppose we wish to estimate a root r of an equation $f(x) = 0$. If we make a first guess, say x_1, then the diagram below suggests that a better estimate of r may be x_2, the point at which the tangent line at $(x_1, f(x_1))$ crosses the x axis.

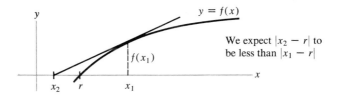

We expect $|x_2 - r|$ to be less than $|x_1 - r|$

To find x_2 explicitly, observe that the slope of the tangent line at $(x_1, f(x_1))$ is $f(x_1)/(x_1 - x_2)$ and is also $f'(x_1)$. Equating these two forms of the slope and solving for x_2 yields

(4)
$$x_2 = x_1 - \frac{f(x_1)}{f'(x_1)}$$

which is meaningful if $f'(x_1)$ is not 0.

Formula (4), which is equivalent to the diagram above, is the basis of Newton's method for estimating a root of an equation. Generally, this formula is applied several times, to increase accuracy. We will illustrate it by an example.

Example 2. Let us estimate the positive square root of 3, that is, the positive root of $x^2 - 3 = 0$. Here $f(x) = x^2 - 3$ and $f'(x) = 2x$. According to (4), if we make a first guess x_1, then our next estimate x_2 should be

$$x_2 = x_1 - \frac{f(x_1)}{f'(x_1)} = x_1 - \frac{x_1^2 - 3}{2x_1} = \frac{x_1 + 3/x_1}{2}$$

a formula which appeared in Example 4, page 68. If we choose as a first estimate,

$x_1 = 2$, then

$$x_2 = \frac{2 + \frac{3}{2}}{2} = 1.75000$$

For a better estimate of $\sqrt{3}$ we repeat the process, using 1.75 instead of 2. Thus

$$x_3 = \frac{x_2 + 3/x_2}{2} = \frac{1.750 + 3/1.750}{2} = 1.73214$$

is our third estimate, to five decimals. Repetition of the process yields, to five decimals, $x_4 = 1.73205$ which is close to $\sqrt{3}$ whose decimal expansion begins 1.732051.

Since the recursive process represented by Newton's method is of practical use and is easily coded for an electronic computer, it is important to know under what circumstances $|x_i - r|$ approaches 0 as $i \to \infty$. The following theorem shows that if $f''(x)$ is not too large nor $f'(x)$ too small, then $|x_i - r|$ does approach 0 as $i \to \infty$.

THEOREM 4. *Let r be a root of $f(x) = 0$ and x_i an estimate of r such that $f'(x_i)$ is not 0. Let*

$$x_{i+1} = x_i - \frac{f(x_i)}{f'(x_i)}$$

If f' and f'' are continuous and M is a number such that

$$\left| \frac{f''(x)}{f'(t)} \right| \leqslant M$$

for all x and t in the interval from x_i to r, then

(5)
$$\left| x_{i+1} - r \right| \leqslant \frac{M}{2} \left| x_i - r \right|^2$$

PROOF. By Theorem 3 we have

(6)
$$0 = f(r) = f(x_i) + f'(x_i)(r - x_i) + \frac{(r - x_i)^2}{2} f''(X)$$

for some X between x_i and r. A little algebra transforms (6) into

(7)
$$x_i - \frac{f(x_i)}{f'(x_i)} - r = \frac{(r - x_i)^2}{2} \frac{f''(X)}{f'(x_i)}$$

The inequality (5) is a consequence of (7). The theorem is proved.

If $f''(x)$ and $f'(x)$ are positive from $x = r$ to $x = x_1 > r$, then, as a sketch [or (7)] shows, $x_1 > x_2 > x_3 > \cdots > r$. Let us consider in this case how swiftly the decreasing sequence $x_1, x_2, x_3 \cdots$ approaches r.

Notice that if x_1 is close to r, say $x_1 - r < 0.1$, then $x_2 - r \leqslant (M/2)(0.1)^2 = (M/2)(0.01)$. Thus, if M is not too large, x_2 is a much better approximation to r than x_1 is. For instance, if $M = 2$, we have $x_2 - r < 0.01$, $x_3 - r \leqslant (M/2)(x_2 - r)^2 < 0.0001$, and so on. Hence if x_1 is an accurate estimate of r to one decimal place, then x_2 is accurate to two decimal places, x_3 is accurate to four decimal places, and so on. The number of decimal places of accuracy tends to double at each step of the Newton recursion. For instance, the Newton recursion formula for $\sqrt{10}\,(=3.162278)$ is

$$x_{i+1} = \frac{x_i + 10/x_i}{2}$$

If we choose $x_1 = 3$, then the following table shows the results of the recursive process:

Step	Estimate	Correct digits	Number of correct decimal digits
1	$x_1 = 3$	3	0
2	$x_2 = 3.166667$	3.16	2
3	$x_3 = 3.162281$	3.1622	4

Example 3. With the aid of Theorem 4, we show that the sequence $x_1, x_2, \ldots$, defined by $x_1 = 2$ and

$$x_{i+1} = \frac{x_i + 3/x_i}{2}$$

approaches $\sqrt{3}$. (In Example 4, page 68, we assumed that this sequence has a limit.) According to (7), in which $f(x)$ is now $x^2 - 3$, $f'(x) = 2x$, and $f''(x) = 2$,

(8)
$$x_{i+1} - \sqrt{3} = \frac{(\sqrt{3} - x_i)^2}{2} \frac{2}{2x_i} = \frac{(x_i - \sqrt{3})^2}{2x_i}$$

Since x_1 is greater than 0, (8) shows that $x_2 - \sqrt{3}$ is greater than 0; that is, x_2 is to the right of $\sqrt{3}$. The same reasoning shows that $x_i > \sqrt{3}$ for each $i = 1, 2, 3, \ldots$. Thus in particular, $x_i > 1$ for each i, and we conclude from (8) that

(9)
$$x_{i+1} - \sqrt{3} < \frac{(x_i - \sqrt{3})^2}{2} < (x_i - \sqrt{3})^2$$

If we denote $x_1 - \sqrt{3}$ by a, then $x_2 - \sqrt{3} < a^2$; $x_3 - \sqrt{3} < a^4$; $x_4 - \sqrt{3}\, a^8$; $\ldots$. Since $a = 2 - \sqrt{3} < 1$, we have $\lim_{n \to \infty} a^n = 0$; hence $\lim_{i \to \infty} (x_i - \sqrt{3}) = 0$.

Example 4. The line $y = 2x/3$ crosses the curve $y = \sin x$ at a point P, whose x coordinate, r, is between 0 and π, as is shown in this diagram:

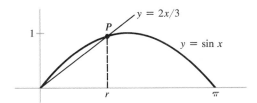

We have $2r/3 = \sin r$, since the graphs have equal y coordinates at $x = r$. Let us use Newton's method to approximate r.

A glance at the graph suggests that r is approximately 1.5. To obtain a better estimate, let us note that we are seeking a root of

$$f(x) = \sin x - \frac{2x}{3} = 0$$

Since $f'(x) = \cos x - \frac{2}{3}$, Newton's method provides this second estimate of r:

$$x_2 = 1.5 - \frac{f(1.5)}{f'(1.5)} = 1.5 - \frac{[(\sin 1.5) - 2(1.5)/3]}{(\cos 1.5) - \frac{2}{3}}$$

Using a table of $\sin x$ and $\cos x$ in radians, we find

$$x_2 = 1.5 - \frac{(0.997 - 1)}{(0.071 - 0.667)} = 1.5 - \frac{0.003}{0.596} = 1.495$$

Incidentally, to three decimals, $r = 1.496$.

EXERCISES

1. Use Theorem 3 to show that $R_n(x) \to 0$ as $n \to \infty$, for $f(x) = e^x$ and any a.
2. Use Theorem 3 to justify the expansion of $\sin x$ in a power series in $(x - \pi)$.
3. (a) Show that $\sqrt{1+x} = 1 + x/2 - x^2/8 + (x^3/16)(1 + X)^{5/2}$ for some X between 0 and x.
   (b) Use (a) to show that $1.21825 < \sqrt{1.5} < 1.21825 + (\frac{1}{128})$.
4. (See Exercise 3.) Using $1 + x/2 - x^2/8$ as an approximation of $\sqrt{1+x}$, estimate $\sqrt{2}$, $\sqrt{1.1}$, $\sqrt{1.01}$.
5. From Theorem 3 deduce that if f, $f^{(1)}$, $f^{(2)}$, $f^{(3)}$ are continuous, then

$$f(a + h) = f(a) + f^{(1)}(a)h + \frac{f^{(2)}(a)h^2}{2} + \frac{f^{(3)}(a + \theta h)h^3}{6}$$

   where $0 \leqslant \theta \leqslant 1$.
6. (a) For $f(x) = \sin^{-1} x$ compute $f(0)$, $f^{(1)}(0)$, $f^{(2)}(0)$, $f^{(3)}(x)$.
   (b) Write the terms of the power series in x, up to x^2, for $\sin^{-1} x$ and the derivative form of $R_2(x)$.
7. (a) For what values of x is the error in approximating $\sin x$ by x surely less than 0.01? (Use the fact that $\sin x = x - x^3/3! + x^5/5! - \cdots$.
   (b) For what values of x is the error in approximating $\sin x$ by $x - x^3/6$ surely less than 0.001?

   [Answer: (a) $x < \sqrt[3]{0.06} = 0.391$; (b) $x < \sqrt[5]{0.12} = 0.654$]
8. A convenient device for expressing a polynomial in powers of $(x - a)$ is Horner's method. We illustrate it for the polynomial $2x^3 - 5x^2 + 6x + 1$ and $a = 3$.

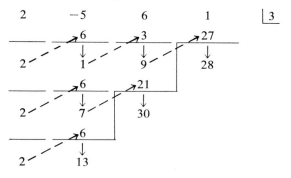

The 3 in the upper right-hand corner is from the expression $x - 3$ (we are expanding around 3). The slanted dashed lines record a multiplication by 3; the horizontal lines record addition; the top row consists of the coefficients of the polynomial. The left column is determined by the leading coefficient of the polynomial, and then the calculation follows the arrows for each line. The expansion in powers of $(x - 3)$ is determined by the outer numbers, 2, 13, 30, 28; it is $28 + 30(x - 3) + 13(x - 3)^2 + 2(x - 3)^2$.

(a) Verify that the expansion is correct.

(b) Apply Horner's method to the same f, but for $a = 2$.

(c) Repeat (b) for $a = 1$. (d) Repeat (b) for $a = -1$.

For a discussion of Horner's method, see J. V. Uspensky: "Theory of Equations," pp. 151–159, McGraw-Hill, New York, 1948, or F. Cajori: "Theory of Equations," pp. 63–66, Macmillan, New York, 1929.

[Answer: (b) $2(x - 2)^3 + 7(x - 2)^2 + 10(x - 2) + 9$;
(d) $2(x + 1)^3 - 11(x + 1)^2 + 22(x + 1) - 12$]

9. Frequently a function f is given by experimental data. To use Newton's method in that case we would first have to estimate the derivative f' by a quotient $\Delta y/\Delta x$. This may introduce large errors. We describe a modification of Newton's method which avoids the derivative by replacing the tangent line by a secant. We make two estimates, x_1 and x_2, of the root r; the third estimate, x_3, is as shown on this diagram, where the secant through $(x_1, f(x_1))$ and $(x_2, f(x_2))$ crosses the x axis:

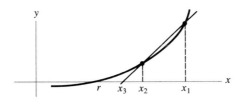

(a) Show that $x_3 = x_2 - \dfrac{f(x_2)}{[f(x_2) - f(x_1)]/(x_2 - x_1)}$.

(b) As $x_2 \to x_1$, what happens to x_3?

10. In estimating $\sqrt{3}$, an electronic computer began with $x_1 = 50$. What does Newton's method give for x_2, x_3, and x_4?

11. (a) Show that Newton's method gives this recursion formula for estimating $\sqrt[3]{7}$:
$x_{i+1} = \frac{2}{3} x_i + \frac{1}{3} (7/x_i^2)$.

(b) Let $x_1 = 1$ and compute x_2 and x_3.

(c) Let $x_1 = 2$, and compute x_2 and x_3.

12. Given the recursion formula in Exercise 11, show that if x_i is in [1,2], then $|x_{i+1} - \sqrt[3]{7}| \leqslant 2|x_i - \sqrt[3]{7}|^2$. [Hint: Use (5).]

13. Let $f(x) = 2x^3 - 4x + 1$.

(a) Show that $f(1) < 0 < f(0)$ and that there must thus be a root r of $f(x) = 0$ in [0,1].

(b) Take $x_1 = 1$, and apply Newton's method to obtain x_2 and x_3, estimates of r.

(c) Graph f, and show what is happening in the sequence of estimates.

[Answer: (b) $x_2 = \frac{3}{2}$, $x_3 = \frac{25}{19}$]

14. Draw the curve $f(x) = x^2 - 2x + 2$. Observe that it does not meet the x axis.
    (a) Let $x_1 = 2$. Draw the tangent lines used in Newton's method, and show where they cut the x axis for x_1, x_2, x_3, and x_4.
    (b) What happens to x_n as $n \to \infty$?
15. Let $f(x) = x^4 + x - 19$.
    (a) Show that $f(2) < 0 < f(3)$ and that f must thus have a root r between 2 and 3.
    (b) Apply Newton's method, starting with $x_1 = 2$. Compute x_2 and x_3, and sketch the pertinent tangent lines on a graph.
    [Answer: (b) $x_2 = 2.030$, $x_3 = 2.030$]
16. (a) Graph $y = e^x$ and $y = x + 2$ relative to the same axes.
    (b) With the aid of (a), estimate a root of $e^x - x - 2 = 0$.
    (c) Use Newton's method and a table of e^x to estimate the root to 3-decimal accuracy.
17. Use Newton's method to estimate $\sqrt{190}$, starting with $x_1 = 1$. What are x_2, x_3, x_4, and x_5?

18. Let f be a function having continuous $f^{(1)}$, $f^{(2)}$, and $f^{(3)}$ for all x. Assume that $\lim_{x \to \infty} f(x) = 1$, and $\lim_{x \to \infty} f^{(3)}(x) = 0$. Prove that $\lim_{x \to \infty} f^{(1)}(x) = 0 = \lim_{x \to \infty} f^{(2)}(x) = 0$.
    [Hint: Express $f(a + 1)$ and $f(a - 1)$ with the aid of Theorem 3.]
19. Let f be defined for all x and have a continuous $f^{(1)}$ and $f^{(2)}$. Prove that if $|f(x)| \leqslant 1$ and $|f^{(2)}(x)| \leqslant 1$ for all x in $[0,2]$, then $|f^{(1)}(x)| \leqslant 2$ for all x in $[0,2]$. [Hint: Use Theorem 3 to express both $f(0)$ and $f(2)$ in terms of derivatives at x.]
20. Let $F_k(x) = \sum_{n=0}^{k} x^n/n!$. Prove that $F_k(x) = 0$ has exactly one real root if k is odd, and no real roots if k is even.
21. Though $f'(a)$ is the limit of $[f(a + \Delta x) - f(a)]/\Delta x$, there is a better way to estimate $f'(a)$ than by that quotient. Assume that f, $f^{(1)}$, $f^{(2)}$, and $f^{(3)}$ are continuous.
    (a) Using Theorem 3, show that

    (10)
    $$\frac{f(a + \Delta x) - f(a)}{\Delta x} = f'(a) + \frac{f^{(2)}(X_1)}{2} \Delta x$$

    for some X_1 between a and $a + \Delta x$, and

    (11)
    $$\frac{f(a + \Delta x) - f(a - \Delta x)}{2\Delta x} = f'(a) + \frac{[f^{(3)}(X_2)]}{6}(\Delta x)^2$$

    where X_2 is in $[a - \Delta x, a + \Delta x]$. (Since the error in using the quotient in (11) involves $(\Delta x)^2$, while the error in using the standard quotient involves Δx, the quotient in (11) is more accurate when Δx is small).
    (b) Test this observation on the function $y = x^3$ at $a = 2$.
22. Assume that f, $f^{(1)}$, and $f^{(2)}$ are continuous and that $f^{(2)}(a) \neq 0$. By the law of the mean (or Theorem 3), we have $f(a + h) = f(a) + hf'(a + \theta h)$, for some θ in $[0,1]$.
    (a) When h is small, why is θ unique?
    (b) Prove that $\theta \to \frac{1}{2}$ as $h \to 0$.
23. We outline a brief alternative proof of Theorem 2. For x fixed, let $g(t) = f(t) + f'(t)(x - t) + f''(t)(x - t)^2/2! + \cdots + f^{(n)}(t)(x - t)^n/n!$

(a) Show that $R_n(x) = g(x) - g(a)$.

(b) Show that $g'(t) = f^{(n+1)}(t)(x - t)^n/n!$

(c) From (a) and (b) deduce Theorem 2.

24. Consider $\int_0^b xe^{-x}\,dx$, when b is a small positive number. Since e^{-x} is then close to $1 - x$, the definite integral behaves like $\int_0^b (x - x^2)\,dx = b^2/2 - b^3/3$, hence approximately like $b^2/2$. On the other hand, $\int_0^b xe^{-x}\,dx = 1 - e^{-b}(1 + b)$, and since e^{-b} is approximately $1 - b$, we have $1 - e^{-b}(1 + b)$ approximately equal to $1 - (1 - b)(1 + b) = b^2$. Hence $\int_0^b xe^{-x}\,dx$ behaves like b^2. Which is correct, $b^2/2$ or b^2? Find the error.

25. (a) When x is sufficiently large, we have $x > 1$; $x^3/3! > x^2/2!$; $x^5/5! > x^4/4!$; . . . ; hence $x + x^3/3! + x^5/5! + \cdots > 1 + x^2/2! + x^4/4! + \cdots$. Also, when x is sufficiently large we have $1 + x^2/2! > x$; $x^4/4! > x^3/3!$; . . . ; hence $1 + x^2/2! + x^4/4! + \cdots > x + x^3/3! + x^5/5! + \cdots$. Explain the paradox.

(b) Which of the two power series in (a) has the larger sum?

26. Justify the second sentence in this statement, quoted from a biological monograph: Hence the probability of extinction $1 - y$ will be given by $1 - y = e^{-(1+k)y}$. If k is small, y is approximately equal to $2k$.

27. Justify this statement, found in a biological monograph: Expanding the equation, $a \ln(x + p) + b \ln(y + q) = M$, we obtain

$$a\left(\ln p + \frac{x}{p} - \frac{x^2}{2p^2} + \frac{x^3}{3p^3} - \cdots\right) + b\left(\ln q + \frac{y}{q} - \frac{y^2}{2q^2} + \frac{y^3}{3q^3} + \cdots\right) = M$$

3. Summary. This chapter has extended the fundamental theorem of calculus and the law of the mean. The fundamental theorem of calculus asserts that *if f' is continuous*, then

$$f(x) = f(a) + \int_a^x f'(t)\,dt$$

and the law of the mean asserts that

$$f(x) = f(a) + f'(X)(x - a)$$

for some X between a and x. Both express the difference between $f(a)$ and $f(x)$ in terms of the derivative of f.

The extension consists in using, instead of $f(a)$, the polynomial

$$P_n(x) = f(a) + \frac{f'(a)}{1!}(x - a) + \cdots + \frac{f^{(n)}(a)}{n!}(x - a)^n$$

Theorem 2 asserts that

$$f(x) = P_n(x) + \int_a^x \frac{(x - t)^n f^{(n+1)}(t)}{n!} dt$$

thus generalizing the fundamental theorem of calculus. Theorem 3 asserts that

$$f(x) = P_n(x) + \frac{f^{(n+1)}(X)(x - a)^{n+1}}{(n + 1)!}$$

for some X between a and x, thus generalizing the law of the mean.

These two theorems were used to prove that certain functions are the sums of power series, to solve the differential equation $d^2y/dx^2 = -y$, and to evaluate the efficiency of Newton's recursion formula,

$$x_{i+1} = x_i - \frac{f(x_i)}{f'(x_i)}$$

Both theorems relate information about the higher derivatives of a function to the function itself.

14

Estimating the definite integral

THE definite integrals

$$\int_0^b \frac{\sin x}{x}\, dx \qquad \int_0^b \left(\frac{\sin x}{x}\right)^2 dx \qquad \int_0^b \frac{1 - e^{-x}}{x}\, dx \qquad \int_0^b e^{-x^2}\, dx$$

are important in information theory, in probability theory, and in the study of electric currents, antennas, and light. None of these integrands has an elementary antiderivative; hence these definite integrals cannot be evaluated by means of the fundamental theorem of calculus. Clearly it is important to be able to obtain accurate estimates of definite integrals.

This chapter presents four ways of estimating a definite integral. The first three methods will be applicable even if we know the values of the integrand at only a few selected values of the variable, while the fourth exploits the Taylor's series for the integrand.

353

METHOD 1 (RECTANGLES). Let $x_0 = a, x_1, \ldots, x_n = b$ be a partition of $[a,b]$ into n sections of equal length $h = (b - a)/n$. Then

(1) $\quad \sum_{i=1}^{n} f(x_i)(x_i - x_{i-1}) = f(x_1)h + \cdots + f(x_n)h = h[f(x_1) + \cdots + f(x_n)]$

approximates the definite integral of f over $[a,b]$. If $f(x)$ is positive for all x, then $f(x_i)h$ can be interpreted as the area of the rectangle whose base has width h and whose height is $f(x_i)$. Hence the sum (1) is the area of the shaded rectangles in this diagram:

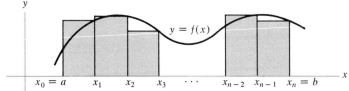

Before we use this method to estimate a definite integral, we should examine the size of the error that may be involved. This we do in the following theorem.

THEOREM 1. *Let M_1 be a number such that $|f'(x)| \leqslant M_1$ for all x in $[a,b]$. Then the error involved in using the rectangular method to approximate $\int_a^b f(x)\,dx$ has absolute value at most $h M_1(b - a)$, where $h = (b - a)/n$. That is,*

(2) $\quad \left| \int_a^b f(x)\,dx - [f(x_1) + f(x_2) + \cdots + f(x_n)]\,h \right| \leqslant h M_1(b - a)$

PROOF. Rewrite the quantity in absolute-value signs in (2) as

(3)

$$\left[\int_a^{x_1} f(x)\,dx - f(x_1)\,h \right] + \left[\int_{x_1}^{x_2} f(x)\,dx - f(x_2)\,h \right] + \cdots + \left[\int_{x_{n-1}}^{b} f(x)\,dx - f(x_n)\,h \right]$$

and consider, for example, the first term in (3),

$$\int_a^{x_1} f(x)\,dx - f(x_1)\,h$$

By Lemma 3, page 143, $\int_a^{x_1} f(x)\,dx = f(X_1)\,h$, for some X_1 in $[a, x_1]$. Thus

(4) $\quad \left| \int_a^{x_1} f(x)\,dx - f(x_1)\,h \right| = \left| f(X_1)\,h - f(x_1)h \right| = h \left| f(X_1) - f(x_1) \right|$

By the law of the mean, $f(X_1) - f(x_1) = f'(X_1^*)(X_1 - x_1)$, for some X_1^* in $[X_1, x_1]$. Thus, since $|f'(X_1^*)| \leqslant M_1$ and $|X_1 - x_1| \leqslant h$, we have

(5) $\quad |f(X_1) - f(x_1)| = |f'(X_1^*)(X_1 - x_1)| \leqslant M_1|X_1 - x_1| \leqslant M_1 h$

From (4) and (5) we obtain

(6) $\quad \left| \int_a^{x_1} f(x)\,dx - f(x_1)\,h \right| \leqslant h M_1 h$

Similar reasoning applies to each of the n terms in (3). We may conclude that the absolute value of the error is then not larger than $nhM_1 h = (b - a) M_1 h = hM_1(b - a)$. The theorem is proved.

Example 1. We estimate $\int_0^1 1/(1 + x^3)\, dx$. Though this definite integral can be evaluated by the fundamental theorem of calculus (by "partial fractions"), it offers a good deal of computational difficulty. Let us instead estimate it, using the rectangular method with $n = 3$, and hence, $h = \frac{1}{3}$. Formula (1) takes the form

$$\frac{1}{3}\left[\frac{1}{1 + (\frac{1}{3})^3} + \frac{1}{1 + (\frac{2}{3})^3} + \frac{1}{1 + (\frac{3}{3})^3}\right]$$

which equals

(7)
$$\frac{27}{3}\left(\frac{1}{28} + \frac{1}{35} + \frac{1}{54}\right)$$

A table of reciprocals shows that (7) equals

$$9(0.03571 + 0.02857 + 0.01852) = 0.745$$

To estimate our error we use Theorem 1 and consider the absolute value of

(8)
$$D\left(\frac{1}{1 + x^3}\right) = \frac{-3x^2}{(1 + x^3)^2}$$

For x in [0,1], we have $x^2 \leqslant 1$ and $(1 + x^3)^2 \geqslant 1$. Hence, by (8),

$$\left|D\left(\frac{1}{1 + x^3}\right)\right| \leqslant \frac{(-3)(1)^2}{(1)^2} = 3$$

which can serve as M_1, an upper bound for the absolute value of the derivative for x in [0,1]. Thus our error is not more than $(\frac{1}{3})(3)(1 - 0) = 1$. As a matter of fact, our error is less than 0.1, since it turns out that $\int_0^1 [1/(1 + x^3)]\, dx = 0.836$ (see Exercise 11(c), page 334).

METHOD 2 (TRAPEZOIDS). In this method we cut [a,b] into n sections of equal length, as shown below, and compute the total area of the indicated trapezoids:

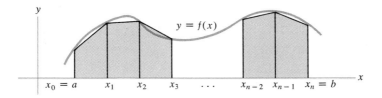

The area of the ith trapezoid is

$$\tfrac{1}{2}[f(x_{i-1}) + f(x_i)](x_i - x_{i-1})$$

Since each $x_i - x_{i-1}$ equals $(b - a)/n$, which we again call h, we have the following approximation to $\int_a^b f(x)\,dx$:

$$\tfrac{1}{2}[f(x_0) + f(x_1)]h + \tfrac{1}{2}[f(x_1) + f(x_2)]h + \cdots + \tfrac{1}{2}[f(x_{n-1}) + f(x_n)]h$$

This simplifies to the *trapezoidal formula*:

(9) $$\frac{h}{2}[f(x_0) + 2f(x_1) + 2f(x_2) + \cdots + 2f(x_{n-1}) + f(x_n)]$$

To contrast (1) with (9), note that in the trapezoidal formula there are $n + 1$ terms [as compared with n terms in (1)] and that $f(x_0) = f(a)$ appears and is given equal weight with $f(x_n) = f(b)$. Note also that if $f(a) = f(b)$, the rectangular and trapezoidal formulas give the same result.

It can be proved that if $|f^{(2)}(x)| \leqslant M_2$ for all x in $[a,b]$, then the error entailed in using the trapezoidal method is at most $h^2 M_2 (b - a)/12$. Note that h^2 is much smaller than h when h is near 0; hence the trapezoidal estimate is usually more accurate than the rectangular method. The error involved in applying the trapezoidal method to estimate $\int_0^1 [1/(1 + x^3)]\,dx$ will be at most $h^2 M_2 (1 - 0)/12$. Now, a straightforward computation shows that

(10) $$\frac{d^2\,[1/(1 + x^3)]}{dx^2} = \frac{6x(2x^3 - 1)}{(1 + x^3)^3}$$

A glance at (10) shows that for x in $[0,1]$ the absolute value of the numerator is not more than $6(1) = 6$ and that the denominator is at least 1. Hence $|f^{(2)}(x)| \leqslant 6$ in this case, and we have

(11) $$|\text{Error}| \leqslant h^2 \frac{6}{12} = \frac{h^2}{2}$$

Example 2. We use the trapezoidal method to estimate $\int_0^1 [1/(1 + x^3)]\,dx$. As in Example 1, let us take $h = \tfrac{1}{3}$. Then $x_0 = 0$, $x_1 = \tfrac{1}{3}$, $x_2 = \tfrac{2}{3}$, $x_3 = \tfrac{3}{3}$. Formula (9) provides the estimate

(12) $$\frac{1}{6}\left[\frac{1}{1 + 0^3} + \frac{2}{1 + (\tfrac{1}{3})^3} + \frac{2}{1 + (\tfrac{2}{3})^3} + \frac{1}{1 + (\tfrac{3}{3})^3}\right]$$

which equals

(13) $$\frac{27}{6}\left[\frac{1}{27} + \frac{2}{28} + \frac{2}{35} + \frac{1}{54}\right]$$

A table of reciprocals helps show that (13) equals 0.829.

According to (11), our error is less than $\tfrac{1}{18} = 0.056$. As a matter of fact, our error is less than 0.007.

METHOD 3 (PARABOLAS: SIMPSON'S FORMULA). In the trapezoidal method we approximate a curve by chords, that is, parts of the graphs of first-degree polynomials, $y = Ax + B$. In Simpson's method we approximate a curve by parts of the graphs of second-degree polynomials, $y = Ax^2 + Bx + C$, that is, parabolas. The basis of the formula is the following theorem.

THEOREM 2: *Prismoidal formula.* If $f(x) = Ax^2 + Bx + C$, then

(14)
$$\int_{c-h}^{c+h} f(x)\,dx = \frac{h}{3}[f(c - h) + 4f(c) + f(c + h)]$$

PROOF. Rather than compute both sides directly and show that they are equal, let us introduce the substitution $u = x - c$, $du = dx$, which changes the definite integral in (14) into

$$\int_{-h}^{h} f(u + c)\,du$$

Define the function g by $g(u) = f(u + c)$. Then (14) takes the form

(15)
$$\int_{-h}^{h} g(u)\,du = \frac{h}{3}[g(-h) + 4g(0) + g(h)]$$

Now g, like f, is a polynomial of degree two, $g(u) = A^*u^2 + B^*u + C^*$. The computation of both sides of (15) is not difficult:

$$\int_{-h}^{h} g(u)\,du \underset{\text{FTC}}{=} \left(A^*\frac{u^3}{3} + B^*\frac{u^2}{2} + C^*u\right)\Bigg|_{-h}^{h} = \tfrac{2}{3}A^*h^3 + 2C^*h$$

and
$$\frac{h}{3}[g(-h) + 4g(0) + g(h)] = \frac{h}{3}[(A^*(-h)^2 + B^*(-h) + C^*) + 4C^* + (A^*h^2 + B^*h + C^*)]$$

$$= \frac{h}{3}[2A^*h^2 + 6C^*] = \tfrac{2}{3}A^*h^3 + 2C^*h$$

Comparison of these two results completes the proof.

Theorem 2 suggests that, *even if f is not a polynomial of degree two*, we use $(h/3)[f(c - h) + 4f(c) + f(c + h)]$ as an estimate of $\int_{c-h}^{c+h} f(x)\,dx$. The following diagram summarizes Theorem 2 and this observation.

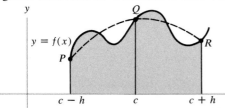

The dashed graph is a parabola, $y = Ax^2 + Bx + C$, through P, Q, R. The area of the region below the parabola is precisely $\frac{h}{3}[f(c - h) + 4f(c) + f(c + h)]$ and is an approximation of the area of the shaded region

In Simpson's method of estimating $\int_a^b f(x)\,dx$ we break $[a,b]$ into an *even* number of sections, each of length $h = (b - a)/2n$, and apply Theorem 2 to each of the n pairs of intervals, as follows: We select

$$x_0 = a, x_1, x_2, \ldots, x_{2n-1}, x_{2n} = b$$

such that $x_i - x_{i-1} = h$ for $i = 1, 2, \ldots, 2n$. Then

$$\int_a^b f(x)\,dx = \int_{x_0}^{x_2} f(x)\,dx + \int_{x_2}^{x_4} f(x)\,dx + \cdots + \int_{x_{2n-2}}^{x_{2n}} f(x)\,dx$$

We approximate the right-hand side by

(16) $\dfrac{h}{3}[f(x_0) + 4f(x_1) + f(x_2)] + \dfrac{h}{3}[f(x_2) + 4f(x_3) + f(x_4)] + \cdots$

$$+ \dfrac{h}{3}[f(x_{2n-2}) + 4f(x_{2n-1}) + f(x_{2n})]$$

Simplifying (16), we obtain *Simpson's formula*:

(17) $\dfrac{h}{3}[f(x_0) + 4f(x_1) + 2f(x_2) + 4f(x_3) + \cdots + 2f(x_{n-2}) + 4f(x_{n-1}) + f(x_{2n})],$

which amounts to an approximation of f with n parabolas like the one shown in the figure above. Notice that $f(x_0) = f(a)$ and $f(x_{2n}) = b$ are weighted less than the other values of f in (17), which receive the (alternating) weights 4 and 2. Since a second-degree curve probably provides a closer fit than a straight line, we may expect Simpson's method to be more accurate than the trapezoidal method. It turns out indeed that there is no error in applying Simpson's formula when the integrand is a third-degree polynomial. More generally, it can be proved that the error is less than $h^4 M_4(b - a)/180$, where M_4 is any number larger than $|f^{(4)}(x)|$ for all x in $[a,b]$. For small h, we find that h^4 is much smaller than h^2; hence the error entailed in Simpson's method is generally much less than that inherent in the trapezoidal method.

    Example 3.   We use Simpson's formula (17) with $2n = 4$ to estimate

$$\int_0^1 \frac{1}{1 + x^3}\, dx$$

In this case $h = \frac{1}{4}$ and $x_0 = 0$, $x_1 = \frac{1}{4}$, $x_2 = \frac{2}{4}$, $x_3 = \frac{3}{4}$, $x_4 = \frac{4}{4}$. Formula (17) gives

$$\frac{\frac{1}{4}}{3}\left[\frac{1}{1 + 0^3} + \frac{4}{1 + (\frac{1}{4})^3} + \frac{2}{1 + (\frac{2}{4})^3} + \frac{4}{1 + (\frac{3}{4})^3} + \frac{1}{1 + (\frac{4}{4})^3}\right]$$

or

$$\frac{64}{12}\left[\frac{1}{64} + \frac{4}{65} + \frac{2}{72} + \frac{4}{91} + \frac{1}{128}\right]$$

which, with the aid of a table of reciprocals, reduces to 0.835. Incidentally, the formula $h^4 M_4(b - a)/180$ in this case is $M_4/[(4)^4 (180)]$. A glance at $f^{(4)}(x) = x^2(360 - 1224x^3 + 360x^6)/(1 + x^3)^5$ shows that $|f^{(4)}(x)| \leqslant |360 - 1224| = 864$ for x in $[0,1]$; the error entailed in our estimate is less than $864/[(4)^4 (180)] = 0.019$. This may be compared with the actual error, 0.001.

    METHOD 4 (THE PARTIAL SUM OF A TAYLOR'S SERIES).   Our first three methods for estimating f depend on the values of f at certain points. The fourth method is useful if we know a few terms of a Taylor's series for f. We illustrate it with an example.

    Example 4.   Let us estimate $\displaystyle\int_0^1 [1/(1 + x^3)]\, dx$. We begin with the identity

$$\frac{1}{1 + t} = 1 - t + t^2 - t^3 + \frac{t^4}{1 + t}$$

(of the type we used on page 332). Replacing t with x^3, we have

$$\frac{1}{1+x^3} = 1 - x^3 + x^6 - x^9 + \frac{x^{12}}{1+x^3}$$

Therefore $1 - x^3 + x^6 - x^9$ is the beginning of a Taylor's series for $1/(1+x^3)$. Thus

(18)
$$\int_0^1 \frac{1}{1+x^3}\,dx = \int_0^1 (1 - x^3 + x^6 - x^9)\,dx + \int_0^1 \frac{x^{12}}{1+x^3}\,dx$$

The second definite integral in (18) is easy to evaluate by the fundamental theorem of calculus. We put a bound on the third definite integral in (18) by noticing that $1 + x^3 \geqslant 1$ when x is in $[0,1]$. Thus

$$\int_0^1 \frac{x^{12}}{1+x^3}\,dx \leqslant \int_0^1 x^{12}\,dx \underset{\text{FTC}}{=} \frac{x^{13}}{13}\Big|_0^1 = \frac{1}{13}$$

Therefore $\int_0^1 (1 - x^3 + x^6 - x^9)\,dx = 1 - \frac{1}{4} + \frac{1}{7} - \frac{1}{10} = 0.793$ is an estimate of $\int_0^1 [1/(1+x^3)]\,dx$, with an error of at most $\frac{1}{13} = 0.077$. The actual error is 0.043.

Our next two examples display the power of Taylor's series for estimating definite integrals. We consider the integrands e^{-x^2} and $(\sin x)/x$, mentioned at the beginning of the chapter.

Example 5. We estimate $\int_0^{1/2} e^{-x^2}\,dx$. Using the first four terms of the Taylor's series for e^t, page 336, and the derivative form of R_9, page 344, we have

(19)
$$e^t = 1 + t + \frac{t^2}{2!} + \frac{t^3}{3!} + \frac{e^T}{4!}t^4$$

for some T between 0 and t. Replacing t with $-x^2$ through (19) yields

$$e^{-x^2} = 1 - x^2 + \frac{x^4}{2!} - \frac{x^6}{3!} + \frac{e^T x^8}{4!}$$

for some T between 0 and $-x^2$. Since T is negative,

$$0 \leqslant \frac{e^T x^8}{4!} \leqslant \frac{e^0 x^8}{4!} = \frac{x^8}{4!}$$

We have
$$\int_0^{1/2} \frac{e^T x^8}{4!}\,dx \leqslant \int_0^{1/2} \frac{x^8}{4!}\,dx \underset{\text{FTC}}{=} \frac{x^9}{(4!)(9)}\Big|_0^{1/2} = \frac{1}{(4!)(9)(2^9)}$$

Hence
$$\int_0^{1/2}\left(1 - x^2 + \frac{x^4}{2!} - \frac{x^6}{3!}\right)dx \underset{\text{FTC}}{=} \frac{1}{2} - \frac{1}{(2^3)(3)} + \frac{1}{(2^5)(5)(2!)} - \frac{1}{(2^7)(7)(3!)} = 0.46127$$

is an estimate of $\int_0^{1/2} e^{-x^2}\,dx$, with an error less than

$$\frac{1}{4!(9)(2^9)} = \frac{1}{110{,}592} < 0.00001$$

Example 6. To estimate $\int_0^1 [(\sin x)/x]\,dx$, we begin with a few terms of the Taylor's series for $\sin x$,

$$\sin x = x - \frac{x^3}{3!} + \frac{x^5}{5!} - \frac{x^7}{7!} + R_7(x)$$

where

$$R_7(x) = \frac{\sin^{(8)}(X)x^8}{8!} = \frac{(\sin X)x^8}{8!}$$

for some X between 0 and x. Thus

$$\frac{\sin x}{x} = 1 - \frac{x^2}{3!} + \frac{x^4}{5!} - \frac{x^6}{7!} + \frac{(\sin X)x^7}{8!}$$

Hence

(20)
$$\int_0^1 \frac{\sin x}{x}\,dx = \int_0^1 \left(1 - \frac{x^2}{3!} + \frac{x^4}{5!} - \frac{x^6}{7!}\right) dx + \int_0^1 \frac{(\sin X)x^7}{8!}\,dx$$

Now, since $0 \leqslant \sin X \leqslant 1$ for X in $[0,1]$, we have

$$0 < \int_0^1 \frac{(\sin X)x^7}{8!}\,dx < \int_0^1 \frac{1x^7}{8!}\,dx \underset{\text{FTC}}{=} \frac{1}{(8)8!} < 0.00001$$

Thus the second definite integral in (20), which can easily be shown to equal 0.94608, is an estimate of $\int_0^1 [(\sin x)/x]\,dx$ with an error of less than 0.00001.

Of the four methods for estimating a definite integral, the last two are the most efficient. The arithmetic involved in each of the first three methods is about the same, but Simpson's method is usually the most accurate. Taylor's series is especially convenient to use if we can find its first few terms easily, and if the error $R_n(x)$ remains small over the interval of integration. This table summarizes the first three methods and their errors.

(21)

Method	Formula	Coefficients	Maximum error
Rectangles	$h\,[f(x_1)+f(x_2)+ \cdots +f(x_n)]$	$1, 1, \ldots, 1$	$hM_1(b-a)$
Trapezoids	$\dfrac{h}{2}[f(x_0)+2f(x_1)+ \cdots +f(x_n)]$	$1, 2, 2, \ldots, 2, 1$	$\dfrac{h^2M_2(b-a)}{12}$
Parabolas (Simpson)	$\dfrac{h}{3}[f(x_0)+4f(x_1)+2f(x_2)+ \cdots +f(x_{2n})]$	$1, 4, 2, \ldots, 2, 4, 1$	$\dfrac{h^4M_4(b-a)^4}{180}$

(In the table h is the length of each equal section of the partition of the x axis and M_k is a number such that $|f^{(k)}(x)| \leqslant M_k$ for all x in $[a,b]$.)

EXERCISES

1. (a) Using $h = 1$, estimate $\int_0^2 x^2\, dx$ by each of the first three methods in order.

   (b) What is the actual error in each?

   (c) What is the bound on the error as given by the formulas in the fourth column of (21)? [Answer: (a) 5, 3, $\frac{8}{3}$; (b) $\frac{7}{3}$, $\frac{1}{3}$, 0; (c) 8, $\frac{1}{3}$, 0]

2. Imagine $[a,b]$ partitioned into n segments of equal length. Form two estimates of $\int_a^b f(x)\, dx$, the first using only right-hand end points as X_i, the second using only left-hand end points. If you average these two sums, what formula results?

3. In Example 1 a crude argument showed that $|f'(x)| \leqslant 3$ for x in $[0,1]$. Find the maximum value of $|f(x)|$ for x in $[0,1]$. [Answer: $(\frac{1}{3}) \sqrt[3]{14} = 0.840$]

4. (a) Show by a diagram that if $f^{(1)}(x)$ is positive throughout $[a,b]$, then the rectangular estimate with all $X_i = x_i$ overestimates $\int_a^b f(x)\, dx$ but with all $X_i = x_{i-1}$ underestimates $\int_a^b f(x)\, dx$.

   (b) Show by a diagram that if $f^{(2)}(x)$ is positive throughout $[a,b]$, then the trapezoidal method overestimates $\int_a^b f(x)\, dx$.

5. The fundamental theorem of calculus is of no help in computing $\int_0^2 e^{-x^2}\, dx$. Use a table of e^{-x} and a partition of $[0,2]$ into four sections of equal length to estimate $\int_0^2 e^{-x^2}\, dx$ by (a) the trapezoidal method; (b) Simpson's method.

   [Answer: (a) 0.881; (b) 0.882]

6. (a) Estimate $\int_0^{1/2} [(\sin x)/\sqrt{x}]\, dx$ with the aid of a Taylor's series.

   (b) Put a bound on the error of your estimate made in (a).

7. Estimate $\int_0^4 [1/(1 + x^5)]\, dx$ by each of the first three methods, using $h = 1$. (A table of decimal expansions of the reciprocals of integers will be useful in this exercise.)

8. The function $\sin x^3$ does not have an elementary antiderivative. Thus the fundamental theorem of calculus is not helpful in evaluating $\int_0^{1/2} \sin x^3\, dx$.

   (a) What is the Taylor's series for $\sin x^3$ in powers of x?

   (b) Using x^3 as an approximation of $\sin x^3$, estimate $\int_0^{1/2} \sin x^3\, dx$.

   (c) Discuss the error in (b). [Hint: See (a).]

   [Answer: (a) $x^3 - x^9/3! + x^{15}/5! - \cdots$; (b) $\frac{1}{64} = 0.015625$; (c) less than $1/(2^{10} \cdot 60)$, which is less than 0.00002]

9. The cross sections $c(x)$ of a certain plane set R are known only when $x = 1$, 1.2, 1.4, 1.6, 1.8, 2, and 2.2. We have $c(1) = 2.03$, $c(1.2) = 2.41$, $c(1.4) = 2.54$, $c(1.6) = 2.76$,

$c(1.8) = 2.32$, $c(2) = 2.41$, and $c(2.2) = 2.01$. Estimate the area of R by (a) the trapezoidal method; (b) Simpson's method.   [Answer: (a) 2.892; (b) 2.939]

10. Estimate $\int_0^1 [1/(1 + x^3)]\, dx$, using $h = \frac{1}{6}$ and (a) the trapezoidal method; (b) Simpson's method.

11. Estimate $\int_{\sqrt{\pi/4}}^{\sqrt{\pi/4 + 0.1}} \sin x^2\, dx$, using series (4), page 336.

12. (a) Estimate $\ln(3) = \int_1^3 (1/x)\, dx$ by using each of the first three methods with $h = \frac{1}{2}$.

   (b) In each case discuss the bound on the error, as given in the fourth column of (21).
   (c) What is the actual error in each case?
                    [Answer: (a) 0.95, 1.117, 1.100; (b) 1, $\frac{1}{48} = 0.021$, $\frac{1}{60} = 0.017$;
                                                         (c) 0.149, 0.019, 0.001]

13. Repeat Exercise 12 for $h = \frac{1}{3}$.

14. (a) From the Taylor's series for $\cos x$ in powers of x, obtain the Taylor's series for $\cos 2x$.
   (b) Exploiting the identity $\sin^2 x = (1 - \cos 2x)/2$, obtain a Taylor's series for $(\sin^2 x)/x^2$.
   (c) Estimate $\int_0^1 \left(\frac{\sin x}{x}\right)^2 dx$ and put a bound on the error entailed in your estimate.

15. Using a Taylor's series, estimate $\int_0^1 [(1 - e^{-x})/x]\, dx$ and put a bound on the error in your estimate.

□ □ □

16. Prove that $(h/3)[f(c - h) + 4f(c) + f(c + h)]$ is equal to $\int_{c-h}^{c+h} f(x)\, dx$ when f is a polynomial of degree 3, $f(x) = Ax^3 + Bx^2 + Cx + D$. (Hint: First review the proof of Theorem 2.)

17. Show that if we use the Taylor's series for f in powers of x through the power x^n as a device for estimating $\int_a^b f(x)\, dx$, then the error is not more than

$M_{n+1}(b^{n+1} - a^{n+1})/(n + 1)!$ where $|f^{(n+1)}(x)| \leqslant M_{n+1}$ for all x in $[a,b]$

18. The cross-sectional area of a sphere, right circular cone, or frustum of such a cone ("bushel basket") can be expressed as second-degree polynomials.
   (a) Show that Theorem 2 implies that the volume of a sphere is $(\frac{4}{3})rA$, where r is the radius of the sphere and A is the area of a disk bounded by a great circle.
   (b) What does Theorem 2 tell us for the case of a cone or frustum?

19. (a) Estimate $\int_0^2 e^{x^2} dx$ by using a Taylor's series. (b) Put a bound on the error in (a).

20. (a) Find the Taylor's series for e^x in powers of $(x - a)$.
   (b) Deduce from (a) that $e^{x+y} = e^x e^y$.

21. Obtain a bound on $|f^{(4)}(x)|$ for x in $[0,1]$, where f is given in Example 3.

15

Further applications of partial derivatives

WE have already used partial derivatives to compute repeated integrals, page 252, and to find the maximum or minimum of a function over a set in the plane, page 311. In this chapter we use partial derivatives to generalize to functions of more than one variable such important concepts as the differential, the chain rule, and Taylor's series.

It should be remembered that a partial derivative is a derivative, just as a higher derivative is a derivative. But since there is a choice among two or more variables, we must specify the derivative we mean; this is accomplished by using the notation z_x, f_x, or $\partial z/\partial x$. (The notation f' would be ambiguous.)

Throughout this chapter and in our later work with partial derivatives, we will tacitly assume that the various functions and their partial derivatives are continuous.

363

1. *The change Δz and the differential dz.* When dealing with a function of only one variable, $y = f(x)$, we found that the differential, $dy = f'(x)\, dx$, is often a good approximation to the change Δy. Moreover, dy records the change as we move along the tangent line. In the case of a function of two variables, a tangent plane plays the role of the tangent line, once again reminding us that calculus is the study of functions whose graphs "microscopically" resemble a straight line or plane.

Let us consider a function f that assigns to a point (x,y) a number z, so that $z = f(x,y)$. For instance, $f(x,y)$ may be total sales when a firm spends x dollars on improving its product and y dollars on advertising; or $f(x,y)$ may be the temperature at the point (x,y) in a sheet of metal.

If we change x by an amount Δx, and y by an amount Δy, then z changes by an amount

$$\Delta z = f(x + \Delta x, y + \Delta y) - f(x,y)$$

as indicated in this diagram:

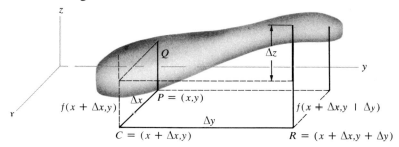

We will *not* take the shortest path from $P = (x,y)$ to $R = (x + \Delta x, y + \Delta y)$ to estimate the change Δz as we travel from (x,y) to $(x + \Delta x, y + \Delta y)$. Rather, we will travel from (x,y) to $C = (x + \Delta x, y)$ and then from C to R. The reason for this detour is simple: From P to C only the x coordinate changes, and from C to R only the y coordinate changes. This route splits our problem into two problems concerning functions of a single variable. We will estimate the change in z as we move first from P to C and then from C to R.

Let us look only at that part of the graph of f which lies above the segments PC and CR, namely, the two curves QU and US in the following diagram, in which the points Q, V, and T lie on one horizontal plane, and the line UW is horizontal.

The curves QU and US lie on the surface whose equation is $z = f(x,y)$

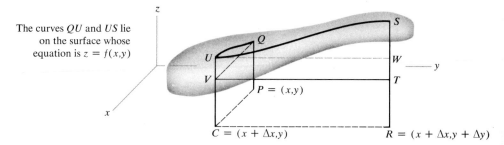

Inspection of the diagram shows that $\Delta z = TS = VU + WS$. Now, by the law of the mean

$$VU = f(x + \Delta x, y) - f(x,y) = f_x(X,y)\,\Delta x$$

for some X between x and $x + \Delta x$ and

$$WS = f(x + \Delta x, y + \Delta y) - f(x + \Delta x, y) = f_y(x + \Delta x, Y)\,\Delta y$$

for some Y between y and $y + \Delta y$. We therefore have this representation of Δz:

(1) $$\Delta z = f_x(X,y)\,\Delta x + f_y(x + \Delta x, Y)\,\Delta y$$

When Δx and Δy approach 0, both (X,y) and $(x + \Delta x, Y)$ approach (x,y); by the continuity of f_x and f_y we have

$$f_x(X,y) = f_x(x,y) + \varepsilon_1 \qquad \text{and} \qquad f_y(x + \Delta x, Y) = f_y(x,y) + \varepsilon_2$$

where $\varepsilon_1 \to 0$ and $\varepsilon_2 \to 0$ as Δx and Δy approach 0. From (1) follows this basic result, which we will need on several occasions:

THEOREM 1.   *If f has continuous partial derivatives f_x and f_y, then Δz, defined as $f(x + \Delta x, y + \Delta y) - f(x,y)$, is of the form*

$$\Delta z = f_x(x,y)\,\Delta x + f_y(x,y)\,\Delta y + \varepsilon_1\,\Delta x + \varepsilon_2\,\Delta y$$

where $\varepsilon_1 \to 0$ and $\varepsilon_2 \to 0$ as Δx and Δy approach 0.

Since $\varepsilon_1\,\Delta x$ and $\varepsilon_2\,\Delta y$ are the products of small quantities when Δx and Δy are sufficiently small, they are usually negligible when compared to $f_x(x,y)\,\Delta x$ and $f_y(x,y)\,\Delta y$ [if $f_x(x,y)$ and $f_y(x,y)$ are not 0]. For this reason, $f_x(x,y)\,\Delta x + f_y(x,y)\,\Delta y$ is often a good estimate of Δz when Δx and Δy are small.

Example 1.   If we change the dimensions of a cylindrical tin can from radius 3 inches and height 4 inches to radius 2.9 inches and height 4.2 inches, by how much do we change the volume? In this case the volume is a function, $V(r,h) = \pi r^2 h$, of the two variables r and h. We wish to estimate

$$\Delta V = V(2.9, 4.2) - V(3, 4)$$

which we can think of as

$$\Delta V = V(3 + (-0.1), 4 + (0.2)) - V(3, 4)$$

Rather than compute ΔV, let us, as the theorem suggested, use $V_r(3, 4)\,\Delta r + V_h(3, 4)\,\Delta h$ as an estimate of ΔV. We have $\Delta r = -0.1$, $\Delta h = 0.2$ and $V_r = 2\pi rh$, $V_h = \pi r^2$. We evaluate V_r and V_h at $(3, 4)$: $V_r(3, 4) = 24\pi$, $V_h = 9\pi$. Hence ΔV is approximately

$$(24\pi)(-0.1) + (9\pi)(0.2) = (-0.6)\pi$$

A direct computation shows that $\Delta V = -0.678\pi$, with the minus sign indicating a decrease in volume.

If z is a function of x and y, we define the *differential* of z as $dz = f_x(x,y)\,dx + f_y(x,y)\,dy$. As Theorem 1 suggests, and Example 1 illustrates, dz is frequently a good approximation to Δz when dx and dy are small.

To compare dz to Δz geometrically, as we compared dy to Δy on page 60, we begin by constructing a certain plane. Denote the curve lying in the graph of f and above the segment from (x,y) to $(x + \Delta x, y)$ by C_x (this is the curve QU in the figure on page 364; similarly, denote the curve above the segment from (x,y) to $(x,y + \Delta y)$ by C_y. Let T_x be the tangent line to C_x at the point above (x,y); similarly let T_y be the tangent line to C_y at the same point.

Then $f_x(x,y)\,\Delta x$ is the change in z as we move along T_x from the point above (x,y) to the point above $(x + \Delta x, y)$; similarly $f_y(x,y)\,\Delta y$ is the change in z as we move from the point above (x,y) to the point above $(x,y + \Delta y)$. Lines T_x and T_y determine a plane (the "tangent plane" which we will discuss in Chap. 16).

The left-hand diagram below shows C_x, T_x, C_y, T_y and the tangent plane; the right-hand diagram shows that dz is the change in z as we move along the tangent plane from the point above (x,y) to the point above $(x + \Delta x, y + \Delta y)$.

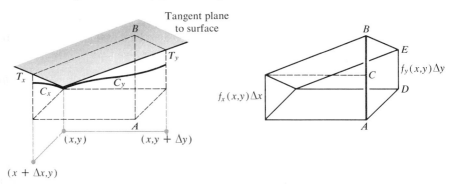

Letting AB in the diagram denote the change in z "along the tangent plane," we have, in fact,

$$AB = AC + CB = f_x(x,y)\,\Delta x + DE = f_x(x,y)\,\Delta x + f_y(x,y)\,\Delta y = dz$$

Theorem 1 is also the basis of the chain rules for functions of more than one variable. Theorems 2 and 3, which follow, are two of the basic chain rules whose proofs depend on Theorem 1.

THEOREM 2: *Chain rule.*   Let $z = f(x,y)$ have continuous partial derivatives f_x and f_y, and let $x = g(t)$ and $y = h(t)$ be differentiable functions of t. Then z is indirectly a function of t and

$$\frac{dz}{dt} = z_x \frac{dx}{dt} + z_y \frac{dy}{dt}$$

PROOF.   The proof is similar to that for the chain rule for functions of one variable (see page 103). We have $dz/dt = \lim_{\Delta t \to 0} (\Delta z/\Delta t)$. Now, Δt induces changes Δx and Δy in x and y, respectively. According to Theorem 1,

$$\Delta z = f_x(x,y)\,\Delta x + f_y(x,y)\,\Delta y + \varepsilon_1 \Delta x + \varepsilon_2 \Delta y$$

where $\varepsilon_1 \to 0$ and $\varepsilon_2 \to 0$ as Δx and Δy approach 0. Thus

$$\frac{\Delta z}{\Delta t} = f_x(x,y)\frac{\Delta x}{\Delta t} + f_y(x,y)\frac{\Delta y}{\Delta t} + \varepsilon_1\frac{\Delta x}{\Delta t} + \varepsilon_2\frac{\Delta y}{\Delta t}$$

and

$$\frac{dz}{dt} = \lim_{\Delta t \to 0}\frac{\Delta z}{\Delta t} = f_x(x,y)\frac{dx}{dt} + f_y(x,y)\frac{dy}{dt} + 0\frac{dx}{dt} + 0\frac{dy}{dt}$$

The theorem is proved.

We illustrate Theorem 2 by examples.

Example 2. We proved that $D(uv) = u\,Dv + v\,Du$, page 98. Theorem 2 provides another proof, which we sketch. Let $z = xy$ and let $g(t)$ and $h(t)$ be differential functions of t. If we replace x by $g(t)$ and y by $h(t)$, then z is a function of t, and according to Theorem 2

$$\frac{dz}{dt} = \frac{\partial z}{\partial x}\frac{dx}{dt} + \frac{\partial z}{\partial y}\frac{dy}{dt}$$

But $\partial z/\partial x = y$ and $\partial z/\partial y = x$. Thus

$$\frac{dz}{dt} = y\frac{dx}{dt} + x\frac{dy}{dt}$$

which is our old formula for the derivative of the product.

Example 3. We discuss the rate of change of the hypotenuse H of a right triangle whose legs x and y change at the rates v and v^*, respectively. We have

$$H = \sqrt{x^2 + y^2}$$

By Theorem 2

$$\frac{dH}{dt} = \frac{\partial H}{\partial x}\frac{dx}{dt} + \frac{\partial H}{\partial y}\frac{dy}{dt}$$

But $\quad \dfrac{\partial H}{\partial x} = \dfrac{x}{\sqrt{x^2 + y^2}} \quad \dfrac{\partial H}{\partial y} = \dfrac{y}{\sqrt{x^2 + y^2}} \quad \dfrac{dx}{dt} = v \quad$ and $\quad \dfrac{dy}{dt} = v^*$

Hence $\quad \dfrac{dH}{dt} = \dfrac{xv}{\sqrt{x^2 + y^2}} + \dfrac{yv^*}{\sqrt{x^2 + y^2}} = \dfrac{xv + yv^*}{\sqrt{x^2 + y^2}}$

The next theorem is a generalization of Theorem 2.

THEOREM 3: *Chain rule.* Let $z = f(x,y)$ have continuous partial derivatives f_x and f_y, and let x and y be differentiable functions of t and u. Then z is indirectly a function of t and u, and we have:

$$\frac{\partial z}{\partial t} = z_x\frac{\partial x}{\partial t} + z_y\frac{\partial y}{\partial t} \qquad \text{and} \qquad \frac{\partial z}{\partial u} = z_x\frac{\partial x}{\partial u} + z_y\frac{\partial y}{\partial u}$$

PROOF. We only sketch the proof, which is virtually the same as that for Theorem 2. To examine $\partial z/\partial t = \lim\limits_{\Delta t \to 0} \Delta z/\Delta t$ we hold u fixed and let t change by an amount Δt. Then x changes by Δx and y changes by Δy. By Theorem 1 we have

(2) $$\Delta z = z_x\,\Delta x + z_y\,\Delta y + \varepsilon_1\,\Delta x + \varepsilon_2\,\Delta y$$

where $\varepsilon_1 \to 0$ and $\varepsilon_2 \to 0$ as Δx and Δy approach 0. Dividing (2) by Δt and recalling that $\lim\limits_{\Delta t \to 0} (\Delta x/\Delta t) = \partial x/\partial t$ and $\lim\limits_{\Delta t \to 0} \Delta y/\Delta t = \partial y/\partial t$, we conclude the proof in the manner of that for Theorem 2.

Example 4. Let $z = x^2y^3$, $x = 3t + 4u$, and $y = 5t^2u$. Then $z_x = 2xy^3$, $z_y = 3x^2y^2$, $x_t = 3$, and $y_t = 10tu$. According to Theorem 3,
$$z_t = (2xy^3)(3) + (3x^2y^2)(10tu)$$
If we wish, we may express z_t in terms of t and u:
$$z_t = 2(3t + 4u)(5t^2u)^3(3) + 3(3t + 4u)^2(5t^2u)^2(10tu)$$
Of course z_t could be computed by writing z as a function of t and u, and calculating z_t directly; z_u can also be calculated both ways.

While we have limited our discussion to functions of two variables, it is only a slight generalization to consider functions of three or more variables. For instance, the number of air conditioners sold in a summer is a function of (at least) four variables: temperature, price, number of new houses, and total spendable income; that is, $A = f(T,p,h,i)$. (We imagine f to be a continuous function, an estimate of the number actually sold.) In this case there are four partial derivatives: $\partial A/\partial T$ measures the influence of temperature, $\partial A/\partial p$ the influence of price, $\partial A/\partial h$ the influence of new construction, and $\partial A/\partial i$ the influence of spendable income. In each of these four partial derivatives the remaining three variables are held constant. As another example, temperature T in a solid depends on position (x,y,z) and time t; that is, $T = f(x,y,z,t)$. Then $\partial T/\partial t$ represents the rate of change of temperature as a function of time at a fixed point; $\partial T/\partial x$ represents the rate of change of temperature along a line parallel to the x axis at a fixed time (with y, z, and t fixed); and so on.

Theorems 1 through 3 generalize without effort to more variables; the only change is in the number of terms in the various sums, which depends on the number of variables under consideration.

Example 5. Some functions f have the property that
$$(3) \qquad\qquad f(kx,ky) = kf(x,y)$$
for all positive numbers k. Such functions are called *homogeneous.* For instance, let $f(x,y)$ denote the total production (in dollars) of a firm employing x workers in a factory costing y dollars. It is reasonable to assume that kx workers employed in a factory costing ky dollars produce k times as much as x workers in a y-dollar factory; in other words, $f(kx,ky) = kf(x,y)$. As a specific example, consider $f(x,y) = \sqrt[3]{x^3 + y^3}$. We have
$$f(kx,ky) = \sqrt[3]{(kx)^3 + (ky)^3} = \sqrt[3]{k^3(x^3 + y^3)} = k\sqrt[3]{x^3 + y^3} = kf(x,y)$$
We will show that such functions also satisfy an equation involving the function and its partial derivatives. Since several variables will be present, it will be convenient to denote f_x by f_1 (differentiation with respect to the "first variable") and f_y by f_2.

Let f be a homogeneous function, that is, satisfy the equation $f(kx,ky) = kf(x,y)$ for all positive k, x, and y. Both sides of this equation represent functions of the three variables k, x, and y. Let us differentiate both sides with respect to k, holding x and y fixed. Then we have

(4)
$$\frac{\partial f(kx,ky)}{\partial k} = \frac{\partial [kf(x,y)]}{\partial k} = f(x,y)$$

Now, $z = f(kx,ky)$ can be expressed as $z = f(u,v)$, where $u = kx$ and $v = ky$. Thus z is a function of u and v, where u and v are functions of k, x, and y. Assuming Theorem 3 for any number of variables, we conclude that

$$\frac{\partial z}{\partial k} = f_1(u,v)\frac{\partial u}{\partial k} + f_2(u,v)\frac{\partial v}{\partial k}$$

But $\partial u/\partial k = \partial(xk)/\partial k = x$ and, similarly, $\partial v/\partial k = y$. Thus

(5)
$$\frac{\partial z}{\partial k} = xf_1(u,v) + yf_2(u,v) = xf_1(kx,ky) + yf_2(kx,ky)$$

Combining (4) and (5), we see that

(6)
$$xf_1(kx,ky) + yf_2(kx,ky) = f(x,y)$$

Setting $k = 1$ in (6) yields $xf_1(x,y) + yf_2(x,y) = f(x,y)$, or in a briefer notation,

(7)
$$xf_x + yf_y = f$$

An economic interpretation of this relation between f and its partial derivatives is presented in Chap. 22.

EXERCISES

1. What are the various symbols we use to denote

    (a) $\lim\limits_{\Delta x \to 0} \dfrac{f(x + \Delta x, y) - f(x,y)}{\Delta x}$?

    (b) $\lim\limits_{\Delta y \to 0} \dfrac{f(x, y + \Delta y) - f(x,y)}{\Delta y}$?

2. If u is a function of x, y, and z, then u_x or $\partial u/\partial x$ denotes the derivative of u with respect to x (where y and z are fixed); we define u_y and u_z similarly. Find u_x, u_y, and u_z if (a) $u = x^2yz$; (b) $u = y \cos x + z$.

3. In our work leading to (1), illustrated on page 364, we showed geometrically that $\Delta z = VU + WS$ (in figure on page 364), where VU is defined as $f(x + \Delta x, y) - f(x,y)$ and WS as $f(x + \Delta x, y + \Delta y) - f(x + \Delta x, y)$. Without using any pictures, obtain that relation.

4. We obtained Theorem 1 by going from (x,y) to $(x + \Delta x, y)$, then to $(x + \Delta x, y + \Delta y)$. Prove Theorem 1 by using the path that passes through $(x, y + \Delta y)$ instead of through $(x + \Delta x, y)$.

5. If $z = 3x + 4y + 7$, show that $dz = \Delta z$ by computing dz and Δz.

6. Let $z = f(x,y)$ have $z_x(x_0,y_0) = A$ and $z_y(x_0,y_0) = B$.
    (a) Show that the function $z = A(x - x_0) + B(y - y_0) + f(x_0,y_0)$ has the same partial derivatives as f at (x_0,y_0).
    (b) Show that its graph has the same ordinate as f at (x_0,y_0).

(c) Show that $dz = f_x \, dx + f_y \, dy$ is the change in z if we go along the plane $z = A(x - x_0) + B(y - y_0) + f(x_0, y_0)$ from the point above (x,y) to the point above $(x + dx, y + dy)$.

7. Verify that the following functions satisfy both the equation $f(kx, ky) = kf(x,y)$ and (7): (a) $\sqrt{x^2 + y^2}$; (b) $x \ln (x/y)$.

8. Let $T = f(x,y,z)$, and let x, y, and z each be functions of t. (For instance, temperature T may depend on position in space, while x, y, and z describe the position of an astronaut in space at time t.)
   (a) State the analog of Theorem 1 for f.
   (b) State the analog of Theorem 2 for dT/dt.

9. (This exercise continues Example 1 and shows how dV compares with ΔV.) Fill in the following table [ΔV denotes $V(3 + \Delta r, 4 + \Delta h) - V(3,4)$, while dV denotes $V_r(3,4) \, \Delta r + V_h(3,4) \, \Delta h$]:

Δr	Δh	dV	ΔV	$\Delta V / dV$
-0.1	0.2	-0.6π	-0.678π	1.13
0.1	0.2			
0.01	0.03			
0.001	-0.001			

10. Let $z = u^3 v^5$, where $u = x + y$ and $v = x - y$.
    (a) Express z explicitly as a function of x and y and use this explicit expression to find z_x and z_y.
    (b) Find z_x and z_y by the chain rule. Do your answers agree? Which method is easier to use?

11. Let $z = e^{uv}$, where $u = y \sin x$ and $v = x + \cos y$.
    (a) Compute z_x and z_y by the chain rule.
    (b) Express z explicitly in terms of x and y and use this expression to compute z_x and z_y.
    (c) Does your answer to (a) agree with your answer to (b)?

12. Let $z = cx^m y^n$, where c, m, and n are constants.
    (a) Show that $dz/z = m(dx/x) + n(dy/y)$.
    (b) Use (a) to show that if you make at most a 3 percent error in measuring r, the radius of a tin can, and at most a 2 percent error in measuring h, its height, then the error introduced in calculating the volume $V = \pi r^2 h$ is likely to be less than 8 percent. (Hint: Consider dr/r, dh/h, and dV/V.)

13. Let (r,θ) be polar coordinates for the point (x,y) given in rectangular coordinates.
    (a) From the relation $r = \sqrt{x^2 + y^2}$ show that $\partial r/\partial x = \cos \theta$.
    (b) From the relation $r = x/\cos \theta$ show that $\partial r/\partial x = 1/\cos \theta$.
    (c) Explain why (a) and (b) are not contradictory.

14. Using Theorem 2, obtain the formula for the derivative of the sum of two functions, $D(u + v) = Du + Dv$.

15. (a) Prove that if $f(kx, ky, kz) = k^3 f(x,y,z)$ for all k, then

$$xf_1 + yf_2 + zf_3 = 3f$$

where f_3, for instance, denotes differentiation with respect to the third variable.
    (b) Verify this for $f(x,y,z) = x^3 + y^3 + z^3$.
    (c) Repeat (b) for $f(x,y,z) = x^3(\ln y - \ln z)$.

16. Let u and v be differentiable functions of t and f continuous.

   (a) Using Theorem 2, show that

$$\frac{d\left(\displaystyle\int_u^v f(x)\, dx\right)}{dt} = f(v)\frac{dv}{dt} - f(u)\frac{du}{dt}$$

   (b) Verify this for the special case $f(x) = \cos x$, $u = t$, $v = t^2$.

17. Verify Theorem 3 by computing dz/dt, dx/dt, dy/dt, z_x, and z_y explicitly in terms of t, if (a) $z = x^2y^3 + y$, $x = \sin t$, $y = e^t$; (b) $z = xy$, $x = t^2$, $y = t^3$.

18. Show by an example that if $z_x = 2x$, then z *need not be of the form* $x^2 + C$, where C is a constant.

19. (See Exercise 12.) The kinetic energy of a particle of mass m and velocity v is given by $K = (\tfrac{1}{2})mv^2$. If the maximum error in measuring m is 1 percent and in measuring v is 3 percent, estimate the maximum error in measuring K.

                                               (Answer: 7 percent)

20. Using differentials, estimate (a) $\sqrt{(3.01)^2 + (4.02)^2}$; (b) $\sqrt{(3.04)^2 + (3.98)^2}$.

                                         [Answer: (a) 5.022; (b) 5.008]

□ □ □

21. Let u be a function of x, y, and z. (For instance, the volume of a rectangular box is the product of its three dimensions, xyz.)

   (a) Obtain the formula for Δu analogous to (1). There are too many variables for our geometric intuition, so use the ideas indicated in Exercise 3.

   (b) From (a) show that $u_x\,\Delta x + u_y\,\Delta y + u_z\,\Delta z$ is a good approximation to Δu.

   (c) Use the result of (a) to generalize Theorem 1.

22. Let $z = f(u,v)$, where u and v are functions of x and y. Then, indirectly, $z = g(x,y)$. Show that if $du = u_x\,dx + u_y\,dy$ and $dv = v_x\,dx + v_y\,dy$, then the two expressions for dz,

$$dz = z_u\,du + z_v\,dv \qquad \text{and} \qquad dz = z_x\,dx + z_y\,dy$$

have equal values.

23. (a) Is there a function $z = f(x,y)$ such that $z_x = 2xy$ and $z_y = 2xy$? If so, find it.

   (b) Is there a function $z = f(x,y)$ such that $z_x = 2xy$ and $z_y = x^2 + 3y^2$? If so, find it.

24. Review the argument in Exercise 14 on page 64 that shows that $\Delta y - dy$ is small when compared to Δx if Δx is small. Prove that $\Delta z - dz$ is small when compared to $\sqrt{(\Delta x)^2 + (\Delta y)^2}$ if Δx and Δy are small.

25. Let (x,y) be rectangular coordinates in the plane, and (X,Y,Z) in space. Assume that F is a one-to-one correspondence between the plane and space, such that x and y depend continuously on X, Y, and Z and have continuous partial derivatives with respect to them. Similarly, assume that through the inverse function F^{-1}, X, Y, and Z are continuous functions of x and y and have continuous partial derivatives with respect to them. From this deduce that $2 = 3$. (Hint: $2 = dx/dx + dy/dy$ and $3 = dX/dX + dY/dY + dZ/dZ$. Use the chain rule.) Incidentally, there *is* a one-to-one correspondence between the plane and space, but it does not have the specified properties of continuity and differentiability.

26. The volume V occupied by a mixture of several gases depends on the pressure p, the temperature T, and the amounts $x_1, x_2, \ldots, x_n$ of the several gases,

$$V = f(p, T, x_1, x_2, \ldots, x_n)$$

(a) Show that $\sum_{i=1}^{n} x_i \, \partial V / \partial x_i = V$.

(b) From (a) deduce that $\sum_{i=1}^{n} x_i \, \partial^2 V / \partial x_j \, \partial x_i = 0$ for each fixed j, with $j = 1, 2, \ldots, n$.

2. Higher partial derivatives and Taylor's series.

Just as we may consider higher-order derivatives, we may also consider higher-order partial derivatives. Most common functions of two variables possess 2 *first-partial derivatives*, f_x and f_y, 4 *second-partial derivatives*, $(f_x)_x$, $(f_x)_y$, $(f_y)_x$, $(f_y)_y$, 8 *third-partial derivatives*, $((f_x)_x)_x$, $((f_x)_x)_y$, ..., $((f_y)_y)_y$, two for each second-partial derivative, and so on. It is customary to omit the parentheses and denote, for instance, $(f_x)_x$ by f_{xx} and $((f_x)_y)_y$ by f_{xyy}. (Note that the differentiations are carried out in the order in which they appear in the subscript, from left to right.) A ∂ notation is also used. Thus

$$f_{xy} = \frac{\partial(\partial f / \partial x)}{\partial y} \qquad \text{is written as} \qquad \frac{\partial^2 f}{\partial y \partial x}$$

and f_{xyy} as $\partial^3 f / \partial y \partial y \partial x$. (Note that in the ∂ notation the differentiations are carried out in the reverse order, that is, from right to left.) If $z = f(x,y)$ then we also use the notations z_{xx}, $\partial^2 z / \partial x^2$, and so on.

Example 1. Let us compute some of the higher partial derivatives of $z = x^2 + x^5 y^7$. We have $z_x = 2x + 5x^4 y^7$ and $z_y = 7x^5 y^6$. Then $z_{xx} = 2 + 20x^3 y^7$ and $z_{xy} = 35x^4 y^6$; also, $z_{yx} = 35x^4 y^6$ and $z_{yy} = 42x^5 y^5$. Let us compute just two of the 8 third-partial derivatives, say z_{xxy} and z_{xyx}. We have $z_{xxy} = (z_{xx})_y = 140x^3 y^6$ and $z_{xyx} = (z_{xy})_x = 140x^3 y^6$.

In Example 1 it turned out that $z_{xy} = z_{yx}$ and $z_{xxy} = z_{xyx}$; in short, the order of the subscripts did not affect the result. The following theorem, whose proof is to be found on page 455, shows that for well-behaved functions, the "mixed" partial derivatives, z_{xy} and z_{yx}, are equal; more generally, the order of subscripts is immaterial.

THEOREM 1. *If $z = f(x,y)$ has continuous partial derivatives z_x, z_y, z_{xy}, and z_{yx}, then $z_{xy} = z_{yx}$.*

From this theorem it follows that if the third-partial derivatives of z are continuous, then $z_{xyx} = z_{yxx} = z_{xxy}$. To see this, note that since $z_{xy} = z_{yx}$, we have $(z_{xy})_x = (z_{yx})_x$; that is, $z_{xyx} = z_{yxx}$. Also, $z_{xxy} = (z_x)_{xy}$, and application of Theorem 1 to z_x (instead of to z) shows that $(z_x)_{xy} = (z_x)_{yx}$. Thus we obtain $z_{xxy} = z_{xyx}$.

For a well-behaved function, when we compute a partial derivative of order $n + m$, with n differentiations with respect to x combined with m differentiations with respect to y, we might as well take all the differentiations with respect to x first, and consider

$$\underbrace{z_{xx \cdots x}}_{n \ x\text{'s}} \underbrace{{}_{yy \cdots y}}_{m \ y\text{'s}}$$

which is usually written as $\partial^{n+m} z / \partial x^n \partial y^m$.

Just as the higher derivatives at a may be of aid in expressing a function of a single variable x in terms of powers of $x - a$, so may the higher derivatives at (a,b) be of aid in expressing a function of two variables in terms of powers of $x - a$ and $y - b$. This may be quite useful. For instance, if we are interested in the behavior of $f(x,y) = xy$ near $(1,2)$, it may be of use to express xy in powers of $x - 1$ and $y - 2$; that is, $xy = (x - 1)(y - 2) + 2(x - 1) + (y - 1) + 1$. (How to find this expression is described below.)

As another example, we may wish to compute $\int_R f(P)\, dA$; however, all the repeated integrals for computing this definite integral may lead, in the first or second step, to an integrand whose antiderivative is not elementary. In that case we may estimate $\int_R f(P)\, dA$ by first expressing f in terms of powers of x and y. (This is how we estimated $\int_0^{1/2} e^{-x^2}\, dx$ on page 359.)

To see how to express $f(P) = f(x,y)$ in terms of powers of $x - a$ and $y - b$, which we will call Δx and Δy, respectively (for convenience and because they are usually small), we exploit Taylor's series for functions of one variable, which we write as

(1) $$F(t) = F(0) + F'(0)\, t + \frac{F^{(2)}(0)}{2!}\, t^2 + \cdots + \frac{F^{(n)}(0)}{n!}\, t^n + R_n$$

where

$$R_n = \frac{F^{(n+1)}(T)}{(n + 1)!}\, t^{n+1}$$

for some T between 0 and t. Equation (1) is simply Theorem 3 of page 344 in a different notation: F plays the role of f, t the role of $x - a$, and T the role of X.

With (1) we shall express $f(a + \Delta x, b + \Delta y)$ as a power series whose typical term is of the type $a_{ij}(\Delta x)^i (\Delta y)^j$, where the a_{ij} are suitable constants that involve the higher partial derivatives of f at (a,b).

To reduce matters to just one variable, we travel from (a,b) to $P = (x,y) = (a + \Delta x, b + \Delta y)$ via a straight line L, and turn the line into a t axis such that when $t = 0$ we are at (a,b), and when $t = 1$ we are at $(a + \Delta x, b + \Delta y)$. Thus a, b, Δx, and Δy will be fixed in our discussion, and t will be free to vary.

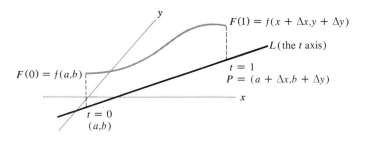

Let us define $F(t)$ to be $f(a + t\,\Delta x, b + t\,\Delta y)$. Then

$$F(0) = (f(a + 0(\Delta x)), b + 0(\Delta y)) = f(a,b) \qquad \text{and} \qquad F(1) = f(a + \Delta x, b + \Delta y)$$

If enough derivatives of F exist, then

(2) $\qquad F(1) = F(0) + F'(0)(1) + \dfrac{F^{(2)}(0)}{2!}(1)^2 + \cdots + \dfrac{F^{(n)}(0)}{n!}(1)^n + R_n$

where

$$R_n = \frac{F^{(n+1)}(T)}{(n+1)!}(1)^{n+1}$$

for some T, $0 < T < 1$. [Of course, $(1)^2 = (1)^3 = \cdots = (1)^{n+1} = 1$.]

We now express $F'(0)$, $F^{(2)}(0)$, $\ldots$, $F^{(n)}(0)$, in terms of f and its partial derivatives at (a,b). Since $F(t) = f(a + t\,\Delta x, b + t\,\Delta y)$ we may build up F as a composite function

$$F(t) = f(x,y) \qquad x = a + t\,\Delta x, y = b + t\,\Delta y$$

Since a, b, Δx, and Δy are held fixed, we have $dx/dt = \Delta x$ and $dy/dt = \Delta y$. By the chain rule (Theorem 2, page 366) we then have

(3) $\qquad F'(t) = f_x(a + t\,\Delta x, b + t\,\Delta y)\,\Delta x + f_y(a + t\,\Delta x, b + t\,\Delta y)\,\Delta y$

Hence $\qquad\qquad\qquad F'(0) = f_x(a,b)\,\Delta x + f_y(a,b)\,\Delta y$

Thus (2) begins

(4) $\qquad f(a + \Delta x, b + \Delta y) = f(a,b) + f_x(a,b)\,\Delta x + f_y(a,b)\,\Delta y + \cdots$

To see how (2) continues, let us compute $F^{(2)}(0)$ in terms of the partial derivatives of f at (a,b). Let us differentiate (3), which we write as

(5) $\qquad\qquad\qquad\qquad F'(t) = f_x\,\Delta x + f_y\,\Delta y$

and keep in mind that f_x and f_y depend indirectly on t, while Δx and Δy are fixed.

Again using the chain rule, we have

(6) $\qquad F^{(2)}(t) = \dfrac{d(F'(t))}{dt} = \dfrac{\partial(f_x\,\Delta x + f_y\,\Delta y)}{\partial x}\dfrac{dx}{dt} + \dfrac{\partial(f_x\,\Delta x + f_y\,\Delta y)}{\partial y}\dfrac{dy}{dt}$

which equals

$$(f_{xx}\,\Delta x + f_{yx}\,\Delta y)\,\Delta x + (f_{xy}\,\Delta x + f_{yy}\,\Delta y)\,\Delta y$$
$$= f_{xx}\,(\Delta x)^2 + f_{yx}\,\Delta y\,\Delta x + f_{xy}\,\Delta x\,\Delta y + f_{yy}\,(\Delta y)^2$$
$$= f_{xx}\,(\Delta x)^2 + 2f_{xy}\,\Delta x\,\Delta y + f_{yy}(\Delta y)^2$$

Thus the third term in (2), $F^{(2)}(0)/2!$, contributes

(7) $\qquad \dfrac{f_{xx}(a,b)\,(\Delta x)^2 + 2f_{xy}(a,b)\,\Delta x\,\Delta y + f_{yy}(a,b)\,(\Delta y)^2}{2!}$

to the series for $f(a + \Delta x, b + \Delta y)$. From (7) we see that $(\Delta x)^2$ has the coefficient $f_{xx}(a,b)/2!$; $\Delta x\,\Delta y$ has the coefficient $2f_{xy}(a,b)/2!$; and $(\Delta y)^2$ has the coefficient $f_{yy}(a,b)/2!$.

The terms contributed by $F^{(3)}(0)/3!$ turn out to be

(8) $\qquad \dfrac{1f_{xxx}(a,b)}{3!}(\Delta x)^3 + \dfrac{3f_{xxy}(a,b)}{3!}(\Delta x)^2\,(\Delta y) + \dfrac{3f_{xyy}(a,b)}{3!}(\Delta x)\,(\Delta y)^2 + \dfrac{1f_{yyy}(a,b)}{3!}(\Delta y)^3$

Notice the resemblance of (8) to the algebraic identity

$$(A + B)^3 = 1A^3 + 3A^2B + 3AB^2 + 1B^3$$

both in the powers to which Δx and Δy are raised and in the subscripts of f that appear in (8). This suggests a much simpler notation for (8):

$$\frac{1}{3!} (\Delta x\, \partial_x + \Delta y\, \partial_y)^3 f \Big|_{\text{at } (a,b)}$$

where we expand $(\Delta x\, \partial_x + \Delta y\, \partial_y)^3$ by a formal "multiplication" and interpret an expression such as $(\partial_x \partial_x \partial_y) f$ as f_{yxx}, which, in this case, equals f_{xxy}.

Example 2. Let us express $f(x,y) = x^2 y$ as a polynomial in $\Delta x = x - 1$ and $\Delta y = y - 2$. [That is, we will expand $f(x,y)$ about the point (1,2).] To do this we compute the partial derivatives of f and evaluate them at (1,2). We have

$$f_x = 2xy \qquad f_{xx} = 2y \qquad f_{xy} = 2x \qquad f_{xxy} = 2 \qquad f_y = x^2 \qquad f_{yy} = 0$$

All higher partial derivatives of f are identically 0. We have $f(1,2) = 2$, $f_x(1,2) = (2)(1)(2) = 4$, and so on. Thus

$$f(x,y) = f(1 + \Delta x, 2 + \Delta y)$$

$$= 2 + 4\Delta x + \Delta y + \frac{4}{2!} (\Delta x)^2 + \frac{4\Delta x\, \Delta y}{2!} + \frac{0}{2} (\Delta y)^2 + \frac{6}{3!} (\Delta x)^2\, \Delta y$$

or

(9) $x^2 y = 2 + 4(x - 1) + (y - 2) + 2(x - 1)^2 + 2(x - 1)(y - 2) + (x - 1)^2(y - 2)$

EXERCISES

1. Let f have continuous partial derivatives through order four. Use Theorem 1 to prove that $f_{xyxy} = f_{yxxy} = f_{yyxx} = f_{xyyx} = f_{xxyy} = f_{yxyx}$.
2. (a) Show that $\partial^7(x^m y^n)/\partial x^3\, \partial y^4$ at (0,0) is 0 if the positive integers m and n are different from 3 and 4, respectively.
   (b) Show that $\partial^7(x^3 y^4)/\partial x^3\, \partial y^4$ at (0,0) is $3!4!$.
3. Find all higher partial derivatives of the polynomial $3x^3 + 2xy^2 + 6x^2 - 5xy + 6x$.
4. The binomial theorem asserts that $f(x,y) = (x + y)^4 = x^4 + 4x^3 y + 6x^2 y^2 + 4xy^3 + y^4$. Expand $f(x,y)$ in a Taylor's series in x and y with the aid of partial derivatives, and see whether the result is in agreement with the binomial theorem.
5. (a) Obtain the first three nonzero terms of a Taylor's series in powers of x and y for $f(x,y) = \sqrt{x^2 + y^2 + 1}$.
   (b) Use the result of (a) to estimate $\int_R f(P)\, dA$, where R is the square whose vertices are (0,0), (0.1,0), (0.1,0), and (0.1,0.1).

[Answer: (b) 0.010033]

6. Obtain Eq. (8). To do this, make use of the equation $F^{(2)}(t) = f_{xx}(\Delta x)^2 + 2f_{xy}\, \Delta x\, \Delta y + f_{yy}(\Delta y)^2$, where $\Delta x = x - a$ and $\Delta y = y - b$, and of the chain rule.
7. (a) Using partial derivatives, obtain the first four nonzero terms in the Taylor's series for e^{x+y^2} in powers of x and y.
   (b) Noticing that $e^{x+y^2} = e^x e^{y^2}$ and using the first few terms of the Taylor's series for e^x and for e^{y^2}, solve (a) again.

8. Verify that the expansion of $\sqrt{1 + x + y}$ begins $1 + x/2 + y/2 - (\frac{1}{8})x^2 - (\frac{1}{4})xy - (\frac{1}{8})y^2 + \cdots$, (a) by using (4) and (7); (b) by using the first three terms of the expansion for $\sqrt{1 + t}$ and replacing t with $(x + y)$.

9. Using Eq. (9), compute the difference in the volumes of these two boxes: one has a square base of side 1 foot and height 2 feet; the other has a square base of side 1.1 feet and height 2.1 feet.

10. Let $T = f(x,y,z)$ be the temperature at the point (x,y,z) within a solid whose surface has a fixed temperature distribution. It can be shown that if T does not vary with time, then $T_{xx} + T_{yy} + T_{zz} = 0$. Similarly, if $P(x,y,z)$ is the work done in moving a particle from a fixed base point in a gravitational field to the point (x,y,z), then $P_{xx} + P_{yy} + P_{zz} = 0$. The equation $f_{xx} + f_{yy} + f_{zz} = 0$ is called Laplace's equation (in three dimensions). Verify that the functions $1/\sqrt{x^2 + y^2 + z^2}$, $x^2 - y^2 - z$, and $e^x \cos y + z$ satisfy Laplace's equation.

11. Here is an f such that $f_{xy}(0,0) \neq f_{yx}(0,0)$: $f(x,y) = 4xy(x^2 - y^2)/(x^2 + y^2)$ if $(x,y) \neq (0,0)$ and $f(0,0) = 0$. Verify this assertion by showing that $f_{xy}(0,0) = -4$ and $f_{yx}(0,0) = 4$.

12. (a) Using partial derivatives, express x^2y^2 as a polynomial in $x - 1$ and $y - 1$.
    (b) Verify your answer to (a) by expanding it.

13. (a) Find the first three nonzero terms of the Taylor's series for $\sqrt[3]{e^x + \sin y}$ in powers of x and y.
    (b) With the aid of (a), estimate $\int_R f(P)\, dA$, where R is the triangle where vertices are $(0,0)$, $(1,0)$, and $(1,2)$ and where f is the function given in (a).

[Answer: (a) $1 + x/3 + y/3$; (b) $1\frac{3}{9}$]

□ □ □

14. Assume that A, B, C are constants and $A > 0$. Show that $f(x,y) = Ax^2 + 2Bxy + Cy^2$ has a relative minimum at $(0,0)$ if $B^2 - AC < 0$. [Hint: Complete the square in $Af(x,y) = A^2x^2 + 2ABxy + ACy^2$.]

15. (See Exercise 14.) Show that if $B^2 - AC > 0$, and $A > 0$, then f has neither a maximum nor a minimum at $(0,0)$. In this case, the surface $z = Ax^2 + 2Bxy + Cy^2$ resembles a saddle in the vicinity of $(0,0)$; the point $(0,0)$ is called a *saddle point*. To see that this is so, examine the behavior and graph of $z = x^2 + 4xy + y^2$ for $y = x$, for $y = -x$, for $y = 0$, and for $x = 0$.

16. What do Exercises 14 and 15 suggest about a function f such that $f_x(0,0) = 0$ and $f_y(0,0) = 0$, but $f_{xx}(0,0) > 0$ and $[f_{xy}(0,0)]^2 > f_{xx}(0,0)\, f_{yy}(0,0)$?

17. Obtain at least 10 terms of a Taylor's series for $f(x,y,z)$ in powers of x, y, and z, assuming, of course, that the function is representable by a Taylor's series.

3. Summary. In this chapter we developed the differential, the chain rule, and Taylor's series for functions of two (or more) variables. We obtained our results by referring matters back to functions of a single variable. For instance, in the proof of Theorem 1 we went from (x,y) to $(x + \Delta x, y + \Delta y)$ along a path on which only one variable changes at a time. Taylor's series for $f(x,y)$ was obtained from that of a function $F(t)$, by introducing a straight path from (a,b) to $(a + \Delta x, b + \Delta y)$.

This table is a summary of the results obtained in this chapter.

For a function of one variable, $y = f(x)$	Analog for a function of two variables, $z = f(x,y)$
Derivative: df/dx	Partial derivatives: $\partial f/\partial x$ and $\partial f/\partial y$
Higher derivatives: $d^2f/dx^2,\ \ldots$	Higher partial derivatives: $\partial^2 f/\partial x^2,\ \partial^2 f/\partial y^2,$ $\partial^2 f/\partial x\,\partial y,\ \partial^2 f/\partial y\,\partial x,\ \ldots$
$\Delta y = f'(x)\,\Delta x + \varepsilon\,\Delta x \qquad (\varepsilon \to 0 \text{ as } \Delta x \to 0)$	$\Delta z = f_x\,\Delta x + f_y\,\Delta y + \varepsilon_1\,\Delta x + \varepsilon_2\,\Delta y$ $(\varepsilon_1 \to 0,\ \varepsilon_2 \to 0 \text{ as } \Delta x \text{ and } \Delta y \to 0)$
dy is defined as $f'(x)\,dx$	dz is defined as $f_x\,dx + f_y\,dy$
dy is change along tangent line	dz is change along tangent plane
Chain rule: $\dfrac{dy}{dx} = \dfrac{dy}{du}\dfrac{du}{dx}$	Chain rule: $\dfrac{dz}{dt} = \dfrac{\partial z}{\partial x}\dfrac{dx}{dt} + \dfrac{\partial z}{\partial y}\dfrac{dy}{dt}$ (where x and y are functions only of t) Chain rule: $\dfrac{\partial z}{\partial t} = \dfrac{\partial z}{\partial x}\dfrac{\partial x}{\partial t} + \dfrac{\partial z}{\partial y}\dfrac{\partial y}{\partial t}$ (where x and y are functions of t and u)

Taylor's series in $x - a$,
  beginning
 	
$f(x) = f(a) + f^{(1)}(a)\,(x - a)$
 	
$\qquad + \dfrac{f^{(2)}(a)}{2!}(x - a)^2 + \cdots$
	Taylor's series in $x - a$ and $y - b$,
	  beginning
	
	$f(x,y) = f(a,b) + f_x(a,b)\,(x - a)$
	
	$\qquad + f_y(a,b)\,(y - b) + \dfrac{f_{xx}(a,b)}{2!}(x - a)^2$
	
	$\qquad + \dfrac{2f_{xy}(a,b)}{2!}(x - a)\,(y - b)$
	
	$\qquad + \dfrac{f_{yy}(a,b)}{2!}(y - b)^2 + \cdots$

16

Algebraic operations on vectors

IN this chapter we discuss vectors and their algebra. This algebra will resemble somewhat the algebra of real numbers. The vectors we consider will generally lie in the plane. As the exercises will show, however, all our results can easily be extended to higher dimensions.

1. The algebra of vectors. An adequate description of the wind must include its speed and its direction. One way to describe a wind of 30 miles per hour from the southwest is to draw an arrow aimed in the direction in which the wind blows, scaled so that its length represents a magnitude of 30.

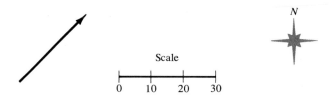

Relative to this same scale, here are some more wind arrows:

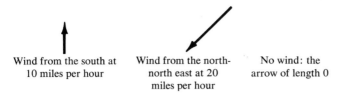

Wind from the south at
10 miles per hour

Wind from the north-
north east at 20
miles per hour

No wind: the
arrow of length 0

Similarly the flow of water on the surface of a stream is best indicated by a few sample arrows:

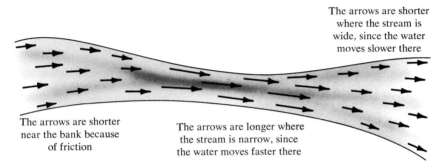

The arrows are shorter
where the stream is
wide, since the water
moves slower there

The arrows are shorter
near the bank because
of friction

The arrows are longer where
the stream is narrow, since
the water moves faster there

Of course, associated with *each* point on the surface is an arrow representing the velocity of the water at that point.

When we push, pull, or lift an object, both the magnitude and the direction of our effort matter. An arrow best describes the force we exert: we use the length of the arrow to represent the magnitude of our force, and the direction of the arrow to represent the direction of our force. For instance, these two forces of equal magnitude but opposite directions pushing against the rock are in equilibrium; the rock doesn't move.

Two forces of equal magnitude
but of opposite directions
pushing against a rock

If we move either of the forces to the right or left, but keep the point of application of the forces on the given line of the original forces, the rock is still in equilibrium.

We keep the forces on
the same line as above;
the rock still doesn't move

From this point of view, two arrows of the same length and direction and situated on the same line have the same effect. But if we move one of the forces (arrows) directly up, the rock will spin. If we remove one of the forces, the rock will move in the direction of the remaining force.

The mathematical word for our arrow is *vector*. A vector is determined by specifying two points P and Q in the plane, one of which is the "tail" of the vector and one the "head." For this reason a *vector* is formally defined as an ordered pair of points P and Q in the plane and is sometimes denoted $\overrightarrow{PQ}$ (P is the tail and Q is the head). If $P = Q$, then $\overrightarrow{PQ}$ is called the zero vector. Sometimes, as in the vectors describing stream flow, the location of the vector is important. The physicist considering the force vector applied to a rock regards two vectors as being the same if they have the same direction and magnitude and lie on the same line. Generally, the location of the vector is of no importance; we will frequently regard two vectors with the same direction and length as being the same; such vectors are sometimes called *free vectors*. We may have a vector associated with each point in some plane region (as in the stream flow illustration). Such a function is called a *vector field*.

We will use boldface letters, such as **A**, **F**, **R**, and **V**, to denote vectors. With pencil or chalk, a vector, such as **A**, is written /A or $\overrightarrow{A}$. We denote the length of **A** by $|\mathbf{A}|$. If we place the origin of a rectangular coordinate system at the tail of **A**, then the head of **A** has coordinates (x,y).

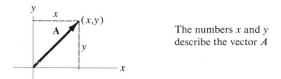

The numbers x and y
describe the vector A

The numbers x and y are the *components* of **A** relative to the coordinate system. Knowing only the two components, we can reconstruct **A** along the diagonal of a rectangle whose sides are $|x|$ and $|y|$. For instance, these four vectors all have x component 3 and y component -4:

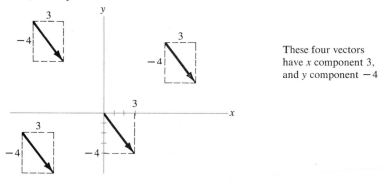

These four vectors
have x component 3,
and y component -4

A vector whose head is at $(13,18)$ and whose tail is at $(10,22)$ also has components 3 and -4. A vector with components x and y will be denoted $\overrightarrow{(x,y)}$ to distinguish it from the point (x,y). It will be a free vector unless otherwise stated. The vector $\overrightarrow{(0,0)}$ of length 0 is the zero vector and is denoted by **0**. Observe that $\overrightarrow{(x_1,y_1)} = \overrightarrow{(x_2,y_2)}$ if and only if $x_1 = x_2$ and $y_1 = y_2$.

THEOREM 1. $|(\overrightarrow{x,y})| = \sqrt{x^2 + y^2}$. *That is, the magnitude of a vector is the square root of the sum of the squares of its components.*

PROOF.   This is simply a restatement of the Pythagorean theorem. That x or y might be negative is immaterial, since both are squared.

As an application of Theorem 1, we see that the vectors in the preceding diagram all have length $\sqrt{3^2 + (-4)^2} = 5$. If $|(\overrightarrow{x,y})| = 1$, then $(\overrightarrow{x,y})$ is called a *unit vector*. For instance $(-1,0)$ and $(\tfrac{1}{2}, \sqrt{3}/2)$ are unit vectors.

We define the *sum* of two vectors $\mathbf{A}_1$ and $\mathbf{A}_2$ as follows. Place $\mathbf{A}_2$ in such a way that its tail is at the head of $\mathbf{A}_1$. Then the vector sum $\mathbf{A}_1 + \mathbf{A}_2$ goes from the tail of $\mathbf{A}_1$ to the head of $\mathbf{A}_2$. Observe that $\mathbf{A}_2 + \mathbf{A}_1 = \mathbf{A}_1 + \mathbf{A}_2$, for both sums lie on the diagonal of a parallelogram.

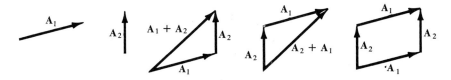

The reader may show that $\mathbf{A}_1 + (\mathbf{A}_2 + \mathbf{A}_3) = (\mathbf{A}_1 + \mathbf{A}_2) + \mathbf{A}_3$, a further similarity of vector addition to ordinary addition.

If $\mathbf{W}$ is a wind vector (describing the motion of the air relative to the earth) and $\mathbf{A}$ is a vector describing the motion of an airplane relative to the air, then $\mathbf{W} + \mathbf{A}$ is the vector describing the motion of the airplane relative to the earth.

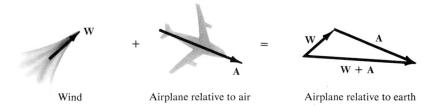

| Wind | Airplane relative to air | Airplane relative to earth |

If $\mathbf{F}_1$ and $\mathbf{F}_2$ describe the forces in two ropes lifting a heavy rock, then a single rope with the force $\mathbf{F}_1 + \mathbf{F}_2$ pulling from the same point has the same effect on the rock.

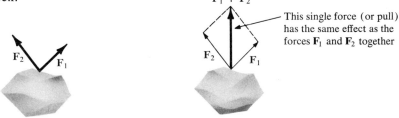

This single force (or pull) has the same effect as the forces $\mathbf{F}_1$ and $\mathbf{F}_2$ together

The difference $x - y$ of the numbers x and y is defined as the number N such that $y + N = x$; that is, $y + (x - y) = x$. This suggests how we will define the difference of two vectors. We define $\mathbf{A}_1 - \mathbf{A}_2$ as the vector $\mathbf{V}$ such that $\mathbf{A}_2 + \mathbf{V} = \mathbf{A}_1$; that is, $\mathbf{A}_2 + (\mathbf{A}_1 - \mathbf{A}_2) = \mathbf{A}_1$:

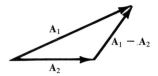

(Observe that $\mathbf{A}_1 - \mathbf{A}_1 = \mathbf{0}$.) We may subtract the vector $\mathbf{A}_2$ from $\mathbf{A}_1$ by constructing a parallelogram in which $\mathbf{A}_2$ lies on a side and $\mathbf{A}_1$ lies on a diagonal. Then $\mathbf{A}_1 - \mathbf{A}_2$ lies on the other side.

The *negative* of the vector $\mathbf{A}_1$ is defined as the vector having the same magnitude as $\mathbf{A}_1$ but the opposite direction:

Observe that $\mathbf{A}_1 + (-\mathbf{A}_1) = \mathbf{0}$, just as with numbers. More generally, subtracting a vector gives the same result as adding its negative; that is, $\mathbf{A}_1 - \mathbf{A}_2 = \mathbf{A}_1 + (-\mathbf{A}_2)$.

Incidentally, when mentioning numbers in a discussion of vectors, it is customary to call numbers *scalars*. Thus 3 and -4 are scalars, but $\overrightarrow{(3,-4)}$ is a vector.

We now let scalars operate on vectors by magnifying or shrinking them. Thus $3\mathbf{A}$ shall mean $\mathbf{A} + \mathbf{A} + \mathbf{A}$, a vector three times as long as $\mathbf{A}$ having the same direction as $\mathbf{A}$. Also $(-3)\mathbf{A}$ shall be $-(3\mathbf{A})$, a vector three times as long as $\mathbf{A}$ but in the opposite direction:

More generally, the product of a scalar c and a vector $\mathbf{A}$, denoted $c\mathbf{A}$ or $\mathbf{A}c$, is the vector defined as follows:

  $c\mathbf{A}$ has magnitude $|c|\,|\mathbf{A}|$;
  $c\mathbf{A}$ has direction the same as $\mathbf{A}$ if c is positive, and opposite if c is negative.
  If $c = 0$, then 0 times $\mathbf{A}$ is $\mathbf{0}$.

The next theorem tells how to compute the sum and difference of vectors if we know their components, and how to compute $c\mathbf{A}$ if we know the components of $\mathbf{A}$.

THEOREM 2.
$$(\overrightarrow{x_1,y_1}) + (\overrightarrow{x_2,y_2}) = (\overrightarrow{x_1 + x_2, y_1 + y_2})$$
$$(\overrightarrow{x_1,y_1}) - (\overrightarrow{x_2,y_2}) = (\overrightarrow{x_1 - x_2, y_1 - y_2})$$
$$c(\overrightarrow{x,y}) = (\overrightarrow{cx,cy}).$$

PROOF. We sketch an appropriate diagram for the first assertion, in the case in which x_1, y_1, x_2, and y_2 are all positive:

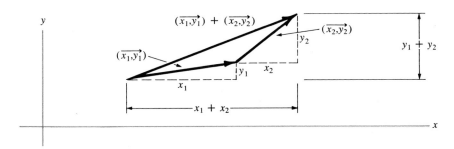

A glance at the diagram shows that $(\overrightarrow{x_1,y_1}) + (\overrightarrow{x_2,y_2})$ has components $x_1 + x_2$ and $y_1 + y_2$. Hence

$$(\overrightarrow{x_1,y_1}) + (\overrightarrow{x_2,y_2}) = (\overrightarrow{x_1 + x_2, y_1 + y_2})$$

The second assertion can be demonstrated similarly.

To establish the third assertion, observe first that $|c(\overrightarrow{x,y})| = |c||(\overrightarrow{x,y})| = |c|\sqrt{x^2 + y^2}$, while $|(\overrightarrow{cx,cy})| = \sqrt{(cx)^2 + (cy)^2} = \sqrt{c^2(x^2 + y^2)} = \sqrt{|c|^2(x^2 + y^2)} = |c|\sqrt{x^2 + y^2}$. Hence $c(\overrightarrow{x,y})$ and $(\overrightarrow{cx,cy})$ have the same magnitude. Furthermore, their directions are the same, for if c is positive, both have the direction of $(\overrightarrow{x,y})$, and if c is negative, both have direction opposite that of $(\overrightarrow{x,y})$; if $c = 0$, the third assertion reduces to the valid equation $\mathbf{0} = \mathbf{0}$.

Example 1. $(\overrightarrow{3,5}) + (\overrightarrow{4,-7}) = (\overrightarrow{7,-2})$; $(\overrightarrow{3,5}) - (\overrightarrow{4,-7}) = (\overrightarrow{-1,12})$; $2(\overrightarrow{3,5}) = (\overrightarrow{6,10})$; $-2.5(\overrightarrow{1,0}) = (\overrightarrow{-2.5,0})$.

We shall also need to be able to divide a vector $\mathbf{A}$ by a scalar $c \neq 0$. We *define* $\mathbf{A}/c$ to be $(1/c)\mathbf{A}$. For instance, $(\overrightarrow{4,6})/2 = (\tfrac{1}{2})(\overrightarrow{4,6}) = ((\tfrac{1}{2})4, (\tfrac{1}{2})6) = (\overrightarrow{2,3})$. Thus $\mathbf{A}/2$ is one-half as long as $\mathbf{A}$ and has the same direction. On the other hand, $\mathbf{A}/(\tfrac{1}{2}) = [1/(\tfrac{1}{2})]\mathbf{A} = 2\mathbf{A}$, a vector twice as long as $\mathbf{A}$ in the same direction.

Example 2. If $\mathbf{A}$ is a vector (other than $\mathbf{0}$), what is the magnitude of

$$\frac{\mathbf{A}}{|\mathbf{A}|}$$

To answer this question let us write $\mathbf{A}$ as $(\overrightarrow{x,y})$ and use Theorem 2. We have

$$\frac{\mathbf{A}}{|\mathbf{A}|} = \frac{(\overrightarrow{x,y})}{\sqrt{x^2 + y^2}} = \left(\overrightarrow{\frac{x}{\sqrt{x^2 + y^2}}, \frac{y}{\sqrt{x^2 + y^2}}}\right)$$

Thus the magnitude of $A/|A|$ is

$$\sqrt{\left(\frac{x}{\sqrt{x^2+y^2}}\right)^2+\left(\frac{y}{\sqrt{x^2+y^2}}\right)^2}=\sqrt{\frac{x^2}{x^2+y^2}+\frac{y^2}{x^2+y^2}}=1$$

Hence $A/|A|$ is a unit vector.

The concepts and results in this section easily extend to vectors in space. In this case a space vector has three components, $A = \overrightarrow{(x,y,z)}$, and Theorems 1 and 2 generalize to such vectors.

EXERCISES

1. Are the components of a vector scalars or vectors?
2. (a) Draw three vectors that have x component 6 and y component -8.
   (b) How long are they? What is their direction?
3. Find the components of A if (a) $|A| = 10$, and A points to the northwest; (b) $|A| = 6$, and A points to the south; (c) $|A| = 9$, and A points to the southeast; (d) $|A| = 5$ and A points to the east. (North is indicated by the positive y axis.)
   [Answer: (b) $\overrightarrow{(0,-6)}$]
4. Write A in the form $\overrightarrow{(x,y)}$ if (a) its tail is at $(1,3)$ and its head at $(3,6)$; (b) its tail is at $(2,7)$ and its head at $(2,4)$; (c) its tail is at $(2,4)$ and its head at $(2,7)$; (d) its tail is at $(5,3)$ and its head at $(-1, -6)$. [Answer: (b) $\overrightarrow{(0,-3)}$]
5. Consider a vector A situated in three-dimensional space.
   (a) Draw a suitable rectangular box of which A is the main diagonal.
   (b) With the aid of the box, show the three components of A.
   (c) What are the components of the vector whose tail is at $(1,3,5)$ and whose head is at $(2,6,7)$?
6. (See Exercise 5.) Draw two examples of the vectors (a) $\overrightarrow{(2,1,0)}$; (b) $\overrightarrow{(0,1,0)}$; (c) $\overrightarrow{(1,2,3)}$; (d) $\overrightarrow{(-1,-2,-3)}$.
7. (See Exercises 5 and 6.) Prove that $|\overrightarrow{(x,y,z)}| = \sqrt{x^2 + y^2 + z^2}$.
8. With a diagram show that $A_1 + (A_2 + A_3) = (A_1 + A_2) + A_3$.
9. Each of three men has tied a rope to a 1-ounce flat gold nugget. They pull with forces F_1, F_2, and F_3, and nothing happens. Using your physical intuition and the vector $F_1 + F_2$ show (a) that $F_1 + F_2 + F_3 = 0$; (b) that the lines on which the three ropes lie pass through the same point.
10. Show with a diagram that $A_1 + (-A_2) = A_1 - A_2$.
11. The production vector P of a firm making x cars and y trucks per year is defined as $\overrightarrow{(x,y)}$. A second firm makes u cars and v trucks per year.
    (a) What is the economic interpretation of $\overrightarrow{(x,y)} + \overrightarrow{(u,v)}$?
    (b) What is the economic interpretation of $3\overrightarrow{(x,y)}$?
12. (See Exercise 11.) A firm that produces five different products has a five-dimensional production vector $P = \overrightarrow{(x_1,x_2,x_3,x_4,x_5)}$.
    (a) If two firms, each producing the same items, have the production vectors $P_1 = \overrightarrow{(30,20,40,70,10)}$ and $P_2 = \overrightarrow{(20,1,10,5,8)}$, what is the production vector of the company formed by their merger?
    (b) If floods cut by 90 percent the production of a company that has the production vector $\overrightarrow{(30,20,40,70,10)}$, what is its new production vector?

13. (a) Which vector has the greater magnitude: $2(\overrightarrow{1,1}) + 2(\overrightarrow{3,5})$ or $(\overrightarrow{4,1}) + 3(\overrightarrow{2,3})$?
    (b) Which has the larger x component?
    (c) Which has the larger y component?
14. Draw a vector **A**. Then draw (a) 3 **A**; (b) (-3)**A**; (c) **A**/3; (d) **A**/0.1.
15. Show pictorially that $(\overrightarrow{2,3}) + (\overrightarrow{-1,2}) = (\overrightarrow{1,5})$.
16. In the expression $|c||\mathbf{A}|$ which of the following are scalars: c, $|c|$, **A**, $|\mathbf{A}|$?
17. Show that the second assertion in Theorem 2 follows from the first.
18. Which three of the following six expressions are meaningful? $3 + (\overrightarrow{4,5})$; $3/(\overrightarrow{4,5})$; $(\overrightarrow{4,5})/3$; $3(\overrightarrow{4,5})$; $(\overrightarrow{4,0}) - (\overrightarrow{3,5})$; $(\overrightarrow{2,1}) - 1$.
19. Frequently the vector $(\overrightarrow{1,0})$ is denoted **i** and the vector $(\overrightarrow{0,1})$ is denoted **j**.
    (a) Show that every vector **A** is expressible in the form $\mathbf{A} = x\mathbf{i} + y\mathbf{j}$, where x and y are appropriate scalars.
    (b) What are the components of $x\mathbf{i} + y\mathbf{j}$? (In the study of mechanics, **A** is sometimes written $\mathbf{i}A_x + \mathbf{j}A_y$.)
20. Generalize Exercise 19 to a vector **A** in three dimensions.

□ □ □

21. In a more abstract approach than the one we have followed, a plane vector is *defined* as an ordered pair of real numbers (x,y). If we had taken this purely algebraic approach, how would we define (a) the vector **0**; (b) the product of a scalar and a vector; (c) the sum of two vectors; (d) the magnitude of a vector?
22. Carry out the analog of Exercise 21 for vectors in three dimensions.
23. (See Exercises 21 and 22.)
    (a) If we regard the sequence $(x_1, x_2, x_3, \ldots, x_n, \ldots)$ as an "infinite-dimensional vector," how would we define its magnitude?
    (b) What is the magnitude of the vector $(\overrightarrow{\frac{1}{2}, \frac{1}{4}, \frac{1}{8}, \frac{1}{16}, \ldots, \frac{1}{2^n}, \ldots})$?
    (c) Show that the vector $(\overrightarrow{1, \frac{1}{2}, \frac{1}{3}, \ldots, 1/n, \ldots})$ has finite magnitude.

2. The dot product of two vectors.

When water is pumped out of a tank, the work done is the product of two scalars: the weight of the water and the vertical distance the water is raised (page 198). However, when a boulder is pulled along the ground with a rope inclined at an angle to the ground, as in this diagram, a little more is involved.

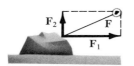

We may replace **F** with $\mathbf{F}_1$ and $\mathbf{F}_2$, which together have the same effect on the boulder as **F**

We may replace **F** with a vertical force $\mathbf{F}_2$ and a horizontal force $\mathbf{F}_1$. Then the force $\mathbf{F}_2$ is not accomplishing any work, since the boulder remains on the ground. The work that **F** accomplishes is only the work that $\mathbf{F}_1$ accomplishes in overcoming friction, and hence equals the product $|\mathbf{F}_1|$ times (distance the boulder moves).

More generally, if a force (vector) **F** moves an object along a straight line from the tail to the head of a vector **R** as in this diagram,

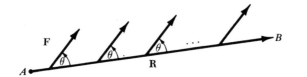

A constant force **F** moves an object from *A* to *B*, perhaps against gravity, air resistance, friction, etc.

the work done is

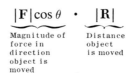

$$|\mathbf{F}|\cos\theta \quad \cdot \quad |\mathbf{R}|$$

Magnitude of   Distance
force in   object
direction   is moved
object is
moved

where θ is the angle between **R** and **F**. This important physical concept justifies our introduction of the *dot product* of two vectors.

DEFINITION: *Dot product.* The dot product of the nonzero vectors $\mathbf{A}_1$ and $\mathbf{A}_2$ is

$$|\mathbf{A}_1||\mathbf{A}_2|\cos\theta$$

where θ is the angle between $\mathbf{A}_1$ and $\mathbf{A}_2$. If $\mathbf{A}_1$ or $\mathbf{A}_2$ is 0, their dot product is 0.

We denote the dot product by $\mathbf{A}_1 \cdot \mathbf{A}_2$; since it is a scalar, it is also called the *scalar product*.

Example 1. If $\mathbf{A}_1 = \overrightarrow{(0,6)}$ is a force and $\mathbf{A}_2 = \overrightarrow{(4,4)}$ is the change in position of an object moved by that force, then the work done is $\mathbf{A}_1 \cdot \mathbf{A}_2 = |\mathbf{A}_1||\mathbf{A}_2|\cos\theta = \sqrt{0^2 + 6^2}\sqrt{4^2 + 4^2}\cos(\pi/4) = 6\sqrt{32}\sqrt{2}/2 = 24$. If the force has a magnitude of 6 pounds and the object is moved a distance $\sqrt{32}$ feet, then the work done is 24 foot-pounds.

Observe that $\mathbf{A} \cdot \mathbf{A} = |\mathbf{A}|^2$ and that if $\mathbf{A}_1$ is perpendicular to $\mathbf{A}_2$, then $\mathbf{A}_1 \cdot \mathbf{A}_2 = 0$. Moreover, if neither $\mathbf{A}_1$ nor $\mathbf{A}_2$ is 0, and if $\mathbf{A}_1 \cdot \mathbf{A}_2 = 0$, then $\cos\theta = 0$ and $\mathbf{A}_1$ is perpendicular to $\mathbf{A}_2$. *Thus the vanishing of the dot product is a test for perpendicularity.*

Example 2. Let $\mathbf{A}_1$ represent the direction and rate of flow of water in a stream as it passes over the edge of a dam. Let $\mathbf{A}_2$ represent a vector perpendicular to the edge of the dam, as shown in this diagram:

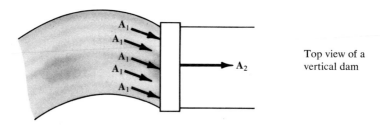

Top view of a
vertical dam

Then the rate at which water escapes over the dam is proportional to $\mathbf{A}_1 \cdot \mathbf{A}_2$, since the component of the motion of the stream parallel to the edge of the dam plays no role in its escape over the edge of the dam.

Just as Theorem 2 showed how to carry out certain vector operations in terms of components, the next theorem tells us how to compute the dot product $\mathbf{A}_1 \cdot \mathbf{A}_2$ if we know the components of $\mathbf{A}_1$ and $\mathbf{A}_2$.

THEOREM 3. $(\overrightarrow{x_1,y_1}) \cdot (\overrightarrow{x_2,y_2}) = x_1x_2 + y_1y_2$ (*a scalar*).

PROOF.   If either one of $(\overrightarrow{x_1,y_1})$ or $(\overrightarrow{x_2,y_2})$ is $\mathbf{0}$, then a simple computation verifies Theorem 3. In the remainder of the proof we assume that neither is $\mathbf{0}$. For convenience we place the tails of $(\overrightarrow{x_1,y_1})$ and $(\overrightarrow{x_2,y_2})$ at the origin, as in this diagram:

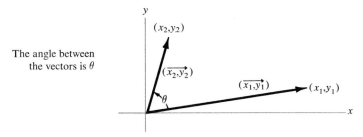

Now, by the definition of the dot product, we have

(1) $$(\overrightarrow{x_1,y_1}) \cdot (\overrightarrow{x_2,y_2}) = \sqrt{x_1^2 + y_1^2}\,\sqrt{x_2^2 + y_2^2}\,\cos \theta$$

To express $\cos \theta$ in terms of x_1, y_1, x_2, and y_2, we apply the law of cosines to the triangle whose vertices are $(0,0)$, (x_1,y_2) and (x_2,y_2).

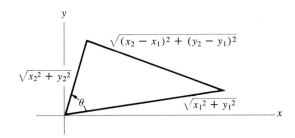

The law of cosines asserts in this case that

$$(\sqrt{(x_2 - x_1)^2 + (y_2 - y_1)^2})^2 = (\sqrt{x_2^2 + y_2^2})^2 + (\sqrt{x_1^2 + y_1^2})^2 - 2\sqrt{x_2^2 + y_2^2}\,\sqrt{x_1^2 + y_1^2}\,\cos \theta$$

Squaring and canceling, we obtain

$$-2x_1x_2 - 2y_1y_2 = -2\sqrt{x_2^2 + y_2^2}\,\sqrt{x_1^2 + y_1^2}\,\cos \theta$$

Hence $$\cos \theta = \frac{x_1x_2 + y_1y_2}{\sqrt{x_1^2 + y_1^2}\,\sqrt{x_2^2 + y_2^2}}$$

Thus, by (1),

$$(\overrightarrow{x_1,y_1})\,(\overrightarrow{x_2,y_2}) = \sqrt{x_1^2 + y_1^2}\,\sqrt{x_2^2 + y_2^2}\,\frac{x_1x_2 + y_1y_2}{\sqrt{x_1^2 + y_1^2}\,\sqrt{x_2^2 + y_2^2}} = x_1x_2 + y_1y_2$$

and the theorem is proved.

Example 3.   We have $\overrightarrow{(8,-2)}\,\overrightarrow{(1,4)} = (8)(1) + (-2)(4) = 0$; hence $\overrightarrow{(8,-2)}$ is perpendicular to $\overrightarrow{(1,4)}$. Also, $\overrightarrow{(3,4)} \cdot \overrightarrow{(3,4)} = (3)(3) + (4)(4) = 25$, in agreement with our observation that $\mathbf{A} \cdot \mathbf{A} = |\mathbf{A}|^2$.

Frequently, as in the following example, the dot product is used algebraically, without regard for its geometric significance.

Example 4.   A person buys 20 pounds of potatoes at 5 cents a pound and 10 pounds of oranges at 12 cents a pound. The vector $\overrightarrow{(20,10)}$ records how much he bought of each item, while the vector $\overrightarrow{(5,12)}$ records the corresponding prices. The dot product

$$\overrightarrow{(20,10)} \cdot \overrightarrow{(5,12)} = (20)(5) + (10)(12) = 220 \text{ cents}$$

records the total cost of the purchase.

The proof of the following important theorem in analytic geometry illustrates the use of the dot product.

THEOREM 4.   *The equation of the line passing through (x_0,y_0) and perpendicular to the vector $\overrightarrow{(A,B)}$ is*

$$A(x - x_0) + B(y - y_0) = 0$$

PROOF.   Let (x,y) be a point on the line perpendicular to $\overrightarrow{(A,B)}$. Then the vector $\overrightarrow{(x - x_0, y - y_0)}$ is perpendicular to $\overrightarrow{(A,B)}$. Hence $A(x - x_0) + B(y - y_0) = 0$.

Conversely, we must show that if $A(x - x_0) + B(y - y_0) = 0$, then (x,y) is on the line through (x_0,y_0) perpendicular to $\overrightarrow{(A,B)}$. We may think of $A(x - x_0) + B(y - y_0)$ as the scalar product of $\overrightarrow{(A,B)}$ and $\overrightarrow{(x - x_0, y - y_0)}$. If this scalar product is zero, the two vectors are perpendicular, and (x,y) lies on the line through (x_0,y_0) perpendicular to $\overrightarrow{(A,B)}$.

An almost identical proof yields the following extension of Theorem 4 to three-dimensional space.

THEOREM 5.   *The equation of the plane passing through (x_0,y_0,z_0) and perpendicular to the vector $\overrightarrow{(A,B,C)}$ is*

$$A(x - x_0) + B(y - y_0) + C(z - z_0) = 0$$

Example 5.   The equation of the line through $(2,-7)$ and perpendicular to the vector $\overrightarrow{(4,1)}$ is $4(x - 2) + 1(y + 7) = 0$, which simplifies to $4x + y - 1 = 0$. The equation of the plane through $(1,5,-6)$ and perpendicular to the vector $\overrightarrow{(5,2,3)}$ is $5(x - 1) + 2(y - 5) + 3[z - (-6)] = 0$, which simplifies to $5x + 2y + 3z + 3 = 0$.

EXERCISES

1. (a) How much work is accomplished by a woman carrying a 10-pound jug of water 15 miles along the seashore, then straight up a 100-foot cliff?
   (b) Describe your computations in the terminology of vectors.

[Answer: (a) 1000 foot-pounds]

2. If $\mathbf{A}_1$ is perpendicular to $\mathbf{A}_2$, then $\mathbf{A}_1 \cdot \mathbf{A}_2 = 0$. Explain why.

3. Explain why $\mathbf{A}_1 \cdot \mathbf{A}_2 = 0$ implies that $\mathbf{A}_1$ is perpendicular to $\mathbf{A}_2$. (Assume $|\mathbf{A}_1| \neq 0 \neq |\mathbf{A}_2|$.)

4. With the aid of Theorem 3, prove that $\mathbf{A} \cdot (\mathbf{B} + \mathbf{C}) = (\mathbf{A} \cdot \mathbf{B}) + (\mathbf{A} \cdot \mathbf{C})$.

5. With the aid of Theorem 3, prove that $(x\mathbf{A}) \cdot (y\mathbf{B}) = xy\,(\mathbf{A} \cdot \mathbf{B})$.

6. (a) Draw the vectors $\overrightarrow{(7,12)}$ and $\overrightarrow{(9,-5)}$.
   (b) Do they seem to be perpendicular?
   (c) Determine whether they are perpendicular by examining their dot product.

7. (a) Estimate the angle between $\overrightarrow{(3,4)}$ and $\overrightarrow{(5,12)}$ by drawing them.
   (b) Find the cosine of the angle between them by using the equation

$$|\mathbf{A}_1|\,|\mathbf{A}_2|\cos\theta = \mathbf{A}_1 \cdot \mathbf{A}_2$$

   (c) With (b) and a trigonometric table, find θ.

   [Answer: (c) $\cos^{-1}(^{63}\!/_{65}) = 14°15'$]

8. (a) Draw the line through $(5,3)$ that is perpendicular to the vector $\overrightarrow{(-1,2)}$.
   (b) Does the point $(1,1)$ lie on this line?
   (c) Check your answer to (b) by using a dot product.

9. (a) Define the dot product of two three-dimensional vectors.
   (b) Prove that $\overrightarrow{(x_1,y_1,z_1)} \cdot \overrightarrow{(x_2,y_2,z_2)} = x_1x_2 + y_1y_2 + z_1z_2$.

10. (a) With the aid of vectors and the dot product, find the cosine of the angle between the diagonal and an edge of a cube.
    (b) What is the angle?

    [Answer: (a) $1/\sqrt{3}$; (b) $54°44'$]

11. Prove that $\overrightarrow{(a,b)}$ is perpendicular to $\overrightarrow{(-b,a)}$. Illustrate with a sketch.

12. Prove that $\mathbf{A} \cdot \mathbf{A} = |\mathbf{A}|^2$, using (a) only the definition of dot product; (b) Theorem 3.

13. Prove that the vector $\overrightarrow{(A,B)}$ is perpendicular to the line $Ax + By + C = 0$. (Hint: Show that the equation of the line is $A(x - x_0) + B(y - y_0) = 0$, where (x_0,y_0) is any fixed point on the line.)

14. Using Theorem 3, prove that if a_1, a_2, b_1, and b_2 are numbers, then $(a_1b_1 + a_2b_2)^2 \leqslant (a_1^2 + a_2^2)(b_1^2 + b_2^2)$. Compare with Exercise 14, page 226.

15. Prove Theorem 5.

16. (a) How long is the vector $\overrightarrow{(3,4)}/|\overrightarrow{(3,4)}|$?
    (b) If $\mathbf{A} \neq 0$, how long is $\mathbf{A}/|\mathbf{A}|$?

17. (a) Let $\mathbf{N}$ have length 1 and be perpendicular to a line passing through (x_0,y_0). Show that the distance from the line to the origin is $|\mathbf{N} \cdot \overrightarrow{(x_0,y_0)}|$.
    (b) Show that $(A/\sqrt{A^2 + B^2}, B/\sqrt{A^2 + B^2})$ is a vector of length 1 perpendicular to the line $Ax + By + C = 0$.
    (c) From (a) and (b) deduce that the distance from $Ax + By + C = 0$ to the origin is $|C/\sqrt{A^2 + B^2}|$.

18. Which of these six expressions are meaningless? $3\overrightarrow{(4,5)}$; $3[\overrightarrow{(4,5)} \cdot \overrightarrow{(5,7)}]$; $\overrightarrow{(3,4)} + \overrightarrow{(5,7)} \cdot \overrightarrow{(6,8)}$; $(4 + 5)\overrightarrow{(6,7)}$; $\overrightarrow{(3,2)}/[\overrightarrow{(3,4)} \cdot \overrightarrow{(4,7)}]$; $3[\overrightarrow{(4,5)}\,\overrightarrow{(6,7)}]$.

19. Draw two vectors, $\mathbf{A}_1$ and $\mathbf{A}_2$, such that (a) $\mathbf{A}_1 \cdot \mathbf{A}_2 > 0$; (b) $\mathbf{A}_1 \cdot \mathbf{A}_2 = 0$; (c) $\mathbf{A}_1 \cdot \mathbf{A}_2 < 0$.

20. Prove that $\overrightarrow{(\cos\theta, \sin\theta)}$ is a unit vector.

□ □ □

21. A firm sells x chairs at C dollars per chair and y desks at D dollars per desk. It costs the firm c dollars to make a chair and d dollars to make a desk. What is the economic interpretation of (a) Cx; (b) $\overrightarrow{(x,y)} \cdot \overrightarrow{(C,D)}$; (c) $\overrightarrow{(x,y)} \cdot \overrightarrow{(c,d)}$; (d) $\overrightarrow{(x,y)} \cdot \overrightarrow{(C,D)} > \overrightarrow{(x,y)} \cdot \overrightarrow{(c,d)}$?

22. The production vector $\overrightarrow{(x,y)}$ in Exercise 21 records the output of a firm that makes two products. The output of a firm that manufactures x_1 washing machines, x_2 refrigerators, x_3 dishwashers, x_4 stoves, and x_5 clothes dryers is recorded by the five-dimensional production vector $\mathbf{P} = \overrightarrow{(x_1,x_2,x_3,x_4,x_5)}$. Similarly the cost vector $\mathbf{C} = \overrightarrow{(y_1,y_2,y_3,y_4,y_5)}$ records the cost of producing each item; for instance, each refrigerator costs the firm y_2 dollars.
    (a) What is the economic significance of $\mathbf{P} \cdot \mathbf{C} = \overrightarrow{(20,0,7,9,15)} \cdot \overrightarrow{(50,70,30,20,10)}$?
    (b) If the firm doubles its production of all items in (a), what is its new production vector?

23. Using the analog of Theorem 3 in space, prove that if a_1, a_2, a_3, b_1, b_2, and b_3 are numbers, then $(a_1b_1 + a_2b_2 + a_3b_3)^2 \leqslant (a_1{}^2 + a_2{}^2 + a_3{}^2)(b_1{}^2 + b_2{}^2 + b_3{}^2)$. Compare with Exercise 14, page 226.

24. Using vectors and dot products, show that the diagonals of a parallelogram are perpendicular if and only if the parallelogram is a rhombus. (Hint: If $\mathbf{V}_1$ and $\mathbf{V}_2$ are adjacent sides of the parallelogram, then $\mathbf{V}_1 - \mathbf{V}_2$ and $\mathbf{V}_1 + \mathbf{V}_2$ are its diagonals.)

25. Is the line through $(1,4,7)$ and $(2,6,5)$ perpendicular to the plane $2x + 3y + 4z = 17$? Explain with the aid of the dot product.

26. Let A, B, and C be the vertices of a triangle, and $\mathbf{A}$, $\mathbf{B}$, and $\mathbf{C}$ vectors from the origin to A, B, and C, respectively.
    (a) Show that the vector $\mathbf{W}$ from A to the midpoint of BC is $(\mathbf{B} + \mathbf{C})/2 - \mathbf{A}$ and the vector $\mathbf{V}$ from B to the midpoint of AC is $(\mathbf{A} + \mathbf{C})/2 - \mathbf{B}$.
    (b) Prove with the aid of (a) that the medians of a triangle intersect at a point that is two-thirds of the way from each vertex to the midpoint of the opposite side.

27. Let p_1 be the profit from selling a washing machine, and p_2, p_3, p_4, and p_5 be defined analogously for the firm of Exercise 22. (Some of the p's may be negative.) What does it mean to the firm to have $\overrightarrow{(p_1,p_2,p_3,p_4,p_5)}$ "perpendicular" to $\overrightarrow{(x_1,x_2,x_3,x_4,x_5)}$?

3. Directional derivatives and the gradient.

If $z = f(x,y)$, then z_x and z_y record the rate of change of z in directions parallel to the x and y axes. But we are free to examine the rate of change of z in any direction. Specifically, let (a,b) be a point in the xy plane and consider a line in the plane through (a,b). On this line introduce a coordinate system with the same scale as the x or y axis: Call the line the t axis and place $t = 0$ at (a,b).

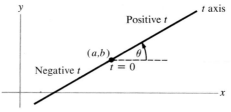

Let θ be the angle from the positive x axis to the positive t axis. Then, if we consider $z = f(x,y)$ only at points (x,y) on the t axis, z is a (composite) function of t;

that is, $z = F(t)$. If we graph z perpendicular to the xy plane and look at the xy plane in perspective, this is how the graph of $z = F(t)$ may appear:

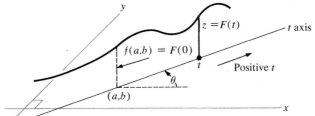

When $t = 0$ we have $(x,y) = (a,b)$. More generally, the point *on the t axis* having coordinate t is

$$(x,y) = (a + t\cos\theta, b + t\sin\theta)$$

DEFINITION: *Directional derivative.*   By the derivative of z at (a,b) in the direction θ we shall mean $F'(t)$ at $t = 0$, where F is defined by $F(t) = f(a + t\cos\theta, b + t\sin\theta)$. A directional derivative at (a,b) is a number that depends on θ, as well as on a and b.

Observe that if $\theta = 0$, the directional derivative is z_x; if $\theta = \pi/2$, the directional derivative is z_y. In the diagram above, the derivative in the direction θ is positive. However, if we point the positive t axis in the opposite direction so that the angle between the positive t axis and the positive x axis is $\theta + \pi$, then the directional derivative will be negative, for in that case, as t increases, z decreases. All these observations are special cases of the next theorem.

THEOREM 6.   *If $z = f(x,y)$ has continuous partial derivatives f_x and f_y, then the directional derivative of z at (a,b) in the direction θ is*

$$f_x(a,b)\cos\theta + f_y(a,b)\sin\theta$$

PROOF. $z = f(x,y)$ where $x = a + t\cos\theta$ and $y = b + t\sin\theta$. The chain rule in the form of Theorem 2, page 366, asserts that

$$\frac{dz}{dt} = f_x\frac{dx}{dt} + f_y\frac{dy}{dt}$$

But $dx/dt = \cos\theta$ and $dy/dt = \sin\theta$. This ends the proof.

Example 1.   We find the derivative of x^2y^3 at $(1,2)$ in the direction $\theta = \pi/3$. First, $f_x = 2xy^3$ and $f_y = 3x^2y^2$. Hence $f_x(1,2) = 16$ and $f_y(1,2) = 12$. Also, $\cos\theta = \frac{1}{2}$ and $\sin\theta = \sqrt{3}/2$. Thus the derivative we seek equals $(16)(\frac{1}{2}) + (12)(\sqrt{3}/2)$, which is $8 + 6\sqrt{3}$.

How should we denote a directional derivative? The symbols $D_\theta z$ or $dz/d\theta$ would be misleading, because both suggest that θ is a variable—even though it is fixed throughout the discussion. Instead of θ, let us use a vector $\mathbf{u}$ whose direction is that of the positive t axis and whose length is 1. In short, let us use the unit vector

$$\mathbf{u} = \overrightarrow{(\cos\theta, \sin\theta)}$$

Then we can denote the directional derivative in the direction described by the angle θ as

$$\overrightarrow{D_{\mathbf{u}}z}$$

where $\mathbf{u} = \overrightarrow{(\cos\theta, \sin\theta)}$.

The formula for $D_{\mathbf{u}}z$ as given by Theorem 6 resembles the formula for the dot product. In order to exploit this similarity, let us introduce the vector whose components are $f_x(a,b)$ and $f_y(a,b)$.

DEFINITION: *Gradient.* The vector $(f_x(a,b), f_y(a,\overrightarrow{b}))$ is the *gradient* of f at (a,b) and is denoted ∇f.

In vector notation, Theorem 6 runs as follows:

THEOREM 6 (rephrased). *If $z = f(x,y)$ has continuous partial derivatives f_x and f_y, then*

$$D_{\mathbf{u}}z = \nabla f \cdot \mathbf{u}$$

Example 2. If $\mathbf{u} = \overrightarrow{(1,0)}$, or equivalently, $\theta = 0$, then $D_{\mathbf{u}}z = \overrightarrow{(f_x,f_y)} \cdot \overrightarrow{(1,0)} = (f_x)(1) + (f_y)(0) = f_x$, which we would expect. If $\mathbf{u} = \overrightarrow{(0,1)}$, then $D_{\mathbf{u}}z = \overrightarrow{(f_x,f_y)} \cdot \overrightarrow{(0,1)} = (f_x)(0) + (f_y)(1) = f_y$, which is again reassuring. If $\mathbf{u} = \overrightarrow{(1,1)}$, then $D_{\mathbf{u}}z = \overrightarrow{(f_x,f_y)} \overrightarrow{(1,1)} = f_x + f_y$.

It might seem that the gradient, ∇f, exists only to simplify the statement of Theorem 6. Actually it is far more useful, as the next theorem shows.

THEOREM 7. *The direction of the gradient at (a,b) is the direction that yields the largest directional derivative at (a,b). The magnitude of the gradient is the largest directional derivative at (a,b).*

PROOF. $D_{\mathbf{u}}z = (\nabla f) \cdot \mathbf{u} = |\nabla f| |\mathbf{u}| \cos\phi$, where ϕ *is the angle between* $\mathbf{u}$ *and* ∇f. Now, $|\mathbf{u}| = 1$. Hence

$$D_{\mathbf{u}}z = |\nabla f| \cos\phi$$

Since $\cos\phi$ attains its maximum, 1, only at $\phi = 0$ (or $2n\pi$), we conclude that to maximize the directional derivative at (a,b) we must choose the direction of $\mathbf{u}$ to be that of ∇f. In that direction, $D_{\mathbf{u}}z = |\nabla f|(1) = |\nabla f|$. This proves the theorem.

Example 3. Let $z = x^2y^3$. What is the largest directional derivative of z at $(2,3)$? In what direction must we go to achieve this maximum directional derivative? In this case, at the point (x,y), we have $\nabla f = \overrightarrow{(2xy^3, 3x^2y^2)}$. At $(2,3)$ we have $\nabla f = \overrightarrow{(108,108)}$, which we sketch below (not to scale). Note that, because its components are equal, it is inclined at an angle of $\pi/4$ radians, its tail is at $(2,3)$, and its head is at $(110,111)$.

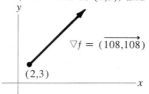

$\nabla f = \overrightarrow{(108,108)}$

$(2,3)$

The maximal directional derivative of $z = x^2y^2$ at $(2,3)$ is $|\nabla f| = 108\sqrt{2}$. This is achieved at the angle $\theta = \pi/4$, relative to the x axis, that is, for $\mathbf{u} = \overrightarrow{(\sqrt{2}/2, \sqrt{2}/2)}$.

The geometric significance of ∇f is best shown by its relation to the level curves of f. A *level curve* of $z = f(x,y)$ consists of all points (x,y) such that $f(x,y) = c$, a fixed value. For instance, the level curves of $3x + 4y$ are the straight lines $3x + 4y = c$; the level curves of $x^2 + y^2$ are the circles $x^2 + y^2 = c$.

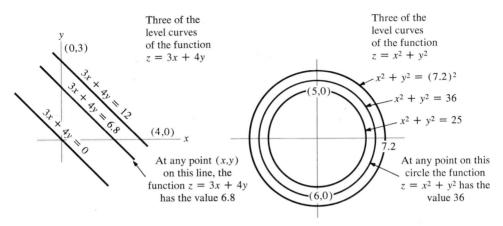

Three of the level curves of the function $z = 3x + 4y$

$3x + 4y = 12$
$3x + 4y = 6.8$
$3x + 4y = 0$

At any point (x,y) on this line, the function $z = 3x + 4y$ has the value 6.8

Three of the level curves of the function $z = x^2 + y^2$

$x^2 + y^2 = (7.2)^2$
$x^2 + y^2 = 36$
$x^2 + y^2 = 25$

At any point on this circle the function $z = x^2 + y^2$ has the value 36

If $f(x,y)$ expresses the air pressure above the point (x,y) on a surface, then the level curves are called *isobars*. A few are shown in the weather map published daily. If $f(x,y)$ is the elevation of the land above the point (x,y), then the level curves are called *contours*. These are shown on U.S. Geological Survey maps. For instance, these contours at 100-foot intervals describe a 530-foot high hill whose gentlest ascent is from the east:

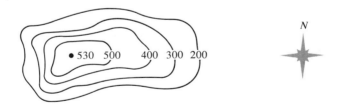

If a hiker walks along a path corresponding to a level curve, he neither ascends nor descends the hill. If he wants the steepest ascent from the point he occupies, he should walk in a direction which on his map is perpendicular to the contour on which he finds himself. This is implied by Theorem 7, together with the next theorem.

THEOREM 8.   *The gradient ∇f at (a,b) is perpendicular to the level curve of f passing through (a,b).*

PROOF.   Let us introduce arc length s as a parameter on the level curve through (a,b). We wish to show that ∇f is perpendicular to a tangent vector to this curve at (a,b).

As a tangent vector we may use $(\overrightarrow{dx/ds, dy/ds})$, since the ratio of its y component to its x component

$$\frac{dy/ds}{dx/ds}$$

equals dy/dx, the slope of the tangent line.

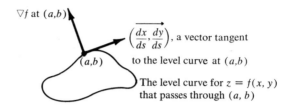

∇f at (a,b)

$\left(\dfrac{dx}{ds}, \dfrac{dy}{ds}\right)$, a vector tangent

(a,b)

to the level curve at (a,b)

The level curve for $z = f(x, y)$ that passes through (a, b)

We wish to prove that ∇f is perpendicular to $(\overrightarrow{dx/ds, dy/ds})$, or, in other words, that

$$\nabla f \cdot \left(\overrightarrow{\frac{dx}{ds}, \frac{dy}{ds}}\right) = 0$$

This dot product equals

$$f_x \frac{dx}{ds} + f_y \frac{dy}{ds}$$

which, by the chain rule, page 366, is dz/ds. But on a level curve, z is constant; hence $dz/ds = 0$. This ends the proof.

Example 4.   Let $f(x,y) = x^2 + y^2$. The typical level curve of f, $x^2 + y^2 = k$, is a circle whose center is at the origin. Now, $\nabla f = (\overrightarrow{2x, 2y}) = 2(\overrightarrow{x,y})$. Thus ∇f at (a,b) is twice the vector from $(0,0)$ to (a,b), and so is parallel to the radius from $(0,0)$ to (a,b). Theorem 8 reminds us that a line through the center of a circle cuts the circle at a right angle.

The electric field created by a charged conductor gives us an important illustration of Theorem 8. In this case, $f(x,y)$ is the work required to move a particle in this field from some base point to (x,y); f is called the potential function. A level curve of f is called an *equipotential curve*. No work is required to push a particle along an equipotential curve, since f is constant there. The direction of the gradient ∇f indicates the direction of force, hence the direction in which a charged particle accelerates in this field.

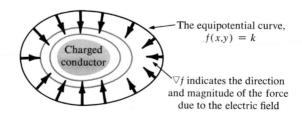

The equipotential curve, $f(x,y) = k$

Charged conductor

∇f indicates the direction and magnitude of the force due to the electric field

When $f(x,y)$ represents the air pressure at (x,y), the gradient ∇f is related to the wind vector, which may be influenced by other factors such as the rotation of the earth. Air does move from high pressure to low pressure, but not usually in paths perpendicular to the isobars.

In order to generalize Theorem 8 to three dimensions, we define the level surfaces and gradient of a function F of x, y, and z. The set of points (x,y,z) such that $F(x,y,z) = k$ is a *level surface* of F. Through each point (a,b,c) where F is defined exactly one level surface passes; on this surface, F has the fixed value $F(a,b,c)$. The gradient of F, denoted ∇F, is $(\overrightarrow{F_x, F_y, F_z})$.

Example 5.   Let $F(x,y,z) = x^2 + y^2 + z^2$. We examine the level surface of F that passes through the point $(2,6,3)$ and its relation to ∇F evaluated at $(2,6,3)$. Since $F(2,6,3)$ equals $2^2 + 6^2 + 3^2 = 49$, the level surface through $(2,6,3)$ has the equation $F(x,y,z) = 49$; that is, $x^2 + y^2 + z^2 = 49$. This is a sphere of radius 7 and center $(0,0,0)$. The gradient ∇F equals $(\overrightarrow{2x,2y,2z})$; at $(2,6,3)$ we have $\nabla F = (\overrightarrow{4,12,6})$, twice the vector from the origin to the point $(2,6,3)$. Note that ∇F is perpendicular to the sphere at $(2,6,3)$:

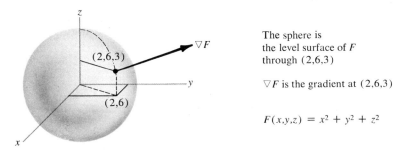

The sphere is
the level surface of F
through $(2,6,3)$

∇F is the gradient at $(2,6,3)$

$F(x,y,z) = x^2 + y^2 + z^2$

Theorem 8, together with Example 5, suggests the next theorem.

THEOREM 9.   *The gradient ∇F at (a,b,c) is perpendicular to any curve through (a,b,c) that lies on that level surface of F which passes through (a,b,c).*

We omit the proof, which differs from that for Theorem 8 only in the number of components in the vectors involved. For instance, a tangent vector to a typical curve referred to in Theorem 9 is defined to be $(\overrightarrow{dx/ds, dy/ds, dz/ds})$, as suggested by the two-dimensional case.

In view of Theorem 8, we make the following definition: The *tangent plane at (a,b,c) to the level surface of F through (a,b,c)* is the plane through (a,b,c) perpendicular to ∇F at (a,b,c) (assuming that ∇F is not 0). Our next example shows that this definition is compatible with the description of the tangent plane on page 366.

Example 6.   Let $z = f(x,y)$ be the equation of some surface. We shall show that the tangent lines T_x and T_y in the left-hand diagram on page 366 lie in the tangent plane as defined above.

In order to express this surface as a level surface of a function of three variables, let us introduce a function F by setting $F(x,y,z) = z - f(x,y)$. Then the surface $z = f(x,y)$ is simply the level surface of the function F given by $F(x,y,z) = 0$.

To compute ∇F, we first find that

$$F_x = -f_x \qquad F_y = -f_y \qquad \text{and} \qquad F_z = 1$$

Thus $\nabla F = (\overline{-f_x, -f_y, 1})$.

To show that T_x lies in the tangent plane at (x,y,z) we will show that T_x is perpendicular to ∇F. Inspection of the left-hand diagram on page 366 shows that $(\overrightarrow{1,0,f_x})$ is a vector parallel to T_x. Is the dot product of ∇F and $(\overrightarrow{1,0,f_x})$ equal to 0? Yes, for we have

$$(\nabla F) \cdot (\overrightarrow{1,0,f_x}) = (\overline{-f_x, -f_y, 1}) \cdot (\overrightarrow{1,0,f_x}) = (-f_x)(1) + (-f_y)(0) + (1)(f_x) = -f_x + f_x = 0$$

In a similar manner it can be shown that T_y is also in the tangent plane. Hence the plane through T_x and T_y is indeed the tangent plane as defined above.

EXERCISES

1. Verify Theorem 6 for the case $f(x,y) = e^x y$, $(a,b) = (0,1)$, and $\theta = \pi/4$ by explicitly expressing z as $F(t)$ and computing $F'(0)$.

2. What does Theorem 6 state for the case in which the angle of inclination θ is 0; $\pi/2$; π?

3. (a) Using Theorem 6, show that $D_{-u}f = -D_u f$. (b) Why is this a reasonable result?

4. Let $f(x,y) = xy$.
   (a) Draw ∇f at $(1,1)$, $(1,2)$, and $(2,3)$, each time placing the tail of ∇f at the point where ∇f is evaluated.
   (b) Draw the level curves $xy = 1$, $xy = 2$, $xy = 6$, which pass through the respective points in (a).
   (c) Does ∇f seem to be perpendicular to the level curve through its tail?

5. Let $f(x,y) = 3x + 4y$.
   (a) Draw three level curves for f. (They are parallel lines.)
   (b) Select a point on each of the three level curves.
   (c) Compute ∇f at each point of (b) and draw it.
   (d) Does ∇f seem to be perpendicular to the level curve through its tail?

6. Let f be such that $\nabla f \neq 0$ at (a,b).
   (a) How many directional derivatives, $D_u f$, at (a,b) are 0?
   (b) How are their directions related to the direction of ∇f?

7. Show that the maximum of $D_u f$ at (a,b) is $\sqrt{f_x^2 + f_y^2}$, where f_x and f_y are evaluated at (a,b).

8. Prove the second part of Theorem 7 without the aid of vectors. That is, prove that the maximum value of $g(\theta) = f_x(a,b) \cos \theta + f_y(a,b) \sin \theta$, is $\sqrt{f_x^2(a,b) + f_y^2(a,b)}$.

9. A hiker is climbing the mountain whose surface has the equation $z = 1{,}000 - 2x^2 - 3y^2$. He is at the point on the mountain corresponding to $(2,1)$ on his map. In which direction should he climb in order to maximize his rate of ascent?

10. Show that if $A \neq 0$, then $A/|A|$ is a unit vector. (Do not use the components of A.)

11. Let $f(x,y) = 1/\sqrt{x^2 + y^2}$; the function f is defined everywhere except at $(0,0)$. (This function is the potential in a gravitational field due to a point mass.) Let $R = \overrightarrow{(x,y)}$.
    (a) Show that $\nabla f = -R/|R|^3$.
    (b) Show that $|\nabla f| = 1/|R|^2$.

12. What happens to ∇f when f has a maximum or minimum? What happens to $D_{\mathbf{u}} f$ there? Explain. (Assume that f is defined in the entire plane and has partial derivatives.)
13. If $f(P)$ is the electric potential at the point P, then the electric field $\mathbf{E}$ at P is given by $-\nabla f$. Calculate $\mathbf{E}$ if $f(x,y) = \sin \alpha x \cos \beta y$, where α and β are constants.

□ □ □

14. (a) Draw the level surface of $F(x,y,z) = 2x + 3y + 4z$ that passes through $(1,0,0)$.
    (b) Compute ∇F at $(1,0,0)$.
    (c) Find two points in the level surface mentioned in (a).
    (d) Using these two points, construct a vector A lying on the surface.
    (e) Compute $\mathbf{A} \cdot \nabla F$.
    (f) Is the answer to (e) reasonable? Why?
15. (a) Draw three level curves of the function f defined by $f(x,y) = xy$. Include the curve through $(1,1)$ as one of them.
    (b) Draw three level curves of the function g defined by $g(x,y) = x^2 - y^2$. Include the level curve through $(1,1)$ as one of them.
    (c) Prove that each level curve of f intersects each level curve of g at a right angle.
    (d) If we think of f as electric potential or air pressure, how should we interpret the level curves of g?
16. (a) Draw a level curve for the function $2x^2 + y^2$.
    (b) Draw a level curve for the function y^2/x.
    (c) Prove that any level curve of $2x^2 + y^2$ crosses any level curve of y^2/x at a right angle.
17. Repeat Exercise 16, for the functions $5x^2 + 3y^2$ and y^5/x^3.
18. The curves $4x^2 + 5y^2 = 24$ and $6x^2 + y^2 = 10$ both pass through the point $(1,2)$. Find the cosine of the angle at which they intersect. (Hint: The gradients of $4x^2 + 5y^2$ and $6x^2 + y^2$ are useful.)
19. We stated Theorem 8 briefly in order not to clutter its essential simplicity. What are some of the assumptions we used about f and its level curves?
20. Let f have continuous partial derivatives f_x, f_y, f_{xy}, and f_{yx} (hence $f_{xy} = f_{yx}$ by Theorem 1, page 372).
    (a) Let $\mathbf{u}_1$ and $\mathbf{u}_2$ be two unit vectors. Prove that $D_{\mathbf{u}_1} D_{\mathbf{u}_2} f = D_{\mathbf{u}_2} D_{\mathbf{u}_1} f$.
    (b) Show that (a) includes, as a special case, $f_{xy} = f_{yx}$.
21. Prove Theorem 9.
22. The surfaces $2x^2 + 3y^2 + z^2 = 6$ and $x^3 + y^3 + z^3 = 3$ pass through the point $(1,1,1)$. At what angle do they cross there?
23. The temperature T in a river at time t and at the point (x,y,z) (relative to a stationary coordinate system) is $T = f(x,y,z,t)$. A skin diver, who has the velocity $\mathbf{V} = (dx/dt, dy/dt, dz/dt)$ relative to the fixed coordinate system, records the temperature of the water as a function of time, $T = g(t)$.
    (a) Show that $dg/dt = f_t + f_x\, dx/dt + f_y\, dy/dt + f_z\, dz/dt$.
    (b) Explain the following equation, which is important in the study of fluids:

$$\frac{dT}{dt} = \frac{\partial T}{\partial t} + \nabla f \cdot \mathbf{V}$$

24. Let $z = f(x,y)$ be a real function defined on the plane and C a curve in the plane. Let s denote arc length along C and $\mathbf{T}$ a unit tangent vector to C at some point P

on C and pointing in the direction of increasing s. Show that $dz/ds = D_{\mathbf{T}}\,f$, where both derivatives are evaluated at P.

4. Summary. This table summarizes our introduction to the algebra of vectors.

Concept	Reminder of definition	Expression in components if $\mathbf{A} = (\overrightarrow{x_1,y_1})$ and $\mathbf{B} = (\overrightarrow{x_2,y_2})$
Vector $\mathbf{A}$	Direction and magnitude $\mathbf{A}$ ╱	$(\overrightarrow{x_1,y_1})$
$|\mathbf{A}|$	Length or magnitude of $\mathbf{A}$	$\sqrt{x_1{}^2 + y_1{}^2}$
$-\mathbf{A}$	$\mathbf{A}$ ╱ ╱ $-\mathbf{A}$	$(-\overrightarrow{x_1}, -\overrightarrow{y_1})$
$\mathbf{A} + \mathbf{B}$	$\mathbf{A}+\mathbf{B}$ $\mathbf{B}$ $\mathbf{A}$	$(\overrightarrow{x_1 + x_2, y_1 + y_2})$
$\mathbf{A} - \mathbf{B}$	$\mathbf{A}-\mathbf{B}$ $\mathbf{B}$ $\mathbf{A}$	$(\overrightarrow{x_1 - x_2, y_1 - y_2})$
$c\mathbf{A}$	$\mathbf{A}$ ╱ ╱ $c\mathbf{A}$ ($c = \tfrac{1}{2}$ here)	$(\overrightarrow{cx_1, cy_1})$
$\mathbf{A} \cdot \mathbf{B}$	$|\mathbf{A}|\,|\mathbf{B}|$ (cosine of angle between $\mathbf{A}$ and $\mathbf{B}$)	$x_1 x_2 + y_1 y_2$

From a function f of x and y we derive the gradient ∇f, a vector defined in terms of components: $\nabla f = (\overrightarrow{f_x, f_y})$. It is perpendicular to the curve $f(x,y) = k$. The directional derivative can be computed with the aid of the gradient. The gradient of a function F of three variables is defined as $\nabla F = (\overrightarrow{F_x, F_y, F_z})$. The tangent plane to a surface was defined with the aid of ∇F.

17

The derivative of a vector function

THE motion of a ball traveling along a straight line is most easily described with the aid of a coordinate system on that line (see page 287). But the motion of a ball along a curved path, or the orbit of a rocket or a space capsule, is most easily described with vectors. This is so partly because the forces influencing the motion are best represented by vectors.

The attraction of the earth on an astronaut's capsule is represented by a vector directed toward the center of the earth.

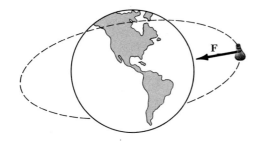

The tug of the earth
upon the capsule

If **F** represents this vector force of gravity, then |**F**| diminishes as the distance between the capsule and the center of the earth increases.

The astronaut influences his flight through small rockets. Their thrust is described by a vector:

When the astronaut fires this engine, he experiences the shove **F** owing to the escaping gas pushing against the capsule

When you spin a weight in a circle at the end of a rope, it is subject to two forces: F_1, toward your hand, and F_2, the pull of gravity straight down.

In this chapter we investigate moving particles whose direction and speed both change with time. Some outside force is always acting on them. Moreover, we will assume that the motion of the particle lies in a plane.

Though we phrase our discussion in terms of "particles" and "time," the results are purely mathematical. For instance, we will obtain a new way of computing the curvature of a curve.

1. The position and velocity vectors. We consider an object moving in the plane. It might be a weight on the end of a rope, a ball, a satellite, a comet, a raindrop, or an astronaut's capsule. We will call this object a "particle" and assume that all of its mass is located at a single point.

The position of the particle at time t relative to an xy coordinate system is (x,y). We shall describe its position with the *position vector* **R**, whose tail is at $(0,0)$ and whose head is at (x,y). Thus $\mathbf{R} = \overrightarrow{(x,y)}$, where x and y depend on time t. Therefore **R** depends on t, and we may also write it as $\mathbf{R}(t)$.

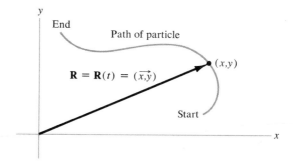

We introduce the *velocity vector*, denoted **V** or $\mathbf{V}(t)$, to describe the motion of the particle at time t. The *magnitude* of **V** is equal to the speed of the particle, ds/dt, where s measures arc length on the path and increases as t increases. The

direction of **V** is along the line tangent to the path at the position (x,y), with the "same sense" as the motion of the particle. We place the tail of **V** at the position of the particle at time t.

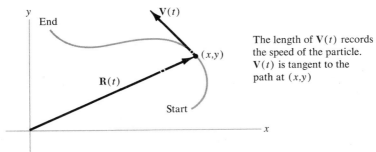

The length of $\mathbf{V}(t)$ records the speed of the particle. $\mathbf{V}(t)$ is tangent to the path at (x,y)

It is easy to compute the components of **V**. The vector $\overrightarrow{(dx/dt, dy/dt)}$, has the direction of **V** since $(dy/dt)/(dx/dt) = dy/dx$, the slope of the tangent line. The magnitude of $\overrightarrow{(dx/dt, dy/dt)}$ is

$$\sqrt{\left(\frac{dx}{dt}\right)^2 + \left(\frac{dy}{dt}\right)^2} = \frac{ds}{dt}$$

the same as the magnitude of **V**. (Recall Theorem 2, page 207.) Hence

$$\mathbf{V} = \left(\frac{dx}{dt}, \frac{dy}{dt}\right)$$

which we may take as the mathematical definition of **V**. The x component of **V** records how fast x changes as the particle moves, and the y component how fast y changes.

Example. Let us examine **R** and **V** when we swing a pail around a circle of radius 10 feet at the rate of 3 revolutions per second. Let us introduce an xy coordinate system such that at time $t = 0$ the pail is at $(10,0)$. Let the angle between **R** and the positive x axis be θ. Assuming that the rotation is counterclockwise, we have $\theta = 3(2\pi t) = 6\pi t$, since the pail sweeps out the circle three times per second. Hence at time t the x component of **R** is $10 \cos\theta$, and the y component is $10 \sin\theta$. We have

$$\mathbf{R} = \overrightarrow{(10\cos\theta, 10\sin\theta)} = \overrightarrow{(10\cos(6\pi t), 10\sin(6\pi t))}$$

Since $\mathbf{V} = \overrightarrow{(dx/dt, dy/dt)}$, we obtain

$$\mathbf{V} = \overrightarrow{(-60\pi\sin(6\pi t), 60\pi\cos(6\pi t))} = 60\pi\overrightarrow{(-\sin(6\pi t), \cos(6\pi t))}$$

From the fact that

$$\left|\overrightarrow{(-\sin(6\pi t), \cos(6\pi t))}\right| = \sqrt{(-\sin(6\pi t))^2 + (\cos(6\pi t))^2} = 1$$

we deduce that $|\mathbf{V}| = 60\pi$. (This is reasonable, since in one second the pail travels three times around a circle of radius 10 feet, hence covers a distance of $3(2\pi)(10) = 60\pi$ feet.) Moreover, **V** is perpendicular to **R**, since

$$\mathbf{V} \cdot \mathbf{R} = 60\pi\overrightarrow{(-\sin\theta, \cos\theta)} \cdot \overrightarrow{(10\cos\theta, 10\sin\theta)}$$

$$= 60\pi[-\sin\theta(10\cos\theta) + \cos\theta(10\sin\theta)] = 0$$

We sketch V and R (not to scale) for a few positions of the pail.

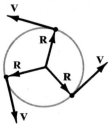

Frequently in mechanics the vector $\mathbf{R} = \overrightarrow{(x,y)}$ is denoted $i x + j y$. The velocity vector $\mathbf{V}$ is written $i V_x + j V_y$. It is important then to keep in mind that the subscripts do *not* indicate partial differentiation. V_x is simply the x component of $\mathbf{V}$, and V_y is the y component of $\mathbf{V}$.

EXERCISES

1. A combination of rockets, ropes, and air resistance influences a particle in such a way that its coordinates are $x = t$ and $y = t^{-1}$ at time $t \geqslant 1$.
   (a) Draw the path of the particle.
   (b) Draw R(1), R(2), and R(3).
   (c) Draw V(1), V(2), V(3).
   (d) As times goes on, what happens to dx/dt, dy/dt, $|\mathbf{V}|$ and $\mathbf{V}$?
2. An electron travels clockwise in a circle of radius 100 feet 200 times a second. At time $t = 0$ it is at (100,0).
   (a) Compute R(t) and V(t).
   (b) Draw R(0), R(⅟₈₀₀), V(0), V(⅟₈₀₀).
   (c) How do $|\mathbf{R}(t)|$ and $|\mathbf{V}(t)|$ behave as time goes on?
   [Answer: $\mathbf{R} = \overrightarrow{(100 \cos 400\pi t, \ -100 \sin 400\pi t)}$;
   $\mathbf{V} = 40{,}000\pi \, (-\sin 400\pi t, \ -\cos 400\pi t)$]
3. At time t a particle is at $(3t^2, 6t^2)$.
   (a) Show that the particle moves on the line $y = 2x$.
   (b) Draw R(0), R(1), R(2) and V(0), V(1), V(2).
4. If the ball thrown from the cliff as described on page 287 is thrown horizontally, then R(t) is $\overrightarrow{(64t, 96 - 16t^2)}$.
   (a) Compute and draw R(0), R(1), R(2) and V(0), V(1), V(2).
   (b) How would V(t) and $|\mathbf{V}(t)|$ behave for large t if there were no ground to stop the ball?
5. At time t a particle is at $(\cos t^2, \sin t^2)$.
   (a) Show that it moves on the circle $x^2 + y^2 = 1$.
   (b) Compute R(t) and V(t).
   (c) How does $|\mathbf{V}(t)|$ behave for large t? What does this say about the particle?
6. At time t a particle is at $\overrightarrow{(4t, 16t^2)}$.
   (a) Show that the particle moves on the curve $y = x^2$.
   (b) Draw R(t) and V(t) for $t = 0$, ¼, ½.
   (c) What happens to $|\mathbf{V}(t)|$ and the direction of V(t) for large t?
7. A ball is thrown up at an initial speed of 200 feet per second and at an angle of 60° from the horizontal. If we disregard air resistance, then at time t it is at the

point $(100t, (100 \sqrt{3}) t - 16t^2)$, as long as it is in flight. Compute and draw $\mathbf{R}(t)$ and $\mathbf{V}(t)$ (a) when $t = 0$; (b) when the ball reaches its maximum height; (c) when the ball strikes the ground.

□ □ □

8. A rock is thrown up at an angle θ from the horizontal and at a speed v_0. Show that $\mathbf{R}(t) = (\overrightarrow{(v_0 \cos \theta) t, (v_0 \sin \theta) t - 16t^2})$. (At time $t = 0$, the rock is at $(0,0)$; the x axis is horizontal.)
9. (See Exercise 8.) The moment a ball is dropped straight down, you shoot an arrow directly at it. Assume that there is no air resistance. Show that if you shoot the arrow fast enough it will hit the ball.
   (a) Solve with the aid of the formulas in Exercise 8.
   (b) Solve with a maximum of intuition and a minimum of formula.
   (c) Must the acceleration be constant for the reasoning in (b) to be valid? Explain.
10. (a) Show that the horizontal distance traveled by the rock in Exercise 8 is the same whether the angle is θ or its complement $(\pi/2) - \theta$.
    (b) What value of θ yields the maximum range?

2. The derivative of a vector function.

When we consider motion on a line, the numerical position function $x = f(t)$ suffices to describe the journey of the moving particle. The velocity of the particle is given by the derivative dx/dt, and its speed by $|dx/dt|$. In this section, growing out of the preceding one, we define the derivative of a vector function, which we apply to the study of motion along a curve.

Let us define the *derivative of a vector function* $\mathbf{R} = \mathbf{F}(t) = \overrightarrow{(x(t), y(t))}$ as the vector $\overrightarrow{(dx/dt, dy/dt)}$; we assume of course that dx/dt and dy/dt exist. In short, we simply differentiate each component function. We will denote the derivative vector as $\mathbf{R}'$ or $d\mathbf{R}/dt$, so that $\mathbf{R}' = \overrightarrow{(dx/dt, dy/dt)}$. *Notice that the derivative of the position vector function is the velocity vector function.* The derivative $d\mathbf{V}/dt$ of the velocity vector function is called the *acceleration* vector function,

$$\mathbf{A}(t) = \overrightarrow{\left(\frac{d^2x}{dt^2}, \frac{d^2y}{dt^2} \right)}$$

Example 1. Let $\mathbf{R}(t) = \overrightarrow{(4t, -16t^2)}$ describe the curved path of a falling ball. Then $\mathbf{V}(t) = \mathbf{R}'(t) = \overrightarrow{(4, -32t)}$ and $\mathbf{A}(t) = \mathbf{V}'(t) = \overrightarrow{(0, -32)}$. Notice that the acceleration vector in this case has the same direction as the vector $\mathbf{F}$ that represents the attractive force of the earth upon the ball. We sketch $\mathbf{V}$ and $\mathbf{A}$ at two points on the path:

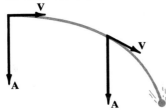

The path of a falling ball

The direction and magnitude of $\mathbf{V}$ change, but its horizontal component is constant.

If there are no forces acting on a moving particle, $\mathbf{V}(t)$ is constant; hence $\mathbf{A}(t) = \mathbf{0}$. That is, if the vector $\mathbf{F}$, representing the forces, is $\mathbf{0}$, then $\mathbf{A} = \mathbf{0}$. Newton's second law asserts universally that $\mathbf{F}$, $\mathbf{A}$, and the mass m of the particle are related by the vector equation:

$$\mathbf{F} = m\mathbf{A}$$

This little equation says several things: (1) The direction of $\mathbf{A}$ is the same as the direction of $\mathbf{F}$. (2) A force $\mathbf{F}$ applied to a heavy mass produces a smaller acceleration vector $\mathbf{A}$ than the same force applied to a light mass. (3) For a given mass, the magnitude of $\mathbf{A}$ is proportional to the magnitude of $\mathbf{F}$.

In Sec. 3 we will study $\mathbf{A}$ in greater detail, but now let us examine some more aspects of the derivative of a vector function. The next theorem describes some useful relations, as we shall see in the example that follows it.

THEOREM 1.   (a) *If f is a scalar function and $\mathbf{F}$ a vector function of t, then* $(f(t)\,\mathbf{F}(t))' = f(t)\,\mathbf{F}'(t) + f'(t)\,\mathbf{F}(t)$. (b) *If $\mathbf{F}$ and $\mathbf{G}$ are vector functions, then* $[\mathbf{F}(t) \cdot \mathbf{G}(t)]' = \mathbf{F}(t) \cdot \mathbf{G}'(t) + \mathbf{G}(t) \cdot \mathbf{F}'(t)$. (c) *If $\mathbf{R} = \mathbf{F}(s)$ and $s = f(t)$, then* $d\mathbf{R}/dt = (d\mathbf{R}/ds)\,(ds/dt)$.

PROOF.   We prove only (b): Let $\mathbf{F}(t) = \overrightarrow{(f_1(t), f_2(t))}$ and $\mathbf{G}(t) = \overrightarrow{(g_1(t), g_2(t))}$; then $\mathbf{F}(t) \cdot \mathbf{G}(t) = f_1(t)\,g_1(t) + f_2(t)\,g_2(t)$. By application of the formula for the derivative of the sum and product of scalar functions (page 98), we obtain

$$[\mathbf{F}(t) \cdot \mathbf{G}(t)]' = f_1(t)\,g_1'(t) + g_1(t)\,f_1'(t) + f_2(t)\,g_2'(t) + g_2(t)\,f_2'(t)$$

The expression on the right side of the equation equals

$$[f_1(t)\,g_1'(t) + f_2(t)\,g_2'(t)] + [g_1(t)\,f_1'(t) + g_2(t)\,f_2'(t)]$$

which is simply $\mathbf{F}(t) \cdot \mathbf{G}'(t) + \mathbf{G}(t) \cdot \mathbf{F}'(t)$

A similar computation disposes of (a), and the chain rule may be used to prove (c).

The strength of (a) will be demonstrated in Sec. 3. We illustrate (b) in the following example.

Example 2.   Let $\mathbf{R} = \mathbf{R}(t)$ be the position vector of a moving particle and let $r = r(t)$ be its magnitude: $r = |\mathbf{R}|$. Then, as we saw on page 386,

(1) $\mathbf{R} \cdot \mathbf{R} = r^2$

Let us differentiate (1). Since r^2 is an ordinary scalar function, $d(r^2)/dt = 2rr'$. Then (b) of Theorem 1 tells us that

(2) $\mathbf{R} \cdot \mathbf{R}' + \mathbf{R}' \cdot \mathbf{R} = 2rr'$ or $\mathbf{R} \cdot \mathbf{R}' = rr'$

Consequently,

(3) $\mathbf{R} \cdot \mathbf{V} = rr'$

From (3) we conclude that in the case in which $\mathbf{V}$ is always perpendicular to $\mathbf{R}$, we must have $r' = 0$. Thus r is constant, and the orbit must be a circle. Conversely, the position and velocity vectors are perpendicular for a circular orbit.

EXERCISES

1. Let $R(t) = \overrightarrow{(10 \cos 2\pi t, 10 \sin 2\pi t)}$ denote the position vector of a particle at time t.
   (a) What is the shape of the path of this particle?
   (b) Compute V and A.
   (c) Draw R, V, and A for $t = \frac{1}{4}$.
   (d) Show that A is always in the direction opposite to that of R.
   (e) Does (d) agree with your experience in whirling a mass at the end of a rope and with the equation $F = mA$?

2. Let $R(t) = \overrightarrow{(4t, -16t^2)}$ describe a falling ball. Compute and draw R, V, and A for $t = 0$, $t = 1$, and $t = 2$.

3. (a) Prove that if the horizontal component of V is constant, then A is vertical.
   (b) Does the assertion in (a) make physical sense? Explain.

4. Let the position vector R be a function of arc length s on a curve. Prove that dR/ds is a *unit* vector tangent to the curve.

5. Prove part (a) of Theorem 1.

6. The momentum of a particle of mass m and velocity vector V is the vector mV. Newton stated his second law in the form $F = (mV)'$.
   (a) Using Theorem 1(a), prove that $F = mA + m'V$.
   (b) Deduce that if m is constant, then $F = mA$.

7. Prove that $[F(t) + G(t)]' = F'(t) + G'(t)$.

8. Verify Theorem 1(a) by direct computation for the case $f(t) = e^t$ and $F(t) = \overrightarrow{(\sin t, \cos t)}$.

9. Verify Theorem 1(b) by direct computation for the case $F(t) = \overrightarrow{(3t, t^2)}$, and $G(t) = \overrightarrow{(t^4, -5t)}$.

10. Prove that if the force $F(t)$ is always perpendicular to the path of the moving particle at the point where F is applied, then the speed of the particle is constant.

11. (a) Prove that if a particle moves in a circular orbit [centered at $(0,0)$] then $R \cdot A + V \cdot V = 0$.
    (b) From (a) deduce that $A \cdot R$ is $\leqslant 0$.
    (c) Is (b) reasonable?

12. A particle moves in the circular orbit $R = \overrightarrow{(\cos t^2, \sin t^2)}$.
    (a) Compute R, V, and A.
    (b) Verify that $R \cdot A \leqslant 0$.

13. (a) What can we say about dR/dt if $R(t)$ is a unit vector for all t?
    (b) Does dR/dt have to be a unit vector too? Justify your answers.

14. At time t a particle has the position vector $R(t) = \overrightarrow{(t + \cos t, t + \sin t)}$.
    (a) Show that A has constant magnitude.
    (b) Sketch the path corresponding to t in $[0, 4\pi]$.
    (c) Sketch R, V, and A for $t = 0$, $\pi/2$, π, $3\pi/2$, and 2π.
    (d) Explain why a satellite in free space ("beyond" gravity), spinning on its own axis, and having one external gas jet that it cannot turn off may follow the path described in this exercise.

15. (a) Verify Theorem 1(c) for the case $R = \overrightarrow{(e^t, \sin t)}$, $t = s^2$, by computing dR/dt, dR/ds, and dt/ds. (b) Prove Theorem 1(c).

□ □ □

16. We defined $\mathbf{R}'$ by referring to the derivative of its component functions. We outline a purely vectorial approach, which depends on the limit of a vector function. Let $\mathbf{F}$ be a vector function of the scalar t. We shall say that $\lim_{t \to a} \mathbf{F}(t) = \mathbf{L}$ if $\lim_{t \to a} |\mathbf{F}(t) - \mathbf{L}| = 0$. Prove that $\mathbf{R}' = \lim_{t \to 0} [\mathbf{R}(t + \Delta t) - \mathbf{R}(t)]/\Delta t$.

17. (See Exercise 16.) (a) Draw a typical $\mathbf{R}(t + \Delta t) - \mathbf{R}(t)$ and $[\mathbf{R}(t + \Delta t) - \mathbf{R}(t)]/\Delta t$. (b) In view of (a), why would you expect $\mathbf{R}'$ to be a vector tangent to the curve traced out by the position vector $\mathbf{R}$?

18. (See Exercise 16.) Prove Theorem 1(b), using only the vectorial definition of the derivative of a vector function. The algebra is simplified by writing $\mathbf{F}(t + \Delta t) = \mathbf{F}(t) + \Delta \mathbf{F}$ and $\mathbf{G}(t + \Delta t) = \mathbf{G}(t) + \Delta \mathbf{G}$.

19. (a) If $\mathbf{V}$ has constant direction, does $\mathbf{A}$ have constant direction? Explain.
(b) If $\mathbf{V}$ has constant magnitude, does $\mathbf{A}$ have constant magnitude? Explain.

3. The tangential and normal components of the acceleration vector A.

The acceleration vector $\mathbf{A}$ is proportional to the force acting on a moving particle. Its x and y components are d^2x/dt^2 and d^2y/dt^2, respectively. These components, though useful, are somewhat artificial, since, like latitude and longitude lines, they depend on an arbitrary choice of axes. We shall present another view of $\mathbf{A}$, a view which is influenced by the position function itself.

To do so we first define the *components* of any vector $\mathbf{R}$ *relative to two perpendicular unit vectors* $\mathbf{u}_1$ and $\mathbf{u}_2$.

DEFINITION: *Components of a vector.* Let $\mathbf{u}_1$ and $\mathbf{u}_2$ be perpendicular unit vectors and $\mathbf{R}$ a vector. Let $\mathbf{R} = \mathbf{R}_1 + \mathbf{R}_2$, where the vector $\mathbf{R}_1$ is parallel to $\mathbf{u}_1$ and the vector $\mathbf{R}_2$ is parallel to $\mathbf{u}_2$. Thus $\mathbf{R}_1 = R_1\mathbf{u}_1$ and $\mathbf{R}_2 = R_2\mathbf{u}_2$. The scalars R_1 and R_2 are the *components* of $\mathbf{R}$ along $\mathbf{u}_1$ and $\mathbf{u}_2$, respectively.

This diagram describes the definition informally.

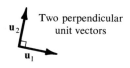

Two perpendicular unit vectors

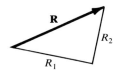

The components of $\mathbf{R}$ relative to $\mathbf{u}_1$ and $\mathbf{u}_2$ are the scalars R_1 and R_2

Observe that the components R_1 and R_2 of $\mathbf{R}$ are scalars. However, $R_1\mathbf{u}_1$ and $R_2\mathbf{u}_2$ are vectors, and we have

(1) $$\mathbf{R} = R_1\mathbf{u}_1 + R_2\mathbf{u}_2$$

THEOREM 2. *The components of* $\mathbf{R}$ *relative to the perpendicular unit vectors* $\mathbf{u}_1$ *and* $\mathbf{u}_2$ *are* $\mathbf{R} \cdot \mathbf{u}_1$ *and* $\mathbf{R} \cdot \mathbf{u}_2$, *respectively.*

PROOF. $\mathbf{R} \cdot \mathbf{u}_1 = |\mathbf{R}| |\mathbf{u}_1| \cos \theta$, where θ is the angle between $\mathbf{u}_1$ and $\mathbf{R}$. Since $|\mathbf{u}_1| = 1$, we have

$$\mathbf{R} \cdot \mathbf{u}_1 = |\mathbf{R}| \cos \theta = R_1$$

A similar proof shows that $\mathbf{R} \cdot \mathbf{u}_2 = R_2$.

There are two unit vectors, perhaps constantly changing in direction, that are of special significance to an astronaut or a driver traveling a curved path. One of them, like a miner's lamp, always points directly ahead, recording the direction of motion; this we call $\mathbf{T}$, for it lies along the tangent to the path. The other is perpendicular to $\mathbf{T}$, and records the direction in which the craft is turning, to the left or to the right; this we call $\mathbf{N}$, for it is normal (perpendicular) to the curve. There are in fact two normals; the one we want is called the *principal normal*.

We now give a precise mathematical definition of $\mathbf{T}$ and $\mathbf{N}$; afterward we shall show that it is equivalent to the physicist's definition in the preceding paragraph. In the definition we make use of the fact that if we divide a vector by its magnitude, we obtain a unit vector.

DEFINITION: $\mathbf{T}$ *and* $\mathbf{N}$.   Let $\mathbf{F}$ be a vector function of t, and let $\mathbf{R} = \mathbf{F}(t)$. If $\mathbf{V} (= \mathbf{R}')$ is not $\mathbf{0}$, then the vector

$$\frac{\mathbf{V}}{|\mathbf{V}|}$$

is a *unit tangent vector* and is denoted $\mathbf{T}$. If $d\mathbf{T}/dt$ is not $\mathbf{0}$, then the vector

$$\frac{d\mathbf{T}/dt}{|d\mathbf{T}/dt|}$$

is a *unit normal vector* and is denoted $\mathbf{N}$.

We show that the formal definition describes the same two vectors described previously. Since both $\mathbf{T}$ and $\mathbf{N}$ are unit vectors, we need to verify only that they have the proper directions. First, because of the way in which it is defined, $\mathbf{T}$ has the same direction as $\mathbf{V}$, and hence "points directly ahead." Second, we examine the direction of $\mathbf{N}$, which is the same as that of $d\mathbf{T}/dt$. If we denote the angle from the positive x axis to the direction of $\mathbf{T}$ by ϕ, then we have

$$\mathbf{T} = (\overrightarrow{\cos \phi, \sin \phi})$$

Thus

$$(2) \qquad \frac{d\mathbf{T}}{dt} = \frac{d\mathbf{T}}{d\phi} \frac{d\phi}{dt} = (\overrightarrow{-\sin \phi, \cos \phi}) \frac{d\phi}{dt} = \left(\overrightarrow{\cos \left(\phi + \frac{\pi}{2}\right), \sin \left(\phi + \frac{\pi}{2}\right)}\right) \frac{d\phi}{dt}$$

the last equality being a consequence of trigonometric identities.

We want to show that $d\mathbf{T}/dt$ is perpendicular to $\mathbf{T}$ and points in the direction "in which the craft is turning." There are two cases: $d\phi/dt > 0$ and $d\phi/dt < 0$. We treat the case $d\phi/dt > 0$, that is, $\mathbf{T}$ is turning counterclockwise. (The other can be treated in a similar way.) Since $d\phi/dt$ is positive, $d\mathbf{T}/dt$ has the same direction as the unit vector $\overrightarrow{(\cos{(\phi + \pi/2))}, \sin{(\phi + \pi/2))}}$, whose angle, $\phi + \pi/2$, is $\pi/2$ larger than that of $\mathbf{T}$. This is precisely the angle that the physicist assigns to $\mathbf{N}$ when $\mathbf{T}$ is turning counterclockwise. Thus $\mathbf{T}$ and $\mathbf{N}$ of the formal definition coincide with $\mathbf{T}$ and $\mathbf{N}$ of the intuitive definition. Note that (2) implies that $|d\mathbf{T}/dt| = |d\phi/dt|$. In particular, if $d\phi/dt > 0$, then $d\mathbf{T}/dt = \mathbf{N}\,d\phi/dt$.

Notice that $\mathbf{T}$ is defined whenever $\mathbf{V}$ is not $\mathbf{0}$ and that $\mathbf{N}$ is defined whenever $d\phi/dt$ is not $\mathbf{0}$. If we introduce the arc length parameter s, we have

$$\frac{d\phi}{dt} = \frac{d\phi}{ds}\frac{ds}{dt}$$

Thus when the curvature $d\phi/ds$ is 0, the vector $\mathbf{N}$ is not defined. (The intuitive definition agrees: the craft is, momentarily, turning neither to the right nor to the left.) We draw some typical $\mathbf{T}$ and $\mathbf{N}$ for this path that stretches from A to B:

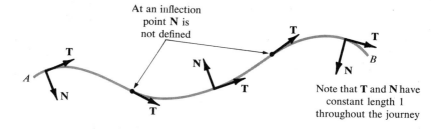

We shall obtain the components of $\mathbf{A}$ along $\mathbf{T}$ and $\mathbf{N}$ for an arbitrary journey. The component of $\mathbf{A}$ along $\mathbf{T}$ is called the *tangential component* A_T; the component of $\mathbf{A}$ along $\mathbf{N}$ is called the *normal component* A_N. Both A_T and A_N are scalars.

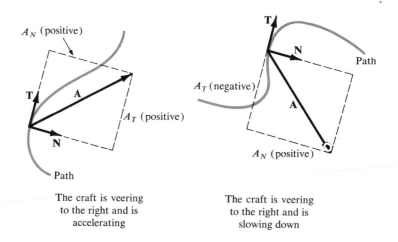

As we might expect, and as Theorem 4 will prove, A_N is always positive.

To get some feeling for **A**, let us examine two special cases: motion on a line and motion with constant speed on a circle. We first consider motion on a line L. We introduce an x axis on L so that x plays the role of arc length s. Let us assume that dx/dt (which is ds/dt) is positive.

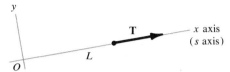

Then $\mathbf{R} = \overrightarrow{(x,0)}$, $\mathbf{V} = \overrightarrow{(dx/dt, 0)} = \overrightarrow{(ds/dt, 0)}$, and $\mathbf{A} = \overrightarrow{(d^2s/dt^2, 0)}$. In this case **A** is parallel to L. A_T is positive if d^2s/dt^2 is positive, that is, if the particle is speeding up; A_T is negative if the particle is slowing down. In linear motion **N** is neither defined nor needed, but note that $A_T = d^2s/dt^2$.

Next, let us consider a particle traveling with constant speed v around a circle of radius r. In this case, which includes that of a mass at the end of a rope, we would expect **A** to be directed toward the center of the circle. Moreover $|\mathbf{A}|$ should be large if the speed is large, since a large force **F** is then required. Let us now show that this guess is correct.

Introduce an xy coordinate system such that $(0,0)$ is at the center of the circle and the particle is at $(r,0)$ at time 0. Let us assume that the particle travels counterclockwise; then θ is positive, as shown in this diagram:

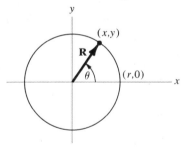

If we measure arc length s counterclockwise from $(r,0)$ then $ds/dt = v$, which is constant; hence $s = vt + C$ for some constant C. Since $s = 0$ when $t = 0$, we have $C = 0$. From the relation $s = r\theta$ we conclude that $\theta = vt/r$. Thus we have

$$\mathbf{R} = \overrightarrow{(x,y)} = \overrightarrow{(r\cos\theta, r\sin\theta)} = \overrightarrow{\left(r\cos\frac{vt}{r}, r\sin\frac{vt}{r} \right)}$$

We are now in a position to compute **V** and **A** explicitly:

$$\mathbf{V} = \frac{d\mathbf{R}}{dt} = \overrightarrow{\left(\frac{-rv}{r}\sin\frac{vt}{r}, \frac{rv}{r}\cos\frac{vt}{r} \right)}$$
$$= \overrightarrow{\left(-v\sin\frac{vt}{r}, v\cos\frac{vt}{r} \right)}$$

Hence $\quad \mathbf{A} = \dfrac{d\mathbf{V}}{dt} = \left(\dfrac{-v^2}{r}\cos\dfrac{vt}{r}, \dfrac{-v^2}{r}\sin\dfrac{vt}{r} \right) = \dfrac{v^2}{r}\overrightarrow{(-\cos\theta, -\sin\theta)}$

From the equation $\mathbf{A} = (v^2/r)\,(-\cos\theta, -\sin\theta)$, we conclude that

$$|\mathbf{A}| = \left| \dfrac{v^2}{r}\overrightarrow{(-\cos\theta, -\sin\theta)} \right| = \dfrac{v^2}{r}\sqrt{(-\cos\theta)^2 + (-\sin\theta)^2} = \dfrac{v^2}{r}$$

Moreover, since $\overrightarrow{(-\cos\theta, -\sin\theta)}$ is pointed directly opposite to $\mathbf{R}$, $\mathbf{A}$ is directed toward the center of the circle. Hence $A_T = 0$ and $A_N = v^2/r$.

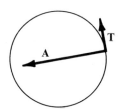

In circular motion with constant speed v, we have $A_T = 0$, $A_N = v^2/r$ (r being the radius of the circle). The unit vector $\mathbf{N}$, not shown, is pointed toward the center of the circle

This was discovered in 1657 by Huyghens while developing a theory of clock mechanisms.

If the "particle" is a pail at the end of a rope, the equation $A_N = v^2/r$ tells us that the tension in the rope is proportional to the square of the speed of the pail, and inversely proportional to the length of the rope.

We now come to motion on any curve. As Theorem 4 will show, the general case is in a sense a mixture of linear and circular motion. For the proof of this general theorem we will need the explicit formulas for $d\mathbf{T}/dt$ provided by Theorem 3.

THEOREM 3. *Let s represent arc length along the path of a moving particle; we assume $v = ds/dt$ is positive. Then*

$$\dfrac{d\mathbf{T}}{dt} = \dfrac{v}{r}\,\mathbf{N}$$

where r is the radius of curvature.

PROOF. We consider the case when the curvature $d\phi/ds$ is positive. The argument when $d\phi/ds$ is negative is similar. Since

$$\dfrac{d\phi}{dt} = \dfrac{d\phi}{ds}\dfrac{ds}{dt}$$

$d\phi/dt$ is also positive. Thus, from (2), $|d\mathbf{T}/dt| = d\phi/dt$ and

$$\dfrac{d\mathbf{T}}{dt} = \mathbf{N}\dfrac{d\phi}{dt} = \mathbf{N}\dfrac{d\phi}{ds}\dfrac{ds}{dt} = \mathbf{N}\left(\dfrac{1}{r}\right)(v) = \dfrac{v}{r}\,\mathbf{N}$$

The theorem is proved.

With Theorem 3 available, we are now in a position to compute A_T and A_N for an arbitrary parameterized curve in the plane. For simplicity we phrase Theorem 4 in terms of a moving particle.

THEOREM 4.   *If a particle moves in a plane curve, and arc length s is measured in such a way that $v = ds/dt$ is positive, then*

$$A = \frac{d^2s}{dt^2} T + \frac{v^2}{r} N$$

where r is the radius of curvature. In other words,

$$A_T = \frac{d^2s}{dt^2} \quad \text{and} \quad A_N = \frac{v^2}{r}$$

PROOF.   We begin with the relation

$$V = vT$$

Differentiation (see Theorem 1, page 404) yields

(3) $$A = V' = v\frac{dT}{dt} + \frac{dv}{dt}T$$

By Theorem 3, we have $dT/dt = (v/r) N$; also, $dv/dt = d^2s/dt^2$. Hence (3) yields

$$A = \frac{v^2}{r} N + \frac{d^2s}{dt^2} T$$

and the theorem is proved.

It is interesting to observe that A_N involves $v = ds/dt$ but not d^2s/dt^2, while A_T involves d^2s/dt^2 but not ds/dt.

Example.   At time t a particle is at $(t^2, (\frac{1}{2}) t^4)$ on the curve $2y = x^2$. We discuss A. First, since $R = (t^2, (\frac{1}{2}) t^4)$, we have $V = (2t, 2t^3)$. Thus, in terms of its x and y components,

$$A = \overrightarrow{(2, 6t^2)}$$

With this information we may conclude that $|A| = \sqrt{4 + 36t^4}$.

Let us sketch A, V, and R at $t = 1$. At that time, we have (see the diagram below)

$$A = \overrightarrow{(2,6)} \qquad V = \overrightarrow{(2,2)} \qquad \text{and} \qquad R = \overrightarrow{(1,\tfrac{1}{2})}$$

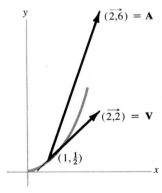

A_T is simply dv/dt, where $v = |V| = \sqrt{4t^2 + 4t^6}$. Thus $A_T = (4t + 12t^5)/\sqrt{4t^2 + 4t^6}$. Rather than compute A_N by the formula $A_N = v^2/r$, which involves computation of the radius of curvature, let us use the Pythagorean relation

$$A_N{}^2 + A_T{}^2 = |A|^2$$

At $t = 1$, for instance, this becomes

$$A_N^2 + \left(\frac{16}{\sqrt{8}}\right)^2 = (\sqrt{40})^2$$

Hence $A_N^2 = 40 - 32 = 8$, and $A_N = 2\sqrt{2}$. We sketch A_N and A_T at $t = 1$:

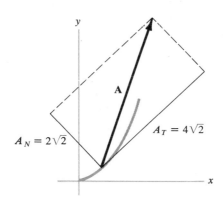

EXERCISES

1. Show that (a) $\mathbf{T} = d\mathbf{R}/ds$, where s denotes arc length, and (h) $\mathbf{N} = d\mathbf{T}/d\phi$, where ϕ denotes the angle of inclination of $\mathbf{T}$, if $d\phi/dt > 0$.
2. Prove Theorem 2 by considering $\mathbf{R} \cdot \mathbf{u}_1 = (R_1\mathbf{u}_1 + R_2\mathbf{u}_2) \cdot \mathbf{u}_1$.
3. Express A_N in terms of the speed of the particle and the rate at which the direction angle ϕ is changing with respect to time.
4. Show that if you want the direction angle ϕ to change at a constant rate, you must have the speed proportional to the radius of curvature of the path.
5. A heavy object swings at the end of a rope. If the speed is doubled, what happens to the tension in the rope? If the length of the rope is doubled, what happens to the tension?
6. If a centrifuge has a 30-foot radius, how many revolutions per minute must an astronaut in training experience to feel an acceleration whose magnitude is 5g? ($g = 32$ feet per second per second.)
   (Answer: $40\sqrt{3}/\pi$, about 23 revolutions per minute)
7. Repeat Exercise 6 for a radius of 7.5 feet.
   (Answer: $80\sqrt{3}/\pi$, about 45 revolutions per minute)
8. Use the computations in Example 2 and the equation $A_N = v^2/r$ to find the radius of curvature of the curve $y = x^2/2$ at $(1,\frac{1}{2})$.
9. At a certain moment a particle has $\mathbf{R} = \overrightarrow{(1,1)}$, $\mathbf{V} = \overrightarrow{(3,4)}$, and $\mathbf{A} = \overrightarrow{(3,-3)}$.
   (a) Draw $\mathbf{R}$, $\mathbf{V}$, and $\mathbf{A}$.
   (b) Is the particle speeding up or slowing down? Explain.
   (c) Estimate A_T and A_N graphically.
   (d) Compute A_T and A_N.
   [Answer: (d) $A_T = -\frac{3}{5}$, $A_N = 21\frac{1}{5}$]
10. Repeat Exercise 9 for $\mathbf{R} = \overrightarrow{(0,0)}$, $\mathbf{V} = \overrightarrow{(-5,12)}$, $\mathbf{A} = \overrightarrow{(3,1)}$.
   [Answer: (b) slowing down; (d) $A_T = -\frac{3}{13}$, $A_N = \frac{41}{13}$]

11. Prove that if a particle travels with a constant speed, then $\mathbf{A}$ is perpendicular to $\mathbf{V}$, (a) by using Theorem 4; (b) by differentiating $\mathbf{V} \cdot \mathbf{V}$.

12. Prove Theorem 3 for negative $d\phi/ds$.

13. Let $\mathbf{R}$ describe the journey in the example.
    (a) Compute and draw $\mathbf{A}$ for $t = 1/\sqrt{6}$.
    (b) From your drawing estimate A_T and A_N at $t = 1/\sqrt{6}$.
    (c) Compute A_T and A_N at $t = 1/\sqrt{6}$.
    (d) Compare (b) and (c) in decimal form.   [Answer: (c) $13/\sqrt{37}$, $4/\sqrt{37}$]

14. At a certain moment, a particle headed northeast is speeding up and veering to the left. Taking north as the positive y axis and east as the positive x axis, draw (a) $\mathbf{T}$; (b) $\mathbf{N}$; (c) enough typical $\mathbf{A}$'s to indicate the directions possible for $\mathbf{A}$.

15. Repeat Exercise 14 for a particle headed north, slowing down, and veering to the left.

16. At time t a particle is at $(\cos t + t \sin t, \sin t - t \cos t)$.
    (a) Show that $|\mathbf{V}| = t$ and $|\mathbf{A}| = \sqrt{1 + t^2}$.
    (b) Show that $A_T = 1$ and $A_N = t$.
    (c) Show that r, the radius of curvature, equals t.

17. An astronaut, traveling at speed v_0 and at an angle ϕ_0 to a fixed line in interstellar space, cannot shut off an external rear gas jet, which remains inclined at an angle of 45° to his path. (We assume that the direction of the axis of the rocket is maintained tangent to the path.) Thus $A_N = A_T = k$, some fixed positive number.
    (a) Show that $v = kt + v_0$.
    (b) Show that $d\phi/dt = k/v$.
    (c) Show that $\phi = \ln(kt + v_0) + \phi_0$.
    (d) Show that he spirals in an (unbounded) path whose curvature approaches 0.

18. (See Exercise 17.) In this case the jet is in front of the rocket, and we have $A_N = k$ and $A_T = -k$, where k is a positive number.
    (a) Show that at time $t = v_0/k$, the speed of the astronaut is 0.
    (b) Show that from time $t = 0$ to time $t = v_0/k$, the astronaut travels the finite distance $v_0^2/2k$.
    (c) Show that during the interval of time from 0 to v_0/k, the astronaut spirals infinitely often on a path converging on the point he will occupy at time $t = v_0/k$.
    (d) What is his average speed with respect to time during the time interval $[0, v_0/k]$?
    (e) What is his average speed with respect to distance traveled, during this trip?
                                    [Answer: (d) $v_0/2$; (e) $2v_0/3$]

19. Since $\mathbf{A} = (d^2x/dt^2, d^2y/dt^2)$, $\mathbf{T} = (dx/ds, dy/ds)$, and $A_T = \mathbf{A} \cdot \mathbf{T}$, we have
$$\frac{d^2s}{dt^2} = \frac{d^2x}{dt^2}\frac{dx}{ds} + \frac{d^2y}{dt^2}\frac{dy}{ds}$$
    Obtain that equation directly, without recourse to vectors.

20. From Theorem 4 deduce this formula for obtaining r, the radius of curvature:
$$\frac{v^4}{r^2} = \left(\frac{d^2x}{dt^2}\right)^2 + \left(\frac{d^2y}{dt^2}\right)^2 - \left(\frac{d^2s}{dt^2}\right)^2$$

21. (See Exercise 20.) The equation in Exercise 20 holds for any differentiable parameterization of the curve. In particular, let x be the parameter, and deduce the formula for curvature as stated on page 292.

22. From the fact that $\mathbf{T}$ is a unit vector, prove directly that $d\mathbf{T}/dt$ is perpendicular to $\mathbf{T}$.

4. *Summary*. In this chapter we introduced the derivative of a vector function **F** and applied it to the study of motion. Using such results as $(f(t)\,\mathbf{F}(t))' = f(t)\,\mathbf{F}'(t) + f'(t)\,\mathbf{F}(t)$, we have examined the components of the acceleration vector. The following table presents some of the main mathematical ideas of this chapter, together with their physical interpretations:

Mathematical formulation	*Physical interpretation*
Vector function **F**	Parameterized path of moving particle
Derivative of **F**, evaluated at t	Velocity vector **V** at time t
Second derivative of **F**, evaluated at t	Acceleration vector **A** at time t
$\mathbf{T} = \dfrac{\mathbf{V}}{|\mathbf{V}|}$	Unit vector "pointing straight ahead"
$\mathbf{N} = \dfrac{d\mathbf{T}/dt}{|d\mathbf{T}/dt|}$	Unit vector perpendicular to path and "pointing in the direction the path is veering"
$\mathbf{A} = \dfrac{d^2s}{dt^2}\,\mathbf{T} + \dfrac{v^2}{r}\,\mathbf{N}$ (Theorem 4)	Acceleration vector is sum of two vectors: one is the acceleration if the particle were moving in a straight line; the other is the acceleration if the particle were moving on a circle whose radius is the radius of curvature

In Chap. 26 we develop another view of the acceleration vector and use it in the determination of planetary orbits.

18

Curve integrals

THE work done by a constant force pushing an object along a straight line is just the product of two numbers (see page 386). If the path of the object is a curve and perhaps the force varies in direction or magnitude, then, as we shall see, the work can be expressed as a curve integral. In this chapter we examine the concept of the curve integral and apply it to fluid flow. It is important to keep in mind that a curve integral is an ordinary definite integral in a special context.

Throughout the chapter we assume the existence of the necessary derivatives of the functions involved.

1. The curve integral of a vector field $(\overrightarrow{P,Q})$. If we push an object along a straight path with a constant force $\mathbf{F}$ (both the magnitude and direction of $\mathbf{F}$ being constant), then the work W which we do is $\mathbf{F} \cdot \Delta \mathbf{R}$, where $\Delta \mathbf{R}$ is the vector from the initial position to the final position of the object:

As an object is moved from A to B the work done is $\mathbf{F} \cdot \Delta \mathbf{R}$

If the force **F** varies in magnitude and direction, and if the path is not straight, then we are faced with the kind of problem on which the calculus thrives.

Let us imagine that an object moves from A to B along a curve C under a varying force **F**, which may be a combination of such forces as gravity, magnetism, and wind resistance.

An object moves from A to B on curve C

What is the total work W done by this varying force during the time interval $[a,b]$? Let us assume that the curve C is given parametrically by the equations

$$x = f(t) \qquad y = g(t)$$

for t in $[a,b]$, and that the force **F** equals $(\overrightarrow{P,Q})$, where P and Q depend on t.

To estimate W we divide the time interval $[a,b]$ into short intervals by means of the partition

(1) $$a = t_0 < t_1 < \cdots < t_n = b$$

and estimate the work done during the typical interval of time $[t_{i-1}, t_i]$. Let (x_i, y_i) be the point on the curve corresponding to time t_i. Let T_i be some number in $[t_{i-1}, t_i]$ and consider $\mathbf{F}(T_i) = (\overrightarrow{P(T_i), Q(T_i)})$. This diagram shows some of these intervals and corresponding $\mathbf{F}(T_i)$'s.

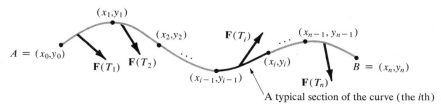

A typical section of the curve (the ith)

It is reasonable to assume that when the partition of $[a,b]$ is very fine, the typical section of the curve from (x_{i-1}, y_{i-1}) to (x_i, y_i) is "almost straight" and that **F** does not vary much in this section. Hence, as an estimate of the work done in moving the object over this typical section of the curve, let us use

$$\mathbf{F}(T_i) \cdot (\overrightarrow{x_i - x_{i-1}, y_i - y_{i-1}}) = P(T_i)(x_i - x_{i-1}) + Q(T_i)(y_i - y_{i-1})$$

Hence

(2) $$\sum_{i=1}^{n} [P(T_i)(x_i - x_{i-1}) + Q(T_i)(y_i - y_{i-1})]$$

is a reasonable estimate of the total work W.

To relate (2) to a definite integral over $[a,b]$ we apply the law of the mean to $x_i - x_{i-1}$ and $y_i - y_{i-1}$. By the law of the mean, we have

$$x_i - x_{i-1} = f'(T_i^*)(t_i - t_{i-1}) \qquad \text{and} \qquad y_i - y_{i-1} = g'(T_i^{**})(t_i - t_{i-1})$$

where T_i^* and T_i^{**} are in $[t_{i-1}, t_i]$. When the mesh of the partition (1) is small, T_i, T_i^*, and T_i^{**} are near each other; we will assume that for small mesh $f'(T_i^*)$ is near $f'(T_i)$ and $g'(T_i^{**})$ near $g'(T_i)$. Thus we expect that

(3) $$\sum_{i=1}^{n} [P(T_i) f'(T_i) + Q(T_i) g'(T_i)] (t_i - t_{i-1})$$

is a good estimate of W when the mesh of the partition of $[a,b]$ is small. For this reason we *define* the work W as a definite integral:

(4) $$W = \int_a^b [P(t) f'(t) + Q(t) g'(t)] \, dt$$

Example 1. We compute the work done by the force **F**, where the value of **F** at (x,y) is $\overrightarrow{(x,y)}$, while moving an object along the curve $x = t^2, y = t^3$ from $(0,0)$ to $(1,1)$. The force at time t is then $\mathbf{F}(t) = (t^2, t^3)$. Also,

$$\frac{dx}{dt} = 2t \qquad \frac{dy}{dt} = 3t^2$$

The definite integral (4) thus takes the form

(5) $$W = \int_0^1 [(t^2)(2t) + (t^3)(3t^2)] \, dt$$

Evaluation of (5) is straightforward:

$$W = \int_0^1 (2t^3 + 3t^5) \, dt = \left(\frac{2t^4}{4} + \frac{3t^6}{6} \right) \Big|_0^1 = \frac{2}{4} + \frac{3}{6} = 1$$

The definition we will now give for a curve integral requires merely that **F** be defined for points of the curve C. In practice **F** is usually defined on a larger set in the plane (as in Example 1), and is usually referred to as a vector field (in analogy with "gravitational field").

DEFINITION: *Curve integral.* Let $\mathbf{F} = (\overrightarrow{P,Q})$ be a vector field defined on a set including the curve C given parametrically by $x = f(t), y = g(t)$. The *curve integral* of **F** over C from $t = a$ to $t = b$ is the definite integral

(6) $$\int_a^b \left[P(x(t), y(t)) \frac{df}{dt} + Q(x(t), y(t)) \frac{dg}{dt} \right] dt$$

For brevity we usually write $(df/dt) \, dt$ as dx and $(dg/dt) \, dt$ as dy. The curve integral (6) is then written simply as

$$\int_a^b (P \, dx + Q \, dy) \qquad \text{or} \qquad \int_C (P \, dx + Q \, dy)$$

For instance, the curve integral that we computed in Example 1 is

$$\int_0^1 (x \, dx + y \, dy)$$

where $(x,y) = (t^2, t^3)$.

Just as in Chap. 1 we were led by various concrete problems to define the definite integral, consideration of force and work have now led us to define the purely mathematical concept of the curve integral. It has other applications than "work"; for instance, Example 4, on page 419, will apply it to fluid flow.

Example 2. We compute $\int_C (y\,dx + x\,dy)$ on two different paths from $(0,0)$ to $(1,2)$:
(a) The path along the parabola $y = 2x^2$ parameterized by $x = t$, $y = 2t^2$. We have $dx = dt$ and $dy = 4t\,dt$. Then

$$\int_0^1 [(2t^2)\,(dt) + (t)\,(4t\,dt)] = \int_0^1 6t^2\,dt = 6(\tfrac{1}{3}) = 2$$

(b) The path which goes in a straight line from $(0,0)$ to $(1,0)$ and then in a straight line from $(1,0)$ to $(1,2)$. Note that this path has the same beginning and end as the path in (a).

In this case the formulas for the parameterization of the curve differ in the two parts of the curve. The horizontal part of the path is described by $x = t$, $y = 0$, for t in $[0,1]$. On this part of the path we have

$$x = t \qquad y = 0 \qquad dx = dt \qquad dy = 0\,dt$$

Hence we have the curve integral

$$\int_0^1 [(0)\,(dt) + (t)\,(0\,dt)] = 0$$

The part of the path from $(1,0)$ to $(1,2)$ can be parameterized as follows

$$x = 1 \qquad y = 2(t - 1)$$

for t in $[1,2]$. (Thus from $t = 0$ to $t = 1$ we are on the horizontal part of the path, and from $t = 1$ to $t = 2$ we are on the vertical part.) Here $dx = 0\,dt$, and $dy = 2\,dt$. The curve integral takes the form

$$\int_1^2 [(2(t - 1))\,(0\,dt) + (1)\,(2\,dt)] = \int_1^2 2\,dt = 2$$

The answers in both (a) and (b) are 2. As we shall see in the next section, if $\mathbf{F}$ is given by the formula $\mathbf{F}(x,y) = \overrightarrow{(y,x)}$, then the integral of $\mathbf{F}$ over the curve C depends only on the beginning and end of C.

If the end points of C are the same ($A = B$), and if C does not otherwise intersect itself, C is called a *simple closed curve.* When C is a simple closed curve (usually assumed to be swept out counterclockwise), $\int_C (P\,dx + Q\,dy)$ is also denoted $\oint_C (P\,dx + Q\,dy)$ or $\oint (P\,dx + Q\,dy)$.

Example 3. We compute $\oint_C(-y\,dx + x\,dy)$ when C is the ellipse described parametrically by

$$x = a\cos t \qquad y = b\sin t$$

for t in $[0,2\pi]$. We have

$$\oint_C (-y\,dx + x\,dy) = \int_0^{2\pi} \left(-y\,\frac{dx}{dt} + x\,\frac{dy}{dt} \right) dt$$

$$= \int_0^{2\pi} [(-b \sin t)(-a \sin t) + (a \cos t)(b \cos t)]\, dt$$

$$= \int_0^{2\pi} ab\,(\sin^2 t + \cos^2 t)\, dt = \int_0^{2\pi} ab\, dt = 2\pi ab$$

As we shall see in the next chapter, $\oint_C (-y\, dx + x\, dy)$ always yields twice the area of the region enclosed by C (if C is counterclockwise).

Our next example shows how the curve integral is of use in the study of fluid flow.

Example 4. Let C be a simple closed curve bounding a region on the surface of a stream (C itself is motionless). The density of fluid per unit surface area is assumed constant. The velocity of flow at (x,y) is denoted by the vector $V(x,y)$. We assume a steady flow; that is, V may depend on (x,y) but not on time. The question we want to consider is this: At what rate is fluid escaping or entering the region bounded by C?

Where V is tangent to C, fluid neither enters nor leaves. Where V is not tangent to C, fluid is either entering or leaving across C, as in this diagram:

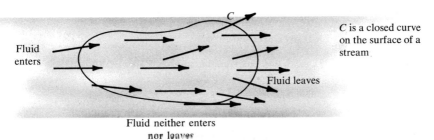

The component of V that interests us is the one perpendicular to C at each point on C. Let us keep a record of this "normal component" by means of a unit vector N, in the plane, perpendicular to C, and pointed to the region of the plane outside C. Then $V \cdot N$ records the rate of flow of the fluid past C:

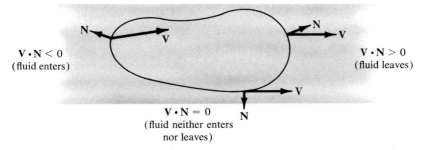

Let us now compute the total net *loss of fluid* across C. The amount of fluid *lost* crossing a short (nearly straight) section of the curve of length Δs is presumably proportional to Δs and is about

(7) $(V \cdot N)\, \Delta s$

where $V \cdot N$ is evaluated at some point in the section.

To put $\mathbf{V} \cdot \mathbf{N}$ into computable form, we introduce an xy coordinate system and express $\mathbf{V}$ and $\mathbf{N}$ in terms of their components along the x and y axes. We write $\mathbf{V} = \overrightarrow{(V_x, V_y)}$. To find the components of $\mathbf{N}$, let us first observe that

$$\left(\overrightarrow{\frac{dx}{ds}, \frac{dy}{ds}} \right) = \overrightarrow{(\cos \phi, \sin \phi)}$$

is a unit tangent vector. (In this equation ϕ is the angle of inclination of the tangent vector to the x axis and s denotes arc length along C.) The unit normal that we want has an angle of inclination $\phi - \pi/2$ (as a quick sketch will show). Hence

$$\mathbf{N} = \overrightarrow{\left(\cos \left(\phi - \frac{\pi}{2} \right), \sin \left(\phi - \frac{\pi}{2} \right) \right)}$$

By trigonometry,

$$\cos \left(\phi - \frac{\pi}{2} \right) = \sin \phi \quad \text{and} \quad \sin \left(\phi - \frac{\pi}{2} \right) = -\cos \phi$$

Hence $$\mathbf{N} = \overrightarrow{(\sin \phi, -\cos \phi)} = \left(\frac{dy}{ds}, -\frac{dx}{ds} \right)$$

Thus

(8) $$\mathbf{V} \cdot \mathbf{N} = V_x \frac{dy}{ds} - V_y \frac{dx}{ds}$$

In view of (7) and (8) we would expect the total net loss of fluid past C to be the curve integral

$$\int_{s=0}^{s=\text{length of } C} \left(V_x \frac{dy}{ds} - V_y \frac{dx}{ds} \right) ds$$

This is expressed in differential notation as

(9) $$\oint_C (V_x \, dy - V_y \, dx) \quad \text{or} \quad \oint_C (-V_y \, dx + V_x \, dy)$$

where the dx is to the left of the dy in the latter form, as is customary.

If in the preceding example we designated the x component of $\mathbf{V}$ as Q, and the y component as $-P$ (which we are free to do), then (9) takes the form

$$\text{Fluid loss} = \oint_C (P \, dx + Q \, dy)$$

Thus we may always interpret the curve integral $\int_C (P \, dx + Q \, dy)$ (where C need not be closed) either as the total work accomplished by the force that at the point (x,y) has the value $\mathbf{F}(x,y) = \overrightarrow{(P,Q)}$, or as the total net loss across the curve C of fluid whose velocity vector at the point (x,y) is $\mathbf{V}(x,y) = \overrightarrow{(Q,-P)}$.

EXERCISES

1. Let C be the straight path from $(a,0)$ to $(b,0)$ parameterized as $x = a + (b - a)t$, $y = 0$, for t in $[0,1]$. Show that $\int_C (f(x) \, dx + 0 \, dy)$ equals (a) the definite integral

$$\int_a^b f(x) \, dx \text{ if } a < b; \text{ or } (b) \int_a^b f(x) \, dx \text{ if } a > b.$$

2. Compute $\int_C x^3 y \, dx$ if C goes from $(0,1)$ to $(1,0)$ along (a) the line $x + y = 1$, with the parameterization $x = t$, $y = 1 - t$; (b) the circle $x^2 + y^2 = 1$, with the parameterization $x = \sin t, y = \cos t$. [Answer: (a) $\frac{1}{20}$; (b) $\frac{2}{15}$]

3. (a) Compute $\oint_C (-y\,dx + x\,dy)$ over the curve bordering the region bounded by the curve $y = x^3$ and the lines $x = a$ and $y = 0$. Assume that a is positive.
(b) Compute the area of the region enclosed by the path.
[Answer: (a) $a^4/2$; (b) $a^4/4$]

4. Let C be the closed curve $x = 2\cos t$, $y = 3\sin t$, for t in $[0,2\pi]$.
(a) Graph C.
(b) Compute $\oint_C [x^2\,dx + (y + 1)\,dy]$.
(c) Devise a work problem whose answer is the integral in (b).
(d) Devise a fluid-flow problem whose answer is the integral in (b).
[Answer: (b) 0]

5. Compute $\oint_C (-y\,dx + x\,dy)$, where C sweeps out the boundary of the rectangle in the first quadrant whose vertices are $(0,0)$, $(a,0)$, (a,b), $(0,b)$. (Answer: $2ab$)

6. Compute $\int_C (xy\,dx + x^2\,dy)$ if C goes from $(0,0)$ to $(1,1)$ on (a) the line $y = x$, parameterized as $x = t$, $y = t$; (b) the line $y = x$, parameterized as $x = t^2$, $y = t^2$; (c) the parabola $y = x^2$, parameterized as $y = t^2$, $x = t$; (d) the polygonal path from $(0,0)$ to $(0,1)$ to $(1,1)$, parameterized conveniently.
[Answer: (a) $\frac{2}{3}$; (b) $\frac{2}{3}$; (c) $\frac{3}{4}$; (d) $\frac{1}{2}$]

7. The gravitational force $\mathbf{F}$ of the earth, located at the origin $(0,0)$ of a rectangular coordinate system, on a certain particle at the point (x,y) is

$$\left(\frac{-x}{(\sqrt{x^2 + y^2})^3}, \frac{-y}{(\sqrt{x^2 + y^2})^3} \right)$$

Compute the total work done by $\mathbf{F}$ if the particle goes from $(2,0)$ to $(0,1)$ along (a) the ellipse $x = 2\cos t$, $y = \sin t$; (b) the line $x = 2 - 2t$, $y = t$.
[Answer: (a) $\frac{1}{2}$; (b) $\frac{1}{2}$]

8. Let the velocity vector $\mathbf{V}$ of fluid at the point (x,y) be $((x + 1)^3, y)$. Let C be the unit circle described parametrically as $x = \cos t$, $y = \sin t$, for t in $[0,2\pi]$.
(a) Draw $\mathbf{V}$ at eight convenient equally spaced points on the circle.
(b) Is fluid tending to leave or enter the region bounded by C; that is, is the net outward flow positive or negative? [Answer on the basis of your diagram in (a).]
(c) Compute the net outward flow with the aid of a curve integral.
[Answer: (c) 3π]

9. Compute
$$\int_C \left(\frac{-y\,dx}{x^2 + y^2} + \frac{x\,dy}{x^2 + y^2} \right)$$

where C goes from $(1,0)$ to $(1,1)$ along (a) the straight line $x = 1$, parameterized as $x = 1$, $y = t$; (b) the curve parameterized as $x = (2t - 1)^2$, $y = t$; (c) the circular path parameterized as $x = \cos 2\pi t$, $y = \sin 2\pi t$, and then followed by the path $x = 1$, $y = t - 1$, t in $[1,2]$. [Answer: (a) $\pi/4$; (b) $\pi/4$; (c) $9\pi/4$]

10. For a certain closed curve C and a certain vector field $\overrightarrow{(P,Q)}$, assume that $\oint (P\,dx + Q\,dy) = 0$. Translate this into an assertion about (a) the total work accomplished by an appropriate force; (b) the total net loss of fluid having an appropriate velocity vector.

11. (a) Let $x = f(t)$, $y = g(t)$ be any parameterization of a curve from $(0,0)$ to $(1,2)$. Show that $\int_C (y\,dx + x\,dy)$ equals 2 (this extends Example 2).
(b) Show that $\int_C (y\,dx + x\,dy)$ depends only on the end points of any curve C.
(c) Show that $\oint_C (x\,dy + y\,dx) = 0$ for any closed curve.

12. As a parameter for C we may use arc length s. If C is a curve from $(1,2)$ to $(3,5)$, evaluate

$$\int_C 7 \frac{dx}{ds}\, ds + 10 \frac{dy}{ds}\, ds.$$

13. Verify that $\oint_C (-y\, dx + x\, dy)$ is twice the area of the region enclosed by C when C is (a) the square path from $(a,0)$ to $(0,a)$ to $(-a,0)$ to $(0,-a)$ and back to $(a,0)$; (b) the triangular path from $(0,0)$ to $(a,0)$ to $(0,b)$ and back to $(0,0)$. Assume that a and b are positive.

$$\square \quad \square \quad \square$$

14. Let C^* be the curve C swept out in the reverse order. That is, if C has the parameterization $x = f(t)$, $y = g(t)$, for t in $[a,b]$, then C^* has the parameterization $x = f(b + a - t)$, $y = g(b + a - t)$, for t in $[a,b]$. Show that $\int_{C^*}(P\, dx + Q\, dy) = -\int_C (P\, dx + Q\, dy)$.

15. Let $(dx/ds,\, dy/ds)$ be the varying unit tangent to the curve C. Show that

$$\int_C \left(\frac{dx}{ds}\, dx + \frac{dy}{ds}\, dy \right)$$

equals the length of C.

16. Our definition of a curve integral involves a parameterization of the curve C. State and prove a theorem asserting that the value of the curve integral does not depend on the particular parameterization we may choose (as long as it sweeps out the curve in the desired direction). (Hint: The substitution theorem, page 185, will be useful.)

17. (a) Let a closed curve C be parameterized by arc length s. Let ϕ be the angle that the tangent vector makes with the x axis. Show that $\oint_C \cos\phi\, ds = 0 = \oint_C \sin\phi\, ds$. (b) If C is not closed, show that $\int_C \cos\phi\, ds$ and $\int_C \sin\phi\, ds$ are determined by the end points of R.

18. The gravitational force of the earth on a satellite located at the point (x,y,z) in space is

$$\left(\frac{-x}{(\sqrt{x^2 + y^2 + z^2})^3},\ \frac{-y}{(\sqrt{x^2 + y^2 + z^2})^3},\ \frac{-z}{(\sqrt{x^2 + y^2 + z^2})^3} \right)$$

Show that the total work done by gravity during one orbit of the satellite is 0.

2. The curve integral of a gradient field ∇F.

One special but important way a vector field $\overrightarrow{(P,Q)}$ arises in practice is as the gradient of a scalar function F. Since $\nabla F = (\partial F/\partial x,\, \partial F/\partial y)$, we have

$$P = \frac{\partial F}{\partial x} \qquad Q = \frac{\partial F}{\partial y}$$

For instance, consider $F(x,y) = 1/\sqrt{x^2 + y^2}$, which is defined for $(x,y) \neq (0,0)$. Then

$$\nabla F = \left(\frac{-x}{(\sqrt{x^2 + y^2})^3},\ \frac{-y}{(\sqrt{x^2 + y^2})^3} \right)$$

By introducing polar coordinates (r,θ), we can write ∇F more simply as

$$\nabla F = \left(\frac{\overrightarrow{-r\cos\theta}}{r^3}, \frac{\overrightarrow{-r\sin\theta}}{r^3}\right) = \frac{1}{r^2}\overrightarrow{(-\cos\theta, -\sin\theta)}$$

Thus the gradient ∇F in this case is always pointed toward the origin. Since $\overrightarrow{(-\cos\theta, -\sin\theta)}$ is a unit vector, the magnitude of ∇F is $1/r^2$, and hence is inversely proportional to the square of the distance of (x,y) from the origin. The gradient field ∇F therefore looks like this:

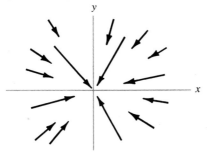

∇F is directed toward the origin; its magnitude diminishes as the point (x,y) recedes from the origin

A physicist would call F the potential function and ∇F the force function of a gravitational field. The most important property of a gradient vector field is expressed in the next theorem, which may be considered a generalization of the fundamental theorem of calculus.

THEOREM 1. *If $\overrightarrow{(P,Q)}$ is a gradient function ∇F, that is, $P = F_x$ and $Q = F_y$, then*

$$\int_C (P\,dx + Q\,dy) = F(B) - F(A)$$

where A is the initial point of the curve C, and B is its terminal point. Consequently the curve integral of a gradient function depends only on the end points of the curve C.

PROOF. Let C have the parameterization $x = f(t), y = g(t)$, where t is in $[a,b]$. Then $A = (f(a), g(a))$ and $B = (f(b), g(b))$. We have

$$\int_C (P\,dx + Q\,dy) = \int_C \left(\frac{\partial F}{\partial x}\frac{df}{dt} + \frac{\partial F}{\partial y}\frac{dg}{dt}\right)dt$$

The right-hand integrand is reminiscent of the chain rule (Theorem 2, page 366). To be specific, let us introduce H, the function of t defined by

$$H(t) = F(f(t), g(t))$$

The chain rule asserts that

$$\frac{dH}{dt} = F_x(f(t), g(t))\frac{df}{dt} + F_y(f(t), g(t))\frac{dg}{dt}$$

Thus our curve integral can be written as

$$\int_C (P\,dx + Q\,dy) = \int_a^b \frac{dH}{dt}\,dt$$

By the fundamental theorem of calculus,

$$\int_a^b \frac{dH}{dt}\, dt = H(b) - H(a) = F(f(b), g(b)) - F(f(a), g(a)) = F(B) - F(A)$$

The theorem is proved.

Example 1. From Theorem 1 we deduce that $\int_C (y\, dx + x\, dy)$ depends only on the end points of C, for $\overrightarrow{(y,x)}$ is the gradient of the function F given by $F(x,y) = xy$. If C is any curve from $A = (x_1,y_1)$ to $B = (x_2,y_2)$, then we have $\int_C (y\, dx + x\, dy) = x_2y_2 - x_1y_1$. This is in agreement with Example 2 on page 418.

The most important physical law derivable from Theorem 1 is that the work involved in moving a particle from one point to another by a gravitational or electric field is independent of the path along which the particle moves.

THEOREM 2. *If $\overrightarrow{(P,Q)}$ is a gradient field ∇F, then*

$$\oint_C (P\, dx + Q\, dy) = 0$$

for any closed path C.

PROOF. This is an immediate consequence of Theorem 1. In the case of a closed path, we have $A = B$; hence $F(B) - F(A)$ equals 0. The proof is done.

In view of Theorem 2, it is of interest to know when a vector field $\overrightarrow{(P,Q)}$ is expressible as a gradient field of some scalar function F. One test, rather negative in character, is provided by the next theorem.

THEOREM 3. *If $\overrightarrow{(P,Q)}$ is expressible as a gradient field of some scalar function F, then*

$$\frac{\partial P}{\partial y} = \frac{\partial Q}{\partial x}$$

PROOF. Assume that $\overrightarrow{(P,Q)}$ is the gradient field of the function F. That is,

$$P = \frac{\partial F}{\partial x} \quad \text{and} \quad Q = \frac{\partial F}{\partial y}$$

Then

$$\frac{\partial P}{\partial y} = \frac{\partial(\partial F/\partial x)}{\partial y} \quad \text{and} \quad \frac{\partial Q}{\partial x} = \frac{\partial(\partial F/\partial y)}{\partial x}$$

Because of the equality of the mixed partials F_{xy} and F_{yx} (see Theorem 1, page 372), we have

$$\frac{\partial P}{\partial y} = \frac{\partial Q}{\partial x}$$

and the theorem is proved.

Example 2. We show that $\overrightarrow{(P,Q)} = \overrightarrow{(e^x \cos y, e^x \sin y)}$ is *not* expressible as a gradient function. We have

$$\frac{\partial P}{\partial y} = -e^x \sin y \qquad \frac{\partial Q}{\partial x} = e^x \sin y$$

Thus $\partial P/\partial y$ is not equal to $\partial Q/\partial x$.

In Chap. 19 we present a method for deciding whether a vector function is a gradient function, and for constructing the pertinent scalar function F if it exists.

We may say, by way of summary, that if the vector function $\overrightarrow{(P,Q)}$ is of the form ∇F for some scalar function F, then $\int_C (P\,dx + Q\,dy)$ depends only on the end points of C, that $\oint (P\,dx + Q\,dy)$ equals 0 for any closed curve, and finally,

$$\frac{\partial P}{\partial y} = \frac{\partial Q}{\partial x}$$

EXERCISES

1. Show that the vector function $\overrightarrow{(3x^2y, 7xy^2)}$ is not a gradient, (a) using Theorem 3; (b) using Theorem 2 and constructing a closed curve around which $\oint_C (3x^2y\,dx + 7xy^2\,dy)$ is not 0.
2. Show that $\overrightarrow{(x + 3y, 3x + 4y)}$ is a gradient by constructing an appropriate F.
3. Show that $\overrightarrow{(e^{-x}\cos y, e^{-x}\sin y)}$ is a gradient by constructing an appropriate F.
4. A particle is moved along a wire from $(0,0)$ to $(1,1)$ by the force $\mathbf{F} = \overrightarrow{(3x^2y, xy)}$. Which of the following three polygonal paths from $(0,0)$ to $(1,1)$ involves the least work? (a) From $(0,0)$ to $(1,0)$ to $(1,1)$; (b) from $(0,0)$ directly to $(1,1)$; (c) from $(0,0)$ to $(0,1)$ to $(1,1)$? Explain.   [Answer: (a)]
5. The electric field $\mathbf{E}$ at any point (x,y) due to a point charge q at $(0,0)$ is equal to

$$\mathbf{E} = \frac{q\mathbf{U}}{4\pi \, \varepsilon r^2}$$

where r is the distance from the charge to the point (x,y), and $\mathbf{U}$ is the unit vector directed from the charge to the point (x,y). Evaluate the work done by the field when a particle is moved from $(1,0)$ to $(2,0)$ along (a) the x axis; (b) the rectangular path from $(1,0)$ to $(1,\frac{1}{2})$ to $(2,\frac{1}{2})$ to $(2,0)$. Is there a difference between the work done in (a) and that done in (b)?
6. Devise a specific velocity vector field for fluid flow such that the net loss of fluid past every closed curve is 0 (other than the trivial case $\mathbf{V}(x,y) = \overrightarrow{(0,0)}$, in which the water is still).
7. Decide whether the following vector fields are gradients (if you answer no, explain; if you answer yes, give an appropriate function F).
   (a) $\overrightarrow{(3x^2y, x^3)}$; (b) $\overrightarrow{(2x^2y, x^3)}$; (c) $\overrightarrow{(2x + 3y, 3x - 4y)}$.
8. Consider the vector field defined by

$$\mathbf{V}(x,y) = \overrightarrow{(P,Q)} = \left(\frac{-y}{x^2 + y^2}, \frac{x}{x^2 + y^2} \right)$$

(a) Verify that $\dfrac{\partial P}{\partial y} = \dfrac{\partial Q}{\partial x}$.

(b) Show that $\oint_C (P\,dx + Q\,dy) \neq 0$, where C is the circle with radius 1 and center at $(0,0)$.

(c) Do (a) and (b) contradict each other? Explain.

□ □ □

9. A motorboat goes back and forth on a straight measured mile at a constant speed V relative to the water. Show that the time required for a round trip is always less

when there is no current than when there is a constant current W. (Assume that the component of W along the route is less than V and greater than 0. If the component along the route were larger than V, the boat couldn't make a round trip.)

10. (See Exercise 9.) An aircraft traveling at constant air speed V traverses a closed horizontal curve marked on the ground. Show that the time required for one complete trip is always less when there is no wind than when there is a constant wind W. (Assume that $W = |\mathbf{W}|$ is less than V, so that the plane never meets an insuperable head wind.)

11. State and prove the analogs of Theorems 1 and 2 for vector fields and curves in three dimensions.

3. Other notations for curve integrals.

Depending on circumstances, various notations are used for the curve integral of a vector field. We first present the *vector notation*. For instance, consider the curve integral for the work done by the varying force $\mathbf{F} = (\overrightarrow{P,Q})$, which is

$$(1) \qquad W = \int_C (P\,dx + Q\,dy)$$

Now, in the case of a *constant* force $\mathbf{F}$ pushing a particle from A to B in a straight path along the vector $\mathbf{R}$, the work done is

$$\mathbf{F} \cdot \mathbf{R}$$

This suggests that even if $\mathbf{F}$ is not constant, we introduce as a memory aid the "formal" vector

$$d\mathbf{R} = \overrightarrow{(dx,dy)}$$

Then Equation (1) takes the convenient and suggestive form

$$W = \int_C \mathbf{F} \cdot d\mathbf{R}$$

In this notation, Theorem 1 now reads: If F is a (scalar) function, then

$$\int_C \nabla F \cdot d\mathbf{R} = F(B) - F(A)$$

In contrast to the vector notation just discussed, the *differential notation* is suggested by the definition of the differential of a function F of two variables:

$$dF = \frac{\partial F}{\partial x}\,dx + \frac{\partial F}{\partial y}\,dy$$

We define a *differential form* as an expression of the form

$$P\,dx + Q\,dy$$

where P and Q are functions of x and y. Then

$$\int_C (P\,dx + Q\,dy)$$

is defined as in Sec. 1. A differential form $P\,dx + Q\,dy$ is called *exact* if it is of the form dF for some function F of x and y. That is, $P\,dx + Q\,dy$ is exact if there is a function F such that

$$P = \frac{\partial F}{\partial x} \quad \text{and} \quad Q = \frac{\partial F}{\partial y}$$

Note that if $P\,dx + Q\,dy$ is an exact differential form, then $\partial P/\partial y = \partial Q/\partial x$. (A differential form is thus the analog of a vector field, while an exact differential form is the analog of a gradient field.) In the differential notation, Theorem 1 takes the terse form

$$\int_C dF = F(B) - F(A)$$

The vector and differential notations are especially convenient for the study in advanced calculus of integrals over surfaces.

EXERCISES

1. (a) Show that $2xy\,dx + x^2\,dy$ is an exact differential form.
   (b) Show that $2xy\,dx - x^2\,dy$ is not exact.
2. Find two different P's that make the differential form $P\,dx + x^3\,dy$ exact.
3. Find two different Q's that make the differential form $xy^3\,dx + Q\,dy$ exact.
4. (a) Compute the differential dF if $F(x,y) = \ln(x^2 + y^2)$.
   (b) Evaluate $\int_C dF$, where C is the arc of a circle given parametrically by $x = 3\cos t$, $y = 3\sin t$, for t in $[0, \pi/2]$.
5. Let $\mathbf{T}$ be the varying unit tangent vector along the curve C. Show that $\int_C \mathbf{T} \cdot d\mathbf{R}$ is the length of C (a) intuitively; (b) by using the definition of curve integral, page 417, and using arc length s as the parameter.
6. Let A, B, m, n, p, and q be constants. Prove that these two statements about the differential form, $P\,dx + Q\,dy = Ax^m y^n\,dx + Bx^p y^q\,dy$, are equivalent: "It is exact." "In this case $\partial P/\partial y = \partial Q/\partial x$."
7. Let $F(x,y) = e^x \sin y + \ln(1 + x^2 + y^2)$, and let C be the curve $x = t^2$, $y = t^3$ from $(1,1)$ to $(4,8)$. Compute (a) $\int_C \nabla F \cdot d\mathbf{R}$, (b) $\int_C dF$.
8. Let $\mathbf{V}$ be the velocity vector of fluid flow. Why do you think $\int_C \mathbf{V} \cdot d\mathbf{R}$ is called the *circulation* around C?
9. Let C be part of a level curve of $z = F(x,y)$. Compute $\int_C \nabla F \cdot d\mathbf{R}$.

□ □ □

10. Assume that P and Q are such that $\oint (P\,dx + Q\,dy) = 0$ for any closed path in the plane. Show that there exists a function F defined on the plane such that $\int_C (P\,dx + Q\,dy) = F(B) - F(A)$, where A is the initial point and B is the terminal point of C, an arbitrary curve in the plane.
11. Show that any F constructed in Exercise 10 has the property that

$$\frac{\partial F}{\partial x} = P \quad \text{and} \quad \frac{\partial F}{\partial y} = Q$$

[Hint: To prove this at (x,y) consider a short curve starting at (x,y) and consisting of just a horizontal or vertical line segment.]
12. (a) Compute dF if $F(x,y) = \tan^{-1}(y/x)$.
    (b) Compute $\oint_C dF$, where C is given parametrically by $x = \cos 2\pi t$, $y = \sin 2\pi t$, for t in $[0,1]$.
    (c) The answer in (b) is not 0. Does this violate Theorem 2 on page 424?

13. The planimeter is a mechanical device for finding the area of a region enclosed by a curve C. It consists of two rods OA and AB hinged at A. Because O is fixed, A moves on an arc of a circle as we guide B around the curve C. A small vertical wheel at the midpoint of AB is free to turn on an axis parallel to AB. In this exercise and in Exercise 21, page 437, we will show that *the distance that the wheel turns as B traverses the curve C is proportional to the area of the region enclosed by C.* Since the wheel is marked in such a way that we can read the distance through which it turns, we can indirectly determine the desired area.

Let AB have length p, let the wheel W sweep out C_W as B sweeps out C_B, and let A be constrained to the arc of a circle C_A. Then let θ be the angle of inclination of AB, as in this diagram:

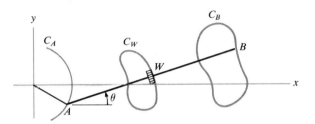

The length of AB is p

Introduce the parameter t, representing time. We now obtain a formula for the distance through which the wheel W turns. (Note that if the plane of the wheel is always perpendicular to C_W, it does not turn at all. On the other hand, if it is always tangent to C_W, then the wheel turns a distance equal to the arc length of C_W.) At time t let $A = (x,y) = (f(t), g(t))$, and $\theta = \theta(t)$.

(a) Show that $W = (x + (p/2) \cos \theta(t), y + (p/2) \sin \theta(t))$.

(b) Show that at time t the wheel has the direction given by that of the unit vector $\mathbf{U} = (-\sin \theta, \cos \theta)$.

(c) Letting $\mathbf{R}$ denote the vector whose tail is at the origin and whose head is at W, show why $\oint_{C_W} \mathbf{U} \cdot d\mathbf{R}$ represents the distance the wheel turns.

(d) With the aid of (a) and (b), show that the curve integral in (c) reduces to

$$\int_a^b \left(-\sin \theta \frac{dx}{dt} + \cos \theta \frac{dy}{dt} + \frac{p}{2} \frac{d\theta}{dt} \right) dt$$

where t goes from a to b.

(e) Show that if the arm OA is not permitted to make a complete revolution, then $\int_a^b (p/2)(d\theta/dt)\, dt = 0$. Thus the total distance through which the wheel turns is simply $\int_a^b [(-\sin \theta)\, dx/dt + (\cos \theta)\, dy/dt]\, dt$. Exercise 21, page 437, where we compute the area of the region enclosed by C_B, will complete the theory of the planimeter.

4. Summary.   In this chapter we introduced the curve integral of a vector field, an ordinary definite integral arising in a special context. The concept has been illustrated by the work done by a variable force and by the net loss of fluid past a curve.

We have shown that if a vector field $\overrightarrow{(P,Q)}$ is the gradient of some function F, that is, $\overrightarrow{(P,Q)} = \nabla F$, then $\int_C (P\,dx + Q\,dy)$ depends only on the end points of C, and not on the particular path joining them.

The "formal vector" and differential notations for curved integrals have been described. For instance, in the formal vector notation, the work done by the force **F** takes the form $\int_C \mathbf{F} \cdot d\mathbf{R}$. The theorem stating that the curve integral of a gradient depends only on the end points of a curve then becomes a theorem on exact differential forms.

The curve integral will be our major tool in Chap. 19.

19

Green's theorem in the plane

THE fundamental theorem of calculus relates the behavior of one function F at the ends of an interval to the behavior of a related function dF/dx throughout the interval:

$$\int_a^b \frac{dF}{dx}\, dx = F(b) - F(a)$$

As we shall soon see, Green's theorem relates an integral around a simple closed curve to a definite integral over the region R bounded by the curve

$$\int_R \left(\frac{\partial Q}{\partial x} - \frac{\partial P}{\partial y} \right) dA = \oint (P\, dx + Q\, dy)$$

Thus Green's theorem may be considered the two-dimensional analog of the fundamental theorem of calculus. We will prove Green's theorem and illustrate it with some important applications.

1. Green's theorem. In order to provide a physical interpretation of Green's theorem, we return to the problem of fluid flow across the curve C, in Example 4,

430

page 419. If we denote the velocity at the point (x,y) by $\mathbf{V}=(\overrightarrow{Q,-P})$, then we see that

$$\text{Net loss of fluid per unit time across } C = \oint_C (P\,dx + Q\,dy).$$

Now, the net loss past C is the same as the net loss of fluid from the region R bounded by C, since the only way that fluid enters or leaves R is across C. Let us calculate the net loss from the viewpoint of R rather than of C. Consider the net loss from a typical small rectangle of dimensions Δx and Δy in R. Let its lower-left-hand corner A have the coordinates (a,b), and let the other vertices be B, C, D, as in this diagram.

The loss from this small rectangle is precisely

$$\int_A^B (P\,dx + Q\,dy) + \int_B^C (P\,dx + Q\,dy) + \int_C^D (P\,dx + Q\,dy) + \int_D^A (P\,dx + Q\,dy)$$

where the integrations are performed along straight paths. Let us estimate this sum when Δx and Δy are small.

First, let us consider the two integrals over the horizontal edges AB and CD. We have

$$\int_A^B (P\,dx + Q\,dy) = \int_A^B P\,dx \qquad \text{and} \qquad \int_C^D (P\,dx + Q\,dy) = \int_C^D P\,dx$$

since in both cases y is constant and thus $dy\ [=(dy/dt)\,dt]$ is 0. Now

$$\int_A^B P\,dx = \int_a^{a+\Delta x} P(x,b)\,dx$$

and

$$\int_C^D P\,dx = -\int_D^C P\,dx = -\int_D^C P(x,b+\Delta y)\,dx = -\int_a^{a+\Delta x} P(x,b+\Delta y)\,dx$$

Hence

(1) $$\int_A^B P\,dx + \int_C^D P\,dx = \int_a^{a+\Delta x} [P(x,b) - P(x,b+\Delta y)]\,dx$$

but, by the law of the mean,

$$P(x,b) - P(x,b+\Delta y) = -P_y(x,Y)\,\Delta y$$

for some Y, with $b < Y < b + \Delta y$. Assuming that P_y is continuous, we have $P_y(x,Y)$ approximately equal to $P_y(a,b)$; hence the last integral in (1) is approximately

$$\int_a^{a+\Delta x} - P_y(a,b)\,\Delta y\,dx = -P_y(a,b)\,\Delta y\,\Delta x$$

We have obtained the estimate

$$\int_A^B (P\,dx + Q\,dy) + \int_C^D (P\,dx + Q\,dy) = -P_y(a,b)\,\Delta y\,\Delta x$$

In a similar manner it can be shown that (approximately)

$$\int_B^C (P\,dx + Q\,dy) + \int_D^A (P\,dx + Q\,dy) = Q_x(a,b)\,\Delta y\,\Delta x$$

Thus the flow out of the typical small rectangle, whose area is $\Delta A = \Delta x\,\Delta y$, is approximately

$$[Q_x(a,b) - P_y(a,b)]\,\Delta A$$

Since the net flow out of R is the sum of the net flows out of all such small rectangles, we may expect that

$$\text{Net flow out of } R = \int_R (Q_x - P_y)\,dA$$

We already have an expression for the net flow through the border C, and thus we expect that

(2) $$\int_R (Q_x - P_y)\,dA = \oint_C (P\,dx + Q\,dy)$$

The study of fluid flow suggested the mathematical assertion (2). We now prove that (2) holds under fairly general conditions.

THEOREM 1: *Green's theorem.*   Let C be a simple, closed curve in the xy plane such that any vertical or horizontal line meets it at most twice. Let R be the region bounded by C. If the functions P and Q have continuous partial derivatives throughout R, then

$$\int_R (Q_x - P_y)\,dA = \oint_C (P\,dx + Q\,dy)$$

where C is swept out counterclockwise.

PROOF.   We shall prove that $\int_R P_y\,dA = -\oint_C P\,dx$. A similar proof will show that $\int_R Q_x\,dA = \oint_C Q\,dy$. Green's theorem is an immediate consequence of these two results.

Let the region R have the following description:

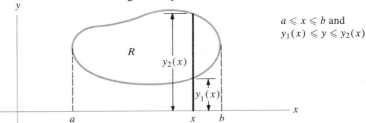

$a \leqslant x \leqslant b$ and
$y_1(x) \leqslant y \leqslant y_2(x)$

Using a repeated integral in rectangular coordinates to evaluate $\int_R P_y\,dA$, we have

$$\int_R P_y\,dA = \int_a^b \left(\int_{y_1(x)}^{y_2(x)} P_y\,dy \right) dx$$

Now,
$$\int_{y_1(x)}^{y_2(x)} P_y \, dy \underset{\text{FTC}}{=} P(x, y_2(x)) - P(x, y_1(x))$$

Hence

(3)
$$\int_R P_y \, dA = \int_a^b P(x, y_2(x)) \, dx - \int_a^b P(x, y_1(x)) \, dx$$

Now let us consider $\oint_C P \, dx$. We break the closed path C into two successive paths, one along the bottom part of R, described by $y = y_1(x)$, the other along the top part of R, described by $y = y_2(x)$. We denote the bottom path C_1 and the top path C_2.

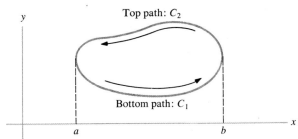

Thus
$$\oint_C P \, dx = \int_{C_1} P \, dx + \int_{C_2} P \, dx$$

but
$$\int_{C_1} P \, dx = \int_a^b P(x, y_1(x)) \, dx$$

and
$$\int_{C_2} P \, dx = \int_b^a P(x, y_2(x)) \, dx = -\int_a^b P(x, y_2(x)) \, dx$$

Thus

(4)
$$\int_C P \, dx = \int_a^b P(x, y_1(x)) \, dx - \int_a^b P(x, y_2(x)) \, dx$$

Comparison of (3) and (4) shows that $\int_R P_y \, dA = -\oint_C P \, dx$. A similar computation shows that $\int_R Q_x \, dA = \oint_C Q \, dy$, and proves Green's theorem.

Green's theorem holds for regions R more general than the type described in Theorem 1. For instance, the border of R may meet the vertical lines $x = a$ and $x = b$ in an interval, not just a single point. (A slight modification of the proof of Theorem 1 shows that Green's theorem holds for such a region.) An analogous statement holds for horizontal lines. Green's theorem thus holds for any triangle (even if one or more of its sides is horizontal or vertical); it can be shown that this implies that it holds for any polygon.

The next two theorems are important consequences of Green's theorem.

THEOREM 2. *If C and R satisfy the hypothesis of Theorem 1, then*

$$Area \ of \ R = \tfrac{1}{2} \oint_C (-y \, dx + x \, dy)$$

where C is swept out counterclockwise.

PROOF. By Green's theorem,

$$\oint_C (-y\, dx + x\, dy) = \int_R \left(\frac{\partial x}{\partial x} - \frac{\partial(-y)}{\partial y} \right) dA = \int_R (1+1)\, dA = 2\,(\text{area of } R)$$

This proves the theorem.

Theorem 2 is already illustrated by Example 3, page 418. It will be applied in the next two sections of this chapter.

For the next theorem we need the concept of a simply connected region. A region S is *simply connected* if, whenever a simple closed curve C lies in S, the region bounded by C is also in S. Thus a simply connected region "has no holes." A square is simply connected but a ring bounded by two concentric circles is *not* simply connected.

THEOREM 3. *Let* $P_y = Q_x$ *throughout a simply connected region* S. *If* C *is a simple closed curve in* S *and satisfies the hypothesis of Theorem 1, then* $\oint_C (P\, dx + Q\, dy) = 0$.

PROOF. Let R be the region bounded by C. Thus R lies in S, and $P_y = Q_x$ throughout R. By Green's theorem, we have

$$\oint_C (P\, dx + Q\, dy) = \int_R (Q_x - P_y)\, dA$$

But throughout R we have $Q_x - P_y = 0$; hence $\int_R (Q_x - P_y)\, dA = 0$. The proof is done.

It follows from Theorem 3 that if $P_y = Q_x$ throughout a simply connected region, then $\int_C (P\, dx + Q\, dy)$ depends only on the end points of C. Letting A be a fixed base point and $B = (x,y)$ be an arbitrary point in the region we define

$$F(B) = \int_C (P\, dx + Q\, dy)$$

where C is any curve in the region from A to B. It can be shown that $F_x = P$ and $F_y = Q$. (See Exercise 11, page 427.) Thus (P,Q) is a gradient field. This is the proper converse of Theorem 3, page 424.

The next example shows that "simply connected" cannot be deleted from the hypothesis of Theorem 3.

Example. Let R be the region bounded by the circles of radius 1 and 3, center $(0,0)$. Let C be the circle of radius 2, center $(0,0)$, parameterized as

$$(x,y) = (2\cos t,\ 2\sin t) \qquad t \text{ in } [0,2\pi]$$

We assert that if

$$P = \frac{-y}{x^2 + y^2} \qquad \text{and} \qquad Q = \frac{x}{x^2 + y^2}$$

then $P_y = Q_x$, yet $\oint_C (P\, dx + Q\, dy)$ is not 0.

A straightforward computation shows that

$$P_y = \frac{y^2 - x^2}{(x^2 + y^2)^2} = Q_x$$

On the other hand, for the circle C we have $dx = -2 \sin t \, dt$, $dy = 2 \cos t \, dt$, and $x^2 + y^2 = 2^2 = 4$. Thus

$$\oint_C (P \, dx + Q \, dy) = \oint_C \left[\left(\frac{-y}{x^2 + y^2} \right) dx + \left(\frac{x}{x^2 + y^2} \right) dy \right]$$

$$= \int_0^{2\pi} \left[\left(\frac{-2 \sin t}{4} \right) (-2 \sin t) + \left(\frac{2 \cos t}{4} \right) (2 \cos t) \right] dt$$

$$= \int_0^{2\pi} (\sin^2 t + \cos^2 t) \, dt = \int_0^{2\pi} 1 \, dt = 2\pi$$

which is not 0.

EXERCISES

1. By computations, verify Green's theorem when R is the disk of radius 1 and center $(0,0)$, and (a) $P = x^2$, $Q = y^2$; (b) $P = y^2$, $Q = x^2$.

2. In the proof of Green's theorem, we showed that $\int_R P_y \, dA$ equals $-\oint_C P \, dx$. Show that $\int_R Q_x \, dA$ equals $\oint_C Q \, dy$.

3. (a) Prove Green's theorem with the hypothesis of Theorem 1, but permit the curve C to overlap the line $x = a$ or the line $x = b$ in an interval. [Thus $y_1(a)$ may be less than $y_2(a)$, and $y_1(b)$ may be less than $y_2(b)$.] Prove only the assertion $\int_R P_y \, dA = -\oint_C P \, dx$.

4. (a) Using Green's theorem, prove that $\oint_C x \, dy = A = -\oint_C y \, dx$, where A is the area of the region bounded by a simple closed curve C.
   (b) Why is (a) a generalization of Theorem 2?

5. Work Exercise 4(a), without using Green's theorem, when C bounds a region of the type discussed in Green's theorem. That is, compute $\oint_C x \, dy$ and $\oint_C y \, dx$, using the definition of curve integrals.

6. Prove that $\oint_C (a \, dx + b \, dy) = 0$, where a and b are constants (a) by Green's theorem; (b) without Green's theorem.

7. (a) Let C be the circle of radius 1, with center at $(0,0)$. Use Green's theorem to compute $\oint_C [(x^2 - y^3) \, dx + (y^2 + x^3) \, dy]$. [Hint: To evaluate $\int_R (Q_x - P_y) \, dA$, use a repeated integral in polar coordinates.]
   (b) Compute the curve integral in (a) directly.

8. (a) Show that Green's theorem can be stated as

$$\int_R (P_x + Q_y) \, dA = \oint_C (\overrightarrow{(P,Q)} \cdot \mathbf{N}) \, ds$$

where $\mathbf{N}$ is the unit outward normal to the curve and s is arc length.
   (b) Interpret (a) in terms of fluid flow in which the velocity vector field is $\overrightarrow{(P,Q)}$.
   (c) Why is $P_x + Q_y$ called the "divergence" of the vector field?

9. The moment of inertia about the z axis of a region R in the xy plane is defined as $\int_R (x^2 + y^2) \, dA$. Show that this equals $\frac{1}{3} \oint_C (-y^3 \, dx + x^3 \, dy)$, where C bounds R.

10. Let R be the square with opposite vertices $(0,0)$ and $(2,2)$, and C its border. Let $P = 3xy^2 + 2y^3$ and $Q = 2x^3 - 3x^2y$. Show that $\int_R (Q_x - P_y) \, dA = \int_C (P \, dx + Q \, dy)$ by a direct computation.

11. The definite integral $\int_R xy \, dA$, called the *product of inertia*, appears in the study of mechanics. Compute it when R is the first quadrant of the ellipse $x^2/a^2 +$

$y^2/b^2 = 1$, and is described parametrically by $x = a \cos t, y = b \sin t$, by (a) setting up an appropriate repeated integral; (b) setting up an appropriate curve integral; (c) evaluating the easier one. [Answer: (c) $a^2b^2/4$]

12. Let $T(x,y)$ be the temperature at the point (x,y) in a sheet of metal. Assume that the temperature is maintained independently of time. Now, at (x,y) heat tends to flow in the direction of the gradient ∇T, at a rate proportional to the magnitude of ∇T. Assuming that the net loss of heat over any closed curve is 0, show that T satisfies Laplace's partial differential equation, $T_{xx} + T_{yy} = 0$.

13. A curve is given parametrically by $x = t(1 - t^2)$, $y = t^2(1 - t^3)$, for t in [0,1].
    (a) Sketch the points corresponding to $t = 0$, 0.2, 0.4, 0.6, 0.8, and 1.0, and use them to sketch the curve.
    (b) Let R be the region enclosed by the curve. What difficulty arises when you try to compute the area of R by a definite integral involving vertical or horizontal cross sections?
    (c) Use Theorem 2 to find the area of R.

[Answer: (c) $^7/_{120}$]

14. Repeat Exercise 13 for $x = \sin \pi t$ and $y = t - t^2$. In (a), let $t = 0$, ¼, ½, ¾, 1.

15. Show how Green's theorem for polygonal regions R would follow from Green's theorem for the special case in which R is triangular.

16. (See Exercise 11, page 427.) Cite a pertinent theorem or exercise, or provide your own justification for the following implications. (For simplicity assume that each assertion holds for the whole xy plane.)

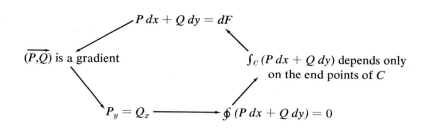

17. (a) Check that

$$\frac{\partial(\tan^{-1}(y/x))}{\partial x} = \frac{-y}{x^2 + y^2} \quad \text{and} \quad \frac{\partial(\tan^{-1}(y/x))}{\partial y} = \frac{x}{x^2 + y^2}$$

(b) Does (a) contradict or illuminate Example 1? Explain.

18. A triangle has vertices $A = (a_1, a_2)$, $B = (b_1, b_2)$, and $C = (c_1, c_2)$ such that the triangular closed path $ABCA$ is counterclockwise.
    (a) Using Theorem 2, find the area of the triangle. (Hint: On each edge, use x or y as the parameter.)
    (b) Check your formula in a simple case.
    (c) Show that if A, B, and C have rational coordinates, the triangle has a rational area.

(d) Are there three points with integral coordinates that are the vertices of an equilateral triangle? If so, give an example; if not, explain.

19. (See Exercise 8.) The *divergence* of a vector function $V = \overrightarrow{(P,Q)}$ is defined as $P_x + Q_y$. It is denoted div V or, in crude shorthand, $\nabla \cdot V$, where ∇ is short for the "operator" $\overrightarrow{(\partial/\partial x, \partial/\partial y)}$.

(a) Show that Green's theorem can be stated as $\int_R \operatorname{div} V \, dA = \int_R (\nabla \cdot V) \, dA = \oint_C (V \cdot N) \, ds$.

(b) Interpret div V and $V \cdot N$ in terms of fluid flow. The equation, $\int_R \operatorname{div} \overrightarrow{V \, dA} = \oint_C (V \cdot N) \, ds$, generalizes to a solid and its surface. In that case we have $V = \overrightarrow{(P,Q,R)}$, $\nabla \cdot V = P_x + Q_y + R_z$, and N is a unit outward normal to the surface S bounding a solid R. The equation

$$\int_R (\nabla \cdot V) \, dV = \int_S (V \cdot N) \, dA$$

is known as the *divergence theorem* or *Gauss' theorem*.

20. Let $V = \overrightarrow{(P,Q)}$ be a vector function. Let curl $V = (Q_x - P_y)k$, when k is a unit vector perpendicular to the xy plane and pointed up. Show that Green's theorem can be stated as

$$\int_R (\operatorname{curl} V) \cdot k \, dA = \oint_C V \cdot dR$$

This theorem generalizes to a curve C bordering a curved surface R in space. In this case k is replaced by a varying unit normal N to the surface, $V = \overrightarrow{(P,Q,R)}$, and curl V is defined as the vector function $(R_y - Q_z, P_z - R_x, Q_x - P_y)$. This generalization, $\int_R (\operatorname{curl} V) \cdot N \, dA = \int_C V \cdot dR$, is known as *Stokes' theorem*.

21. (See Exercise 13, page 428.)

(a) Show that $B = (x + p \cos \theta, y + p \sin \theta)$.

(b) Using Theorem 2, show that the area of the region enclosed by C_B is equal to

$$\frac{1}{2} \int_a^b \left(-y \frac{dx}{dt} + x \frac{dy}{dt} \right) dt + \frac{p}{2} \int_a^b \left(-\sin \theta \frac{dx}{dt} + \cos \theta \frac{dy}{dt} \right) dt$$

$$+ \frac{p}{2} \int_a^b \left(x \cos \theta \frac{d\theta}{dt} + y \sin \theta \frac{d\theta}{dt} \right) dt + \frac{p^2}{2} \int_a^b \frac{d\theta}{dt} \, dt$$

(c) Why are the first and last definite integrals in (b) equal to 0?

(d) Using integration by parts, show that $\int_a^b x \cos \theta \, (d\theta/dt) \, dt = -\int_a^b \sin \theta \, (dx/dt) \, dt$

and that $\int_a^b y \sin \theta \, (d\theta/dt) \, dt = \int_a^b \cos \theta \, (dy/dt) \, dt$.

(e) From (d) deduce that the third definite integral in (b) equals the second definite integral in (b).

(f) Combining Exercise 13, page 428, with (b), (c), and (e) of this exercise, deduce that the area of the region within C_B equals $p \cdot$ (distance the wheel turns); this relation is the basis of the planimeter.

22. (See Exercise 21.) Show that the wheel does not have to be at the midpoint of AB.

23. (See Exercise 18.)

(a) How can you decide *without the use of a picture*, but with the knowledge of the coordinates of A, B, and C, whether the closed path around the triangle A, B, C in the order A, B, C, A is counterclockwise or clockwise?

(b) Test your criterion on three (non-colinear) points of your choice.

2. Magnification in the plane: the Jacobian.   In our discussion of the slide and screen, pages 46 and 51, we saw that magnification at a point was represented by a derivative. In this section we shall generalize the concept of magnification to plane sets, but let us consider for a moment more the linear slide projected onto the linear screen. Let the coordinate on the slide be u and the coordinate of its image on the screen be x; we have $x = f(u)$. The magnification at u is the derivative f' evaluated at u. For instance, if $x = 2u$, then $dx/du = 2$ for all u. There is a magnification by a factor of 2 at all points. If $x = -2u$, the magnification is -2 at all points; the negative value records the interchange of left and right.

For convenience let us assume that the magnification by the function f, with $x = f(u)$, is positive. Let us consider an interval $R = [a,b]$ on the slide. Its projection on the screen is $S = [A,B]$.

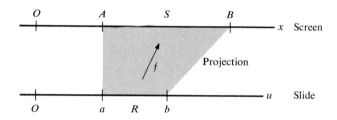

We have

$$\text{Length of } S = B - A = f(b) - f(a) = \int_a^b \frac{df}{du}\, du = \int_a^b (\text{magnification})\, du$$

The *definite integral of the magnification function over an interval R therefore tells us the length of S, the image of R.*

We are now ready to consider the two-dimensional analog. Consider a set R in the uv plane and a set S in the xy plane. Let F be a function that assigns to each point in R a point in S. Assume that F is a one-to-one correspondence, that is, each point in S is expressible in the form $F(P)$ for exactly one point P in R. (We may think of S as the image on the xy screen of R on the uv slide; F is the projection.)

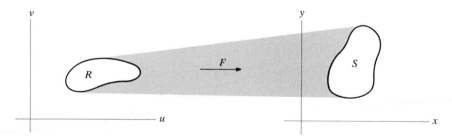

Near some points P in R, the projection F may shrink areas in projecting them to S, while near other P in R, the projection F may expand them. How shall we define and compute the magnification of F at a point P? Or to put it another way, what function defined on R should we integrate in order to obtain the area of S? (The answer to the analogous question for lengths was "the derivative.") Before we answer this question for areas, let us consider a specific example.

Example 1. Let $F(u,v) = (2u,3v)$. For instance, $F(0,0) = (0,0)$, $F(1,0) = (2,0)$, $F(1,1) = (2,3)$, and $F(0,1) = (0,3)$; F doubles the abscissa and triples the ordinate of any point. It therefore magnifies by 2 horizontally and by 3 vertically. It can be shown that it therefore magnifies any area by 6; F has the magnification 6 everywhere. Note, for instance, the image S of the square R whose vertices are $(0,0)$, $(1,0)$, $(1,1)$, $(0,1)$:

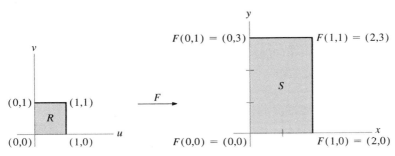

The area of S is six times that of R.

The function F is so simple we can easily calculate its magnification. But what if $F(u,v) = (2u - 3v, 5u - 7v)$ or $F(u,v) = (u \cos v, u \sin v)$? More generally, let us consider the magnification of F, if F has the formula

$$F(u,v) - (f(u,v), g(u,v))$$

where f and g are two real-valued functions that possess continuous derivatives. [In Example 1, we have $f(u,v) = 2u$ and $g(u,v) = 3v$.] The next theorem shows that the magnification of F should be defined as $f_u g_v - f_v g_u$.

THEOREM 4: *Magnification in the plane.* Let R be a region in the uv plane bounded by the curve C_R. Let S be a region on the xy plane bounded by the curve C_S. Let $F = (f,g)$ be a one-to-one correspondence from R to S. Then

$$\text{Area of } S = \int_R (f_u g_v - f_v g_u)\, dA$$

if $f_u g_v - f_v g_u$ is positive everywhere in R. [If $f_u g_v - f_v g_u$ is negative everywhere in R, then the area of S equals $-\int_R (f_u g_v - f_v g_u)\, dA$.]

PROOF.   By Theorem 2, if C_S is counterclockwise, then

(1) $\text{Area of } S = \frac{1}{2}\oint_{C_S} (-y\, dx + x\, dy)$

We will express $\oint_{C_S} (-y\, dx + x\, dy)$ as a curve integral over C_R. To do this we will use the same parameter t for both C_R and C_S. Specifically, let us assume that the counterclockwise curve C_R is given parametrically as $u = p(t)$, $v = q(t)$, where t is in $[0,1]$. (This restriction on the interval does not limit the generality of the proof.)

Then a parameterization of C_S is $x = f(p(t), q(t))$, $y = g(p(t), q(t))$, where t is in $[0,1]$. (After the proof is done, we will show why the parameterization of C_S is also counterclockwise, a fact we will need in order to apply Theorem 2, page 433.) Thus, by the chain rule, Theorem 2, page 366,

$$\frac{dx}{dt} = f_u(p(t), q(t))\frac{dp}{dt} + f_v(p(t), q(t))\frac{dq}{dt}$$

and

$$\frac{dy}{dt} = g_u(p(t), q(t))\frac{dp}{dt} + g_v(p(t), q(t))\frac{dq}{dt}$$

Writing $(p(t), q(t))$ as (u,v), we have therefore

$$\oint_{C_S} (-y\,dx + x\,dy) = \int_0^1 \left\{ -g(u,v)\left[f_u(u,v)\frac{dp}{dt}\,dt + f_v(u,v)\frac{dq}{dt}\,dt \right] \right.$$
$$\left. + f(u,v)\left[g_u(u,v)\frac{dp}{dt} + g_v(u,v)\frac{dq}{dt}\,dt \right] \right\}$$

or more briefly,

$$\oint_{C_S} (-y\,dx + x\,dy) = \int_0^1 \left\{ -g\,[f_u\,du + f_v\,dv] + f\,[g_u\,du + g_v\,dv] \right\}$$

The last definite integral is *a curve integral over* C_R. With terms collected, it becomes

(2)
$$\oint_{C_R} [(-gf_u + fg_u)\,du + (fg_v - gf_v)\,dv]$$

We next apply Green's theorem to relate (2) to an integral over R. Keeping in mind that in this case

$$P = fg_u - gf_u \qquad \text{and} \qquad Q = fg_v - gf_v$$

we see that (2) is equal to

(3)
$$\int_R \left[\frac{\partial(fg_v - gf_v)}{\partial u} - \frac{\partial(fg_u - gf_u)}{\partial v} \right] dA$$

Computing the partial derivatives in (3) and exploiting the identities $f_{uv} = f_{vu}$ and $g_{uv} = g_{vu}$, we see that (3) becomes

(4)
$$\int_R [(fg_{vu} + g_v f_u - gf_{vu} - f_v g_u) - (fg_{ur} + g_u f_v - gf_{uv} - f_u g_v)]\,dA$$
$$= \int_R (g_v f_u - f_v g_u - g_u f_v + f_u g_v)\,dA = 2\int_R (f_u g_v - f_v g_u)\,dA$$

Combining this with (1), we obtain

$$\text{Area of } S = \int_R (f_u g_v - f_v g_u)\,dA$$

and the theorem is proved.

REMARK. Why is the parameterization of C_S counterclockwise? Recall that we have assumed that $f_u g_v - f_v g_u$ is positive. Thus $\int_R (f_u g_v - f_v g_u)\,dA$ is positive, as the area of S must be. If C_S were *clockwise*, then $\frac{1}{2}\int_{C_S} (-y\,dx + x\,dy)$ would be the *negative* of the area of S, and hence a negative number. But our computations showed that $\frac{1}{2} \int_{C_S} (-y \, dx + x \, dy)$ equals $\frac{1}{2} \int_R (f_u g_v - f_v g_u) \, dA$, a positive number. Hence it is the assumption that $f_u g_v - f_v g_u$ is positive that assures us that F takes the counterclockwise C_R into a counterclockwise C_S. We may conclude that just as the sign of dx/du records the preservation or interchange of right and left on a line, so does the sign of $f_u g_v - f_v g_u$ record the preservation or interchange of counterclockwise and clockwise in the plane.

Let us now use Theorem 4 to determine the magnification of F at a point P_0. Consider a set R containing P_0 and assume that $f_u g_v - f_v g_u$ is positive. Then the image of R has area $\int_R (f_u g_v - f_v g_u) \, dA$. Thus, since $f_u g_v - f_v g_u$ is continuous, when R is sufficiently small the area of the image of R is approximately

$$(f_u g_v - f_v g_u)_{\text{at } P_0} \cdot \text{area of } R$$

Thus $f_u g_v - f_v g_u$ describes the local magnification of F, just as dx/du does in the linear case $x = f(u)$. (If $f_u g_v - f_v g_u$ is negative, then F switches clockwise and counterclockwise, and the geometric magnification is $|f_u g_v - f_v g_u|$.)

The function $f_u g_v - f_v g_u$ is known as the *Jacobian* of the function $F = (f,g)$ and was introduced by Jacobi in 1841. It is usually denoted

$$\frac{\partial(f,g)}{\partial(u,v)} \qquad \text{or} \qquad \frac{\partial(x,y)}{\partial(u,v)}$$

For instance, the Jacobian of the function in Example 1, where $x = 2u$, $y = 3v$, is

$$\frac{\partial x}{\partial u} \frac{\partial y}{\partial v} - \frac{\partial x}{\partial v} \frac{\partial y}{\partial u} = (2)(3) - (0)(0) = 6$$

This agrees with our observation that the function magnifies areas sixfold.

Example 2. Let us study the function F such that $F(u,v) = (2u - 3v, 5u + 7v)$. The Jacobian of F is

$$\frac{\partial(2u - 3v)}{\partial x} \frac{\partial(5u + 7v)}{\partial v} - \frac{\partial(2u - 3v)}{\partial v} \frac{\partial(5u + 7v)}{\partial u} = (2)(7) - (-3)(5) = 29$$

Hence F magnifies areas everywhere by the factor 29. Moreover, since the Jacobian is positive, F sends a counterclockwise curve into a counterclockwise curve.

Before we examine the effect of the projection of F on a particular region R, let us show that F carries straight lines into straight lines. Let $au + bv + c = 0$ be the equation of a straight line in the uv plane. Solving the simultaneous equations

$$x = 2u - 3v \qquad y = 5u + 7v$$

for u and v as functions of x and y, we obtain

(5) $$u = \frac{7}{29}x + \frac{3}{29}y \qquad v = \frac{2}{29}x - \frac{5}{29}y$$

Thus any point (x,y) on the image of the typical line $au + bv + c = 0$ satisfies the equation

$$a\left(\frac{7}{29}x + \frac{3}{29}y\right) + b\left(\frac{2}{29}x - \frac{5}{29}y\right) + c = 0$$

Equivalently,

(6) $(7a + 2b) x + (3a - 5b) y + 29c = 0$

Since a and b are fixed, so are $7a + 2b$ and $3a - 5b$. Thus (6) is the equation of a line in the xy plane.

Now let us find the image S in the xy plane of the triangular region R in the uv plane that has the vertices $(u,v) = (0,0)$, $(1,0)$, and $(0,1)$. Since $F(0,0) = (0,0)$, $F(1,0) = (2,5)$, and $F(0,1) = (-3,7)$, and since F takes straight lines into straight lines, S is the triangle with vertices $(x,y) = (0,0)$, $(2,4)$, and $(-3,7)$.

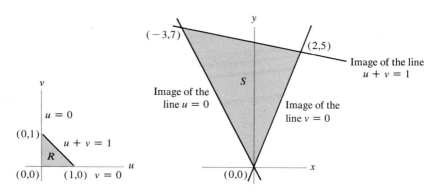

According to Theorem 4, the area of S is $\int_R [\partial(x,y)/\partial(u,v)] \, dA = \int_R 29 \, dA = 29 \int_R dA = 29 \, (\text{area of } R) = (29)\,(\tfrac{1}{2}) = {}^{29}\!/_2$, a result which the reader may wish to check by elementary geometry.

The next example provides an alternative proof that a repeated integral in polar coordinates has an r in its integrand.

Example 3. Let F be defined by the equation

(7) $x = u \cos v \qquad y = u \sin v$

In order to make F one-to-one, let us consider $F(u,v)$ only when (u,v) is on the strip described by $u > 0$ and $0 \leqslant v < 2\pi$. Let R be a region in the uv plane and S its image in the xy plane. Since

$$\frac{\partial x}{\partial u} = \cos v \qquad \frac{\partial x}{\partial v} = -u \sin v \qquad \frac{\partial y}{\partial u} = \sin v \qquad \frac{\partial y}{\partial v} = u \cos v$$

the Jacobian of F is

$$(\cos v)\,(u \cos v) - (-u \sin v)\,(\sin v) = u(\cos^2 v + \sin^2 v) = u$$

Thus

$$\text{Area of } S = \int_R u \, dA$$

Now, assume that R has the description

$$\alpha \leqslant v \leqslant \beta \qquad f_1(v) \leqslant u \leqslant f_2(v)$$

Then, as we saw in Chap. 9,

$$\int_R u \, dA = \int_\alpha^\beta \left(\int_{f_1(v)}^{f_2(v)} u \, du \right) dv$$

Now u and v, rectangular coordinates in the uv plane, can, by virtue of (7), be considered polar coordinates r and θ in the xy plane. Thus the area of S equals

(8)
$$\int_\alpha^\beta \left(\int_{f_1(\theta)}^{f_2(\theta)} r \, dr \right) d\theta$$

This shows that the factor r that is present in repeated integrals in polar coordinates is in fact a Jacobian.

The Jacobian is also used for transforming definite integrals over plane and solid sets and in the study of the inverse of functions F of several variables.

EXERCISES

1. (a) Carry out the details of solving for u and v as functions of x and y in Example 2.
   (b) Show that F of Example 2 takes the circle $u^2 + v^2 = 1$ into a curve that is not a circle. Draw the image of this circle by calculating at least six points in the image.
   (c) Let G be the transformation from the xy plane to the uv plane defined by (5). Its Jacobian is defined as $\partial u/\partial x \, \partial v/\partial y - \partial u/\partial y \, \partial v/\partial x$. Compute the Jacobian of G. Why do you suppose the Jacobian of G is related to the Jacobian of F as it is?
2. Let R be the rectangle in the uv plane whose vertices are $(1,0)$, $(2,0)$, $(2,\pi/2)$, and $(1,\pi/2)$.
   (a) Draw S, the image of R under F, if $F(u,v) = (2u,3v)$.
   (b) Draw S, the image of R under F, if $F(u,v) = (2u - 3v, 5u - 7v)$.
3. Let R be the same as in Exercise 2, but let $F(u,v) = (u \cos v, u \sin v)$. Draw S, the image of R. (Note that if $x = u \cos v$ and $y = u \sin v$, then $x^2 + y^2 = u^2$ and $y/x = \tan v$.) (Answer: S is a quadrant of the ring between two concentric circles)
4. Let $F(u,v) = (u^2, 2v)$ and R be the triangle bordered by $u = v$, $v = 0$, and $u = 1$. Let S be the image of R.
   (a) Draw S, which has one curved side.
   (b) Compute the area of S with the aid of Theorem 4.
   (c) Compute the area of S directly.
5. Consider only positive u and $0 \leqslant v \leqslant \pi/2$.
   (a) Show that if $x = u \cos v$ and $y = u \sin v$, then $u = \sqrt{x^2 + y^2}$ and $v = \tan^{-1}(y/x)$.
   (b) Show that $\partial(u,v)/\partial(x,y) = 1/\sqrt{x^2 + y^2}$.
   (c) Show that $\partial(u,v)/\partial(x,y)$ is the reciprocal of $\partial(x,y)/\partial(u,v)$.
   (d) Why is (c) to be expected? (Think optically.)
6. Show that $F(u,v) = (u \cos \theta - v \sin \theta, u \sin \theta + v \cos \theta)$, where θ is any fixed constant, preserves area. (A transformation "preserves area" if the area of the image of R by the transformation is equal to the area of R for all regions R of the type we consider.)
7. Let $(x,y) = F(u,v) = (u - v, 2u + v)$. Let R be the triangular region in the uv plane that has the vertices $(0,0)$, $(1,0)$, and $(0,1)$. Let C_R be its border, and let S be the image of R and C_S the image of C_R.
   (a) Draw $F(0,0)$, $F(1,0)$, and $F(0,1)$ in the xy plane.
   (b) As you sweep out C_R counterclockwise, in what direction does F sweep out the curve C_S?
   (c) Compute the Jacobian of F. Are your answers to (b) and (c) compatible?

8. Let $F(u,v) = (e^u \cos v, 1 + e^u \sin v)$. Find the magnification of F at (a) $(u,v) = (1,3)$; (b) $(u,v) = (-1,2)$. [Answer: (a) e^2; (b) $1/e^2$]

9. (See Exercise 6.) (a) Prove that the function F defined by $F(u,v) = (x,y) = (u - v^2 - 2vu^2 - u^4, v + u^2)$ preserves areas.
   (b) Sketch the image of the square whose vertices are $(0,0)$, $(1,1)$, $(1,0)$, and $(0,1)$.

10. Let $(x,y) = F(u,v) = (u^2 - v^2, 2uv)$ and let R be the square whose vertices are $(1,0)$, $(2,0)$, $(2,1)$, and $(1,1)$.
    (a) Show that when $u = 1$, the projection $F(u,v) = (1 - v^2, 2v)$ lies on the curve $x = 1 - (y/2)^2$.
    (b) Show that when $u = 2$, the projection $F(u,v) = (4 - v^2, 4v)$ lies on the curve $x = 4 - (y/4)^2$.
    (c) Show that the image of the line $v = 0$ is the positive x axis.
    (d) Show that the image of the line $v = 1$ is the curve $x = (y/2)^2 - 1$.
    (e) Draw S, the image of R. (It has three curved sides and one straight side.)
    (f) Find the area of S. [Answer: (f) $32/3$]

11. Consider only $u, v, x, y > 0$. Define $F(u,v) = (x,y) = (u^{1/3}v^{2/3}, u^{2/3}v^{1/3})$.
    (a) Show that $x^2 = uy$ and $y^2 = vx$.
    (b) Let R in the uv plane be the rectangle bordered by the lines $u = 1$, $u = 2$, $v = 3$, and $v = 4$. Let S be the image in the xy plane of R. Show that S is bordered by the four parabolas $x^2 = y$, $x^2 = 2y$, $y^2 = 3x$, and $y^2 = 4x$.
    (c) Draw S.
    (d) Compute the area of S by integrating the Jacobian of F over R. [Answer: (d) $1/3$]

12. From the knowledge that the area of $S = \int_R g(P)\, dA$, where S is the image of R and R is arbitrary, deduce that as the diameter of $R \to 0$, then area of S/area of R $\to g(P_0)$, where P_0 is fixed in the R under consideration. (Diameter is defined on page 32.) Assume that g is continuous.

13. Let F be a one-to-one correspondence from R in the uv plane to S in the xy plane. Then x and y are functions of u and v, and u and v are functions of x and y $[(u,v) = F^{-1}(x,y)]$.
    (a) Using a chain rule, show that

$$1 = x_u u_x + x_v v_x \qquad 0 = x_u u_y + x_v v_y$$
$$1 = y_u u_y + y_v v_y \qquad 0 = y_u u_x + y_v v_x$$

    (b) With the aid of (a), show that the Jacobians of F and F^{-1} are reciprocals of each other.
    (c) State (b) in optical terms. Is (b) to be expected?

14. Prove Theorem 4 for $f_u g_v - f_v g_u$ negative at all points in R.

15. Verify (a) that $F(u,v) = (-u,v)$ has negative Jacobian and (b) that as P runs counterclockwise around the unit circle whose center is at $(0,0)$, then $F(P)$ runs clockwise.

16. Let F be a one-to-one correspondence from R in the uv plane to S in the xy plane. Let f be a real-valued function on S. Why would you expect $\int_S f\, dA$ to be

$$\int_R (f \circ F)\, [\partial(x,y)/\partial(u,v)]\, dA$$

where $f \circ F$ is the composite function? What result concerning definite integrals over intervals is analogous to this?

17. Let F be a function from the uv plane to the xy plane, and let G be a function from the xy plane to the st plane. Then $G \circ F$ is a function from the uv plane to the st plane.

(a) Why would you expect the Jacobian of $G \circ F$ to be the product of the Jacobians of F and G?

(b) Prove the theorem suggested in (a).

(c) What theorem about functions of a single variable does (a) generalize?

18. Let F, R, and S be the same as in Exercise 4. Use the Jacobian of F to compute $\int_S xy \, dA$.

19. Let F be a function from the u, v, w rectangular coordinate system to the x, y, z rectangular coordinate system: $F(u,v,w) = (f(u,v,w), g(u,v,w), h(u,v,w))$. The Jacobian of F is defined as

$$(f_u)(g_v h_w - g_w h_v) - (f_v)(g_u h_w - g_w h_u) + (f_w)(g_u h_v - g_v h_u).$$

Show that if $x = u \sin v \cos w$, $y = u \sin v \sin w$, and $z = u \cos v$, then the Jacobian of F is $u^2 \sin v$. What expression involving spherical coordinates does $u^2 \sin v$ remind you of?

3. The hyperbolic functions.

The hyperbolic functions are derived from the hyperbola $x^2 - y^2 = 1$, as the trigonometric functions are derived from the circle $x^2 + y^2 = 1$. To make this analogy clear, it is important to consider $\cos \theta$ and $\sin \theta$ from a slightly different point of view than that generally offered in trigonometry.

Notice that the area of a sector of angle θ in a unit circle is $\theta/2$. [The area of a sector of radius r and angle θ is $(\pi r^2)(\theta/2\pi) = \theta r^2/2$.]

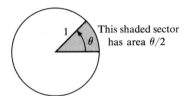
This shaded sector has area $\theta/2$

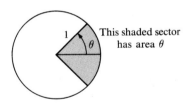
This shaded sector has area θ

Hence the shaded sector on the right, which is twice as large as the sector on the left, has area θ. Therefore the trigonometric functions $\cos \theta$ and $\sin \theta$ for $0 \leqslant \theta < \pi$ can be defined as follows.

Consider in the unit circle the sector AOB whose area is θ and which is symmetric with respect to the x axis:

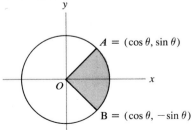

In the circle $x^2 + y^2 = 1$, the shaded sector has area θ

Then the x coordinate of A is $\cos\theta$, and the y coordinate of A is $\sin\theta$. If θ is negative, we use B instead of A to define $\cos x$ and $\sin x$. It is this definition of the trigonometric functions that parallels the definition of the hyperbolic functions, which we now give. (Incidentally, observe that since A is on the unit circle, $\cos^2\theta + \sin^2\theta = 1$.)

Let u be a positive real number. Consider the point $A = (x,y)$ in the first quadrant and on the hyperbola $x^2 - y^2 = 1$ such that the area of the region bounded by the curve $x^2 - y^2 = 1$, the line segment from the origin to A, and the line segment from the origin to $B = (x,-y)$ is u:

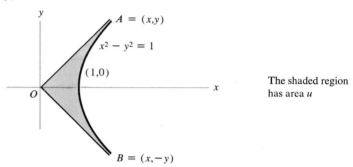

The shaded region has area u

Then the x coordinate of A is called the *hyperbolic cosine* of u, and the y coordinate of A is called the *hyperbolic sine* of u. For brevity, the former is written $\cosh u$ and the latter $\sinh u$. (If u is negative, then we use B instead of A to define $\cosh u$ and $\sinh u$.) Note that the u in $\cosh u$ refers to the area of the shaded region AOB, and not to angle. From the preceding diagram, we see that

$$\cosh 0 = 1 \qquad\qquad \sinh 0 = 0$$
$$\cosh(-u) = \cosh u \qquad\qquad \sinh(-u) = -\sinh u$$
$$\cosh^2 u - \sinh^2 u = 1 \qquad\qquad \cosh u \geqslant 1$$

$$\text{Both } \cosh u \text{ and } \sinh u \text{ are unbounded}$$

We now proceed to show that

(1) $$\cosh u = \frac{e^u + e^{-u}}{2} \qquad \text{and} \qquad \sinh u = \frac{e^u - e^{-u}}{2}$$

Our approach is indirect. We will show that if we choose A to be the point $((e^u + e^{-u})/2, (e^u - e^{-u})/2)$, then the area of OBA is simply u.

Consider the point

(2) $$(x,y) = \left(\frac{e^t + e^{-t}}{2}, \frac{e^t - e^{-t}}{2}\right)$$

where t is an arbitrary real number. Observe that

$$x^2 - y^2 = \left(\frac{e^{2t} + 2 + e^{-2t}}{4}\right) - \left(\frac{e^{2t} - 2 + e^{-2t}}{4}\right) = 1$$

Hence (2) provides a parameterization of the right branch of curve $x^2 - y^2 = 1$. This parameterization will be of use in the following lemma, on which (1) rests.

LEMMA 1.   Let u be a positive number and R the region bounded by the x axis, the hyperbola $x^2 - y^2 = 1$, and the line segment from the origin to the point

$$\left(\frac{e^u + e^{-u}}{2}, \frac{e^u - e^{-u}}{2} \right)$$

Then the area of R is $u/2$.

PROOF.   Let $O = (0,0)$, $D = (1,0)$, and $C = ((e^u + e^{-u})/2, (e^u - e^{-u})/2)$. As this diagram shows, O, C, and D are the three "corners" of R:

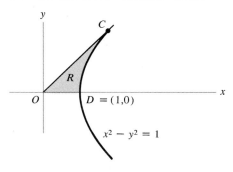

By Theorem 2, page 433, the area of R equals $(\frac{1}{2}) \oint (-y\,dx + x\,dy)$, where the integration is around the boundary of R from O to D to C and then back to O.

From O to D, we see that $y = 0$ and is constant; hence $\int_O^D (-y\,dx + x\,dy)$ is 0.

On OC we have $y/x = dy/dx$, and thus $y\,dx = x\,dy$; hence $\int_C^O (-y\,dx + x\,dy)$ is 0. Lastly we consider $\int_D^C (-y\,dx + x\,dy)$ along the hyperbola $x^2 - y^2 = 1$. If $x = (e^t + e^{-t})/2$ and $y = (e^t - e^{-t})/2$, then $dx/dt = (e^t - e^{-t})/2$ and $dy/dt = (e^t + e^{-t})/2$. Thus $\int_D^C (-y\,dx + x\,dy)$ equals

(3)
$$\int_0^u \left[-\frac{(e^t - e^{-t})}{2} \frac{(e^t - e^{-t})}{2} + \frac{(e^t + e^{-t})}{2} \frac{(e^t + e^{-t})}{2} \right] dt$$

which simplifies to $\int_0^u 1\,dt = u$. Hence $\oint(-y\,dx + x\,dy) = u$, and the area of R is $u/2$. The lemma is proved.

We could have defined $\cosh u$ as $(e^u + e^{-u})/2$, and $\sinh u$ as $(e^u - e^{-u})/2$, but this approach does not expose the fundamental analogy to the circular functions, $\cos \theta$ and $\sin \theta$. Once we have the formulas (1), however, we may dispense with the hyperbola, as the following example illustrates.

Example 1.   We compute the derivatives of $\cosh u$ and $\sinh u$:

$$D(\cosh u) = D\left(\frac{e^u + e^{-u}}{2} \right) = \frac{e^u - e^u}{2} = \sinh u$$

and
$$D(\sinh u) = D\left(\frac{e^u - e^{-u}}{2}\right) = \frac{e^u + e^{-u}}{2} = \cosh u$$

Note that while $D(\cos x) = -\sin x$, we have $D(\cosh u) = \sinh u$; there is no minus sign in the hyperbolic case.

Example 2. In determining the shape of a hanging cable (Example 3, below) it will be important to know that $y = a \cosh(x/a)$ satisfies the differential equation

$$(4) \qquad \frac{d^2y}{dx^2} = \frac{1}{a}\sqrt{1 + \left(\frac{dy}{dx}\right)^2}$$

where a is a constant. Let us show here that this is the case. We have

$$\frac{dy}{dx} = a\left(\sinh\frac{x}{a}\right)\frac{1}{a} = \sinh\frac{x}{a}$$

and
$$\frac{d^2y}{dx^2} = \cosh\left(\frac{x}{a}\right)\frac{1}{a}$$

by Example 1 and the chain rule. Replacing dy/dx with $\sinh(x/a)$ and d^2y/dx^2 with $(1/a)\cosh(x/a)$, we see that (4) becomes

$$(5) \qquad \frac{1}{a}\cosh\left(\frac{x}{a}\right) = \frac{1}{a}\sqrt{1 + \left[\sinh\left(\frac{x}{a}\right)\right]^2}$$

To show that (5) is a valid equation, recall that $\cosh^2(x/a) = 1 + \sinh^2(x/a)$ and that $\cosh(x/a)$ is positive; hence

$$\cosh\frac{x}{a} = \sqrt{1 + \left(\sinh\frac{x}{a}\right)^2}$$

Thus (5) holds, and $a\cosh(x/a)$ is a solution of (4). Note that $y = a\cosh(x/a) + k$ also satisfies (4).

Example 3. Galileo believed that the shape of a chain of uniform linear density hanging from its end points was part of a parabola. This is not the case. The curve it forms, called a *catenary* (from *catena*, Latin for chain) has an equation involving the hyperbolic cosine. To see why, consider a typical section of the chain, stretching from its lowest point L to a typical point $P = (x, y)$. Three forces operate on the section LP. Two of them, **H** (horizontal) and **T** (tangent to the curve and of inclination ϕ), are the pull of the rest of the chain on LP, whereas **W**, the vertical pull of the earth on the section LP, has a magnitude equal to the weight of LP.

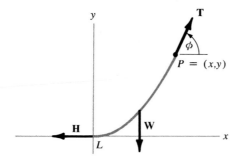

Three forces, **H**, **T**, and **W**, operate on LP

Since the section LP moves neither right nor left, the horizontal components of the forces $\mathbf{H}$ and $\mathbf{T}$ must balance. Denoting $|\mathbf{H}|$ by H and $|\mathbf{T}|$ by T, we have, for the horizontal forces,

(6) $$H = T \cos \phi$$

The balancing of the vertical components gives

(7) $$W = T \sin \phi$$

where $W = |\mathbf{W}|$. From (6) and (7) we obtain

(8) $$\frac{W}{H} = \frac{T \sin \phi}{T \cos \phi} = \tan \phi = \frac{dy}{dx}$$

Furthermore, $W = ws$, where w is the weight of one foot of the chain and s the length of LP in feet. From (8) it follows that

(9) $$\frac{ws}{H} = \frac{dy}{dx}$$

Differentiation of (9) with respect to x yields

(10) $$\frac{w}{H}\frac{ds}{dx} = \frac{d^2y}{dx^2}$$

which is equivalent to

(11) $$\frac{d^2y}{dx^2} = \frac{w}{H}\sqrt{1 + \left(\frac{dy}{dx}\right)^2}$$

Equation (11) has the form of (4), where $a = H/w$. For any k, as Example 2 showed, $y = [a \cosh (x/a)] + k$ satisfies (4). But since the chain passes through $(0,0)$, we must choose k so that $0 = a \cosh (0/a) + k$, that is, so that $k = -a$. Hence

(12) $$y = \frac{H}{w}\left[\cosh\left(\frac{wx}{H}\right) - 1 \right]$$

is a function that satisfies (11) and passes horizontally through the origin. It can be proved that (12) is the only function that does so. Therefore a chain hangs in a curve that is given, essentially, by the hyperbolic cosine.

EXERCISES

1. Show that $\cosh u \geqslant 1$ by (a) using formula (1); (b) inspecting the hyperbola $x^2 - y^2 = 1$.
2. Show that $\sinh (-u) = -\sinh u$ by (a) using formula (1); (b) inspecting the hyperbola $x^2 - y^2 = 1$.
3. Define $\tanh u$ as $(\sinh u)/(\cosh u)$. Show that $\lim_{u \to \infty} \tanh u = 1$ by (a) using formula (1); (b) inspecting the hyperbola $x^2 - y^2 = 1$.
4. Consider $u = \cosh^{-1} x$, the inverse function of cosh. Here, $u \geqslant 0$ and $x \geqslant 1$.
   (a) Show that $x = \cosh u = (e^u + e^{-u})/2$.
   (b) Show that $u = \cosh^{-1} x = \ln (x + \sqrt{x^2 - 1})$. [Hint: Solve the equation in (a) for u.]
   (c) Show that $\cosh^{-1} u = \int (1/\sqrt{u^2 - 1})\, du$.
   (d) Compute $\int (1/\sqrt{u^2 - 1})\, du$ without using hyperbolic functions.
5. Graph $u = \cosh x$.

6. Graph (a) $u = \sinh x$; (b) $u = \tanh x$. (See Exercise 3 for the definition of $\tanh x$.)
7. In Chap. 4 we found that $D(\sin^{-1} x) = 1/\sqrt{1 - x^2}$. Use a similar method to show that $D(\sinh^{-1} x) = 1/\sqrt{1 + x^2}$.
8. According to Example 3, a rope supported at the points $(1, [(e + e^{-1})/2] - 1) = (1, 0.54)$ and $(-1, 0.54)$ and passing through $(0,0)$ follows the curve $y = (\cosh x) - 1$.
   (a) With a rope or string carry out the experiment and trace the curve in which it hangs.
   (b) On the same paper graph $y = (\cosh x) - 1$.
   (c) Are the curves in (a) and (b) close to each other?
9. Show that the arc length of the catenary $y = \cosh x$ from $x = 0$ to $x = a$ is $\sinh a$.

10. Prove that $\cosh (x + y) = \cosh x \cosh y + \sinh x \sinh y$.
11. Prove that $\sinh (x + y) = \sinh x \cosh y + \cosh x \sinh y$.
12. Let i denote the complex number whose square is -1 and whose ordinate (imaginary part) is positive. Define $e^{i\theta}$ as $1 + i\theta + (i\theta)^2/2! + (i\theta)^3/3! + \cdots$. This is suggested by Eq. (3) on page 336. Assume that the series makes sense and converges when x is any complex number $x = a + bi$, where a and b are real.)
   (b) From (a), which links the exponential and the trigonometric functions, deduce that $\cos \theta = (e^{i\theta} + e^{-i\theta})/2$ and $\sin \theta = (e^{i\theta} - e^{-i\theta})/2i$.
   (c) Compare the formulas in (b) with Eq. (1). From (b) we see that the trigonometric functions can be defined in terms of the exponential function. So can the function "log to the base e," for it is the inverse of the exponential function. And the power function x^a, $x > 0$, with a fixed, can be defined in terms of the logarithm and exponential functions: $x^a = e^{a \ln x}$. Clearly the exponential function may be considered the most important function in the calculus.

4. Summary.   The main result in this chapter is Green's theorem, which asserts that under fairly general circumstances,

$$\oint_C (P\, dx + Q\, dy) = \int_R (Q_x - P_y)\, dA$$

where C is the boundary of R and the curve integral is taken counterclockwise. This theorem was used in determining the magnification of a transformation F from the uv plane to the xy plane. If $F(u,v) = (f(u,v), g(u,v))$, then the expression $f_u g_v - f_v g_u$, the Jacobian of F, measures the magnification of F.

When $P = -y$ and $Q = x$, Green's theorem becomes $\oint_C (-y\, dx + x\, dy) = \int_R (1 + 1)\, dA = 2$ (area of R). Thus the area of R equals $\frac{1}{2} \oint_C (-y\, dx + x\, dy)$. This result was used in developing the Jacobian and hyperbolic functions.

20

The interchange of limits

ARE the mixed partial derivatives, f_{xy} and f_{yx}, equal? Can we differentiate "under the integral sign"? That is, can we assert that

$$\frac{d \int_a^b f(x,y)\, dx}{dy} = \int_a^b \frac{\partial f}{\partial y}\, dx$$

As we shall see in this chapter, these and many other questions concerning functions can be translated into questions concerning the interchange of limits. We shall present examples that show the dangers involved in the interchange of limits, as well as some theorems which assure us that under suitable conditions we may safely interchange limits.

Our first example is a simple illustration of the interchange of limits and the attendant risks.

Example 1. We define a function f on the xy plane as follows:

$$f(x,y) = \begin{cases} 1 & \text{if } x \geqslant y \\ 0 & \text{if } x < y \end{cases}$$

451

Thus in the shaded region of this diagram $f(x,y) = 0$, while outside of it, $f(x,y) = 1$:

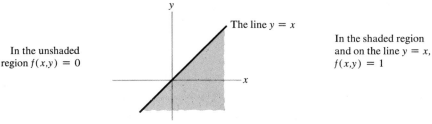

In the unshaded region $f(x,y) = 0$

The line $y = x$

In the shaded region and on the line $y = x$, $f(x,y) = 1$

Let us compute $\lim_{x \to \infty} [\lim_{y \to \infty} f(x,y)]$ and $\lim_{y \to \infty} [\lim_{x \to \infty} f(x,y)]$

First, consider $\lim_{y \to \infty} f(x,y)$. Here x is fixed, and we examine $f(x,y)$ for (x,y) on a fixed vertical line. Now on a fixed vertical line, when y is sufficiently large, (x,y) lies in the unshaded region in the figure, and $f(x,y) = 0$. Thus

$$\lim_{y \to \infty} f(x,y) = 0 \quad \text{and} \quad \lim_{x \to \infty} [\lim_{y \to \infty} f(x,y)] = \lim_{x \to \infty} 0 = 0$$

On the other hand, considering the behavior of f on horizontal lines, we can show similarly that

$$\lim_{x \to \infty} f(x,y) = 1 \quad \text{and} \quad \lim_{y \to \infty} [\lim_{x \to \infty} f(x,y)] = \lim_{y \to \infty} 1 = 1$$

In this case we obtain a different result when we interchange the order of the limits.

Example 2. For $n = 1, 2, 3, \ldots$, let the function f_n be defined by the formula $f_n(x) = (1/n) \sin nx$. Then define f as the limit of f_n; that is, $f(x) = \lim_{n \to \infty} f_n(x)$. Since $-1 \leqslant \sin nx \leqslant 1$, it is clear that $\lim_{n \to \infty} (1/n) \sin nx = 0$. Thus $f(x) = 0$ for all x. We ask whether

$$\lim_{n \to \infty} f_n'(0) = f'(0)$$

(Is the limit of the derivative equal to the derivative of the limit?)

This question actually concerns an interchange of limits, for we have

$$\lim_{n \to \infty} f_n'(0) = \lim_{n \to \infty} \left[\lim_{h \to 0} \frac{f_n(h) - f_n(0)}{h} \right]$$

and $$f'(0) = \lim_{h \to 0} \frac{f(h) - f(0)}{h} = \lim_{h \to 0} \left[\lim_{n \to \infty} \frac{f_n(h) - f_n(0)}{h} \right]$$

In this particular case the answer is no. On the one hand, we have $f_n'(x) = \cos nx$; hence

$$\lim_{n \to \infty} f_n'(0) = \lim_{n \to \infty} \cos(n0) = \lim_{n \to \infty} 1 = 1$$

On the other hand,

$$f'(0) = 0$$

since f is constant.

Example 2 should help us to appreciate the following theorem, which says that when the f_n's are the polynomials associated with a Taylor's series, the derivative of the limit is the limit of the derivative.

THEOREM 1. *Let $a_0 + a_1x + a_2x^2 + \cdots + a_nx^n + \cdots$ converge at least throughout the open interval $(-c,c)$, and let its sum be $f(x)$. Then f has a derivative, and $f'(x) = a_1 + 2a_2x + 3a_3x^2 + \cdots + na_nx^{n-1} + \cdots$*

To relate this theorem to Example 2, define the functions $f_1, f_2, \ldots$, as the partial sums of a series expansion of $f(x)$; that is

$$f_n(x) = a_0 + a_1x + \cdots + a_nx^n$$

Then $f_n'(x) = a_1 + 2a_2x + \cdots + na_nx^{n-1}$. We have $f(x) = \lim_{n \to \infty} f_n(x)$. The theorem asserts that in this case $f'(x) = \lim_{n \to \infty} f_n'(x)$—that the derivative of the limit is the limit of the derivative. A proof may be found in any advanced calculus text (for example, R. C. Buck, "Advanced Calculus," 2d ed., p. 198, McGraw-Hill, N.Y., 1965). As a particular illustration, let us apply Theorem 1 to the case

$$\frac{1}{1-x} = 1 + x + x^2 + \cdots + x^n + \cdots \qquad \text{for } -1 < x < 1$$

Theorem 1 implies that $1/(1-x)^2 = 1 + 2x + 3x^2 + \cdots + nx^{n-1} + \cdots$, for $-1 < x < 1$, a result we obtained on page 325.

Example 3. In Example 2 we asked: "Does the derivative of the limit equal the limit of the derivative?" Now let us ask: "Does the definite integral of the limit equal the limit of the definite integral?" More precisely, we let $f_1, f_2, \ldots$, be a sequence of functions. We then let $f(x) = \lim_{n \to \infty} f_n(x)$, and ask whether

$$\int_a^b f(x)\, dx = \lim_{n \to \infty} \int_a^b f_n(x)\, dx$$

To put it another way, we ask: "Can we move 'lim' past an integral sign?" That is, we ask whether

$$\int_a^b \lim_{n \to \infty} f_n(x)\, dx = \lim_{n \to \infty} \int_a^b f_n(x)\, dx$$

Since a definite integral is itself defined as a limit, these questions concern the interchange of limits. The answer is "not always," as this diagram suggests:

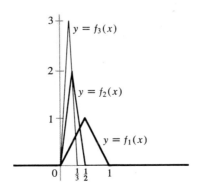

Let the graph of f_n consist of an isosceles triangle whose base is the interval $[0, 1/n]$ and whose altitude is n, together with the portion of the x axis outside of $[0, 1/n]$. Then $f_n(x) = 2n^2x$ for $0 \leqslant x \leqslant 1/2n$, $f_n(x) = 2n - 2n^2x$ for $1/2n \leqslant x \leqslant 1/n$, and $f_n(x) = 0$ for $x > 1/n$ or $x < 0$. We evaluate

$$\int_0^1 \lim_{n \to \infty} f_n(x)\, dx \quad\quad \text{and} \quad\quad \lim_{n \to \infty} \int_0^1 f_n(x)\, dx$$

As $n \to \infty$, $f_n(x) \to 0$; hence $\int_0^1 \lim_{n \to \infty} f_n(x)\, dx = \int_0^1 0\, dx = 0$. On the other hand, $\int_0^1 f_n(x)\, dx$ equals the area of an isosceles triangle whose base has length $(1/n)$ and whose altitude is n. Thus $\int_0^1 f_n(x)\, dx = \frac{1}{2}\left(\dfrac{1}{n}\right) n = \frac{1}{2}$. Hence $\lim_{n \to \infty} \int_0^1 f_n(x)\, dx = \lim_{n \to \infty} \frac{1}{2} = \frac{1}{2}$.

Since $0 \neq \frac{1}{2}$, the definite integral of the limit is not equal to the limit of the definite integral in this case.

However, if f_n is the partial sum of a Taylor's series for f, then the two limits,

$$\lim_{n \to \infty} \int_a^b f_n(x)\, dx \quad \text{and} \quad \int_a^b \lim_{n \to \infty} f_n(x)\, dx,$$

are equal. This is the substance of the next theorem, whose proof is sketched in Exercise 23.

THEOREM 2.   *Let* $f(x) = a_0 + a_1x + a_2x^2 + \cdots + a_nx^n + \cdots$, *and assume that the series converges at least throughout the open interval* $(-c, c)$. *Then if a and b are in $(-c, c)$, we have*

$$\int_a^b f(x)\, dx = \lim_{n \to \infty} \int_a^b (a_0 + a_1x + \cdots + a_nx^n)\, dx$$

For instance, as we saw on page 332,

$$\frac{1}{1 + x^2} = 1 - x^2 + x^4 - x^6 + x^8 - x^{10} + \cdots \quad\quad \text{for } -1 < x < 1$$

According to Theorem 2, if b is in $(-1, 1)$, we have

$$\int_0^b \frac{1}{1 + x^2}\, dx = \lim_{n \to \infty} \int_0^b [1 - x^2 + \cdots + (-1)^n x^{2n}]\, dx$$

hence $\displaystyle\int_0^b \frac{1}{1 + x^2}\, dx = \lim_{n \to \infty} \left[b - \frac{b^3}{3} + \frac{b^5}{5} + \cdots + (-1)^n \frac{b^{2n+1}}{2n + 1} \right]$

In other words, for b in $(-1, 1)$,

$$\tan^{-1} b = b - \frac{b^3}{3} + \frac{b^5}{5} + \cdots + (-1)^n \frac{b^{2n+1}}{2n + 1} + \cdots$$

a result we proved, even for $b = 1$, on page 332.

Example 4.   Is the limit of a sequence of continuous functions necessarily continuous? More precisely, let $f_1, f_2, \ldots, f_n, \ldots$ be a sequence of continuous functions, and let $f(x) = \lim_{n \to \infty} f_n(x)$. Is f continuous?

This is again a question about the interchange of limits. When we ask whether f is continuous, we are asking whether

$$\lim_{x \to a} f(x) = f(a)$$

Since $\lim_{x \to a} f_n(x) = f_n(a)$, we may rephrase this, asking instead whether

$$\lim_{x \to a} \lim_{n \to \infty} f_n(x) = \lim_{n \to \infty} \lim_{x \to a} f_n(x)$$

The answer is "not always." As an example consider x in $[0,1]$ and let $f_n(x) = x^n$. Each f_n is continuous, but it is not difficult to see that the limiting function f is given as follows:

$$f(x) = \begin{cases} 0 & \text{if } 0 \leqslant x < 1 \\ 1 & \text{if } x = 1 \end{cases}$$

The function f "jumps" at $x = 1$. It is not continuous.

In most cases met in practice the limit of a sequence of continuous functions is continuous. In advanced calculus we introduce the notion of *uniform approach* in order to state the hypotheses which guarantee that the limit is continuous.

The four examples show that the interchange of limits is a delicate matter. Theorems 1 and 2, which we did not prove, assure us, however, that under certain fairly general circumstances the interchange of limits is permissible. Each of the three Theorems (3, 4, and 5) that follow can be interpreted as an "interchange-of-limits" theorem. We will include their proofs.

We first prove that $f_{xy} = f_{yx}$ for most common functions. (A counter example is to be found in Exercise 11, page 376.)

THEOREM 3. *Let $z = f(x,y)$ be a function defined on the xy plane. Then f_{xy} and f_{yx} are equal if they are continuous.*

PROOF. We will prove that $f_{xy}(0,0) = f_{yx}(0,0)$. We have

(1)
$$f_{xy}(0,0) = \frac{\partial(f_x)}{\partial y}\bigg|_{\text{(at 0,0)}} = \lim_{k \to 0} \frac{f_x(0,k) - f_x(0,0)}{k}$$

But $\quad f_x(0,k) = \lim_{h \to 0} \dfrac{f(h,k) - f(0,k)}{h} \quad$ and $\quad f_x(0,0) = \lim_{h \to 0} \dfrac{f(h,0) - f(0,0)}{h}$

Thus

(2)
$$f_{xy}(0,0) = \lim_{k \to 0} \left\{ \lim_{h \to 0} \frac{[f(h,k) - f(0,k)] - [f(h,0) - f(0,0)]}{hk} \right\}$$

Similarly $\quad f_{yx}(0,0) = \lim_{h \to 0} \dfrac{f_y(h,0) - f_y(0,0)}{h}$

(3)
$$= \lim_{h \to 0} \left\{ \lim_{k \to 0} \frac{[f(h,k) - f(h,0)] - [f(0,k) - f(0,0)]}{hk} \right\}$$

Inspection of (2) and (3) and a little algebra show that $f_{xy}(0,0)$ and $f_{yx}(0,0)$ differ only in the order in which limits are taken.

We will prove that the repeated limit (3) equals $f_{xy}(0,0)$. This will prove the theorem. We begin by applying the law of the mean twice to the numerator in (3),

(4) $$[f(h,k) - f(h,0)] - [f(0,k) - f(0,0)]$$

Note that the second bracketed expression in (4) can be obtained from the first bracketed expression in (4) by replacing h with 0. For this reason we introduce the function u, defined by

$$u(x) = f(x,k) - f(x,0)$$

Then (4) equals

(5) $$u(h) - u(0)$$

By the law of the mean,

(6) $$u(h) - u(0) = hu'(H)$$

for some H between 0 and h. But

$$u'(H) = \frac{d(f(x,k) - f(x,0))}{dx}\bigg|_{(\text{at } x = H)}$$

That is,

(7) $$u'(H) = f_x(H,k) - f_x(H,0)$$

By (6) and (7), we see that (4) equals

(8) $$h[f_x(H,k) - f_x(H,0)]$$

This is a major step, for it relates f_x to f_{yx}, and brings us halfway to relating f_{xy} to f_{yx}.

To continue the proof, observe that if we introduce the function v, defined by $v(y) = f_x(H,y)$, then

(9) $$f_x(H,k) - f_x(H,0) = v(k) - v(0)$$

Applying the law of the mean to v, we have

(10) $$v(k) - v(0) = kv'(K)$$

for some K between 0 and k. Since $v(y)$ equals $f_x(H,y)$, we have $v'(K) = f_{xy}(H,K)$. Combining (8), (9), and (10) shows that

(11) $$[f(h,k) - f(h,0)] - [f(0,k) - f(0,0)] = hk\, f_{xy}(H,K)$$

for some H between 0 and h and some K between 0 and k. Thus, by (11),

$$f_{yx}(0,0) = \lim_{h \to 0}\left[\lim_{k \to 0} \frac{hkf_{xy}(H,K)}{hk} \right] = \lim_{h \to 0} [\lim_{k \to 0} f_{xy}(H,K)]$$

Since f_{xy} is continuous,

$$f_{yx}(0,0) = \lim_{h \to 0} [\lim_{k \to 0} f_{xy}(H,K)] = \lim_{h \to 0} f_{xy}(H,0) = f_{xy}(0,0)$$

The theorem is proved for the point $(0,0)$. A similar proof, in which $(0,0)$ is replaced by (a,b), establishes the theorem at any point (a,b).

Our next theorem is suggested by a diagram. Let g and f be two differentiable functions of t, and assume that $g(a) = 0 = f(a)$. The curve whose parametric equations are $x = g(t), y = f(t)$ passes through the origin:

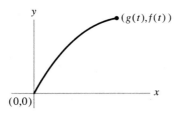

The chord from $(0,0)$ to $(g(t), f(t))$ has the slope $f(t)/g(t)$. The curve has the slope $f'(t)/g'(t)$, as we saw on page 401. It is reasonable to expect that when t is sufficiently near a, the chord and the curve will have approximately the same slope. That is, there are grounds for expecting that

$$(12) \qquad \lim_{t \to a} \frac{f(t)}{g(t)} = \lim_{t \to a} \frac{f'(t)}{g'(t)}$$

Now, (12) can be written as an equality involving an interchange of limits. To see this, note that

$$\lim_{t \to a} \frac{f'(t)}{g'(t)} = \lim_{t \to a} \left(\lim_{\Delta t \to 0} \frac{\dfrac{f(t + \Delta t) - f(t)}{\Delta t}}{\dfrac{g(t + \Delta t) - g(t)}{\Delta t}} \right)$$

$$= \lim_{t \to a} \left[\lim_{\Delta t \to 0} \frac{f(t + \Delta t) - f(t)}{g(t + \Delta t) - g(t)} \right]$$

thus the right side of (12) is a repeated limit. But so is the left side, for

$$\lim_{\Delta t \to 0} \left[\lim_{t \to a} \frac{f(t + \Delta t) - f(t)}{g(t + \Delta t) - g(t)} \right] = \lim_{\Delta t \to 0} \frac{f(a + \Delta t) - f(a)}{g(a + \Delta t) - g(a)}$$

which, since $f(a) = 0 = g(a)$, equals

$$(13) \qquad \lim_{\Delta t \to 0} \frac{f(a + \Delta t)}{g(a + \Delta t)}$$

But (13) is equal to $\qquad \lim_{t \to a} \dfrac{f(t)}{g(t)}$

Thus (12) is a conjecture concerning the equality of two repeated limits.

In order to prove that (12) holds under suitable conditions, we will need the following lemma.

LEMMA: *The generalized law of the mean.* Let f and g be continuous in the closed interval $[a,b]$ and differentiable in the open interval (a,b). Assume also that $g'(t)$ is never 0 for t in (a,b). Then $g(b) - g(a)$ is not 0, and there exists a number T

in (a,b) such that

(14)
$$\frac{f'(T)}{g'(T)} = \frac{f(b) - f(a)}{g(b) - g(a)}$$

PROOF.   First, note that if $g(b) = g(a)$, Rolle's theorem, page 121, would assert that g' takes on the value 0 somewhere in (a,b). Since g' is assumed not to take on the value 0, we conclude that $g(b) - g(a)$ is not 0. Thus the right-hand side of (14) is meaningful.

Our proof now proceeds like that of the law of the mean given on page 123. We introduce a function h that measures the vertical distance from the line L through $(g(a), f(a))$ and $(g(b), f(b))$ to the point $(g(t), f(t))$:

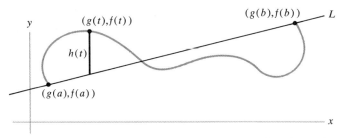

Let $h(t)$ = vertical distance from line L to $(g(t), f(t))$

Note that $h(a) = 0 = h(b)$; let $h(t)$ be positive if $(g(t), f(t))$ is above L, and negative if it is below L. We will apply Rolle's theorem to the function h, which we now compute explicitly.

The line L has slope $[f(b) - f(a)]/[g(b) - g(a)]$; hence the equation of L is

$$\frac{y - f(a)}{x - g(a)} = \frac{f(b) - f(a)}{g(b) - g(a)}$$

which we express as

(15)
$$y = f(a) + [x - g(a)] \frac{f(b) - f(a)}{g(b) - g(a)}$$

The x coordinate of the point on L directly below (or above) the point $(g(t), f(t))$ is $g(t)$. Hence, as (15) shows, the y coordinate of this point on L is

(16)
$$f(a) + [g(t) - g(a)] \frac{f(b) - f(a)}{g(b) - g(a)}$$

Therefore the vertical distance from $[g(t), f(t)]$ on the curve to L is

(17)
$$h(t) = f(t) - \left\{ f(a) + [g(t) - g(a)] \frac{f(b) - f(a)}{g(b) - g(a)} \right\}$$

By Rolle's theorem, there is a number T in (a,b) such that $h'(T) = 0$. In view of (17),

(18)
$$0 = h'(T) = f'(T) - g'(T) \frac{f(b) - f(a)}{g(b) - g(a)}$$

Division of (18) by $g'(T)$, which is not 0, followed by a transposition, yields

$$\frac{f'(T)}{g'(T)} = \frac{f(b) - f(a)}{g(b) - g(a)}$$

The proof is done.

Now we are ready to prove the theorem that our geometric intuition suggested. For simplicity we state it for right-hand limits.

THEOREM 4: *L'hôpital's rule.* Let f and g be differentiable in the open interval (a,b) and continuous throughout the closed interval $[a,b]$. Assume that

$$f(a) = 0 = g(a)$$

and that $g'(t) \neq 0$ for each t in (a,b). Then if

$$\lim_{t \to a^+} \frac{f'(t)}{g'(t)}$$

exists, so does

$$\lim_{t \to a^+} \frac{f(t)}{g(t)}$$

and the two limits are equal.

PROOF. Note first that $g(t) \neq 0$, since otherwise Rolle's theorem would yield a number T such that $g'(T) = 0$. We may write

$$\frac{f(t)}{g(t)} = \frac{f(t) - f(a)}{g(t) - g(a)}$$

and by the lemma conclude that

(19) $$\frac{f(t)}{g(t)} = \frac{f'(T)}{g'(T)}$$

for some T between a and t. Since the limit of the function on the right of (19) exists, so does the limit of the function on the left of (19). Thus $\lim_{t \to a^+} f(t)/g(t)$ exists and equals $\lim_{t \to a^+} f'(t)/g'(t)$. The proof is done.

L'hôpital's rule transforms one limit problem into another limit problem, which may be easier.

Example 5. According to L'hôpital's theorem,

$$\lim_{x \to 0^+} \frac{10^x - e^x}{x} = \lim_{x \to 0^+} \frac{10^x \ln 10 - e^x}{1} = 10^0 \ln 10 - 1 = \ln 10 - 1$$

As another instance, we have

$$\lim_{x \to 0^+} \frac{1 - \cos x}{x^2} = \lim_{x \to 0^+} \frac{\sin x}{2x} = \lim_{x \to 0^+} \frac{\cos x}{2} = \tfrac{1}{2}$$

The reader should verify that the hypotheses of L'hôpital's rule apply.

There are several variations of L'hôpital's rule. Making suitable changes of the hypotheses in Theorem 4, we may replace a^+ with a or with ∞. Similarly, instead of assuming that $f(a) = 0 = g(a)$, we may assume that $\lim_{t \to a} f(t) = \infty = \lim_{t \to a} g(t)$. In this case too, a may be replaced with ∞. Thus, if $\lim_{t \to \infty} f(t) = \infty = \lim_{t \to \infty} g(t)$, and if $\lim_{t \to \infty} f'(t)/g'(t)$ exists, then $\lim_{t \to \infty} f(t)/g(t)$ also exists, and the two limits are equal. For instance,

$$\lim_{x \to \infty} \frac{3x^2 + x + 1}{6x^2 - x + 2} = \lim_{x \to \infty} \frac{6x + 1}{12x - 1} = \lim_{x \to \infty} \tfrac{6}{12} = \tfrac{1}{2}$$

Our next theorem shows that under certain conditions

(20)
$$\frac{d\left(\int_a^b f(x,y) \, dx \right)}{dy} = \int_a^b f_y(x,y) \, dx$$

Since the derivative and the definite integral are defined as limits, (20) is a statement about the interchange of limits. It can be proved that if f and f_y are continuous, then the derivative on the left-hand side of (20) exists and equals the definite integral on the right-hand side of (20) (see R. C. Buck, "Advanced Calculus," 2d ed., p. 120, McGraw-Hill, N.Y., 1965). We will content ourselves with the proof of a more elementary result.

THEOREM 5.   *Let f be a function defined on the plane, and let a and b be two numbers, $a < b$. If f and f_y are continuous and if f_{yy} exists and is bounded, then the function F, defined by*

$$F(y) = \int_a^b f(x,y) \, dx$$

has a derivative equal to $\int_a^b f_y(x,y) \, dx$.

PROOF.   We will show that the quotient

(21)
$$\frac{F(y + h) - F(y)}{h} = \int_a^b \left[\frac{f(x,y + h) - f(x,y)}{h} \right] dx$$

approaches $\int_a^b f_y(x,y) \, dx$ as $h \to 0$. This will prove the theorem.

By the law of the mean, the quantity in brackets on the right of (21) may be written

$$\frac{f(x,y + h) - f(x,y)}{h} = \frac{h f_y(x,y + H)}{h} = f_y(x,y + H)$$

for some H between 0 and h. (H depends on x and h; y is fixed throughout the proof.) Thus the definite integral on the right-hand side of (21) equals

(22)
$$\int_a^b f_y(x,y + H) \, dx$$

We hope to prove that

(23) $$\lim_{h \to 0} \int_a^b f_y(x,y + H)\, dx = \int_a^b f_y(x,y)\, dx$$

To show this, observe that

(24) $$\int_a^b f_y(x,y + H)\, dx - \int_a^b f_y(x,y)\, dx = \int_a^b [f_y(x,y + H) - f_y(x,y)]\, dx$$

Now, by the law of the mean,

(25) $$f_y(x,y + H) - f_y(x,y) = H f_{yy}(x,y + H^*)$$

where H^* is between 0 and H, and depends on x and H. Combining (24) and (25), we obtain

(26) $$\int_a^b f_y(x,y + H)\, dx - \int_a^b f_y(x,y)\, dx = \int_a^b H f_{yy}(x,y + H^*)\, dx$$

But f_{yy} is bounded; hence there is a fixed number M such that $M \geqslant |f_{yy}(x,y + H^*)|$. Moreover, $|H| \leqslant |h|$. Hence we have

(27) $$\left| \int_a^b H f_{yy}(x,y + H^*)\, dx \right| \leqslant \left| \int_a^b h M\, dx \right| = |h| M(b - a)$$

Since M and $(b - a)$ are fixed, we see that $\int_a^b H f_{yy}(x,y + H^*)\, dx$ approaches 0 as $h \to 0$. Thus the left-hand side of (26) approaches 0 as $h \to 0$ and hence (23) holds. Consequently

$$\lim_{h \to 0} \frac{F(y + h) - F(y)}{h} = \int_a^b f_y(x,y)\, dx$$

and the theorem is proved.

We should realize that, on the basis of the examples presented, the interchange of limits is not an automatic procedure. Indeed many theorems in the calculus are basically theorems about the "legality" of an interchange of limits. For instance, Theorem 2 assures us that we can integrate a power series term by term over an interval in which it converges. Theorem 3 assures us that under fairly general conditions $f_{xy} = f_{yx}$. Theorem 4 (L'hôpital's rule) says that under certain circumstances $\lim_{t \to a} f(t)/g(t) = \lim_{t \to a} f'(t)/g'(t)$. Theorem 5 tells us that it is usually safe to differentiate under the integral sign; that is, $d\left[\int_a^b f(x,y)\, dx \right]/dy = \int_a^b (\partial f/\partial y)\, dx$. Each of these theorems can be phrased in such a way as to emphasize that they are about an interchange of limits.

EXERCISES

1. Let $f(x,y) = 1$ if $x > y$, 0 if $x < y$, and x^2 if $x = y$. Show that the repeated limits $\lim_{x \to \infty} [\lim_{y \to \infty} f(x,y)]$ and $\lim_{y \to \infty} [\lim_{x \to \infty} f(x,y)]$ are the same as in the f of Example 1.

2. Verify Theorem 1 in the cases (a) $e^x = 1 + x + x^2/2! + \cdots$; (b) $\sin x = x - x^3/3! + x^5/5! - \cdots$.

3. (a) Using Theorem 1, differentiate the relation $x/(1 - x)^2 = x + 2x^2 + 3x^3 + 4x^4 + \cdots$, with $-1 < x < 1$, to obtain $(x + 1)/(1 - x)^3 = 1 + 2^2x + 3^2x^2 + \cdots$.

   (b) Use (a) to sum $1 + 2^2(\frac{1}{2}) + 3^2(\frac{1}{2})^2 + 4^2(\frac{1}{2})^3 + \cdots$.

   [Answer: (b) 12]

4. Show that $\lim_{x \to 0} [\lim_{n \to \infty} nx/(1 + nx)] = 1$, while $\lim_{n \to \infty} [\lim_{x \to 0} nx/(1 + nx)] = 0$.

5. Let $f_n(x) = \dfrac{nx}{1 + n^2x^4}$. Show that $\displaystyle\int_0^\infty \lim_{n \to \infty} f_n(x)\, dx = 0$, but

$$\lim_{n \to \infty} \int_0^\infty f_n(x)\, dx = \frac{\pi}{4}.$$

6. Show that $\displaystyle\int_0^\infty \left[\int_0^1 (2xy - x^2y^2)\, e^{-xy}\, dx\right] dy = 1$, but

$$\int_0^1 \left[\int_0^\infty (2xy - x^2y^2)\, e^{-xy}\, dy\right] dx = 0$$

7. Let $f_n(x) = x^{2n}/(1 + x^{2n})$.

   (a) Let $f(x) = \lim_{n \to \infty} f_n(x)$. Graph f_4 and f.

   (b) For which a is $\lim_{n \to \infty} [\lim_{x \to a} f_n(x)] = \lim_{x \to a} [\lim_{n \to \infty} f_n(x)]$?

8. Show that $\lim_{x \to 0} [\lim_{y \to 0} x^2/(x^2 + y^2)]$ is not equal to $\lim_{y \to 0} [\lim_{x \to 0} x^2/(x^2 + y^2)]$.

9. Let $f_n(x) = n\pi \sin(n\pi x)$ if $0 \leqslant x \leqslant 1/n$, and 0 otherwise.

   (a) Graph f_1, f_2, and f_3.

   (b) Show that $\lim_{n \to \infty} \int_0^1 f_n(x)\, dx = 2$, but $\int_0^1 \lim_{n \to \infty} f_n(x)\, dx = 0$.

10. Let $f(x) = \lim_{n \to \infty} (1 + nx^2)/(1 + nx)$ for $x \geqslant 0$.

    (a) Compute $f(0)$.

    (b) Compute $f(x)$ if $x > 0$.

    (c) Show that f is not continuous.

11. Verify Theorem 5 by direct computations when $[a,b] = [0,1]$ and $f(x,y)$ is (a) x^2y^3; (b) $\tan^{-1} xy$; (c) $\cos xy$.

12. (a) Show that in the proof of Theorem 3 we did not use the fact that f_{yx} is continuous.

    (b) Prove this theorem: If f_{xy} is continuous and f_{yx} exists everywhere, then f_{yx} is continuous.

13. Compute

$$\lim_{y \to 0} \left[\lim_{x \to \infty} \frac{\left(1 + \dfrac{2y}{x}\right)^x - \left(1 + \dfrac{y}{x}\right)^x}{y}\right] \quad \text{and} \quad \lim_{x \to \infty} \left[\lim_{y \to 0} \frac{\left(1 + \dfrac{2y}{x}\right)^x - \left(1 + \dfrac{y}{x}\right)^x}{y}\right]$$

(Answer: 1, 1)

14. Show that the generalized law of the mean, page 457, includes the law of the mean, page 123, as a special case.

15. (a) Compare

$$\lim_{x \to \infty} \left(\lim_{y \to \infty} \frac{x^2}{x^2 + y^2 + 1}\right) \quad \text{and} \quad \lim_{y \to \infty} \left(\lim_{x \to \infty} \frac{x^2}{x^2 + y^2 + 1}\right)$$

(b) Compare

$$\lim_{x \to \infty} \left(\lim_{y \to \infty} \frac{x}{x^2 + y^2 + 1} \right) \quad \text{and} \quad \lim_{y \to \infty} \left(\lim_{x \to \infty} \frac{x}{x^2 + y^2 + 1} \right)$$

16. (a) What geometric statement does the generalized law of the mean make about the graph of the curve in the xy plane given parametrically as $x = g(t), y = f(t)$, for t in $[a,b]$?

(b) Does the geometric statement in (a) generalize to a curve in three-dimensional space given parametrically as $x = g(t), y = f(t), z = h(t)$, for t in $[a,b]$? Explain.

(c) What does the generalized law of the mean imply about a particle moving in the plane in such a way that at time t it is at $(g(t), f(t))$?

(d) At time t, one car is at $f(t)$ and another at $g(t)$, both on straight paths. What does the generalized law of the mean imply about these two cars?

17. Assume the following theorem, which is another form of L'hôpital's rule. Theorem: Let the functions f and g be differentiable for all $x \geqslant c$, where c is some fixed number. Assume that

$$\lim_{x \to \infty} f(t) = 0 = \lim_{x \to \infty} g(t)$$

and that $g'(t) \neq 0$ for $t \geqslant c$. Then if $\lim_{t \to \infty} f'(t)/g'(t)$ exists, so does $\lim_{t \to \infty} f(t)/g(t)$, and the two limits are equal. Use the theorem, when needed, to find

(a) $\lim_{x \to \infty} \dfrac{\ln \dfrac{x+1}{x-1}}{1/x}$; (b) $\lim_{x \to \infty} \dfrac{e^{-x}}{1/x}$.   [Answer: (a) 2; (b) 0]

18. We state another variant of L'hôpital's rule. Theorem: Assume that f and g are differentiable in the open interval (a,b) and that

$$\lim_{t \to a^+} f(t) = \infty \quad \text{and} \quad \lim_{t \to a^+} g(t) = \infty$$

Assume also that $g'(t) \neq 0$ for each t in (a,b). Then if $\lim_{t \to a^+} f'(t)/g'(t)$ exists, so does $\lim_{t \to a^+} f(t)/g(t)$, and the two limits are equal. (A similar theorem holds when a^+ is replaced with a or ∞.) Using these theorems, if they are needed, find the following limits:

(a) $\lim_{x \to \infty} \dfrac{\ln x}{x}$ (e) $\lim_{x \to \infty} \dfrac{x^2 + 3}{x^2 - 1}$

(b) $\lim_{x \to \infty} \dfrac{x}{e^x}$ (f) $\lim_{x \to \pi/2} \dfrac{\tan x}{\sec x}$

(c) $\lim_{x \to \infty} \dfrac{\sin x}{x}$ (g) $\lim_{x \to 0} \left(\dfrac{1}{\sin x} - \dfrac{1}{x} \right)$

(d) $\lim_{x \to 0^+} \dfrac{x}{\ln x}$

[Answer: (a) 0; (b) 0; (c) 0; (d) 0; (e) 1; (f) 1; (g) 0]

19. Take logarithms first and then use some variant of L'hôpital's rule to find (a) $\lim_{x \to \infty} (2^x + x^2)^{1/x}$; (b) $\lim_{x \to 0} x^x$; (c) $\lim_{x \to 0} (1 + \sin x)^{\tan x}$.   [Answer: (a) 2; (b) 1; (c) e]

□ □ □

20. Obtain the theorem stated in Exercise 17 from Theorem 4. [Hint: Introduce the functions F and G, where $F(t) = f(1/t)$ and $G(t) = g(1/t)$.]

21. In the diagram below, the unit circle is centered at the origin; BQ is a vertical tangent line; and $BQ = BP$. Prove that $R \to -2$ as $P \to B$.

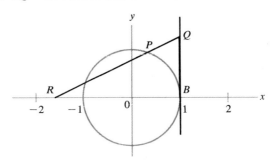

22. Use a variant of L'hôpital's rule, when applicable, to compute

(a) $\lim\limits_{x \to 1} \dfrac{x^3 - 1}{x^2 - 1}$ (d) $\lim\limits_{x \to \pi/2} \dfrac{\sin 3x}{\sin x}$

(b) $\lim\limits_{x \to 1} \dfrac{x^3 + 1}{x^2 + 1}$ (e) $\lim\limits_{x \to 0} \dfrac{5^x - 3^x}{x}$

(c) $\lim\limits_{x \to 0} \dfrac{\sin 3x}{\sin x}$ (f) $\lim\limits_{x \to 1} \dfrac{5^x - 3^x}{x}$

[Answer: (a) $\tfrac{3}{2}$; (b) 1; (c) 3; (d) -1; (e) $\ln \tfrac{5}{3}$; (f) 2]

(Note the happy coincidence: L'hôpital's rule can be applied only when you need it.)

23. In Theorem 5 we assumed that f_{yy} is bounded. Show that it is sufficient to assume that on every rectangle in the plane f_{yy} is bounded. (It can be proved that if f_{yy} is continuous, it is bounded on every rectangle.) (Hint: Look closely at the proof of Theorem 5.)

24. This exercise outlines a proof of Theorem 2 and uses the notation introduced in its statement. Select A such that $|a| < A$, $|b| < A$, and $A < c$.
    (a) Show that for n suitably large, $|a_n A^n| \leqslant 1$.
    (b) Let t be the larger of $|b|/A$ and $|a|/A$. Note that $0 < t < 1$. Show that there is an integer N such that $|a_n x^n| \leqslant t^n$ for all $n \geqslant N$ and for all x in $[a,b]$.
    (c) From (b) deduce that $|f(x) - (a_0 + a_1 x + \cdots + a_n x^n)| \leqslant t^{n+1}/(1 - t)$ for $n \geqslant N$.
    (d) From (c) deduce Theorem 2.

25. Define f by setting $f(x) = \lim\limits_{n \to \infty} \{ \lim\limits_{m \to \infty} [\cos (n! \, \pi x)]^{2m} \}$. Recalling that π is irrational (Exercise 29, page 301), prove that $f(x) = 1$ if x is rational and $f(x) = 0$ if x is irrational. (Thus the function f that is 1 at the rationals and 0 at the irrationals is the limit of a sequence of functions that are themselves limits of sequences of continuous functions. It can be proved that f is *not* the limit of a sequence of continuous functions.)

26. Let $F(y) = \displaystyle\int_0^1 [(x^y - 1)/\ln x] \, dx$ for $y \geqslant 0$.

(a) Assuming that one may differentiate F by differentiating under the integral sign, show that $dF/dy = 1/(1 + y)$.
(b) From (a) deduce that $F(y) = \ln (1 + y) + C$.
(c) Show that the constant C in part (b) is 0 by examining the case $y = 0$.

27. Devise an example of a function f such that $\sum_{m=1}^{\infty} [\sum_{n=1}^{\infty} f(m,n)]=0$ but $\sum_{n=1}^{\infty} [\sum_{m=1}^{\infty} f(m,n)]=1$.

Suggestion: Place $f(m,n)$ on the point (m,n). Let us call the points (m,n) for fixed m, *column m* and for fixed n, *row n*. First fill in row 1 in such a way that $\sum_{m=1}^{\infty} f(m,1) = \frac{1}{2}$. Then choose $f(1,2)$ to be the negative of $f(1,1)$, and all remaining $f(1,n) = 0$; hence $\sum_{n=1}^{\infty} f(1,n) = 0$. Fill in row 2 in such a way that its sum is $\frac{1}{4}$, and then column 2 in such a way that its sum is 0. For instance, we may begin as follows:

$\cdot\,0$	$\cdot\,0$					
$\cdot\,0$	$\cdot\,0$					
$\cdot\,0$	$\cdot\,0$					
$\cdot\,0$	$\cdot\,0$					
$\cdot\,0$	$\cdot -\frac{3}{8}$	$\cdot$	$\cdot$	$\cdot$		
$\cdot -\frac{1}{4}$	$\cdot\,\frac{1}{4}$	$\cdot\,\frac{1}{8}$	$\cdot\,\frac{1}{16}$	$\cdot\,\frac{1}{32}$	$\cdot\,\dots$	Row 2
$\cdot\,\frac{1}{4}$	$\cdot\,\frac{1}{8}$	$\cdot\,\frac{1}{16}$	$\cdot\,\frac{1}{32}$	$\cdot\,\frac{1}{64}$	$\cdot\,\dots$	Row 1

28. The trouble with the f_n's in Example 3 is that they don't look much like f. We present a stronger definition of the limit of a sequence of functions, $f_1, f_2, \dots$. We shall say that $\lim_{n\to\infty} f_n = f$ if for any positive ε there exists an N such that $|f_n(x) - f(x)| < \varepsilon$ for any $n \geqslant N$ and for all x. (In other words, when n is sufficiently large $f_n(x)$ is close to $f(x)$ *for all x* under consideration.)

(a) Prove that if $\lim_{n\to\infty} f_n = f$ and $\int_0^1 f_n(x)\,dx$ and $\int_0^1 f(x)\,dx$ exist, then

$$\lim_{n\to\infty} \int_0^1 f_n(x)\,dx = \int_0^1 f(x)\,dx.$$

(b) Prove that if f_n is continuous, then so is f.

29. Exercise 23, page 232, shows that $\int_0^\infty [(\sin x)/x]\,dx$ is convergent. Fill in the details and find all the gaps or assumptions in the following argument that $\int_0^\infty [(\sin x)/x]\,dx = \pi/2$: Set $F(y) = \int_0^\infty e^{-yx} [(\sin x)/x]\,dx$. We are interested in $F(0)$. Differentiating under the integral sign, we have $F'(y) = -\int_0^\infty e^{-yx} \sin x\,dx$, which, by the fundamental theorem of calculus, equals $-1/(1 + y^2)$. Hence $F(y) = C - \tan^{-1} y$. To find C, observe that $0 = \lim_{y\to\infty} F(y) = C - \pi/2$. Thus $C = \pi/2$, and we have $F(y) = (\pi/2) - \tan^{-1} y$. Hence $F(0) = \pi/2$.

30. Using Theorem 5, solve Exercise 30, page 343.

PART III

Further applications
of the calculus

We now apply the mathematical tools that we have developed to the fields of biology, economics, and psychology, and to problems concerned with traffic, rockets, and gravity. These applications, much more extensive than those scattered through Parts I and II, show that the mathematical way of approaching a problem can help us understand the world around us, and that sometimes the problem may in turn illuminate our understanding of mathematics.

The particular illustrations in these chapters were chosen for their importance and interest. While we do not wish to convey the impression that most of biology, economics, and psychology involves mathematics, it is true that mathematics is being used to an increasing degree in the biological and social sciences. Having applied the ideas of elementary statistics for decades, researchers in these disciplines are now turning to the calculus, linear programming, and abstract algebra in order to discover a structure within masses of data, and to develop a precise language for communicating complex theories.

The first, and still one of the greatest, of such applications of mathematics is Newton's theory of gravity, presented in Chap. 26. Before examining any of the chapters in Part III, it would be wise to read Newton's own description of what he termed "the mathematical way," beginning on page 542.

21

Growth in the
natural world

ONE of the most menacing of the problems that face mankind is the size of the human population, which is increasing at the rate of 1.8 percent per year. In some underdeveloped countries population growth more than neutralizes hard-won improvements in agriculture and housing. In industrialized ("advanced") countries, population growth diverts attention from other pressing problems: The school superintendent plans more schools while the old ones fall into disrepair; the city council tries to control new subdivisions while the provision of adequate community facilities for the present population is neglected. The mathematical theory of population growth is relatively simple. It puts the problem of overpopulation in precise terms, as we shall see in the first example in this chapter devoted to "growth equations" and their various applications in the natural world.

To construct a mathematical model for the simplest type of growth, we assume that the rate of change of the size of a population is proportional to the population size. That is, if P is the population size at time t, then we have

(1) $$\frac{dP}{dt} = kP$$

469

where k is some fixed number. (If k is positive, there is growth; if k is negative, decay.) When the world population was 3 billion, it was increasing at the rate of 54 million per year; thus we estimate k as $(54 \cdot 10^6)/(3 \cdot 10^9) = 0.018 = 1.8$ percent. As we saw in Example 3, page 124, the function

$$(2) \qquad\qquad P(t) = P_0 e^{kt}$$

where P_0 is any fixed number, is the only type of function that satisfies the growth equation (1). If we set $t = 0$ in (2) we see that $P(0) = P_0 e^{k0} = P_0 e^0 = P_0$; thus the constant P_0 is the population at time $t = 0$.

Example 1 (*Human population*).　One-quarter of an acre is required to provide food for one person. The world contains 10 billion acres of arable land; hence the world population would seem to be limited to 40 billion. If the population continues to grow at the rate of 1.8 percent, when will it reach this figure?

To keep the arithmetic simple, let us introduce a time scale such that $t = 0$ for the year 1965, when the population was 3 billion $= 3 \cdot 10^9$. The equation of growth is

$$(3) \qquad\qquad P(t) = 3 \cdot 10^9 \, e^{0.018t}$$

We seek t such that

$$(4) \qquad\qquad P(t) = 40 \cdot 10^9 \qquad \text{or} \qquad 40 \cdot 10^9 = 3 \cdot 10^9 \, e^{0.018t}$$

That is, we wish to solve the equation

$$(5) \qquad\qquad e^{0.018t} = \frac{40 \cdot 10^9}{3 \cdot 10^9} = 13.3$$

By the definition of logarithm to the base e, we have $0.018t = \ln 13.3$. Using a table of natural logarithms, we find that $\ln 13.3 \, (= \ln 10 + \ln 1.33) = 2.303 + 0.285 = 2.588$. Thus $0.018t = 2.588$ and so $t = 144$. We conclude that in the year $1965 + 144 = 2109$, the world will have reached its saturation point.

Our next example is from genetics.

Example 2 (*Gene frequency*).　Two genes that can occupy the same position in a chromosome and determine a certain characteristic, such as hair color, are called alleles. Let us assume that there are only two alleles, A_1 and A_2, for a certain position, and that the probability that A_1 mutates (changes) to A_2 in one generation is 2 percent, while the probability that A_2 mutates to A_1 is 1 percent. What will happen to the distribution of A_1 and A_2 in the population in future generations?

We assume first that two-thirds of the people have A_1, and one-third have A_2. Thus the frequency of A_1 is now ⅔, and that of A_2 is now ⅓. The frequency of mutation of A_1 to A_2 is thus (¹⁄₁₀₀) (⅔), and that of A_2 to A_1 is (²⁄₁₀₀) (⅓). Hence the frequency of A_1 in the next generation is

$$(6) \qquad\qquad \tfrac{2}{3} - (\tfrac{1}{100}) (\tfrac{2}{3}) + (\tfrac{2}{100}) (\tfrac{1}{3}) = \tfrac{2}{3}$$

and the frequency of A_2 in the next generation is

$$(7) \qquad\qquad \tfrac{1}{3} - (\tfrac{2}{100}) (\tfrac{1}{3}) + (\tfrac{1}{100}) (\tfrac{2}{3}) = \tfrac{1}{3}$$

Equations (6) and (7) tell us that if the frequencies of A_1 and A_2 happen to be ⅔ and ⅓, respectively, then these frequencies remain constant forever: we have genetic equilibrium. Many characteristics are in genetic equilibrium. For instance, the frequencies of the various hair colors do not seem to change with the generations.

However, if we do not begin with the frequencies $\frac{2}{3}$ and $\frac{1}{3}$, we do not have genetic equilibrium. Let us see what happens to the frequencies if the initial frequency of A_1 is p_0, and that of A_2 is q_0. Let p_n and q_n be the frequency of genes A and B in the nth generation. (We call the initial generation the *zeroth* generation.) Whatever p_n and q_n may be, we have

$$(8) \qquad\qquad p_n + q_n = 1$$

so it suffices to examine p_n. Consider

$$\Delta p = p_{n+1} - p_n$$

We have

$$\Delta p = -\tfrac{1}{100}\, p_n + \tfrac{2}{100}\, q_n = -\tfrac{1}{100}\, p_n + \tfrac{2}{100}\,(1 - p_n) = \tfrac{2}{100} - \tfrac{3}{100}\, p_n$$

which we write as

$$(9) \qquad\qquad \Delta p = -\tfrac{3}{100}\,(p_n - \tfrac{2}{3})$$

in order to relate p_n to the equilibrium value, $\frac{2}{3}$.

Now, in (9), Δp and p_n are defined only for $n = 0, 1, 2, \ldots$. Since we are interested in changes taking place from one generation to the next, it is convenient to introduce a time scale such that the basic unit corresponds to the time interval between generations (one generation is about 30 years). Thus Δp is the change in frequency corresponding to a change in time of one unit, that is, corresponding to the change $\Delta t = 1$. We may therefore rewrite (9) as

$$\Delta p = \frac{\Delta p}{1} = \frac{\Delta p}{\Delta t} = -\tfrac{3}{100}\,(p_n - \tfrac{2}{3})$$

For convenience, let us imagine that p is defined for all t, not just at integral values of t. This will enable us to introduce the machinery of the calculus. Indeed, since $\Delta p / \Delta t$ is an estimate of dp/dt, the preceding equation suggests that we hypothesize that the function p satisfies the differential equation

$$(10) \qquad\qquad \frac{dp}{dt} = -\tfrac{3}{100}\,(p - \tfrac{2}{3})$$

which says that the rate of change of the frequency p is proportional to $(p - \frac{2}{3})$. Equation (10) is similar to the natural growth equation (1), but *the rate of change is not proportional to the amount itself*. However, since $d(\frac{2}{3})/dt = 0$, we can rewrite dp/dt as $d(p - \frac{2}{3})/dt$, and (10) as

$$(11) \qquad\qquad \frac{d(p - \tfrac{2}{3})}{dt} = -\tfrac{3}{100}\,(p - \tfrac{2}{3})$$

which is precisely the form (1). We therefore have, as in (2),

$$(12) \qquad\qquad p - \tfrac{2}{3} = (p_0 - \tfrac{2}{3})\, e^{-3t/100}$$

Equation (12) tells us that no matter what the initial frequency p_0 is, $p - \frac{2}{3}$ approaches 0 as time, measured in generations, goes on. Thus, as the generations pass, p_n approaches the equilibrium value, $\frac{2}{3}$; hence q_n approaches $\frac{1}{3}$. This means that if a viable new allele is formed, it will eventually become a stable characteristic of the population; the eventual frequency of the characteristic is determined by its mutation rate and that of its allele.

The equation we met in Example 2 is of the type

$$(13) \qquad\qquad \frac{dx}{dt} = k(x - C)$$

where k and C are constants. It asserts that x changes at a rate proportional to the difference between x and C. Since $dC/dt = 0$, we can rewrite (13) as

$$(14) \qquad\qquad \frac{d(x - C)}{dt} = k(x - C),$$

which asserts that the quantity $x - C$ changes at a rate proportional to itself. Thus

$$(15) \qquad\qquad x - C = Ae^{kt}$$

where A is, like k, some constant. Usually, as in Example 2, k is negative. Thus, as t grows, $e^{kt} \to 0$ and so $x - C$ shrinks toward 0. Therefore we have, for the time-dependent behavior of the quantity x,

$$(16) \qquad\qquad \lim_{t \to \infty} x = C$$

In other words, C is the value which x approaches with the passage of time. The quantity A in (15) is simply the difference between x at time 0 and its limit, since by (15), we have $x(0) - C = Ae^{k0} = A$

Example 3 (Newton's law of cooling or warming). Newton assumed that the rate at which the temperature of a body changes is proportional to the difference between its temperature and that of the surrounding medium. (Experiments and theory support a more complicated law, which is approximated by Newton's law of cooling.) Let T be the temperature of the body, and m the fixed temperature of the surrounding medium. We assume that

$$(17) \qquad\qquad \frac{dT}{dt} = k(T - m)$$

so that we have an equation of the form (13). As our examination of (13) shows, $T \to m$ as $t \to \infty$; this asserts that if fruit is cooled in a refrigerator, its temperature approaches the refrigerator temperature, or if a potato is baked in an oven, its temperature approaches the oven temperature. In the present symbols, (15) takes the form

$$(18) \qquad\qquad T - m = Ae^{kt}$$

Let us consider a specific illustration of Newton's law. A chef puts some meat of temperature 70° into a warm oven. An hour later the meat thermometer reads 120°; in another hour it reads 140°. What is the oven temperature? When will the meat temperature be 150°? What is k? (For simplicity we assume that the interior of the meat has the same temperature as the surface.)

Let T denote the meat temperature, and m the oven temperature. We introduce our time scale in such a way that $t = 0$ when the meat is put into the oven. Then we have

$$(19) \qquad 70 - m = Ae^{(k)\,(0)} \qquad 120 - m = Ae^{(k)\,(1)} \qquad 140 - m = Ae^{(k)\,(2)}$$

which simplify to

$$(20) \qquad\qquad 70 - m = A \qquad 120 - m = Ae^{k} \qquad 140 - m = Ae^{2k}$$

The three equations (20) enable us to find the three unknowns, A, k, and m.

From (20) we obtain

$$(21) \qquad\qquad 120 - m = (70 - m)\,e^{k} \qquad \text{and} \qquad 140 - m = (70 - m)\,e^{2k}$$

From (21) it follows that

(22) $$\frac{120 - m^2}{70 - m} = (e^k)^2 = e^{2k} = \frac{140 - m}{70 - m}$$

Equation (22) gives us an equation for m,

(23) $$\frac{120 - m^2}{70 - m} = \frac{140 - m}{70 - m}$$

which reduces to

(24) $$30m = 4600$$

from which we learn the oven temperature:

$$m = 153\tfrac{1}{3}°$$

To find k, we use either the second or the third equation in (20). If we use the second, first equation in (20), which gives us

$$70 - 153\tfrac{1}{3} = A$$

thus $A = -83\tfrac{1}{3}°$.

To find k, we use either the second or the third equation in (20). If we use the second, we have

(25) $$120 - 153\tfrac{1}{3} = (-83\tfrac{1}{3})\, e^k$$

which yields

(26) $$e^k = 0.4$$

From a handbook of tables, we find that $k = -0.91$, approximately. Finally, the meat reaches a temperature of $150°$ when

$$150 - 153\tfrac{1}{3} = (-83\tfrac{1}{3})\, e^{kt}$$

Since $e^{kt} = (e^k)^t = (0.4)^t$, we may rewrite this equation as $-3\tfrac{1}{3} = (-83\tfrac{1}{3})(0.4)^t$, or more simply as $^{10}\!/_{250} = 0.04 = (0.4)^t$. To solve the equation $(0.4)^t = 0.04$, we take logarithms of both sides (to base 10, say), obtaining $t(-0.398) = -1.398$. Thus $t = 3.54$. In 3.54 hours the meat temperature will reach $150°$.

If the human population continued to grow as described in Example 1, and found unlimited sources of food, in about 7 centuries there would be one person per square foot of ground. Well before then, inhibitory influences would have begun to restrict our growth. In the dense cities epidemics would probably be devastating. With agricultural land exploited to the maximum, a single crop failure could lead to mass starvation. The next example shows one mathematical way of describing restricted growth.

Example 4 (Inhibited growth). Let us assume that as the population P increases, the growth rate may be forced to decline. For simplicity, let us assume that circumstances prevent P from exceeding the value M. In addition let us assume that the growth rate of P is proportional to the product of P and the difference $M - P$. When the amount left to grow, $M - P$, is small, the growth rate shrinks. Instead of (1), we have

(27) $$\frac{dP}{dt} = kP(M - P)$$

where k is a positive constant. To find P explicitly as a function of time we first rewrite (27) in terms of differentials:

$$(28) \qquad \frac{dP}{P(M - P)} = k \, dt$$

The left side of (28), by partial fractions or elementary algebra, equals

$$(29) \qquad \left[\frac{1}{MP} + \frac{1}{M(M - P)} \right] dP$$

while the right side of (28) equals $d(kt)$. Now, (29) can be written as

$$d \left(\frac{\ln P}{M} \right) - d \left(\frac{\ln (M - P)}{M} \right) = d \left(\frac{\ln P - \ln (M - P)}{M} \right) = d \left(\frac{1}{M} \ln \frac{P}{M - P} \right),$$

and so we may write (28) as

$$d \left(\frac{1}{M} \ln \frac{P}{M - P} \right) = d(kt)$$

Since two functions that have equal differentials differ by a constant, we have

$$(30) \qquad \frac{1}{M} \ln \frac{P}{M - P} = kt + C$$

where C is fixed. To solve (30) for P, we rewrite it as

$$\ln \frac{P}{M - P} = Mkt + MC$$

Hence

$$\frac{P}{M - P} = e^{Mkt + MC} = e^{Mkt} e^{MC}$$

Denoting $e^{Mkt} e^{MC}$ by s, we have $P/(M - P) = s$, an algebraic equation that yields

$$(31) \qquad P = \frac{sM}{1 + s} \qquad s = e^{Mkt} e^{MC}$$

As $t \to \infty$, $e^{Mkt} \to \infty$, since $k > 0$ for growth; hence $s \to \infty$. We see therefore that as $t \to \infty$, $s/(1 + s) \to 1$ and, by (31), we have $P \to M$, as we would expect.

In order to make (31) more accessible to the intuition, we will let P_0 denote the population at $t = 0$. Observe that when $t = 0$, we have $s = e^{MC}$. Hence by (31),

$$(32) \qquad P_0 = \frac{e^{MC} M}{1 + e^{MC}}$$

Solving (32) for e^{MC}, we find that

$$(33) \qquad e^{MC} = \frac{P_0}{M - P_0}$$

Combining (31) and (33), we obtain, after some algebra,

$$(34) \qquad P = \frac{MP_0}{P_0 + (M - P_0) e^{-Mkt}}$$

Equation (34) provides a close approximation to the growth of a population of fruit flies in a jar, the spread of epidemics in the human population, and the strength of certain chemical reactions. It is called the *logistic* or *saturation* equation. As Exercise 27 shows, the graph of (34) has an inflection point where $P = M/2$.

We summarize this chapter by sketching the solutions of the three growth equations (1), (13), and (27):

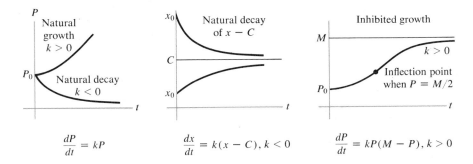

$$\frac{dP}{dt} = kP \qquad\qquad \frac{dx}{dt} = k(x - C), k < 0 \qquad\qquad \frac{dP}{dt} = kP(M - P), k > 0$$

The three equations,

$$\frac{dP}{dt} = kP \qquad \frac{dx}{dt} = k(x - M) \qquad \text{and} \qquad \frac{dP}{dt} = kP(M - P)$$

all lead us to formulas involving the exponential function. They are theoretical models of growth. As man extends his control over the natural world, and sometimes unbalances forces that have been in equilibrium for thousands of years, these and other theoretical models will be of increasing value in the attempt to minimize the damage he inflicts on this planet during the next few decades or centuries of genetic inequilibrium.

EXERCISES

1. Solve the equation $e^{0.018t} = 2$, using the (a) e^x table; (b) $\log_{10} x$ table; (c) $\ln x$ table. [This result shows that if (1) continues to hold, the world population will double between 1965 and 2003.]
2. (a) Using formula (3), estimate the world population in the year 1800, that is, when $t = -165$.
   (b) The estimate in (a) is too small because the growth rate was less than that used in obtaining formula (3). The best estimates indicate that the world population in 1800 was about 1 billion. What growth rate k, assumed constant from 1800 to 1965, would describe the growth in that interval of time?
   [Answer: (a) 0.15 billion; (b) $k = 0.0066$]
3. (a) Read the discussion in Chap. 22 of the value of 1 dollar t years from now, and
   (b) show that it provides an example of natural growth.
4. A radioactive substance disintegrates at a rate proportional to its mass.
   (a) Show that the amount N remaining at time t is of the form $N = N_0 e^{-kt}$, where k is positive.
   (b) The time necessary for one-half the substance to disintegrate is its *half-life*. Show that the substance has a half-life of $(\ln 2)/k$ or approximately $0.69/k$. Half-life is denoted $t_{1/2}$.

5. (See Exercise 4.) The half-life of radium is about 1,600 years (actually 1,590 years).
(a) From this, find k in Eq. (2).
(b) With the aid of Eq. (2), find how long it takes 75 percent of the radium to disintegrate.
(c) Solve (b) without using the calculus.
(d) How long will it take for 90 percent of the radium to disintegrate?
(e) Without the calculus, show that the answer to (d) is between 4,800 and 6,400.
[Answer: (a) 0.00043; (b) 3,200 years; (d) 5,300 years;
all rounded off to two significant figures]

6. Show that if a quantity is growing or shrinking at a rate proportional to the amount present, then its changes in successive equal intervals of time form a geometric progression.

7. At one point in his study of a falling body starting from rest, Galileo conjectured that its speed is proportional to the distance s it has dropped.
(a) Show that if this conjecture were correct, s would grow exponentially as a function of time.
(b) With the aid of (a), show that the speed would also grow exponentially.
(c) Recalling that the initial speed is 0, show that (b) leads to an absurd conclusion. Galileo later was to discover that ds/dt is proportional to time t rather than distance s.

8. In the spectrophotometry of solutions, the intensity of light passing through a solution is studied. The fraction of light that is absorbed by a very thin lamina is roughly proportional to the amount of light striking the lamina and to its thickness. From this assumption, show that the amount of light penetrating an object of thickness x is proportional to e^{kx}, where k is a negative constant. That is, show that I, the intensity of the light penetrating the lamina, has the form $I = I_0 e^{kx}$, where x is the thickness of the lamina and I_0 is the intensity of illumination at the surface. The conclusion holds in particular for the intensity of sunlight at a depth x in the ocean.

9. Draw a typical graph of P in Eq. (2) as a function of time if k is (a) positive; (b) negative.

10. Draw a typical graph of x in Eq. (15) as a function of time if k is (a) positive; (b) negative.

11. Verify that the function $y = ae^{kx}$ satisfies the equation $dy/dx = ky$.

12. (See Exercise 4.) A radioactive substance disintegrates at the rate of 0.05 grams per day when its mass is 10 grams.
(a) How much of the substance will remain t days from now?
(b) What is its half-life?
[Answer: (a) $10e^{-0.005t}$ grams; (b) 138 days]

13. The number of bacteria in a culture grew from 100 to 400 in 24 hours. What was the population after the first 12 hours? Solve the problem, (a) without the calculus, (b) with the aid of Eq. (2).

14. Show that if the growth of the human population continues at the present rate, then in seven centuries humanity will be packed like sardines. Assume that 1 square foot per person is "sardine packing," that the radius of the earth is 4,000 miles, and that a quarter of its surface is land.

15. Let x be the concentration of cells and s be the concentration of some nutrient on which they feed. Both x and s depend on time t.
(a) If the cells require energy both to maintain themselves and to reproduce, why is it reasonable to assume that $dx/dt + ax = b\, ds/dt$, where a and b are some constants?

(b) Calling $b\, ds/dt$ the "feeding rate" F, and assuming that it is constant, deduce that $x = (F/a)(1 - e^{-at}) + x_0 e^{-at}$, where x_0 is the cell concentration at time $t = 0$.

16. If the population P satisfies the equation $dP/dt = kP$, where k is a positive constant, then, as we saw, $P \to \infty$ as $t \to \infty$. Assume that because families are increasing in size we have $dP/dt = kP^{1.01}$, with $k > 0$.

    (a) Find P explicitly as a function of time, and sketch the general shape of its graph.

    (b) Why is $dP/dt = kP^{1.01}$ called a "doomsday equation"?

17. An indoor thermometer, reading 60°, is placed outdoors. In 10 minutes it reads 70°, and in another 10 minutes it reads 76°.

    (a) Using no calculus, guess the outdoor temperature.

    (b) Find the outdoor temperature with aid of (15).   (Answer: 85°)

18. Review Example 2.

    (a) If $p_0 = 0.1$, in how many generations will p_n reach 0.5?

    (b) If $p_0 = 0.9$, in how many generations will p_n reach 0.7?

19. Review Example 2.

    (a) If A_1 mutates to A_2 at the rate p (instead of 0.01) and A_2 mutates to A_1 at the rate q (instead of 0.02), show that at genetic equilibrium, the frequency of A_1 is $q/(p + q)$, and that of A_2 is $p/(p + q)$.

    (b) Show that no matter what the initial frequencies of A_1 and A_2 are, as the generations pass, the population approaches equilibrium.

20. Carbon-14 (chemical symbol, C^{14}), one of the three isotopes of carbon, is radioactive and has a half-life of about 5,570 years. If the C^{14} concentration in the carbon from a plant, shell, fish, or piece of wood of unknown age were half that of the C^{14} concentration in a present-day live specimen, then we would place its age at about 5,570 years. (This technique of radiocarbon dating is dependable up to an age of 70,000 years.) Show that if A_0 and A are the radioactivities of samples prepared from contemporary and undated materials, respectively, then the age of the undated material is about $t = 8040 \ln(A_0/A)$. (For specific examples, see Radiocarbon Dating in the "McGraw-Hill Encyclopedia of Science and Technology," McGraw-Hill, N.Y.)

21. Graph Eq. (34) for $t \geqslant 0$, if $P_0 = M/10$ and $k = 1/(2M)$. In particular, show that it has an inflection point, and that at this point, $P = M/2$.

22. Graph Eq. (34), for $t \geqslant 0$, if $P = 3M/4$ and $k = 1/(2M)$. In particular, show that it has no inflection point.

23. The data from an experiment concerning the growth of a plant look like this:

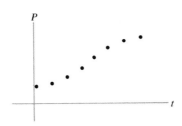

Which growth formula, (1), (13), or (27), would you use to approximate P as a function of time?

24. Assume that the birth rate is proportional to the population size and that the death rate is proportional to the square of the population size; that is, there are constants b and m such that

$$\frac{dP}{dt} = bP - mP^2$$

an equation first considered by Quételet in 1835.

(a) Show that there is a constant c such that $P = be^{bt}/(c + me^{bt})$.

(b) How does P behave as t increases indefinitely?

(c) Show that Eq. (27) is a special case of the equation considered in this exercise.

25. (See Exercise 4.) The mass of atoms that disintegrates between time t and time $t + \Delta t$ is approximately $(dN/dt)\,\Delta t$; hence the fraction that disintegrates in that interval of time is $(1/N_0)(dN/dt)\,\Delta t$, where N_0 is the initial mass.

    (a) Why would $(1/N_0)\displaystyle\int_0^\infty t\,(dN/dt)\,dt$ represent the average life expectancy of all the atoms present at time 0?

    (b) Using (a), show that the average life expectancy is $1/k$, the reciprocal of the constant of decay.

26. A spherical raindrop evaporates at a rate proportional to its surface area. Find a formula for its volume V as a function of time t, $V = f(t)$.

27. (a) Show that if $P_0 < M/2$, then the curve of Eq. (34) has an inflection point at a unique $t > 0$. (See page 283 for the definition of inflection point.)

    (b) Show that $P = M/2$ at the inflection point. We may think of this inflection point, where the growth rate dP/dt begins to shrink, as the place where the effect of inhibition in the form of the barrier M begins to dominate the growth.

28. One person in a population of size P is infected with a certain disease. All the members of the population are susceptible to the disease, and an epidemic spreads from this person, eventually infecting everybody. At time t let $s(t)$ be the number of those not yet infected and $i(t)$ the number of those who are infected. We have $s(t) + i(t) = P$. Assume that $ds/dt = -ks(t)\,i(t)$, where k is some positive constant.

    (a) Find an explicit formula for $s(t)$.

    (b) Graph $y = -ds/dt$, the rate at which new cases occur.

29. Two species living in the same region feed on the same plants and on each other. Let the population of one species be P_1 and the population of the other species be P_2; both P_1 and P_2 are functions of time t. Assume that P_1 and P_2 are positive and that

$$\frac{dP_1}{dt} = 20(P_2 - P_1)P_2{}^3 \qquad \text{and} \qquad \frac{dP_2}{dt} = 8(P_1 - P_2)P_1{}^3$$

    (a) Show that when P_1 exceeds P_2, population P_1 is decreasing and P_2 is increasing.

    (b) Show that when P_2 exceeds P_1, population P_1 is increasing and P_2 is decreasing.

    (c) Show that the point (P_1, P_2) remains on a curve of the form $2x^4 + 5y^4 = \text{constant}$.

30. Let S be the number of people in a large city who are susceptible to measles, and let I be the number of people who have measles. Both S and I are functions of time t.

    (a) Argue for the plausibility of these two assumptions:

$$\frac{dS}{dt} = a - bIS \qquad \text{and} \qquad \frac{dI}{dt} = bIS - cI$$

where a, b, and c are positive constants.

(b) Show that $I + S$ is increasing when I is larger than a/c; and decreasing when I is less than a/c.

(c) Examine the change of I when S is larger than c/b and when S is less than c/b.

(d) Show that if there are no epidemics—that is, I is constant—then $I = a/c$ and $S = c/b$.

31. Assume that a certain species is sparsely distributed throughout a large forest, that the number of females equals the number of males, and that the birth rate is proportional to the product of the number of males and the number of females.

(a) Obtain a differential equation for P, the size of the population, as a function of time.

(b) Find P explicitly.

32. Review probability density and distribution, pages 233–237.

(a) Assume that a certain culture of cells is growing exponentially, each cell splitting into two "daughter" cells. Show that if the population at time t is $N_0 e^{kt}$, where t may be positive or negative, then the rate of formation of new cells is $2kN_0 e^{kt}$.

(b) The time between the birth of a cell and its division is its "generation time," which varies from cell to cell. Let f be the theoretical probability density for these generation times; that is, $\int_0^{t_0} f(t)\,dt$ is a theoretical estimate of the fraction of cells that have a generation time less than or equal to t_0, for all $t_0 \geqslant 0$. Now, at a certain instant we take a sample of the culture and record the time required for these cells to divide. This time we call the "life expectancy." Let P be a theoretical probability density for these life expectancies. Show that if we take our sample at time 0, then

$$N_0 \int_0^{u_0} P(u)\,du = \int_0^{u_0} \left[2kN_0\, e^{-kt} \int_t^{u_0} f(u)\,du \right] dt$$

(c) Deduce from (b) that

$$N_0 \int_0^{u_0} P(u)\,du = \int_0^{u_0} \left[2kN_0 \int_0^u e^{-kt} f(u)\,dt \right] du = N_0 \int_0^{u_0} 2f(u)\,(1 - e^{-ku})\,du$$

(d) From (b) deduce that $P(u_0) = 2f(u_0)\,(1 - e^{ku_0})$, an explicit relation between the functions P and f. This is due to P. Painter.

33. Experimental results had suggested to several biologists that the expected generation time, $\overline{T} = \int_0^\infty tf(t)\,dt$, of the cells described in Exercise 32 is always at least as large as the time required for the cell population to double, namely $(\ln 2)/k$. We outline a proof for this assertion from Reference 4 below.

(a) Recalling Exercise 32, show that $\int_0^\infty 2e^{-kt} f(t)\,dt = 1$.

(b) Show that $1 - x \leqslant e^{-x}$ for all x.

(c) Show that

$$\int_0^\infty 2e^{-kt} f(t)\,dt = 2e^{-k\overline{T}} \int_0^\infty e^{-k(t-\overline{T})} f(t)\,dt \geqslant 2e^{-k\overline{T}} \int_0^\infty [1 - k(t - \overline{T})] f(t)\,dt = 2e^{-k\overline{T}}$$

(d) Combining (a) and (c), deduce the conjectured inequality.

REFERENCES

1. D'ancona, U.: The Struggle for Existence, "Bibliotheca Biotheoretica," vol. 6, E. J. Brill, Leiden, 1954. (This contains many applications of the calculus; Chap. 27 considers a justification for applying mathematics in biology.)
2. Bartlett, M. S.: "Stochastic Population Models in Ecology and Epidemiology," Wiley, New York, 1960. (The calculus is used throughout this study of birth-and-death processes, prey–predator systems, competition between species, epidemic size, and recurrent epidemics.)
3. von Foerster, H., P. M. Mora, and L. W. Amiot: Doomsday: Friday, 13 November, A.D. 2026, *Science*, 132:2, 1291–1295 (1960). (This compares data with the doomsday type of equation.)
4. Painter, P. R., and A. G. Marr: Inequality of Mean Interdivision Time and Doubling Time, submitted to *J. Gen. Microbiol.*
5. Marr, A. G., E. H. Nilson, and D. J. Clark: The Maintenance Requirement of Escherichia coli, *Ann. N. Y. Acad. Sci.*, 102:536–548 (1963).

22

Business management
and economics

A complex business organization must continually make decisions. How many warehouses should be built, and where should they be? How often should orders be placed? How should hundreds of delivery trucks be routed? How many echelons of command would be most efficient? Mathematics is often called upon to help obtain quantitative answers.

Governments struggle with such questions as these: What is the cause of periodic recessions? What will be the immediate and long-range impact of a tax cut or of a reduction in the military budget? What should be done about inflation or recession? Mathematics helps obtain insights into these questions of economic theory.

We will present a few illustrations of the uses of mathematics in economic theory and practice. For brevity we may introduce assumptions to simplify both the economics and the mathematics. Thus each of the examples in this chapter should be considered as only the first step into rather complex theories.

481

Example 1 (Ideal lot problem). A firm sells A units of a certain item at a constant rate during one year. (We are assuming that there are no peak periods and no element of chance.) Goods purchased in a single order are delivered in one lot. If the firm orders all A units delivered at the beginning of the year, then it saves on *re-order* costs (such as secretarial work and delivery fees), but it incurs higher *carrying* costs (since the average inventory throughout the year is $A/2$). If it orders every day, it keeps the average inventory low, but then the re-order costs may become prohibitive. To arrive at the happy mean, the firm wishes to minimize cost as a function of the size of the order.

Let $C(x)$ be the total annual carrying and re-order costs when the firm orders x units in each lot. It therefore places A/x orders per year. Let us assume that the cost of placing one order is made up of a fixed cost F (for instance, stationery) and a cost Px which is a linear function of the size of the order (such as packaging and shipping). Then the total re-order cost for the year is

(1)
$$(F + Px)\frac{A}{x}$$

[Note in (1) that smaller lots increase re-order cost.] Let us assume that the annual carrying cost for one unit is I. When the lot size is x, the average inventory is $x/2$. Thus the carrying cost for 1 year is

(2)
$$I\frac{x}{2}$$

[Note in (2) that smaller lots decrease annual carrying costs.] Combining (1) and (2):

(3)
$$C(x) = \frac{Ix}{2} + \frac{(F + Px)A}{x} = \frac{Ix}{2} + \frac{FA}{x} + PA$$

To study the function C (for $x > 0$), we examine dC/dx and d^2C/dx^2. We have

(4)
$$\frac{dC}{dx} = \frac{I}{2} - \frac{FA}{x^2} = \frac{Ix^2 - 2FA}{2x^2}$$

and

(5)
$$\frac{d^2C}{dx^2} = \frac{2FA}{x^3}$$

From (5) we see that the graph of $y = C(x)$ is concave upward for all $x > 0$. From (4) we see that dC/dx is negative when x satisfies the inequality $Ix^2 < 2FA$, but positive when x satisfies $Ix^2 > 2FA$. When $Ix^2 = 2FA$, that is (since x is positive), when

(6)
$$x = \sqrt{\frac{2FA}{I}}$$

$dC/dx = 0$. Thus $C(x)$ decreases when x is less than $\sqrt{2FA/I}$, and increases when x is greater than $\sqrt{2FA/I}$. For all positive x the curve is concave upward and at $x = \sqrt{2FA/I}$ it reaches a minimum value. We sketch the graph:

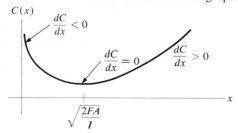

Since $\dfrac{d^2C}{dx^2} > 0$ for all $x > 0$, the graph is concave upwards for all $x > 0$

Formula (6) tells the firm that, since F and I are fixed, the ideal order size x is proportional to $\sqrt{A}$. If sales are quadrupled, say by an intensive advertising campaign, then for maximum efficiency the order size should be *doubled*; hence the frequency of ordering should be *doubled*. It is wiser to double both the order size and the frequency than to quadruple the order size and keep the same frequency.

A more thorough analysis considers back orders and sales lost due to inadequate inventory. (See Reference 3 for further details.)

Example 2 (Present value). Both business and government frequently face the question: "What is 1 dollar t years in the future worth today?" Implicit in this question are such considerations as "the present value of a business depends on its future profit," and "the cost of a dam is weighed against its future revenue."

To begin our analysis, we consider a related question: "How much is 1 dollar today worth t years from now?" We shall interpret this to mean "If 1 dollar is deposited today in a bank that pays an interest rate r, how much will be in the account t years from now?" We will assume that r does not change with time.

In practice r is between 0.02 and 0.20. If the bank compounds interest annually, then in 1 year the account holds $1 + r$ dollars, and in t years 1 dollar grows to $(1 + r)^t$ dollars. (See Example 6, page 69 for a discussion of a similar problem.) If the bank compounds n times a year, then in t years 1 dollar becomes

$$(7) \qquad \left(1 + \frac{r}{n}\right)^{tn} \qquad \text{dollars}$$

Now,

$$(8) \qquad \left(1 + \frac{r}{n}\right)^{tn} = \left(1 + \frac{r}{n}\right)^{(n/r)\,tr} = \left[\left(1 + \frac{r}{n}\right)^{n/r}\right]^{rt}$$

Since $\lim_{x \to 0} (1 + x)^{1/x} = e$ (see page 76), we see from (8) that for large n (that is, when the bank compounds interest frequently) $[(1 + r/n)^{n/r}]^{rt}$ is approximately e^{rt}. For simplicity we *define the value t years from now of 1 dollar today as e^{rt}.*

Now it is easy to answer the question "What is 1 dollar t years in the future worth today?," which we rephrase as "What amount A put in the bank today will grow to 1 dollar t years from now?" Assuming the interest rate is r, we want to find A such that

$$(9) \qquad Ae^{rt} = 1$$

Solving (9) for A, we obtain

$$(10) \qquad A = \frac{1}{e^{rt}} = e^{-rt}$$

Thus we define the *present value of 1 dollar t years in the future as e^{-rt}*, which is, as we would expect, less than 1.

The future profit of a business (or future revenue of a dam) is spread out over time. Let us say that the profit flow t years from now is $f(t)$ dollars per year. This rate may vary within the year, and we will consider f to be a continuous function of time. The profit in the small interval of time Δt, from time t to time $t + \Delta t$, would be approximately $f(t)\,\Delta t$. The future profit, $F(T)$, from now, when $t = 0$, to some time in the future, when $t = T$, is therefore

$$(11) \qquad F(T) = \int_0^T f(t)\,dt$$

But the *present value* of the future profit is *not* given by (11). We must consider the present value of the profit earned in a typical short interval of time from t to $t + \Delta t$. According to (10) its present value is approximately

(12) $$e^{-rt} f(t) \, \Delta t$$

Hence the present value of future profit from $t = 0$ to $t = T$ is given by a definite integral:

(13) $$\int_0^T e^{-rt} f(t) \, dt$$

The present value of all future profit is therefore the improper integral $\int_0^\infty e^{-rt} f(t) \, dt$.

(This is a convenient idealization; in practice, an economist usually restricts the future to a finite period.)

Let us denote by $P(r)$ the present value of all future revenue when the interest rate is r; that is,

(14) $$P(r) = \int_0^\infty e^{-rt} f(t) \, dt$$

If the interest rate r is raised, then according to (14), the present value of a business declines. An investor choosing between investing in a business or placing his money in a bank account finds the bank account more attractive when r is raised.

In the simplest case, when f is constant [that is, when the profit flow remains constant, say, at k dollars per year $(k > 0)$], then the total future profit is clearly infinite, but

(15) $$P(r) = \int_0^\infty e^{-rt} k \, dt = \lim_{T \to \infty} \frac{ke^{-rt}}{-r} \bigg|_0^T = \lim_{T \to \infty} \frac{k}{r}(1 - e^{-rt}) = \frac{k}{r}$$

is finite. For a constant profit function, the present value is inversely proportional to the interest rate. If the banks double their interest rate, then the present value of such a business promising a constant profit flow is halved.

Equation (14) assigns to a profit function f (which is a function of t) a present-value function P, which is a function of r, the interest rate. In the theory of differential equations P is called the Laplace transform of f and is frequently used in the solution of complicated differential equations.

Example 3 (Marginal analysis). In economic theory and practice the derivative (or partial derivative) is frequently used to analyze the desirability of certain procedures. For instance, suppose that a firm that employs L workers and has a capital investment of C dollars produces $Q = f(L,C)$ units. Then, assuming that production is proportional to input, we saw in Example 5, page 368, that

(16) $$Q = L\frac{\partial Q}{\partial L} + C\frac{\partial Q}{\partial C}$$

Now, what are the meanings of $\partial Q/\partial L$ and $\partial Q/\partial C$? The partial derivative $\partial Q/\partial L$ records the rate at which production increases when the number of workers increases but the capital investment is not changed. It is called the *marginal product of labor*. Similarly, $\partial Q/\partial C$ is the *marginal product of capital*. Equation (16) asserts that the total product is the sum of a contribution due to labor and a contribution due to capital. The contribution due to labor is equivalent to the contribution by each worker of the marginal product $\partial Q/\partial L$ to the product (and similarly for the contribution of capital).

Let us examine the derivative of Q/L with respect to L. We have

(17)
$$\frac{\partial(Q/L)}{\partial L} = \frac{L(\partial Q/\partial L) - Q}{L^2}$$

We may think of Q/L as the average production of a worker. Now, (17) shows that as long as $L(\partial Q/\partial L) - Q$ is positive, that is, as long as $\partial Q/\partial L$ is greater than Q/L, the average production per worker increases as the size of the labor force increases. However, when $\partial Q/\partial L$ is less than Q/L, the average production per worker decreases as new workers are added [since the right-hand side of (17) becomes negative]. Thus, for maximum productivity per worker, the marginal product $\partial Q/\partial L$ must coincide with the average product Q/L.

This diagram summarizes our observations.

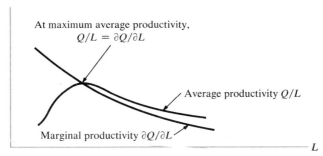

At maximum average productivity, $Q/L = \partial Q/\partial L$

Average productivity Q/L

Marginal productivity $\partial Q/\partial L$

Marginal analysis is also of use in deciding how much of its product a firm should sell in each of two separate markets. (Resale between the two markets is assumed impossible.) Let $c(x)$ be the cost of producing x items. Let $R_1(x_1)$ be the revenue from the sale of x_1 items in the first market, and $R_2(x_2)$ the revenue from the sale of x_2 items in the second market. The profit from the sale of the $x_1 + x_2$ items is thus

(18)
$$R_1(x_1) + R_2(x_2) - c(x)$$

where $x = x_1 + x_2$. Note that $\partial x/\partial x_1 = 1 = \partial x/\partial x_2$. If x_1 and x_2 are to be chosen to maximize (18), we must have

$$0 = \frac{\partial(R_1(x_1) + R_2(x_2) - c(x))}{\partial x_1} = \frac{dR_1}{dx_1} + \frac{dR_2}{dx_2}\frac{\partial x_2}{\partial x_1} - \frac{dc}{dx}\frac{\partial x}{\partial x_1} = \frac{dR_1}{dx_1} - \frac{dc}{dx}$$

Thus $dR_1/dx_1 = dc/dx$. Similarly, $dR_2/dx_2 = dc/dx$.

Hence, for maximization,

(19)
$$\frac{dR_1}{dx_1} = \frac{dR_2}{dx_2}$$

that is, *marginal revenue* in both markets should be equal. Since the company can estimate the functions R_1 and R_2, (19) can be of aid in reaching a decision.

These three examples illustrate some of the simpler applications of the calculus in economics. A more complicated problem encountered is that of maximizing a function of several variables, where the variables are related by an equation. (Compare with Example 3, page 305.) As government and business face more complex issues, they will turn increasingly to mathematics, not only for the objectivity and precision of its language, but for the insight obtained from its theoretical results.

EXERCISES

1. What does Eq. (6) advise us to do (a) if the fixed cost F of placing an order quadruples; (b) if the inventory cost I quadruples?
2. Why is it reasonable that P does not appear in (6)?
3. A more realistic expression than $F + Px$ for the re-order cost may be $F + P\sqrt{x}$, which increases more slowly than $F + Px$. Show that in this case the most economical re-order quantity x satisfies the equation $Ix^2 = PA\sqrt{x} + 2FA$.
4. (a) Graph the inventory of Example 1 as a function of time.
   (b) Where is it not continuous?
5. A printer is planning to produce 200,000 copies of an advertisement. It costs 2 dollars per hour to run his press, which can turn out 1,200 impressions per hour. A metal copy of set type costs 55 cents. How many copies of the type should the printer make and set on his press to minimize his cost? (Assume that he does not use the original type.)   (Answer: about 25)
6. Show that, mathematically speaking, the lot order problem (Example 1), the truck problem in Exercise 17, page 307, and the printer's problem in Exercise 5 of this chapter are basically the same.
7. A delivery service is deciding how many warehouses to set up in a large city. The warehouses will serve similarly shaped regions of equal area A, and, let us assume, an equal number of people.
   (a) Why would transportation costs per item presumably be proportional to $\sqrt{A}$?
   (b) Assuming that the warehouse cost per item is inversely proportional to A, show that C, the cost of transportation and storage per item, is of the form $t\sqrt{A} + w/A$, where t and w are appropriate constants.
   (c) Show that C is a minimum when $A = (2w/t)^{2/3}$.
8. Use a table of the exponential function e^{-x} to find e^{-rt} when (a) $r = 0.02$ and $t = 1$; (b) $r = 0.02$ and $t = 2$; (c) $r = 0.02$ and $t = 4$. (d) In view of Eq. (10), what is the present value of 1 dollar 1 year, 2 years, and 4 years in the future if the interest rate is 2 percent?   [Answer: (d) approximately 98¢, 96¢, 92¢]
9. Show that the present value of 1 dollar 10 years from now, at an interest rate of 3 percent, is the same as the present value of 1 dollar 5 years from now, at an interest rate of 6 percent.
10. Which is worth more today, 100 dollars 8 years from now or 80 dollars 5 years from now? Assume $r = 0.04$. Explain.   (Answer: 100 dollars 8 years from now)
11. Repeat Exercise 10 for $r = 0.08$.   (Answer: 80 dollars 5 years from now)
12. Using the definition of the definite integral, justify Eq. (13).
13. (a) Show that $\int_0^\infty e^{-rt}\, dt = 1/r$ and that $\int_0^\infty te^{-rt}\, dt = 1/r^2$.

   (b) For a certain business the rate of profit $f(t)$ is growing and is proportional to $t : f(t) = kt$. Show that the firm's present value is inversely proportional to the square of the interest rate.

14. (a) Using your financial intuition, but no calculus, explain why $1 = \int_0^\infty e^{-rt}r\, dt$, where r is a positive number.

   (b) From (a) deduce that $1/r = \int_0^\infty e^{-rt}\, dt$.

15. The acquisition cost of a certain machine is A. Its scrap value t years from now will be $S(t)$. Let $f(t)$ be the net revenue flow due to the machine t years from now. Let the interest rate be r, independent of time. How long should the machine be kept before scrapping?

    (a) Show that we wish to find the value of T that maximizes the function g, where

$$g(T) = -A + \int_0^T f(t)\, e^{-rt}\, dt + S(T)\, e^{-rT}$$

    (b) Show by the calculus that, at a maximum of g, $f(T) + S'(T) = rS(T)$.
    (c) Using your economic intuition, interpret $f(T)$, $S'(T)$, and $rS(T)$ and explain why the equation in (b) is reasonable.

16. The cost of an electric stove is E, and that of a gas stove is G. The cost of electricity (per year, say) is A, and that of gas is B. If we have $E < G$ and $A > B$, then the decision which stove to purchase may be complicated.

    (a) Using the notion of present values, and assuming fixed interest rate r, show by the calculus that the electric stove is more economical when $r(G - E)$ is larger than $A - B$.
    (b) Does the answer in (a) agree with your economic intuition? Explain.

17. An optometrist knows that when the price of sunglasses is p, for $0 \leqslant p \leqslant 3$, then the number he can sell is $9 - p^2$ thousands.

    (a) What is the maximum revenue if the optometrist has to set a single fixed price?
    (b) How should the optometrist set the prices to achieve a maximum revenue if he can set two fixed prices, one of them 1 dollar higher than the other?
                [Answer: (a) $6\sqrt{3} = 10.4$; (b) the lower price should be $(\sqrt{22} - 1)/3$]

18. (This continues Exercise 17.) Denote $9 - p^2$ by $f(p)$. Assume that the optometrist charges "what the traffic will bear."

    (a) Show that if $p_0 = 0 < p_1 < \cdots < p_n = 3$, then $\sum_{i=0}^{n-1} [f(p_i) - f(p_{i+1})]\, p_i$ is an estimate of his total revenue.

    (b) Using (a), deduce that his total revenue is $-\int_0^3 p\,(df/dp)\, dp$.

    (c) Using integration by parts, show that his total revenue is $\int_0^3 f(p)\, dp$.

    (d) Evaluate his total revenue.
                                                        [Answer: (d) 18]

19. Explain why, in Example 3, the marginal product $\partial Q/\partial L$ is approximately the increase in production due to the addition of one worker.

20. Let $U(x,y,z) = x^{1/2}y^{1/3}z^{1/6}$ be the "utility" or "desirability" to a given consumer of the amounts x, y, and z of three different commodities. Their prices are, respectively, 2 dollars, 1 dollar, and 5 dollars, and the consumer has 60 dollars to spend. How much of each product should he buy to maximize the utility?
                                    (Answer: $x = 15$, $y = 20$, $z = 2$)

21. Assume that the profits of two firms depend on the amount each produces. For the first firm let the profit be P_1 and its output Q_1; let P_2 and Q_2 be similarly defined

for the second firm. Assume that

$$P_1 = 48Q_1 - 2Q_1{}^2 - 3Q_2{}^2 + 1{,}000 \qquad \text{and} \qquad P_2 = 60Q_2 - 3Q_2{}^2 - 2Q_1{}^2 + 2{,}000$$

Thus the profit for each firm is dependent in part on the output of the other.

(a) If each firm acts to maximize its own profit, what will Q_1, Q_2, P_1, P_2, and $P_1 + P_2$ be?

(b) If the firms agree to work together in order to maximize $P_1 + P_2$, what will Q_1, Q_2, P_1, P_2, and $P_1 + P_2$ be?

[Answer: (a) 12, 10, 988, 2,012, 3,000; (b) 6, 5, 1,141, 2,153, 3,294]

REFERENCES

1. Allen, R. G. D.: "Mathematical Analysis for Economists," Macmillan, New York, 1938. (The development in this text relies heavily on calculus.)
2. Meier, R. C., and S. H. Archer: "An Introduction to Mathematics for Business Analysis," McGraw-Hill, New York, 1960. (This is an elementary introduction to several mathematical topics used in business analysis.)
3. Hadley, G., and T. M. Whitin: "Analysis of Inventory Systems," Prentice-Hall, Englewood Cliffs, N.J., 1963. (Chapter 9 discusses the problems of implementing theoretical results. A glance at earlier chapters will show that several branches of mathematics are used in inventory analysis.)
4. Howell, J. E., and D. Teichroew: "Mathematical Analysis for Business Decisions," Irwin, Homewood, Ill., 1963. (See pp. 51, 74–94, 101, 134–140, 160, and 222–224 for more illustrations of management problems.)
5. Bowen, E. K.: "Mathematics, with Applications in Management and Economics," Irwin, Homewood, Ill., 1963. (This is an elementary introduction to calculus, linear programming, and probability for economists.)
6. Kooros, A.: "Elements of Mathematical Economics," Houghton Mifflin, Boston, 1965. (This text develops various mathematical theories and applies them to economics.)
7. Baumol, W. J.: "Economic Theory and Operations Analysis," Prentice-Hall, Englewood Cliffs, N.J., 1965. (Chapter 4 includes further applications of the derivative. In particular, the technique of Lagrange multipliers, widely used in economics to maximize a function whose variables are restrained, is illustrated on pp. 60–65. Other chapters present many concrete and theoretical applications of mathematics to economics.)
8. Horowitz, I.: "An Introduction to Quantitative Business Analysis," McGraw-Hill, New York, 1965. (This is an introduction to decision theory, using only elementary statistics and algebra.)

23

Psychology

A wide variety of mathematical methods are employed in the study of how people perceive, choose, and act. We shall present examples of the use of calculus in psychophysics, learning theory, and control theory.

Example 1 (Psychophysics). Psychophysics is concerned with the degree of sensation caused by a certain intensity, or a change in intensity, of a stimulus. If the length of a line is doubled, do we perceive it as doubled? If not, by what fraction do we judge it changed? By what amount must a line segment be lengthened or shortened in order for the difference to be noticeable? Similar questions may be raised concerning our reactions to weights, areas, volumes, intensity of electrical shock, brightness, loudness, pitch, and color.

Some stimuli involve more than one variable. For instance, rectangles of various shapes and colors involve three variables: length, width, and the frequency of the color. In most experiments an attempt is made to study one variable at a time, with other

489

variables kept as constant as possible. Throughout this chapter we restrict our attention to one-variable stimuli; a single number suffices to describe the stimulus. (For an experiment dealing with three variables, see Reference 8.)

Let x denote the magnitude of a stimulus (in units of pounds for weight, lumens for brightness, decibels for loudness, frequency for pitch or color, and so on). Then x refers to something in the physical world; engineers can measure it as accurately as may be necessary.

Let y denote the magnitude of the sensation caused by the stimulus. What y measures within a person may not yet be fully understood—whether it is the amount of a chemical produced, or the intensity of an electrical discharge, or whatever. In experiments y may simply measure some verbal or physical reaction of the subject upon whom an experiment is being performed. It is usually hypothesized that y depends on x:

$$(1) \qquad\qquad y = f(x)$$

Equation (1) already contains the hypothesis that for a given subject the sensation y depends only on the stimulus x: if the subject is exposed to the same stimulus on various similar occasions, the sensation y will be the same each time. A psychologist studies the form of this equation theoretically and experimentally.

What can we say in general about f? Since a slight change in the stimulus induces only a slight change in sensation, we may assume that f is continuous. Moreover, the sensation increases when the stimulus increases, and thus f is an increasing function.

How much does the sensation change when we change the stimulus x by a small amount Δx? One theory hypothesizes that the change in sensation is proportional not to the change in stimulus Δx, but to the ratio $(\Delta x)/x$. For instance, the change from a 10-pound weight to an 11-pound weight would be just as noticeable as a change from a 100-pound weight to a 110-pound weight. This hypothesis asserts that Δy is roughly proportional to $\Delta x/x$, when Δx is small. Dividing by Δx, we may rephrase this as

$$\frac{\Delta y}{\Delta x} \text{ is roughly proportional to } \frac{1}{x} \text{ when } \Delta x \text{ is small}$$

Now, when Δx is small, $\Delta y/\Delta x$ is a good approximation to the derivative, dy/dx; hence the hypothesis is best stated in terms of the derivative:

$$\frac{dy}{dx} \text{ is proportional to } \frac{1}{x}$$

or equivalently,

$$(2) \qquad\qquad \frac{dy}{dx} = k\,\frac{1}{x}$$

for some fixed positive number k. From (2) we obtain the "logarithmic law for sensation,"

$$(3) \qquad\qquad y = k \ln x + C$$

where k and C are constants that depend on the type of stimulus, the units in which it is measured, and the subject (see Corollary 2, page 125).

More recent experiments suggest that the hypothesis "Δy is proportional to the relative stimulus $(\Delta x)/x$" does not always hold. A different hypothesis asserts that for small Δx the *relative* sensation $(\Delta y)/y$ is proportional to the relative stimulus $(\Delta x)/x$. This suggests the approximate equation

$$\frac{\Delta y}{y} \cong k\left(\frac{\Delta x}{x}\right) \qquad \text{or} \qquad \frac{\Delta y}{\Delta x} \cong k\,\frac{y}{x}$$

In the limit this becomes

(4) $$\frac{dy}{dx} = k\,\frac{y}{x}$$

To find y explicitly in terms of x, we rewrite (4) first as

$$\frac{dy}{y} = k\,\frac{dx}{x}$$

and then as

(5) $$d(\ln y) = d(k \ln x)$$

Now, two functions with the same differential differ only by a constant, and thus

(6) $$\ln y = k \ln x + C$$

Denoting e^C by a, we then have

(7) $$\ln y = \ln x^k + \ln a = \ln (ax^k)$$

Hence we obtain

(8) $$y = ax^k$$

the "power law for sensation."

While hypothesis (2) leads us to a logarithmic function, hypothesis (4) leads us to power functions such as $y = ax$, $y = ax^2$, or $y = ax^{1/2}$. To determine the exponent k experimentally, we must measure not only x, which is relatively easy, but also y, which is not so easy. The measurement and meaning of y are the source of much controversy.

In one method of determining k, the subject, exposed to a variety of different intensities, is asked to assign a number proportional to the intensity (brightness, loudness, length, and so on) as he judges it. In various experiments the exponent k varies from 0.3 for brightness to 3.5 for electrical shock. For the subject's estimation of length the exponent is close to 1. The graphs of $y = x^{0.3}$ and $y = x^{3.5}$ show that it takes a relatively large change in the intensity of illumination to persuade us that there is much change, but that we are very sensitive to changes in intensity of electric shock.

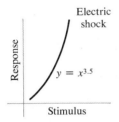

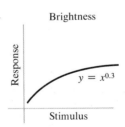

Another approach in the study of sensation involves the "just noticeable difference," usually abbreviated jnd. For instance, when one listens to a very low note of 31 cycles per second, a frequency change of 4 cycles per second can occur before the change of pitch is noticed. However, at a pitch of 500 cycles per second (about an octave above middle C), the jnd is about 8 cycles per second. Here is a table of x (the frequency) and Δx (the jnd) for a pure tone at the fixed loudness of 5 decibels. Note that Δx increases with x; we should not think of Δx as necessarily being small.

Frequency (x)	Δx (jnd)
31	4.00
62	6.05
125	7.60
250	8.88
500	8.15
1,000	9.40
2,000	15.80
4,000	24.00
8,000	50.40
11,700	80.70

(9)

The frequencies increase from 31 cycles per second (the threshold of hearing) approximately by octaves to 8,000, and then to 11,700 (near the upper limit of perception).

Let us see how the jnd is related to the sensation function f. We know that a change in stimulus Δx induces a change Δy in sensation. Let us assume that Δy must reach a certain fixed threshold value t before Δx is noticed. Now, Δy is approximately $f'(x)\,\Delta x$, so let us say that

$$t = f'(x)\,\Delta x$$

from which it follows that

(10)
$$\Delta x = \frac{t}{f'(x)}$$

Equation (10) tells us that the jnd is inversely proportional to the derivative $f'(x)$. For instance, if we assume the "power law" (8), then $f'(x) = kax^{k-1}$. Thus

(11)
$$\Delta x = \frac{t}{kax^{k-1}} = \left(\frac{t}{ka}\right)x^{1-k}$$

We could say therefore that

(12)
$$\text{jnd} = \Delta x = cx^{1-k}$$

where c is constant and equals t/ka.

Let us assume that the sensation function in our specific example is of the form $y = ax^k$, and hence that $\Delta x = cx^{1-k}$. We will now show how to estimate k and c from tabulated data. To find k, we first find $1 - k$ by measuring jnd's. For convenience, let

(13)
$$K = 1 - k$$

We suspect that the table (9) corresponds to a function of the form

(14)
$$\Delta x = cx^K$$

To find the best-fitting c and K, we first take logarithms to the base 10 of (14):

(15)
$$\log_{10}(\Delta x) = (\log_{10} c) + K \log_{10} x$$

(Any base would suffice, but base 10 is the most convenient arithmetically.) Let us denote $\log_{10}(\Delta x)$ by Y, and $\log_{10} x$ by X. Then (15) yields this simple relation between X and Y:

(16)
$$Y = (\log_{10} c) + KX$$

The data in table (9) are equivalent to the following relations between $X = \log_{10} x$ and $Y = \log_{10} (\Delta x)$.

(17)

X	Y
1.49	0.602
1.79	0.782
2.10	0.881
2.40	0.948
2.70	0.911
3.00	0.973
3.30	1.199
3.60	1.380
3.90	1.702
4.07	1.907

We graph the ten points (X,Y) of (17) to show that they may be approximated by a linear relation between X and Y:

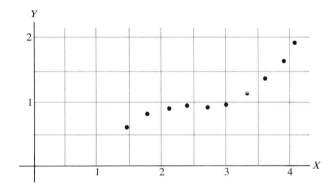

To obtain the line $Y = mx + b$ best fitting these data (the line of regression), we use equations (3) and (4) on page 312. In this case they become

$$(m)\,(88.5) + (b)\,(28.3) = 35.2 \qquad \text{and} \qquad (m)\,(28.3) + 10b = 11.3$$

Solving these simultaneous equations, we obtain $m = 0.308$ and $b = 0.347$. The regression line is

(18)
$$Y = 0.308X + 0.347$$

Substituting for X and Y in (18), we obtain

(19)
$$\log_{10} \Delta x = 0.308 \log_{10} x + 0.347$$

Hence
$$10^{\log_{10}\Delta x} = (10^{\log_{10}x})^{0.308}\, 10^{0.347}$$

or
$$\Delta x = x^{0.308}\, 10^{0.347} = 2.22 x^{0.308}$$

Thus $1 - k = 0.308$, and $k = 0.692$, which is closer to the exponent for brightness than to that for electric shock.

With the aid of these formulas, let us find the number of steps or jnd's in a scale from frequency 31 to frequency 11,700. The number of these steps would be important in the design of an "ideal" piano, whose successive notes are as close as possible and yet are distinguishable. To estimate this number, n, let us denote in cycles per second the successive just noticeably different pitches by

$$x_0, x_1, x_2, \ldots, x_n$$

where $x_0 = 31$ and $x_n = 11,700$. For instance, the theoretical x_1 is near 35, since the observed Δx is 4, according to (9). In any case,

(20) $$x_i = x_{i-1} + \Delta_{i-1}$$

where Δ_{i-1} is the jnd corresponding to the frequency x_{i-1}. Now, $\Delta_{i-1} = 2.22x_{i-1}^{0.308}$, so (20) yields

$$x_i - x_{i-1} = 2.22x_{i-1}^{0.308}$$

or

(21) $$\frac{x_i - x_{i-1}}{2.22x_{i-1}^{0.308}} = 1 \quad \text{or} \quad \frac{x_{i-1}^{-0.308}}{2.22}(x_i - x_{i-1}) = 1$$

Summing (21) for $i = 1, 2, \ldots, n$, we obtain

(22) $$\sum_{i=1}^{n} \frac{1}{2.22} x_{i-1}^{-0.308}(x_i - x_{i-1}) = \sum_{i=1}^{n} 1 = n$$

The sum on the left-hand side of (22) is an approximating sum for the definite integral

$$\int_{31}^{11,700} \left(\frac{1}{2.22}\right) x^{-0.308} dx$$

Hence, for computational purposes, we shall say that

(23) $$n = \int_{31}^{11,700} \left(\frac{1}{2.22}\right) x^{-0.308} dx$$

The fundamental theorem of calculus enables us to evaluate (23) quickly, since the function

(24) $$\frac{x^{-0.308+1}}{(2.22)(-0.308+1)} = 0.651x^{0.692}$$

is an antiderivative of the integrand in (23). We obtain, by (23) and (24),

(25) $$n = 0.651x^{0.692} \Big|_{31}^{11,700} = (0.651)(11,700^{0.692} - 31^{0.692})$$

which is about 419. This means that a piano designed to cover the range considered with the smallest perceptible intervals should have 420 keys; this is an average of about 50 keys per octave.

Example 2 (Learning theory). Our first example required only one theoretical assumption, but our next example, a classic contribution of Thurston to learning theory, requires several. Nevertheless, the learning equation (43) that follows from them is in reasonable agreement with experimental results. Though a present-day psychologist might consider its foundation flimsy, it nevertheless gives us some idea of the role of model-building in psychology.

In the process of learning a maze or the words of a foreign language, there are a hypothetical number S of successful acts and a hypothetical number E of erroneous ones. Let

(26) $$p = \frac{S}{S + E}$$

a quotient which we call *the probability of a successful response*. Clearly $0 \leqslant p \leqslant 1$, since both S and E are positive or 0. Let

(27) $$q = \frac{E}{S + E}$$

be the *probability of an erroneous response*. Then

(28) $$p + q = \frac{S}{S + E} + \frac{E}{S + E} = 1$$

The rate of change of p with respect to time, dp/dt, depends on the rate at which S and E change with respect to time. If the subject is learning, we have $dp/dt > 0$. Let us hypothesize that

(29) $$\frac{dS}{dt} = kp$$

and

(30) $$\frac{dE}{dt} = -kq$$

where k is a fixed number that depends on the experiment and the subject, but not on time. Equation (29) is a specialized form of "nothing succeeds like success," while equation (30) asserts that "we learn by our mistakes." We assume that the constants of proportionality in (29) and (30) are the same; more recent theories do not make this assumption.

We might expect that p is initially close to 0, but with learning experience, p approaches 1. It turns out that the preceding hypotheses are compatible with this expectation.

From (26), (27), (29), and (30) we shall deduce an explicit formula linking p with time. We begin by determining dp/dt as a function of time. Observe first that, from (29) and (30),

(31) $$\frac{d(SE)}{dt} = S\frac{dE}{dt} + E\frac{dS}{dt} = S(-kq) + E(kp) = k(-Sq + Ep)$$

Using (26) and (27), we obtain

$$k(-Sq + Ep) = k\left(\frac{-SE}{S + E} + \frac{ES}{S + E}\right) = 0$$

Thus $d(SE)/dt = 0$, and SE is a constant, which we shall call m:

(32) $$SE = m$$

Observe that (32) implies that as the number of successful responses likely to be made increases, the number of erroneous responses decreases. One may think of m as a measure of the difficulty of the task to be learned.

Now we differentiate (26), obtaining

(33) $$\frac{dp}{dt} = \frac{[(S + E)(dS/dt) - S\,d(S + E)/dt]}{(S + E)^2}$$

Substituting (29) and (30) in (33), we obtain

$$(34) \qquad \frac{dp}{dt} = \frac{(S+E)(kp) - S(kp - kq)}{(S+E)^2} = \frac{k(Ep + Sq)}{(S+E)^2}$$

From the definitions of p and q and (34), it follows that

$$(35) \qquad \frac{dp}{dt} = \frac{k(qp + pq)}{S+E} = \frac{2pqk}{S+E}$$

With the aid of (26), which implies that $S + E = S/p$, we remove $S + E$ from (35):

$$(36) \qquad \frac{dp}{dt} = \frac{2p^2qk}{S}$$

To eliminate S from (36), we recall that $SE = m$ [equation (32)]; hence

$$(37) \qquad S^2 = S\frac{m}{E} = m\frac{S}{E} = m\frac{p(E+S)}{q(E+S)} = \frac{mp}{q}$$

Thus $S = \sqrt{mp/q}$, and we have, after combining (36) and (28),

$$(38) \qquad \frac{dp}{dt} = \frac{2p^2qk}{\sqrt{mp/q}} = \frac{2k}{\sqrt{m}} p^{3/2} q^{3/2} = \frac{2k}{\sqrt{m}} p^{3/2} (1-p)^{3/2}$$

a formula *expressing the rate of learning dp/dt as a function of p.*

To find p as a function of t, we rewrite (38) as

$$(39) \qquad \frac{dp}{p^{3/2}(1-p)^{3/2}} = \frac{2k}{\sqrt{m}} dt$$

an equation in differentials. As a table of integrals shows, or as one may check by differentiation, the left side of (39) equals

$$(40) \qquad d\left(\frac{4p-2}{\sqrt{p-p^2}}\right)$$

while the right side of (39) equals

$$(41) \qquad d\left(\frac{2kt}{\sqrt{m}}\right)$$

Since two functions with equal differentials differ by a constant, say C, we have

$$(42) \qquad \frac{4p-2}{\sqrt{p-p^2}} = \frac{2kt}{\sqrt{m}} + C$$

an equation relating p and t. If we measure time t from the instant when $p = \frac{1}{2}$ (so that the probabilities of correct and erroneous responses are equal), then (42) forces C to be zero [set $t = 0$ and $p = \frac{1}{2}$ in (42)]. Hence

$$(43) \qquad \frac{4p-2}{\sqrt{p-p^2}} = \frac{2kt}{\sqrt{m}}$$

an equation in which $2k/\sqrt{m}$ is some constant. Observe that in (43), as $t \to -\infty$, we have $p \to 0$, and as $t \to \infty$, we have $p \to 1$, in agreement with our expectation of the behavior of p: At the beginning the probability of success is negligible; as the subject learns, the probability of success approaches "certainty" or 1. Equation (43), linking probability of success p with duration of learning t, is a likely candidate for a formula approximating the data from an experiment in learning.

Example 3 (Control theory). In control theory a psychologist studies the reactions of a subject as expressed in such actions as turning knobs or pushing buttons in a control panel.

In one experiment the subject is asked to keep centered a certain movable spot on an oscilloscope. The stimulus consists not only of the motion given the spot by the experimenter, but also the motion given it by the subject in trying to center it.

Let H denote the position of the controlling handle, and A the position of the spot. For convenience, let us assume that there is only one handle and that the position of the spot and the handle are restricted to a horizontal line. Then H and A are numbers depending on time t: $H = h(t)$ and $A = a(t)$.

In one theory it is proposed that the *rate* at which the subject turns the handle depends on the velocity of the moving spot and its position. The formula suggested is

(44)
$$\frac{dh}{dt} = c_1 \frac{da}{dt} + c_2 a(t)$$

where c_1 and c_2 are constants. Taking antiderivatives of both sides of (44), we obtain

(45)
$$h(t) = c_1 a(t) + c_2 \int a(t)\, dt + c_3$$

where c_3 is some constant. Equation (45) asserts that the position of the handle depends not only on the position of the spot but on a function that involves the subject's cumulative memory of past locations of the spot. Moreover, since it has been observed there is a reaction time or delay of 0.3 second in the response of the hand to simuli, we should revise (45) to read

(46)
$$h(t + 0.3) = c_1 a(t) + c_2 \int a(t)\, dt + c_3$$

By proper choice of coordinates we may force c_3 to be 0.

If we wished to include the effect of the acceleration of the spot, $d^2 a / dt^2$, we could easily generalize (46) to

(47)
$$h(t + 0.3) = c_1 a(t) + c_2 \int a(t)\, dt + c_3 + c_4 \frac{da}{dt}$$

where c_1, c_2, c_3, and c_4 are constants.

Each of the three examples discussed in this chapter concerns highly controlled laboratory experiments that attempt to isolate one variable. Yet the analysis of behavior in even such a simplified situation requires such mathematical notions as the derivative and the definite integral. As experiments become more complicated and deal with more variables simultaneously (as people do in daily life), we may be sure that their interpretation will require a variety of mathematical tools, and indeed may require the invention of new mathematics.

EXERCISES

1. Let $y = f(x)$ denote a sensation function, Eq. (1). Show that the number of steps (jnd's) that we may insert between stimulus $x = a$ and stimulus $x = b$ is proportional to the definite integral $\int_a^b [1/f'(x)]\, dx$. [Hint: review the argument employed in obtaining Eqs. (10), (20), (21), and (22).]

2. Go through the details of obtaining the regression line of page 493.

3. How many of the 420 keys of our "ideal" piano would be used to span the octave from $x = 500$ to $x = 1,000$? From $x = 1,000$ to $x = 2,000$?

4. Let f^{-1} be the inverse of the sensation function f and $f(x_1) = y_1$, $f(x_2) = y_2$. Justify these equations:

$$y_2 - y_1 = \int_{x_1}^{x_2} f'(x)\, dx \qquad \text{and} \qquad x_2 - x_1 = \int_{y_1}^{y_2} (f^{-1})'(y)\, dy = \int_{y_1}^{y_2} \frac{1}{f'(f^{-1}(y))}\, dy$$

5. In proceeding from Eq. (39) to (42), we computed an antiderivative of $1/[p^{3/2}(1 - p)^{3/2}]$. Find an antiderivative (a) by using the substitution $p = \sin^2 \theta$; (b) by using a table of integrals. [Hint: for (b) first write $p(1 - p)$ as $p - p^2$.]

6. Assume that $c_3 = 0$ in (47). Another way of expressing (47) is then

$$h(t) = c_4 \frac{da}{dt} + c_1\, a(t) + c_2 \int a(t)\, dt$$

with delay 0.3. Another formulation is the following "operator" equation:

(48) $$h = [(c_4 D + c_1 + c_2 D^{-1})e^{-0.3D}]a$$

where D denotes differentiation, D^{-1} denotes antidifferentiation, and $e^{-0.3D}$ denotes an operator which we shall define.

(a) Verify, using the Theorem 2 on page 339, that

(49) $$a(t + \Delta t) = \sum_{n=0}^{\infty} \frac{D^n(a)}{n!} (\Delta t)^n$$

where $D^n(a)$ is evaluated at t.

(b) The similarity of the right side of (49) to the right side of $e^x = 1 + x + \cdots + x^n/n! + \cdots$, suggests that we formally define the operator $e^{(\Delta t)D}$ by the equation

$$e^{(\Delta t)D} = \sum_{n=0}^{\infty} \frac{[(\Delta t)\, D]^n}{n!}$$

Justify Eq. (48).

7. In the usual geometric representation of the positive numbers as a line, the number x is marked at a point whose distance from the point marked "0" is proportional to x. In the logarithmic scale, representing the numbers $x \geqslant 1$, the number x is marked at a point whose distance from the point marked "1" is proportional to $\log_{10} x$, as is shown in this diagram:

Note that the powers of a given number, such as $2^0 = 1, 2^1, 2^2, 2^3, \ldots$, are equally spaced in the logarithmic scale. (The scale on a slide rule is logarithmic.) In log-log graphing paper, both the x and y axes are logarithmic. In semi-log paper, one axis is logarithmic and the other is the usual scale.

(a) Graph the equation $y = 6x^2$ on log-log paper.

(b) If a psychologist suspects that the sensation function he is studying is a power function $y = ax^n$, how can he estimate n by drawing the data on log-log graph paper?

(c) If the psychologist suspects that the sensation function is logarithmic $y = a + b \log_{10} x$, on what kind of graph paper should he sketch his data? Explain.

8. (a) Graph the data of (9) on log-log paper. The graph should resemble that on page 493.

(b) Fit "by eye" a straight line to the points sketched in (a).

(c) What is the equation of the line that you drew in (b)? The use of log-log paper eliminates the need for computing the logarithms of the data [as in (17)].

9. In a study of the perception of the number of elements in a set a subject was shown cards containing from 17 to 74 spots. Let x denote the number of spots and y the corresponding sensation of numerosity, determined experimentally. We record $x, y, X = \log_{10} x$, and $Y = \log_{10} y$.

x	17	26	37	50	74
X	1.23	1.42	1.57	1.70	1.87
y	2.3	4	5.2	7.0	8.2
Y	0.36	0.60	0.72	0.85	0.91

(a) Graph the five points (x,y).

(b) Graph the five points (X,Y).

(c) Fit "by eye" a straight line to the points sketched in (b).

(d) What is the equation of the line that you drew in (c)?

(e) From (d) obtain a formula for the sensation function, $y = f(x)$.

10. Weber, in 1834, asserted that the jnd is proportional to the stimulus: jnd $= kx$.

(a) For brightness $k = 0.016$, and for loudness $k = 0.33$. Why might we say that we are more sensitive to changes in brightness than to changes in loudness?

(b) On the basis of Weber's assertion, obtain the form of the sensation function f. [Hint: consider Eq. (10)]

11. In an experiment on "saltiness" some subjects felt that water containing no salt had some saltiness. Thus a stimulus of value zero induced a nonzero sensation value a. Letting $y = f(x)$ be the sensation function for saltiness and assuming that $\Delta y/(y - a)$ is "approximately" proportional to $\Delta x/x$ for small Δx, deduce that $y = a + bx^n$ for suitable constants b and n.

12. If $z = f(x,y)$ is a function of x and y, let us denote z by $x \otimes y$. Show that, for $x \otimes y = (x + y)/2$, the arithmetic mean of x and y, we have (a) $x \otimes x = y$; (b) $x \otimes y = y \otimes x$; (c) $(x \otimes y) \otimes (z \otimes w) = (x \otimes z) \otimes (y \otimes w)$.

13. Repeat Exercise 12 for the functions $x \otimes y = \sqrt{xy}$ (the geometric mean), and $x \otimes y = \sqrt{(x^2 + y^2)/2}$.

14. (See Exercises 12 and 13.) A weight of x grams is placed in a subject's left hand and a weight of y grams in his right hand. Denote by $x \otimes y$ the weight that the subject judges to be midway between the two weights.

(a) Would you expect conditions (a) and (b) of Exercise 12 to hold?

(b) In an experiment, a subject judges a weight $0.7y$ to be one-half as heavy as the weight y (see reference 5). Express this in terms of the $\otimes$ notation.

(c) Which of the three functions cited in Exercises 12 and 13 is compatible with the experimental result in (b)?

15. Solve Eq. (43) for p as a function of time.

16. A learning experiment was set up in such a way that a dog could avoid an electric shock by jumping over a hurdle within 10 seconds after being placed in a compartment. Each dog tested gradually learned to avoid the shock, though none knew how to avoid it at the beginning of the experiment. We describe a theoretical model of the learning process: Let p be the probability that the dog avoids the shock at a certain trial. If he avoids the shock, then the probability that he will avoid it on the next trial is $0.80p + 0.20$. If he is shocked, then the probability that he will avoid the shock on the next trial is $0.92p + 0.08$.

(a) What is p at the beginning of the experiment?

(b) What is p when the dog fully understands how to avoid the shock?

(c) Let us use p as a measure of the dog's understanding of the experiment. Does the dog's understanding increase at each trial? Is the dog's understanding increased more by his being shocked or by his jumping in time?

(d) Show that p is at least 0.08 at the second trial and at least 0.1536 at the third trial.

(e) Show that p approaches 1 as the trials continue. (Hint: assume that a set of numbers with an upper bound has a least upper bound, as discussed on page 569.)

The behavior of 30 statistical dogs (stat-dogs) run off randomly on a computer in accordance with this theory is in remarkably close agreement with that of 30 real dogs. (See especially Reference 6, Table 11.7, p. 252.) The development in Reference 6 encounters several infinite series, definite integrals, and derivatives.

17. Let x and y denote the arms budgets of two rival nations. L. F. Richardson, a pioneer in the application of mathematics to political science, made these two assumptions about the rate at which the budget changes with respect to time:

$$\frac{dx}{dt} = k_1 y - k_2 x + k_3 \qquad \frac{dy}{dt} = c_1 x - c_2 y + c_3$$

where k_1, k_2, k_3, c_1, c_2, and c_3 are constants (k_1, k_2, c_1, and c_2 are positive).

(a) Which term represents "fatigue"?

(b) Which term represents the "threat of the rival's actions"?

(c) Which term represents the "general attitude" of one nation about the other? These equations have been used to analyze Russian-American relations, in particular to decide whether Russia is motivated by ideology or nationalism (see Reference 10).

REFERENCES

1. Lewis, D.: "Quantitative Methods in Psychology," pp. 197–200, 438–441, 455–480, McGraw-Hill, New York, 1960. [Table (9) in this chapter, due to Shower and Biddulph, is on p. 197.]

2. Miller, G. A.: "Mathematics and Psychology," pp. 1–14, 59, 95, 116, 138–146, 150–151, 201–206, Wiley, New York, 1964.

3. Guilford, J. P.: "Psychometric Methods," pp. 37–42, McGraw-Hill, New York, 1954.

4. Gulliksen, H.: Mathematical Solutions of Psychological Problems, *American Scientist,* **47**: 178–201 (1959). (This is an article of general interest.)

5. Harper, R. S., and S. S. Stevens: A Psychological Scale of Weight and a Formula for Its Derivation, *Am. J. Psych.,* **61**: 343–351 (1948).

6. Bush, R. R., and R. Mosteller: "Stochastic Models for Learning," Wiley, New York, 1955. (See Exercise 16 in this chapter.)

7. Rapoport, A.: Mathematical Models of Social Interaction, chap. 14 in R. D. Luce, R. R. Bush, and E. Galanter (eds.), "Handbook of Mathematical Psychology," vol. 2, Wiley, New York, 1963. (Even a few minutes spent with this chapter will acquaint the reader with the mathematical approach to several types of social interactions and structures.)

8. Turner, E. D., and W. Beran: Simultaneous Indication of Multiple Anchor Effects in the Judgment of Form, *J. Exp. Psych.*, **64**, 589–592 (1962). (This article describes an experiment involving the area, shape, and brightness of rectangles.)

9. Arrow, K., S. Karlin, and P. Suppes (eds.): "Mathematical Methods in the Social Sciences," Stanford University Press, Stanford, Calif., 1959. (Part 3, pp. 205–365, contains papers by several authors on learning, choice, utility, and so on.)

10. Schwartz, H.: Social Scientists Relying on Math, *New York Times,* Dec. 29, 1965, p. 16. (This is a report on a meeting of the American Association for the Advancement of Science.)

11. Stevens, S. S., The Psychophysics of Sensory Function, in W. A. Rosenblith (ed.): "Sensory Communication," M.I.T., Cambridge, Mass., 1961. (This contains a discussion of a broad range of psychophysical studies.)

12. Stevens, S. S., The Quantification of Sensation, *Daedulus*, **88**: 606–621 (1959). (This discusses the introduction of mathematics into psychophysics.)

13. Amerine, M. A., R. M. Pangborn, and E. B. Roessler: "Principles of Sensory Evaluation of Food," Academic, New York, 1965. (This is a review and discussion of psychophysics, particularly the psychology of taste. See chap. 5 for a discussion of the theory.)

24

Traffic

ONE of the major problems faced by a densely packed population is traffic. In Manhattan commercial traffic moves more slowly now than in horse and buggy days. Los Angeles, a city in which no two places are less than 10 miles apart, has given 49 percent of its downtown area to the automobile and constructed extensive high-speed arteries, all without solving its traffic problem. In this chapter we shall examine, in terms of a very simple model of traffic flow, the delay at an intersection. Some of our reasoning will apply to other forms of traffic, such as telephone calls, customers arriving at a checkout counter, accidents, and machine breakdowns.

1. Preliminaries.   A single lane of traffic moves east. All cars travel at the same speed, but the gaps between them may vary from car to car. A car traveling north (let us say) waits until there is an adequate gap before crossing the traffic. Seen from above, the traffic looks like this:

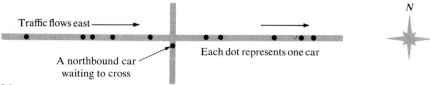

Traffic flows east ⟶

Each dot represents one car

A northbound car waiting to cross

N

502

We shall be interested in the delay of the northbound car. This delay will depend on such factors as the density of eastbound traffic, its speed, and the size of the gaps. In order to deal with these mathematically, we must use probability theory.

To study the gaps we introduce a distribution function F. If $x \geqslant 0$, then $F(x)$ is the fraction of gaps that have a length at most x. This function can be studied by observing the traffic. On the other hand, we may, on the basis of hypotheses concerning the traffic, derive a theoretical distribution function for the gaps. If the theory is to be of value, the theoretical distribution function should be in reasonable agreement with the experimentally observed distribution of gaps. In the next section, where we shall construct a theoretical model for the traffic, we shall meet the distribution function $F(x) = 1 - e^{-kx}$.

Next, consider the typical northbound car as just arrived to cross the east-west road. A certain fraction of such northbound cars will not have to wait at all; in other words they will "cross after 0 eastbound cars pass." This fraction we denote by $p(0)$. A certain fraction may be able to cross after only one car passes; this fraction we denote by $p(1)$. More generally, let $p(n)$ denote the fraction of northbound cars which cross after n eastbound cars (but before $n + 1$ cars) pass. [When the sequence $p(0), p(1), \ldots, p(n), \ldots$ is given by experimental data, then $p(n) = 0$ when n is beyond a certain integer.] In either case we have

$$p(0) + p(1) + \cdots + p(n) + \cdots = 1$$

since every northbound driver presumably manages to cross the traffic. In Sec. 3 we compute $p(0), p(1), \ldots, p(n), \ldots$ on the basis of a theoretical traffic model; in that case it will turn out that the sequence $p(0), p(1), p(2), \ldots, p(n), \ldots$ is geometric, that is, $p(n) = ar^n$ for suitable constants a and r.

For instance, when, of 10 northbound cars, five cross with no delay, three cross after one car passes, one crosses after two cars pass, and one crosses after four cars pass, we have the observed

$$p(0) = \tfrac{5}{10}, p(1) = \tfrac{3}{10}, p(2) = \tfrac{1}{10}, p(3) = 0, p(4) = \tfrac{1}{10} \quad \text{and} \quad p(n) = 0 \quad \text{for } n \geqslant 5$$

The observed average number of eastbound cars that pass before the northbound driver crosses is therefore

(1) $$\frac{0 \cdot 5 + 1 \cdot 3 + 2 \cdot 1 + 3 \cdot 0 + 4 \cdot 1}{10} = 0.9$$

To relate (1) to $p(0), p(1), \ldots, p(n), \ldots$ let us rewrite it as

(2) $$0 \cdot \tfrac{5}{10} + 1 \cdot \tfrac{3}{10} + 2 \cdot \tfrac{1}{10} + 3 \cdot \tfrac{0}{10} + 4 \cdot \tfrac{1}{10}$$
$$= 0\,p(0) + 1p(1) + 2p(2) + 3p(3) + 4p(4)$$

When $p(n)$ is given theoretically, (2) suggests that we *define* the expected (average) number of cars that pass as

(3) $$\sum_{n=0}^{\infty} np(n)$$

This is analogous to the definition of expected value of a probability density, as $\int_0^\infty tf(t)\,dt$ (see page 237).

In the remainder of this chapter we shall use some notions from elementary probability theory, most easily illustrated in terms of thrown dice. Assume that the probability of throwing any one of 1, 2, 3, 4, 5, and 6 with a single die is $\frac{1}{6}$. Then the probability of throwing a 3 with one die and a 5 with a second die is $\frac{1}{6} \cdot \frac{1}{6}$. We shall assume in general that the probability of several independent events occurring simultaneously is the *product* of their respective probabilities. We shall also assume that the probability of at least one of several mutually exclusive events occurring is the *sum* of their respective probabilities. Thus the probability of throwing at least one of 2 or 6 is $\frac{1}{6} + \frac{1}{6}$.

Example. What is the probability of obtaining a sum of at most 4 when throwing two dice? According to the second assumption made above, this probability is

Probability that sum is 2 + probability that sum is 3 + probability that sum is 4

The probability that the sum is 2 is $\frac{1}{6} \cdot \frac{1}{6} = \frac{1}{36}$. The sum 3 is obtainable by throwing a 1 with the first die and a 2 with the second die, or a 2 with the first die and a 1 with the second. Hence the probability of obtaining the sum 3 is $\frac{1}{36} + \frac{1}{36} = \frac{2}{36}$. Similarly the probability of throwing a sum of 4 is $\frac{3}{36}$. Thus the probability of throwing a sum of at most 4 is $\frac{1}{36} + \frac{2}{36} + \frac{3}{36} = \frac{6}{36} = \frac{1}{6}$.

Utilizing these notions from probability theory, we shall construct in Sec. 2 a theoretical model to represent the eastbound traffic.

EXERCISES

1. A helicopter photograph of eastbound traffic provided the following data concerning 100 gaps.

Length of gap less than	100 feet	200 feet	300 feet	400 feet	500 feet	600 feet	700 feet
Number of such gaps observed	32	56	76	88	95	99	100

On the basis of this table, (*a*) compute $F(0)$, $F(200)$, $F(700)$; (*b*) estimate $f(200)$ and $f(600)$, where f is the probability density associated with F (see page 235); (*c*) estimate the expected gap. [Answer: (*a*) 0,0.56, 1; (*b*) 0.20, 0.01; (*c*) 204 feet]

2. One theoretical model of the eastbound traffic has the distribution function F given by $F(x) = 1 - e^{-2x}$.
   (*a*) Graph F.
   (*b*) Graph the probability density $f = F'$.
   (*c*) Compute the expected gap $\int_0^\infty x f(x)\,dx$.

3. One theoretical model of the eastbound traffic has the distribution function F given by $F(x) = (2/\pi) \tan^{-1} x$.

(a) Graph F and $f = F'$.

(b) Compute the expected gap, $\int_0^\infty x f(x)\, dx$.

4. Let F be a distribution function such that $F(3) = 0.62$, $F(3.01) = 0.64$, and $F(6) = 0.80$. Let $f = F'$. Estimate (a) $f(3)$; and (b) the probability that x is between 3 and 6.
[Answer: (a) 2; (b) 0.18]

5. One theoretical model for the eastbound traffic leads to $p(n) = 3^n e^{-3}/n!$, for $n = 0, 1, 2, \ldots$, where $p(n)$ is the probability that a northbound car crosses after exactly n eastbound cars pass. Show that (a) $\sum_{n=0}^{\infty} p(n) = 1$; and (b) $\sum_{n=0}^{\infty} np(n) = 3$.

6. One theoretical model for the eastbound traffic yields $p(n) = (\frac{1}{2})^{n+1}$, for $n = 0, 1, 2, \ldots$.

(a) Verify that $\sum_{n=0}^{\infty} p(n) = 1$.

(b) Show that the expected number of cars passing before a northbound car can cross is 1. [Hint: for (b) recall Example 2, page 325.]

7. Assume that the probability of exactly n eastbound cars passing before the northbound driver can cross is $p(n) = (\frac{1}{2})^{n+1}$. Find the probability that (a) the northbound driver is not delayed; (b) at most five cars pass before a crossing; (c) at least seven cars pass before a crossing.
[Answer: (a) $\frac{1}{2}$; (b) $\frac{63}{64}$; (c) $\frac{1}{128}$]

8. Assume that the probability of heads turning up when a penny is thrown is $\frac{1}{2}$. What is the probability of obtaining, in three throws (a) no heads; (b) exactly one head; (c) exactly two heads; (d) exactly three heads? (e) Toss three pennies 20 times and compare the observed frequencies with the theoretical probabilities.
[Answer: (a) $\frac{1}{8}$; (b) $\frac{3}{8}$; (c) $\frac{3}{8}$; (d) $\frac{1}{8}$]

9. Let $P(n)$ be the theoretical probability that the sum is n when two dice are tossed.
(a) Compute $P(n)$ for $n = 2, 3, \ldots, 12$.

(b) Verify that $\sum_{n=2}^{\infty} P(n) = 1$.

(c) Which sum is most likely to occur?
(d) Compare (a), (b), and (c) with results that you obtain by tossing two dice.

□ □ □

10. A penny is tossed until it turns up heads.
(a) Find the theoretical probability that exactly n tosses are required.
(b) On the basis of (a), find the expected number of tosses.
(c) Compare (a) and (b) with results that you obtain by tossing a penny.

11. Assuming that the probability that a baby will be a boy equals the probability that it will be a girl, compute the probability that in a family of five children, there is at most one boy.
(Answer: $\frac{6}{32}$)

12. When n Christmas cards are placed in n envelopes at random, what is the probability $g(n)$ that none is in the correct envelope?
(a) Compute $g(1)$, $g(2)$, $g(3)$, and $g(4)$.
(b) Verify that $(n + 1)[g(n + 1) - g(n)] = g(n - 1) - g(n)$ for $n = 2$ and $n = 3$.
(c) Show that if (b) holds for all $n \geqslant 2$, then $g(n) = \frac{1}{2!} - \frac{1}{3!} + \cdots + (-1)^n 1/n!$ for $n \geqslant 2$.
(d) If (b) holds for all n, find $\lim_{n \to \infty} g(n)$.

2. The exponential (Poisson) model of random traffic.

We shall now construct a mathematical model for the eastbound traffic. First of all, we shall disregard the lengths of the cars and treat each car as a point. It is therefore possible theoretically to have an arbitrarily large number of cars in a finite interval. Moreover, we shall assume that all cars travel at the same speed (say, the speed limit), but that each car enters the traffic flow independently of the other cars. (These assumptions are more realistic for sparse than for dense traffic.)

To construct our model we introduce the functions $P_0, P_1, P_2, \ldots, P_n, \ldots$ where $P_n(x)$ shall be the probability that any interval of length x contains exactly n cars (independently of the location of the interval). Thus $P_0(x)$ is the probability that an interval of length x is empty. We shall assume that

$$P_0(x) + P_1(x) + \cdots + P_n(x) + \cdots = 1 \qquad \text{for any } x$$

We also shall assume that $P_0(0) = 1$ ("the probability is 1 that a given *point* contains no cars").

For our model we make the following two major assumptions:

(*a*) The probability that exactly one car is in any fixed short section of the road is approximately proportional to the length of the section. That is, there is some positive number k such that

$$\lim_{\Delta x \to 0} \frac{P_1(\Delta x)}{\Delta x} = k$$

(*b*) The probability that there is more than one car in any fixed short section of the road is negligible, even when compared to the length of the section. That is,

(1) $$\lim_{\Delta x \to 0} \frac{P_2(\Delta x) + P_3(\Delta x) + P_4(\Delta x) + \cdots}{\Delta x} = 0$$

We shall now put assumptions (*a*) and (*b*) into more useful form. If we let

(2) $$\varepsilon = \frac{P_1(\Delta x)}{\Delta x} - k$$

where ε depends on Δx, assumption (*a*) tells us that $\lim_{\Delta x \to 0} \varepsilon = 0$. Thus, solving (2) for $P_1(\Delta x)$, we see that assumption (*a*) can be phrased as

(3) $$P_1(\Delta x) = k \, \Delta x + \varepsilon \, \Delta x$$

where $\varepsilon \to 0$ as $\Delta x \to 0$.

Since $P_0(\Delta x) + P_1(\Delta x) + \cdots + P_n(\Delta x) + \cdots = 1$, assumption (*b*) may be expressed as

(4) $$\lim_{\Delta x \to 0} \frac{1 - P_0(\Delta x) - P_1(\Delta x)}{\Delta x} = 0$$

In view of assumption (*a*), equation (4) is equivalent to

(5) $$\lim_{\Delta x \to 0} \frac{1 - P_0(\Delta x)}{\Delta x} = k$$

In the manner in which we obtained (3), we may deduce that

$$1 - P_0(\Delta x) = k \Delta x + \delta \Delta x,$$

where $\delta \to 0$ as $\Delta x \to 0$. Thus

(6) $$P_0(\Delta x) = 1 - k \Delta x - \delta \Delta x$$

where $\delta \to 0$ as $\Delta x \to 0$. *On the basis of (a) and (b), as expressed in (3) and (6), we shall obtain an explicit formula for each P_n.*

Let us determine P_0 first. Observe that a section of length $x + \Delta x$ is vacant if its left-hand part of length x is vacant and its right-hand part of length Δx is also vacant.

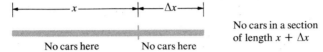

No cars in a section of length $x + \Delta x$

Since the cars move independently of each other, the probability that the whole interval of length $x + \Delta x$ being empty is the product of the probabilities that the two smaller intervals of lengths x and Δx are both empty. Thus we have

(7) $$P_0(x + \Delta x) = P_0(x) P_0(\Delta x)$$

Recalling (6), we write (7) as

(8) $$P_0(x + \Delta x) = P_0(x)(1 - k \Delta x - \delta \Delta x)$$

which a little algebra transforms to

(9) $$\frac{P_0(x + \Delta x) - P_0(x)}{\Delta x} = -(k + \delta)P_0(x)$$

Taking limits on both sides of (9) as $\Delta x \to 0$, we obtain

(10) $$P_0{}'(x) = -kP_0(x)$$

From (10) it follows that there is a constant A such that $P_0(x) = Ae^{-kx}$ (see Example 3, page 124). Since $1 = P_0(0) = Ae^{-k0} = A$, we conclude that $A = 1$, hence

(11) $$P_0(t) = e^{-kx}$$

This explicit formula for P_0 is reasonable; e^{-kx} is a decreasing function of x, so that the larger an interval, the less likely that it is empty.

Now let us determine P_1. To do so, we examine $P_1(x + \Delta x)$ and relate it to $P_0(x), P_0(\Delta x), P_1(x)$ and $P_1(\Delta x)$, with the goal of finding an equation involving the derivative of P_1. Again, imagine an interval of length $x + \Delta x$ cut into two intervals, the left-hand subinterval of length x and the right-hand subinterval of length Δx. Then there is precisely one car in the whole interval if *either* there is exactly one car in the left-hand subinterval and none in the right-hand subinterval *or* there is none in the left-hand subinterval and exactly one in the right-hand subinterval.

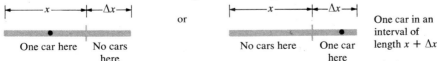

or

One car in an interval of length $x + \Delta x$

Thus we have

(12) $$P_1(x + \Delta x) = P_1(x)P_0(\Delta x) + P_0(x)P_1(\Delta x)$$

In view of (3) and (6), we may write (12) as

$$P_1(x + \Delta x) = P_1(x)(1 - k\,\Delta x - \delta\,\Delta x) + P_0(x)(k\,\Delta x + \varepsilon\,\Delta x)$$

which a little algebra changes to

(13) $$\frac{P_1(x + \Delta x) - P_1(x)}{\Delta x} = -(k + \delta)P_1(x) + (k + \varepsilon)P_0(x)$$

Letting $\Delta x \to 0$ in (13) and remembering that $\delta \to 0$ and $\varepsilon \to 0$ as $\Delta x \to 0$, we obtain $P_1'(x) = -kP_1(x) + kP_0(x)$; recalling that $P_0(x) = e^{-kx}$, we deduce that

(14) $$P_1'(x) = -kP_1(x) + ke^{-kx}$$

From (14) *we shall obtain an explicit formula for* $P_1(x)$. Since $P_0(x)$ involves e^{-kx} and so does (14), it is reasonable to guess that $P_1(x)$ involves e^{-kx}. Therefore let us express $P_1(x)$ as $g(x)e^{-kx}$ and determine the form of $g(x)$. (Since we have the identity $P_1(x) = [P_1(x)e^{kx}]e^{-kx}$, we know that $g(x)$ exists.) According to (14) we have $[g(x)e^{-kx}]' = -kg(x)e^{-kx} + ke^{-kx}$; hence

$$g(x)(-ke^{-kx}) + g'(x)e^{-kx} = -kg(x)e^{-kx} + ke^{-kx}$$

from which it follows that $g'(x) = k$. Hence $g(x) = kx + c_1$, where c_1 is some constant. Thus $P_1(x) = (kx + c_1)e^{-kx}$. Since $P_1(0) = 0$, we have $P_1(0) = (k0 + c_1)e^{-k0} = c_1$, and hence $c_1 = 0$. Thus we have shown that

(15) $$P_1(x) = kxe^{-kx}$$

and P_1 is completely determined.

To obtain P_2 we argue as we did in obtaining P_1. Instead of (12) we have

(16) $$P_2(x + \Delta x) = P_2(x)P_0(\Delta x) + P_1(x)P_1(\Delta x) + P_0(x)P_2(\Delta x)$$

an equation which records the three ways in which two cars in a section of length $x + \Delta x$ can be situated in a section of length x and a section of length Δx:

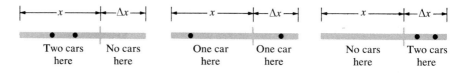

Two cars here	No cars here	One car here
One car here	No cars here	Two cars here

Making use of (3) and (6), we rewrite (16) as

$$P_2(x + \Delta x) = P_2(x)(1 - k\,\Delta x - \delta\,\Delta x) + P_1(x)(k\,\Delta x + \varepsilon\,\Delta x) + P_0(x)P_2(\Delta x)$$

Hence

(17) $$\frac{P_2(x + \Delta x) - P_2(x)}{\Delta x} = -kP_2(x) - \delta P_2(x) + kP_1(x) + \varepsilon P_1(x) + P_0(x)\frac{P_2(\Delta x)}{\Delta x}$$

Recalling (1), we see that $\lim_{\Delta x \to 0} P_2(\Delta x)/\Delta x = 0$. Letting $\Delta x \to 0$ in (17), we obtain

$$(18) \qquad\qquad P_2'(x) = -kP_2(x) + kP_1(x)$$

Now, $P_1(x) = kxe^{-kx}$. In view of our experience with P_1, let us write $P_2(x) = h(x)e^{-kx}$. Then (18) becomes

$$-kh(x)e^{-kx} + h'(x)e^{-kx} = -kh(x)e^{-kx} + k^2xe^{-kx}$$

which yields $h'(x) = k^2x$. Thus h is determined up to a constant c_2:

$$h(x) = \frac{k^2x^2}{2} + c_2$$

To determine c_2, we use the information that $P_2(0) = 0$. Since $P_2(x) = h(x)e^{-kx} = [(k^2x^2/2) + c_2]\,e^{-kx}$, we have $P_2(0) = c_2$; thus $c_2 = 0$. Therefore P_2 is completely determined:

$$(19) \qquad\qquad P_2(x) = \frac{k^2x^2}{2}e^{-kx}$$

Similar reasoning carried out inductively shows that

$$(20) \qquad\qquad P_n(x) = \frac{(kx)^n}{n!}e^{-kx}$$

We have obtained in (20) *the formulas on which the rest of our analysis will be based.* Note that these formulas refer to a road section of any length, though the assumptions (a) and (b) refer only to short sections. What has enabled us to go from the "microscopic" to the "macroscopic" is the additional assumption that the traffic in any one section is independent of the traffic in any other section. The formulas (20) are known as the *Poisson formulas.*

Example 1 (The significance of k).   The expected number of cars in a section of length x is defined as $\sum_{n=0}^{\infty} nP_n(x)$, which we will now compute. We have

$$\sum_{n=0}^{\infty} nP_n(x) = \sum_{n=1}^{\infty} nP_n(x) = \sum_{n=1}^{\infty} n\frac{(kx)^n e^{-kx}}{n!}$$

$$= kxe^{-kx} \sum_{n=1}^{\infty} \frac{(kx)^{n-1}}{(n-1)!} = kxe^{-kx} \sum_{n=0}^{\infty} \frac{(kx)^n}{n!} = kxe^{-kx}e^{kx} = kx$$

Thus the expected number of cars in a section is proportional to the length of the section. This shows that the k appearing in assumption (a) is a measure of traffic density, the number of cars per unit length of road.

Example 2 (Traffic at a checkout counter).   Customers arrive at a checkout counter at the rate of 15 per hour. What is the probability that exactly five customers will arrive in any given 20-minute period? We may assume that the probability of exactly one customer coming in a short interval of time is roughly proportional to the duration of that interval. Also, there is only a negligible probability that more than one customer may arrive in a brief interval of time. Therefore conditions (a) and (b) hold, if we replace "length of section" by "length of time." Without further ado, we conclude that the probability of exactly n customers arriving in a period of x minutes is given by (20). Moreover, the "customer density" is one per 4 minutes; hence $k = \frac{1}{4}$, and thus the probability that exactly five customers arrive during a 20-minute period, $P_5(20)$, is

$$(\tfrac{1}{4} \cdot 20)^5 \frac{e^{-(\frac{1}{4} \cdot 20)}}{5!} = \frac{5^5 e^{-5}}{120} = 0.18$$

Example 3 (Airport traffic). Planes arrive randomly at an airport at the rate of one per 2 minutes. What is the probability that more than three planes arrive in a 1-minute interval?

Let $P_n(t)$ be the probability that exactly n planes arrive in a time interval of t minutes. Because of the random nature of the arrivals we conclude that $P_n(t) = e^{-kt}(kt)^n/n!$ where $k = \frac{1}{2}$. The probability that *more* than three planes arrive in a 1-minute interval is $P_4(1) + P_5(1) + \cdots = 1 - P_0(1) - P_1(1) - P_2(1) - P_3(1)$ Since $P_n(1) = e^{-\frac{1}{2}}(\frac{1}{2})^n/n!$, the probability in question is

$$1 - e^{-\frac{1}{2}} - e^{-\frac{1}{2}}(\tfrac{1}{2}) - \frac{e^{-\frac{1}{2}}(\frac{1}{2})^2}{2!} - \frac{e^{-\frac{1}{2}}(\frac{1}{2})^3}{3!}$$

which equals $1 - e^{-\frac{1}{2}}(1 + \frac{1}{2} + (\frac{1}{2})^2/2! + (\frac{1}{2})^3/3!) = 1 - 0.99818 = 0.00182$. Thus the "odds" are about 1 in 600 that more than three planes arrive in a given 1-minute period.

EXERCISES

1. (*a*) Why would you expect that $P_0(a + b) = P_0(a) \cdot P_0(b)$ for any a and b?
   (*b*) Verify that $P_0(x) = e^{-kx}$ satisfies the equation in (*a*).
2. Write x^2 in the form $g(x)e^{-kx}$.
3. Show that $P_3(x) = (kx)^3 e^{-kx}/3!$.
4. (*a*) Why would you expect $P_3(a + b) = P_0(a)P_3(b) + P_1(a)P_2(b) + P_2(a)P_1(b) + P_3(a)P_0(b)$?
   (*b*) Do the formulas (20) satisfy the equation in (*a*)?
5. (*a*) Why would you expect $\lim\limits_{n \to \infty} P_n(x) = 0$?
   (*b*) Using Eq. (20), show that the limit is 0.
6. (*a*) Why would you expect $\lim\limits_{x \to \infty} P_n(x) = 0$?
   (*b*) Using Eq. (20), show that the limit is 0.
7. Describe the behavior of $P_n(x)$, with $n > 0$, for small x and for large x, (*a*) using only your intuition; (*b*) using Eq. (20).
8. From the fact that $P_n(x) = (kx)^n e^{-kx}/n!$, deduce the Taylor's series for e^x about the point $x = 0$.
9. We obtained $P_0(x) = e^{-kx}$ and $P_1(x) = kxe^{-kx}$. Verify that $\lim\limits_{\Delta x \to 0} P_1(\Delta x)/\Delta x = k$, and $\lim\limits_{\Delta x \to 0} P_0(\Delta x)/\Delta x = 1 - k$. Hence show that $\lim\limits_{\Delta x \to 0} [P_2(\Delta x) + P_3(\Delta x) + \cdots]/\Delta x = 0$, and that assumptions (*a*) and (*b*) on page 506 are indeed satisfied.
10. What length of road is most likely to contain exactly one car? That is, what x maximizes $P_1(x)$? (Answer: $1/k$)
11. What length of road is most likely to contain three cars? (Answer: $3/k$)
12. In a large continually operating factory there are, on the average, two accidents per hour. Let $P_n(x)$ denote the probability that there are exactly n accidents in an interval of time of length x hours.

(a) Why is it reasonable to assume that there is a constant k such that $P_0(x)$, $P_1(x)$, . . . satisfy conditions (a) and (b) on page 506?

(b) Assuming that these conditions are satisfied, show that $P_n(x) = (kx)^n e^{-kx}/n!$.

(c) Why must k equal 2?

(d) Compute $P_0(1), P_1(1), P_2(1), P_3(1)$, and $P_4(1)$.

[Answer: (d) 0.13, 0.27, 0.27, 0.18, 0.09]

13. Obtain assumption (a) from Eq. (3); Eq. (6) from assumption (b); assumption (b) from Eq. (6).

14. A brief rain left, on the average, two raindrops per square inch on a large flat surface. Let $P_n(x)$ be the probability that exactly n drops fell on a region of area x square inches. Explain carefully why you would expect $P_n(x) = (2x)^n e^{-2x}/n!$.

15. A typesetter makes an average of one mistake per page. Let $P_n(x)$ be the probability that a section of x pages (x need not be an integer) has exactly n errors.

(a) Why would you expect $P_n(x) = x^n e^{-x}/n!$?

(b) Approximately how many pages would be error-free in a 300-page book?

[Answer: (b) about 110]

16. A cloud chamber registers an average of four cosmic rays per second.

(a) What is the probability that no cosmic rays are registered in the next 6 seconds?

(b) What is the probability that exactly two are registered in the next 4 seconds?

[Answer: (a) 0.22; (b) 0.21]

17. Telephone calls during the busy hour arrive at a rate of three per minute. What is the probability that none arrives in a period of (a) ½ minute; (b) 1 minute; (c) 3 minutes?

[Answer: (a) 0.22; (b) 0.05; (c) 0.0001]

18. (a) Look at 25 consecutive pages of an illustrated dictionary and record the number of pages that have $0, 1, 2, . . .$ illustrations.

(b) What is the average number of illustrations per page?

(c) Let $P_n(x)$ be the probability that x pages have exactly n illustrations. With the data in (a), estimate $P_n(1)$ for $n = 0, 1, . . . , 6$.

(d) Compare the result in (c) with $P_n(x) = (kx)^n e^{-kx}/n!$, where k is given in (b).

19. (a) From newspaper records or some other reference, find the number of events of a certain type (and of a random character) over a period of time (perhaps the number of automobile fatalities in each of the last 100 days in a certain region; perhaps the number of births in each of the last 100 days).

(b) How do the data compare with the theory that we developed?

□ □ □

20. (a) Obtain Eq. (20) for $n = 4$ and $n = 5$.

(b) Using mathematical induction, establish (20) for all n.

21. (See Exercise 1.) Assuming that f is a continuous function and that $f(x + y) = f(x)f(y)$ for all x and y, show that $f(x) = a^x$ for some fixed number a.

22. How was it shown that P_0, P_1, and P_2 are differentiable?

3. Cross traffic and the gap between cars.

We now examine the distribution of gaps in order to compute the average delay of a northbound car at the intersection. First we will find $F(x)$, the probability that a gap has a length of at most x.

The gap between a car and the one immediately behind it is at most x if the section of road of length x immediately behind the front car is *not empty*. The probability of its being *not empty* is $1 - P_0(x) = 1 - e^{-kx}$. Thus

(1) $$F(x) = 1 - e^{-kx}$$

From (1) it follows that the density function for gaps is given by

(2) $$f(x) = F'(x) = ke^{-kx}$$

Since f is a decreasing function and $f(0) = k$, the graph of f looks like this:

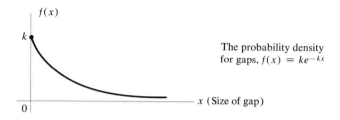

The probability density for gaps, $f(x) = ke^{-kx}$

Thus *short gaps are more frequent than long gaps.* In other words *traffic tends to move in clusters.*

Example 1. Let us compute the expected gap in the traffic, that is, $\int_0^\infty x f(x)\, dx$. We have

$$\int_0^\infty x f(x)\, dx = \int_0^\infty xke^{-kx}\, dx = \frac{1}{k}$$

by Example 7, page 230. *Thus the expected gap is the reciprocal of the traffic density,* just as it would be if all the gaps were equal.

Example 2. A driver just arriving at the intersection from the south observes a gap between the last eastbound car to pass the intersection before he arrives and the next eastbound car to pass the intersection. Let us call this the *initial gap*.

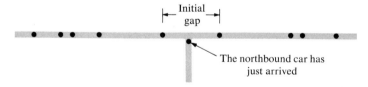

The northbound car has just arrived

What is the expected value of the initial gap?

At first we might guess that the expected value of initial gap is also $1/k$, but this is not so. A driver arriving from the south provides a biased viewpoint. He will tend to notice a longer gap more than he notices a short gap *because a longer gap remains at the intersection longer to be observed.* (Compare this with a similar bias in the measurements of average velocity, page 222.) We shall assume that the density function i for initial gaps is of the form

(3) $$i(x) = qxke^{-kx}$$

where q is constant. That is, the chance of having an initial gap of length about x is proportional not only to the density of such gaps in the traffic, ke^{-kx}, but also to their length. We shall now determine the constant q in (3).

Since i is a probability density, we have

(4)
$$\int_0^\infty qxke^{-kx}\,dx = 1$$

from which we find q. Since $\int_0^\infty xke^{-kx}\,dx = 1/k$, we have $\int_0^\infty qxke^{-kx}\,dx = q/k$. In view of (4), q must equal k. Thus $i(x) = k^2xe^{-kx}$, which is quite different from the probability density f for gaps in the traffic. *The expected value of the initial gap is*

(5)
$$\int_0^\infty x\,i(x)\,dx = \int_0^\infty k^2x^2e^{-kx} = \left[\lim_{b\to\infty} e^{-kx}\left(-kx^2 - 2x - \frac{2}{k}\right)\right]\Big|_0^b = \frac{2}{k}$$

which is twice as long as the expected gap between the cars. The expected initial gap in the traffic as seen by an arriving northbound driver is exactly twice as long as the expected gap as seen by eastbound drivers. But since the *expected distance* between someone who has just arrived at the intersection from the south and the first car coming from the west is one-half the expected initial gap, it coincides with the expected gap between eastbound cars.

A northbound driver, when he arrives at the intersection, is interested primarily in the distance between himself and the first car coming from the west. Let us call this the *initial distance.* (We have just shown that the expected initial distance is $1/k$.)

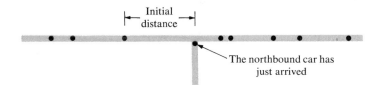

The northbound car has just arrived

The distribution function for initial distances determines the delay of the northbound driver, as we shall now show. Now, the initial distance is less than or equal to x when the section of road of length x and immediately west of the intersection is *not* empty. Since the probability of its being empty is $P_0(x) = e^{-kx}$, the *probability that the initial distance is less than x is $1 - e^{-kx}$. Thus the distribution function for initial distances is $1 - e^{-kx}$.

We are now in a position to compute the delay of the northbound driver, which we shall express in terms of the expected length of the line of eastbound traffic that passes before he can cross. Let us assume that the northbound driver waits to cross until the distance from himself to the first driver coming from the west is at least c. The probability that he crosses without delay is the probability that the initial distance is at least c; hence the *probability of no delay* is e^{-kc} (the probability that a section of length c is empty).

If the initial distance is less than c, then the northbound driver must wait until the first car goes by. The expected distance to cars that are initially too close to the intersection (within a distance c) is a major influence on the total delay of the northbound car. *We define w as the expected value of those initial distances that are less than c.* Clearly w is less than c.

The probability that the initial distance is less than c is $1 - e^{-kc}$. Let F^* be the distribution function of initial distances *that are less than c.* We have $F^*(x) = 1$ for $x \geqslant c$. For

$x \leqslant c$, we have

(6)
$$F^*(x) = \frac{\text{probability that initial distance is less than } x}{\text{probability that initial distance is less than } c} = \frac{1 - e^{-kx}}{1 - e^{-kc}}$$

From (6) we obtain the density function f^* for initial distances that are less than c:

(7)
$$f^*(x) = D F^*(x) = D\left(\frac{1 - e^{-kx}}{1 - e^{-kc}}\right) = \frac{ke^{-kx}}{1 - e^{-kc}}$$

Now w, the expected initial distance (of those distances less than c), is defined as $\int_0^c x f^*(x)\, dx$. We have

(8)
$$w = \int_0^c x f^*(x)\, dx = \int_0^c \frac{xke^{-kx}}{1 - e^{-kc}}\, dx = \frac{k}{1 - e^{-kc}} \int_0^c xe^{-kx}\, dx$$

Since
$$\int_0^c xe^{-kx}\, dx = \left[e^{-kx}\left(-\frac{x}{k} - \frac{1}{k^2}\right)\right]\Big|_0^c$$

$$= e^{-kc}\left(-\frac{c}{k} - \frac{1}{k^2}\right) - e^{-k0}\left(-\frac{0}{k} - \frac{1}{k^2}\right)$$

$$= \frac{1}{k^2}[1 - e^{-kc}(1 + kc)]$$

we have
$$w = \frac{k}{1 - e^{-kc}}\frac{1}{k^2}[1 - e^{-kc}(1 + kc)]$$

which reduces to

(9)
$$w = \frac{e^{kc} - 1 - kc}{k(e^{kc} - 1)}$$

If the initial distance is less than c, then the northbound driver waits until the first car passes. If the distance to the second car is also less than c, he still cannot cross. The average delay due to the second car is also w. If the northbound driver has to wait for 10 cars to pass (and then crosses immediately after the tenth car) his expected delay is $10w$. The total expected delay is just the product of w and the expected number of cars that pass before he crosses. In other words, the total expected delay, which we denote by W, is

(10)
$$W = w \sum_{n=0}^{\infty} np(n)$$

To compute W, as given in (10), we must determine $p(n)$ for $n = 0, 1, \ldots$. First of all, $p(0) = e^{-kc}$. Next, $p(1)$ is the probability that the northbound driver will cross between the first and second car. This is

$$\underset{\substack{\text{Probability that he}\\ \text{does not cross before}\\ \text{first car}}}{(1 - e^{-kc})} \cdot \underset{\substack{\text{Probability that gap}\\ \text{between first car and}\\ \text{second car is at least } c}}{e^{-kc}}$$

Similarly, $p(2)$ is equal to

$$\underset{\substack{\text{Probability that he}\\ \text{does not cross be-}\\ \text{fore first car}}}{(1 - e^{-kc})} \cdot \underset{\substack{\text{Probability that, having}\\ \text{waited for the first car,}\\ \text{he does not cross between}\\ \text{the first and second cars}}}{(1 - e^{-kc})} \cdot \underset{\substack{\text{Probability that gap}\\ \text{between second and}\\ \text{third car is at least } c}}{e^{-kc}}$$

or $(1 - e^{-kc})^2 e^{-kc}$. More generally,

(11)
$$p(n) = (1 - e^{-kc})^n e^{-kc}$$

By (10) and (11), the total expected delay W is

(12)
$$W = w \sum_{n=0}^{\infty} n(1 - e^{-kc})^n e^{-kc}$$

which we evaluate as follows:

$$w \sum_{n=0}^{\infty} n(1 - e^{-kc})^n e^{-kc} = we^{-kc} \sum_{n=1}^{\infty} n(1 - e^{-kc})^n$$

which, by Example 2, page 325, equals

(13)
$$we^{-kc} \frac{(1 - e^{-kc})}{(e^{-kc})^2} = \frac{w(1 - e^{-kc})}{e^{-kc}} = w(e^{kc} - 1)$$

Combining (9) and (13), we obtain W, the total expected delay:

(14)
$$W = \frac{e^{kc} - 1 - kc}{k(e^{kc} - 1)} (e^{kc} - 1) = \frac{1}{k} (e^{kc} - 1 - kc)$$

Now, W is the expected *length* of the traffic line that passes before the crossing is made. The expected *waiting time* is easily derived from W, as illustrated in the next example.

Example 3. On a certain street it is observed that the expected gap between cars is 132 feet, and that the traffic moves at 30 miles per hour. What is the expected waiting time of a northbound driver who requires 6 seconds to cross the intersection?

Let us express all lengths in feet; in particular, 30 miles per hour is 44 feet per second. Since the expected gap is $1/k$ (by Example 1), we see that $k = 1/132$. Since the northbound driver requires 6 seconds to cross, he must wait for a gap $c = 6 \cdot 44 = 264$ feet. The expected delay (in seconds) is $W/44$ or, if we substitute in (14),

$$\frac{W}{44} = \frac{1}{44} (132) \left(e^{(1/132)264} - 1 - \frac{1}{132} 264 \right) = 3(e^2 - 1 - 2) = 3(7.389 - 3)$$

$$= 13.2 \text{ seconds}$$

A child who requires 12 seconds to cross traffic needs a traffic gap $c = 528$ feet. Hence his expected delay is

$$\frac{W}{44} = \frac{1}{44} (132) \left(e^{(1/132)528} - 1 - \frac{1}{132} 528 \right) = 3(e^4 - 5) = 3(54.60 - 5) = 149 \text{ seconds}$$

The expected delay is far more than twice that of the driver, even though the child needs only twice as long to cross.

Example 4. Formula (14) for W shows that the nuisances of civilization grow much faster than the population. For instance, let us say that the expected gap, $1/k$, is 100 feet and that $c = 100$ feet. Then

$$W = 100 \left(e^{(1/100)100} - 1 - \frac{1}{100} 100 \right) = 100(e^1 - 2) = 71.8 \text{ feet}$$

In a few years the population quadruples and so does the traffic density, though it still moves at the same speed. The expected gap is now 25 feet, so k is now $1/25$. The northbound car still requires a gap $c = 100$ feet. The new W is

$$W = 25 \left(e^{(1/25)100} - 1 - \frac{1}{25}100 \right) = 25(e^4 - 5) = 1{,}265 \text{ feet}$$

which is about 18 times as large as the original delay. *When the population quadruples, the delay is magnified* 18-fold!

To make matters worse, let us note that the northbound traffic also may quadruple. At a rush hour, when each car must wait for the car in front to cross, the expected delay grows not just 18-fold, but 72-fold.

Delay and congestion are thus sensitive barometers of growth. The new discipline of traffic engineering has only started to cope with them. Little is known about such important facets of traffic as waiting times at intersections where traffic in four directions meets; the effect of delays due to slow or turning drivers; car-following and car-passing patterns; the timing of red, green, and amber traffic lights to maximize metropolitan flow; or the capacity of an *m*-lane freeway as a function of *m*. The traffic engineers who will help us use our highways most efficiently may in the long run contribute more than the civil engineers who build them.

EXERCISES

1. A bus company runs 6 buses every hour: on the hour and 5, 15, 30, 45, and 50 minutes after the hour. The buses travel at 10 miles per hour.
   (*a*) What is the expected gap between buses?
   (*b*) What is the expected initial gap noticed by a person arriving to wait for a bus?
   [Answer: (*a*) 1.67 miles; (*b*) 1.94 miles]

2. Let $F(x)$ be the probability that the initial distance between the arriving northbound driver and the first eastbound car to pass the intersection is $\leqslant x$.
   (*a*) Show that $F'(x) = ke^{-kx}$.
   (*b*) With the aid of (*a*), show that the expected value of the distance mentioned in (*a*) is $1/k$.
   (*c*) From (*b*) deduce, once again, that the expected initial gap observed by a northbound car is $2/k$.

3. Since w is positive, Eq. (9) shows that $e^{kc} - kc - 1$ is positive. Prove directly that $e^{kc} - kc - 1$ is positive.

4. If c is very large, w, as given in Eq. (9), is approximately $1/k$. Is this reasonable? Explain.

5. For traffic on a particular highway the expected gap, $1/k$, is 100, and $c = 200$.
   (*a*) Compute $p(0)$, the probability of crossing without delay.
   (*b*) Compute $p(2)$, the probability that the crossing occurs after the second car passes.
   [Answer: (*a*) 0.135; (*b*) 0.110]

6. What is the expected number of cars that pass before the car in Exercise 5 can cross?
   (Answer: 6.3)

7. Traffic moving at 44 feet per second passes at the average rate of one car per second.
   (*a*) What is the average gap (in feet)?
   (*b*) What is k?
   (*c*) If a car requires 2 seconds to cross the traffic, what is c?
   (*d*) How many seconds, on the average, must a car wait before crossing?
   [Answer: (*a*) 44 feet; (*b*) 1/44; (*c*) 88; (*d*) 4.39 seconds]

8. Repeat Exercise 7 for traffic moving at 60 miles per hour.

[Answer: (a) 88 feet; (b) $\frac{1}{88}$; (c) 176; (d) 4.39 seconds]

9. We assumed that there was only one lane of traffic, that moving eastbound. Assume now that there are equal amounts of traffic moving eastbound and westbound, each with the same k. Show that the probability of crossing without delay is e^{-2kc}.

10. Assume that $k = 2$.

(a) Graph W, as given in Eq. (14), as a function of c.

(b) If a car, with $c = 1$, waits an average of 10 seconds, how long will a pedestrian, with $c = 3$, usually wait?

[Answer: (b) about 15 minutes]

11. Show that doubling c has twice the effect on W as doubling k. (Moral: It is better to face twice the density of traffic than to require a gap twice as long to cross.)

12. Assume that $c = 1$. Graph W as a function of k.

13. Assume that the eastbound traffic is controlled in such a way that all gaps are 100 feet. A northbound driver who requires a gap of 50 feet reaches the intersection. Compute (a) the probability $p(0)$ that he is not delayed; (b) probabilities $p(1)$, $p(2)$, . . . ; (c) the expected distance to the first car, if he has to wait.

[Answer: (a) $\frac{1}{2}$; (b) $p(1) = \frac{1}{2}$; (c) 25 feet]

14. Random eastbound traffic, traveling at 60 miles per hour, passes at the rate of one car in 4 seconds.

(a) Find k, if length is measured in feet.

(b) A northbound car requires 3 seconds to cross. Find c.

(c) Find $p(n)$, with $n = 0, 1, 2, \ldots$.

(d) Find the expected duration (in seconds) of the time spent waiting to cross.

(e) What is the expected number of cars that pass before the crossing is made?

[Answer: (a) $\frac{1}{352}$; (b) 264 feet; (c) $p(n) = (0.528)^n(0.472)$;

(d) 1.46 seconds; (e) 1.1]

15. The time required to check out a customer at a supermarket depends on the size of his order. Let us assume that the probability that a customer is checked out in less than t minute is $1 - e^{-t/2}$.

(a) What is the expected checkout time?

(b) If the clerk has just begun checking out the customer first in line, what is the expected time before the tenth customer in line is checked out?

[Answer: (a) 2 minutes]

□ □ □

16. Traffic *(not necessarily random)* flows at a constant speed. Let $F(x)$ be the probability that a gap between cars is less than or equal to x, and assume that $f = F'$ is continuous. Let $i(x)$ denote the probability density of initial gaps.

(a) Why would $i(x)$ be proportional to $xf(x)$?

(b) Let $i(x) = bxf(x)$, where b is some constant. Show that $b = 1/ \displaystyle\int_{c}^{\infty} xf(x)\, dx$.

(c) Show that the expected gap between cars, $\displaystyle\int_{0}^{\infty} xf(x)\, dx$, is less than or equal

to $\displaystyle\int_{0}^{\infty} xi(x)\, dx$, the expected initial gap. [Hint: This reduces to the inequality

$$\int_0^\infty xf(x)\,dx \leqslant \left[\int_0^\infty x^2 f(x)\,dx\right]^{1/2}$$, which is a consequence of Exercise 16, page 226.)

(*d*) Can equality occur in (*c*)? Explain.

17. Fill in the details in the evaluation of Eq. (5).
18. If the expected distance between cars is 100 feet, what is the probability that a section of the road of length 200 feet is empty?

REFERENCES

1. Cohen, J. W.: A Survey of Queueing Problems Occurring in Telephone and Telegraph Traffic Theory, "Proceedings of the First International Congress on Operational Research," 138–146 (1957). (This brief historical survey emphasizes telephone traffic but points out similarities to problems in other fields.)
2. Feller, W.: "An Introduction to Probability Theory and Its Applications," vol. 1, 2d ed., Wiley, New York, 1957. (Pages 407–421 include a discussion of the repair of machines subject to random breakdown.)
3. Riordan, J.: "Stochastic Service Systems," Wiley, New York, 1962. (The preface and introduction describe many problems in traffic theory.)
4. Haight, F. A.: "Mathematical Theories of Traffic Flow," Academic, New York, 1963. (This text concentrates on road traffic.)
5. Cox, D. R., and W. L. Smith: "Queues," Wiley, New York, 1963. (The introduction, pp. 1–30, discusses many types of practical problems.)
6. Stoller, D. S.: "Operations Research: Process and Strategy," University of California Press, Berkeley, Calif., 1964. (Pages 27–68 contain a discussion of such topics as the length of a waiting line.)
7. Barlow, R. E., F. Proschan, and L. C. Hunter: "Mathematical Theory of Reliability," Wiley, New York, 1965. (Pages 1–5 present the history of reliability theory.)
8. Bone, A. J., B. V. Martin, and T. N. Harvey: "The Selection of a Cycle Length for Fixed Time Traffic Signals," School of Engineering, the Massachusetts Institute of Technology, Cambridge, Mass. (This is an example of the interplay of concrete data and abstract theory.)
9. Horowitz, I.: "An Introduction to Quantitative Business Analysis," McGraw-Hill, New York, 1965. (Waiting lines in businesses are discussed on pp. 213–234.)

25

Rockets

IN this chapter we discuss the mathematical basis of rocket propulsion and such related topics as escape velocity, orbit velocity, and the time required to orbit the earth. For simplicity we consider only rockets moving in a straight line or in a circle. (In the next chapter we examine the general orbit.) The derivative, the definite integral, the improper integral, and the antiderivative will be used in our analysis.

A typical rocket burns its fuel for a period of 30 seconds to 20 minutes at a constant rate; the speed of the exhaust gas relative to the rocket may be anywhere from 1 to 2 miles per second. The exhaust gases propel the rocket just as escaping air propels a toy balloon:

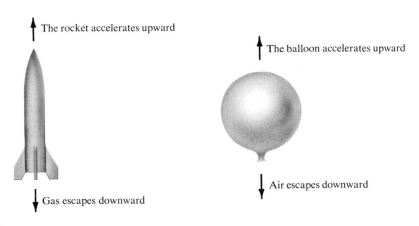

The rocket accelerates upward

Gas escapes downward

The balloon accelerates upward

Air escapes downward

The exhaust exerts a "thrust" of 2,000 to 8,000,000 pounds on the rocket. If the thrust is less than the weight of the rocket, the rocket remains on its launching pad; if the thrust exceeds the weight, the rocket rises.

As we shall see, it is frequently advisable to combine several rockets in "stages." As many as five stages have been used, but three is most common. A typical large three-stage rocket has these features:

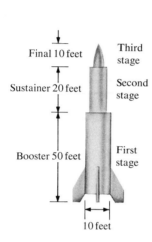

Purpose	Thrust (pounds)	Duration of burn (seconds)
Accurate final control	Less than 2000	30-1000
Intermediate lift	2000-150,000	120-400
Lift vehicle off ground	Up to 8,000,000	50-150

Final 10 feet — Third stage
Sustainer 20 feet — Second stage
Booster 50 feet — First stage
10 feet

We shall study the motion of rockets in a straight line in outer space (where we assume there is no gravitational force), and then the motion of a payload launched either to escape the gravitational field of the earth or to move in a circular orbit.

1. The basic equation of rocket propulsion.

Consider a rocket whose (varying) mass is m, whose exhaust velocity is c, and whose velocity is v, *moving in a straight line in outer space:*

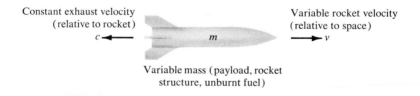

Constant exhaust velocity (relative to rocket) $c \leftarrow$

m

Variable rocket velocity (relative to space) $\longrightarrow v$

Variable mass (payload, rocket structure, unburnt fuel)

As the fuel burns, m decreases and the rocket accelerates.

In order to see how the velocity of the rocket varies with time, we consider what happens in a small interval of time Δt, from t to $t + \Delta t$. We shall introduce a fixed x axis parallel to the line on which the rocket moves. At time t the velocity of the rocket is v and the momentum of the rocket (including its unburnt fuel) is mv:

Situation at time t

Mass: m Velocity: v

Momentum: mv

x axis fixed in space

In the interval of time $[t, t + \Delta t]$, a small mass of fuel burns and is ejected with a velocity of $-c$ relative to the rocket, and hence with a velocity of $v - c$ relative to the fixed axis. Since the mass of the rocket and remaining fuel decreases, the change in rocket mass Δm is negative; *the mass of the ejected fuel is* $-\Delta m$, a positive quantity. Its velocity relative to the fixed axis is $v - c$. The velocity of the rocket increases by an amount Δv, owing to the thrust exerted on the rocket by escaping gas.

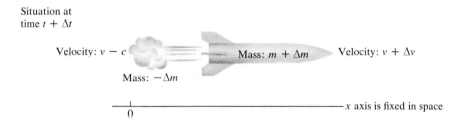

Situation at time $t + \Delta t$

Velocity: $v - c$ Mass: $m + \Delta m$ Velocity: $v + \Delta v$

Mass: $-\Delta m$

x axis is fixed in space

Not only is the total mass of this system conserved,

$$m = (m + \Delta m) + (-\Delta m)$$

but *since we assume that there is no external force acting on the system,* the total momentum is also conserved:

(1) $$\underset{\substack{\text{Momentum of}\\\text{system at time } t}}{mv} = \underset{\substack{\text{Momentum of rocket}\\\text{(including unburnt}\\\text{fuel) at time}\\ t + \Delta t}}{(m + \Delta m)(v + \Delta v)} + \underset{\substack{\text{Momentum of}\\\text{fuel burnt}\\\text{during}\\\text{interval}\\ [t, t + \Delta t]}}{(-\Delta m)(v - c)}$$

From (1) we obtain

$$mv = mv + m\,\Delta v + (\Delta m)v + \Delta m\,\Delta v - (\Delta m)v + (\Delta m)c$$

Hence $$0 = m\,\Delta v + \Delta m\,\Delta v + (\Delta m)c$$

which reduces to

(2) $$m\,\Delta v = -\Delta m(c + \Delta v)$$

Dividing (2) by Δt, we obtain

$$m\frac{\Delta v}{\Delta t} = -\frac{\Delta m}{\Delta t}(c + \Delta v)$$

Taking limits as $\Delta t \to 0$, we arrive at

(3)
$$m\frac{dv}{dt} = -c\frac{dm}{dt}$$

the basic equation of rocket propulsion in the absence of external forces. Since dv/dt is the acceleration of the rocket, and since dm/dt is negative, Equation (3) tells us that *the rocket has a positive acceleration;* hence *its velocity* (which is positive) *is increasing.* Moreover, if we write (3) in the form

(4)
$$\text{Acceleration} = \frac{dv}{dt} = c\frac{1}{m}\left(-\frac{dm}{dt}\right)$$

we see that the acceleration is proportional to the rate at which the fuel is consumed and *inversely proportional to the remaining mass m.* Since m decreases with time, the acceleration increases.

We also learn from (4) the importance of a high exhaust speed, for the *acceleration is also proportional to c.* High exhaust speed is obtained by the use of fuels that burn at high temperatures (above $4,000°$ fahrenheit) and whose exhaust consists of small (easily accelerated) molecules.

Example 1. The *thrust* of a rocket engine *is defined as* $c(-dm/dt)$, the product of the exhaust speed and the rate at which fuel is consumed. Let us find the relation between thrust and the motion of the rocket. We have, from (4),

(5)
$$\text{Mass} \cdot \text{acceleration} = c\left(-\frac{dm}{dt}\right) = \text{thrust}$$

If we want swift acceleration, we must design the rocket to have a large thrust; this is achieved by a large exhaust velocity and a high rate of fuel consumption. Note, by (5), that if the thrust remains constant, the acceleration increases.

Early in this century some physicists rejected the possibility of a long rocket journey because they felt that the velocity of the rocket could never exceed its exhaust velocity. As a matter of fact, a simple equation shows us that v can grow to be much larger than c. To show this, we divide (2) by Δm and obtain

(6)
$$m\frac{\Delta v}{\Delta m} = -(c + \Delta v)$$

We consider v now as a function of the mass remaining, m. When Δm is sufficiently small, the velocity of the rocket changes only by a small amount. That is, as Δm approaches 0, so does Δv. Letting $\Delta m \to 0$ in (6), we obtain

(7)
$$m\frac{dv}{dm} = -c$$

or

(8)
$$\frac{dv}{dm} = \frac{-c}{m}$$

Thus

(9)
$$v = (-c \ln m) + k \qquad \text{where } k \text{ is some constant}$$

Now let m_0 be the initial mass of the rocket and its fuel, and let v_0 be its initial velocity. Let m_1 and v_1 be its mass and speed when the fuel is used up. From (9) we have

$$v_1 = (-c \ln m_1) + k$$

and

$$v_0 = (-c \ln m_0) + k$$

Subtracting, we arrive at

(10) $\qquad$ Change in velocity $= v_1 - v_0 = c \ln \dfrac{m_0}{m_1}$

Equation (10) shows that the increase in velocity is proportional to the exhaust velocity and to $\ln(m_0/m_1)$. This means that *we can achieve a velocity much higher than the exhaust velocity by making the ratio between the initial mass and the final mass very large.* (This is accomplished by making m_0 large—using a great deal of fuel—and by making m_1 small—using small payloads and very light metals in the rocket frame and shell.) The important quotient m_0/m_1 is called the *mass ratio*.

Example 2. A 1-ton rocket carrying 3 tons of fuel is initially motionless in space. It burns all its fuel in one minute. If its exhaust velocity is 2 miles per second, what is its velocity at burnout?

Using (10) with $m_0 = 4, m_1 = 1, c = 2$, and $v_0 = 0$, we obtain the final velocity $v_1 = v_1 - v_0 = 2 \ln \frac{4}{1} = 2.77$ miles per second, which is greater than the exhaust velocity. Note that the duration of burning is irrelevant.

Example 3. A certain rocket has an exhaust velocity of two miles per second and an unloaded mass of 500 pounds. How much fuel is needed to give it a velocity of 6 miles per second?

In this case $v_1 = 6, v_0 = 0, c = 2$, and $m_1 = 500$. If x denotes the mass of the fuel, then $m_0 = 500 + x$. Equation (10) becomes

$$6 - 0 = 2 \ln \frac{500 + x}{500}$$

or

$$\ln \frac{500 + x}{500} = 3$$

Thus

$$\frac{500 + x}{500} = e^3 = 20.086$$

from which we obtain $500 + x = 10{,}430$. Hence $x = 9{,}930$ pounds.

2. Escape velocity. Now we are ready to examine the motion of a rocket in the earth's gravitational field. We disregard the rotation of the earth and the resistance of the air in order not to be distracted from the essentials, and we assume that rockets are launched vertically.

How much work is done against gravity if we send a payload to "infinity"? (If the work turned out to be infinite, it would be impossible to escape the earth's gravitational field using only a finite amount of fuel.) We begin by computing the work done in lifting a 1-pound payload from the surface of the earth to "infinity."

Let the mass of the payload be 1 pound. The farther it is from the center of the earth, the less it weighs, for the force of the earth on the mass is inversely proportional to the square of the distance of the mass from the center of the earth. Thus the force on the payload is given by k/r^2, where k is a constant which we shall determine in a moment, and r is the distance from the payload to the center of the earth. When $r = 4{,}000$ (miles), the force is 1 pound; thus

$$1 = \frac{k}{(4{,}000)^2}$$

From this we conclude that $k = (4{,}000)^2$ and therefore that the gravitational force on a 1-pound mass is, in general, $(4{,}000/r)^2$ pounds. As the payload recedes from the earth it loses weight (but not mass), as recorded on this diagram:

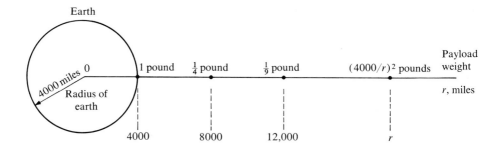

The work done in lifting the payload from point r to point $r + \Delta r$ is approximately

$$\underbrace{\left(\frac{4{,}000}{r}\right)^2}_{\text{Force}} \underbrace{(\Delta r)}_{\text{Distance}}$$

Hence the total work required to move the 1-pound mass from the surface of the earth to infinity is given by the improper integral $\int_{4{,}000}^{\infty} (4{,}000/r)^2 \, dr$. Now

$$\int_{4{,}000}^{\infty} \left(\frac{4{,}000}{r}\right)^2 dr = \lim_{b \to \infty} \int_{4{,}000}^{b} \left(\frac{4{,}000}{r}\right)^2 dr = \lim_{b \to \infty} \frac{-4{,}000^2}{r}\Big|_{4{,}000}^{b}$$

$$= \lim_{b \to \infty} \left[\frac{-4{,}000^2}{b} + \frac{4{,}000^2}{4{,}000}\right] = 4{,}000 \text{ mile-pounds}$$

The total work is finite. It is just as if we had lifted the payload 4,000 miles against a constant gravitational force equal to that at the surface of the earth.

Encouraged by this result, *we compute the escape velocity* (the velocity that a payload must have at burnout if it is not to fall back to earth). We begin by studying the motion of a projectile fired with an initial velocity of v_0 miles per second from the surface of the earth, and for this purpose introduce a coordinate system whose origin is at the center of the earth:

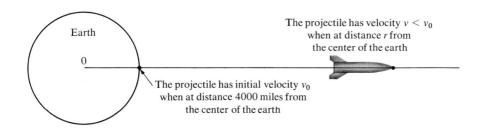

The velocity of the projectile is defined as

$$v = \frac{dr}{dt}$$

and its acceleration as $d^2r/dt^2 = dv/dt$. We shall assume that the *acceleration* due to gravity *is proportional to the force of gravity* on the particle; that is,

(11) $$\text{Acceleration} = \frac{dv}{dt} = \frac{-K}{r^2}$$

where K is some positive constant. [The negative sign in (11) reminds us that gravity slows the projectile.]

Before we analyze (11) further, we determine K. At the surface of the earth, where $r = 4,000$ miles, the acceleration due to gravity is -32 feet per second per second, which is approximately -0.006 mile per second per second. Thus K satisfies the equation

$$-0.006 = \frac{-K}{4,000^2}$$

and

(12) $$K = (4,000)^2 (0.006)$$

Now we deal with (11), which links velocity, time, and distance. We shall eliminate time by using the chain rule:

$$\frac{dv}{dt} = \frac{dv}{dr}\frac{dr}{dt} = v\frac{dv}{dr}$$

Thus (11) is now simply

(13) $$v\frac{dv}{dr} = \frac{-K}{r^2}$$

an equation linking velocity and distance. We may rewrite (13) as

$$\frac{d(v^2/2)}{dr} = \frac{d(K/r)}{dr}$$

so that we can say that

(14)
$$\frac{v^2}{2} = \frac{K}{r} + C$$

where C is some constant. To determine C, we again use information available at the surface of the earth, namely, $v = v_0$ when $r = 4,000$. From (14) it follows that

$$\frac{v_0^2}{2} = \frac{K}{4,000} + C$$

and

(15)
$$C = \frac{v_0^2}{2} - \frac{K}{4,000}$$

Combining (12), (14), and (15), we obtain

$$\frac{v^2}{2} = \frac{K}{r} + \left(\frac{v_0^2}{2} - \frac{K}{4,000}\right) = \frac{v_0^2}{2} + K\left(\frac{1}{r} - \frac{1}{4,000}\right)$$

$$= \frac{v_0^2}{2} + (4,000)^2 (0.006)\left(\frac{1}{r} - \frac{1}{4,000}\right)$$

Hence

(16)
$$v^2 = v_0^2 + (4,000)^2 (0.012)\left(\frac{1}{r} - \frac{1}{4,000}\right)$$

Equation (16) *describes v as a function of r. If v in* (16) *is never* 0, that is, if the payload never reaches a maximum distance from the earth, *then the payload will not fall back to the earth.* Thus, by (16), if v_0 is such that the equation

(17)
$$0 = v_0^2 + (4,000)^2 (0.012)\left(\frac{1}{r} - \frac{1}{4,000}\right)$$

has no solution r, then v_0 is large enough to send the payload on an endless journey. To find such v_0 we rewrite (17) as

(18)
$$(4,000) (0.012) - v_0^2 = (4,000)^2 (0.012)\left(\frac{1}{r}\right)$$

If the left side of (18) is greater than 0, then there is a solution for r, and the payload will reach a maximum distance; if the left side of (18) is less than or equal to 0, *then there is no solution for r.* The *smallest* v_0 that satisfies the inequality $(4,000) (0.012) - v_0^2 \leqslant 0$ is

$$v_0 = \sqrt{(4,000) (0.012)} = \sqrt{48} = 6.92 \text{ miles per second}$$

The escape velocity is 6.92 miles per second.

3. Orbit velocity.   If, instead of sending a payload to infinity, we wanted to put it into a circular orbit around the earth, with what initial velocity should we provide it? We disregard the resistance of the air and assume that the launch is made *horizontally* from a high tower:

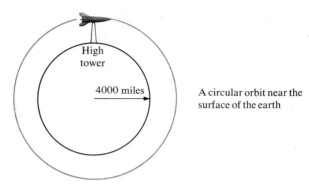

A circular orbit near the surface of the earth

The rocket would then be swung around the earth like a pail at the end of a rope. Instead of the tension on a rope, we have the force of gravity pulling the rocket in toward the earth from a linear path. Now, if a particle moves in a circle of radius 4,000 miles with velocity v, it has an acceleration toward the center of the earth of

(19) $$\frac{v^2}{4,000}$$

(see page 410). This acceleration coincides with the acceleration 32 feet per second per second = 0.006 mile per second per second, which gravity imparts to any object at the surface of the earth. Thus $0.006 = v^2/4,000$ and

(20) $$\text{Orbital velocity} = v = \sqrt{(4000)(0.006)} = \sqrt{24}$$
$$= 4.90 \text{ miles per second}$$

The velocity necessary to maintain an object in orbit at the surface of the earth is 4.90 miles per second, which is much less than the escape velocity, 6.92 miles per second. (In Chap. 26 we shall see that if the velocity is different from 4.90 miles per second, the rocket will move in an ellipse, parabola, or hyperbola.)

Now let us turn our attention to the return of the payload and examine its motion as it falls vertically through the atmosphere. Let us assume that the *drag* (or decelerating force) *of the air on an object moving through it is proportional to the speed of the object.* (Actually the drag varies in a much more complicated way, partly because the density of the atmosphere is not constant.) With this assumption, *we shall show that the velocity of a falling body does not get arbitrarily large.* (Experiments show that a falling man reaches a speed of about 180 miles per hour, and a falling feather less than 1 mile per hour.)

We introduce a vertical y axis to record the position of the falling object at time t. Then its velocity v is equal to dy/dt. If there were no air, the acceleration, dv/dt, would be -32 feet per second per second. (We are simplifying matters by assuming that in the fall the force of gravity is constant.) But, because of the drag due to the air, which we assume is proportional to velocity, we have

$$(21) \qquad \frac{dv}{dt} = -32 - kv$$

where k is some positive constant. Note that since v is negative, $-kv$ is positive; thus the acceleration, $-32 - kv$, is less (in absolute value) than the acceleration in a vacuum. On the basis of (21), we shall find v as a function of t.

We first observe that

$$\frac{d(32 + kv)}{dt} = k\frac{dv}{dt}$$

But from (21), we have $k\, dv/dt = k(-32 - kv)$, and thus

$$(22) \qquad \frac{d(32 + kv)}{dt} = -k(32 + kv)$$

Thus the derivative of the function $32 + kv$ is proportional to the function itself. By Example 3, page 124,

$$(23) \qquad 32 + kv = Ce^{-kt}$$

where C is some constant. To determine C, recall that at time $t = 0$ the object is at zero velocity above the earth and just begins to fall; that is, $v = 0$. Thus (23) yields

$$(24) \qquad 32 + k0 = Ce^{-k0} \qquad \text{or} \qquad C = 32$$

Solving (23) for v, and replacing C by 32, we obtain v as a function of time,

$$(25) \qquad v = \frac{32}{k}(e^{-kt} - 1)$$

As t increases without bound, v *approaches* $(32/k)(0 - 1) = -32/k$. *Thus a falling object tends toward a limiting velocity.* This implies that its acceleration tends toward 0. As a matter of fact, the acceleration equals

$$(26) \qquad -32 - kv = -32 - k\frac{32}{k}(e^{-kt} - 1) = -32e^{-kt}$$

and fades exponentially.

We have treated only a few aspects of rocket theory. But the calculus remains the key tool in many other problems related to rockets, such as the design of propulsion systems, the choice of economical trajectories, and the study of the motion of a rocket as it rises against both air resistance and the force of gravity.

EXERCISES

1. Without fuel, a rocket weighs 1 ton. If it is motionless in interstellar space, how much fuel is required to give it a velocity (*a*) equal to its exhaust velocity; (*b*) equal to twice its exhaust velocity? (Hint: See Example 2.)   [Answer: (*a*) 1.72 tons; (*b*) 6.39 tons]
2. Which has the greatest effect on the final velocity of a rocket in free space: doubling

its fuel $(m_1 - m_0)$, doubling its exhaust velocity c, or doubling its rate of consumption of fuel dm/dt? Which has the least effect? [Hint: Interpret (10).]

3. In its present design, a certain rocket weighs 1 ton and requires 1 ton of fuel. Which would be a more effective improvement: cutting the weight of the rocket in half or doubling its fuel capacity? (Assume that c remains constant and that the goal is high velocity in interstellar space.) Explain.

4. If the rocket of Example 2 is redesigned so that when empty it weighs 250 pounds instead of 500 pounds, how much fuel is needed?   (Answer: 4,750 pounds)

5. A two-stage rocket is more efficient than a one-stage rocket because the mass of the first stage is ejected when its fuel is used up. The first stage of a certain two-stage rocket consists of a 100-pound rocket containing 300 pounds of fuel and the second stage consists of a 25-pound rocket containing 75 pounds of fuel. Each has the same exhaust speed, c.

(a) Show that at burnout of the first rocket $v = c \ln \frac{5}{2}$, but that at burnout of the second rocket v has increased to $c \ln 10$.

(b) Show that the rocket obtained by strapping the two together attains only $v = c \ln 4$.

6. (a) Show that if gravitational attraction decreased as $1/r$, instead of as $1/r^2$, then the work involved in lifting a payload to "infinity" would be infinite.

(b) What if the gravitational attraction decreased as $1/r^{1.01}$?

7. Show that half the work of lifting an object from the surface of the earth to "infinity" is accomplished in the first 4,000 miles.

8. How much work is done in lifting a 1-pound brick to a height of 82 miles?

(Answer: about 80 mile-pounds)

9. A projectile is launched with an initial velocity of 8 miles per second.

(a) Using Eq. (16), show that it will not return to the earth.

(b) What is $\lim_{r \to \infty} v$?

10. What burnout velocity is required to launch a projectile to the moon, 240,000 miles away? Assume a straight path, and disregard air resistance and the moon's gravitational field. [Hint: Use (16).]   (Answer: $\sqrt{47.2}$ miles per second)

11. Repeat Exercise 10, for a rocket to Mars, 40,000,000 miles away.

(Answer: $\sqrt{47.9952}$ miles per second)

Note in Exercises 10 and 11 how close these velocities are to the escape velocity.

12. If a projectile is launched with precisely the escape velocity, what is $\lim_{r \to \infty} v$? [Hint: Use (16).]

13. Show that the orbital velocity (20) is $(1/\sqrt{2})$ times the escape velocity.

14. The acceleration that gravity imparts to an object decreases with the square of the distance of the object from the center of the earth.

(a) Show that if an object is r miles from the center of the earth, it has an acceleration of $(0.006)(4,000/r)^2$ miles per second per second.

(b) With the aid of (a) and Eq. (19), find the velocity of a satellite in orbit at an altitude of 1,000 miles.   [Answer: (b) $\sqrt{19.2} = 4.38$ miles per second]

15. How long would it take a satellite to orbit the earth just above the earth's surface? One hundred miles above the earth's surface? One thousand miles above the surface?

(Answer: 85.5 minutes, 88.7 minutes, 119.5 minutes)

16. What altitude must an orbiting satellite have in order to stay directly above a fixed spot on the equator?   (Answer: about 22,000 miles; that is, $r = 26,000$ miles)

17. An object millions of miles away falls toward the earth. Discuss its velocity at the

moment it strikes the earth. Can it be arbitrarily large if it falls from a point sufficiently remote?

18. A certain satellite in circular orbit goes around the earth once every 92 minutes.
How high is it above the earth?   (Answer: about 900 miles)

19. Show that if an object is dropped from a height y_0 at time 0, and satisfies Eq. (21),
then at time t it has a height

$$y = (c/k^2)(1 - e^{-kt}) - (g/k)t + y_0$$

20. Graph as functions of time the acceleration (26), velocity (25), and height (see
Exercise 19) of a body falling through the air after being dropped toward the earth.

21. A projectile is fired directly up with an initial velocity v_0. Assume that the acceleration of gravity is constant and that the resistance of the air is proportional to the
velocity of the projectile.
  (a) Show that $dv/dt = -32 - kv$, where k is a positive constant, just as in the case
  in which the projectile was falling [Eq. (21)].
  (b) Show that $v = (1/k)(ce^{-kt} - 32)$, where c is some constant.
  (c) Show that $v(0) = (c - 32)/k$; hence $c > 32$.
  (d) Show that $y = (c/k^2)(1 - e^{-kt}) - (32t)/k$.

22. (See Exercise 21.) Show that the projectile in Exercise 21 reaches its maximum
height, $(c - 32)/k^2 - (32/k^2)\ln(c/32)$, at time $T = (1/k)\ln(c/32)$.

23. Prove that $(\ln x)^2 < 2(x - 1 - \ln x)$ for $x > 1$. (Hint: Let $y = \ln x$, and write the
inequality in terms of y.)

24. (See Exercise 22.) In each of two experiments, a ball is thrown straight up, reaches
a maximum height, and then falls. One experiment is carried out in vacuum, the
other in air. Both balls reach the same maximum height. Which takes longer
going up?
  (a) Guess the answer.
  (b) Use the calculus. [In (b), Exercise 23 may be useful.]

25. Could it happen that a projectile shot straight out from the earth, as on page 523,
neither returns nor travels to "infinity" but approaches a certain finite limiting
position? Explain your answer.

26. How long would it take the projectile in Exercise 10 to reach the moon? (Hint:
Consider $\int_{4,000}^{240,000} \dfrac{dr}{v}$.)

REFERENCES

1. Ley, W.: "Rockets, Missiles, and Space Travel," Viking, New York, 1961. (This is a
nontechnical introduction to the history and technology of rockets.)

2. Ordway, F. I., J. P. Gradner, and M. R. Shayne: "Basic Astronautics," Prentice-Hall,
Englewood Cliffs, N.J., 1962. (See pages 8–26 for a history of the development of
the rocket.)

3. "Space Facts," General Electric Co., 3198 Chestnut St., Philadelphia, Pennsylvania.
(This little handbook contains data related to many aspects of space flight.)

26

Gravity

AFTER hundreds of pages of computation based on the observations made by the astronomer Tycho Brahe in the last three decades of the sixteenth century, plus lengthy detours and lucky guesses, Kepler arrived at these three laws of planetary motion:

    I. Every planet travels around the sun in an elliptical orbit such that the sun is situated at one focus (discovered 1605, published 1609).

    II. The velocity of a planet varies in such a way that the line joining the planet to the sun sweeps out equal areas in equal times (discovered 1602, published 1609).

    III. The square of the time required by a planet for one revolution around the sun is proportional to the cube of its mean distance from the sun (discovered 1618, published 1619).

To arrive at these laws Kepler first had to show that the orbit of each planet lies in a plane, that the planes of the planets all pass through the sun, and that the orbit of a planet is not a circle or a simple compound of circles.

The work of Kepler shattered the crystal spheres which for 2,000 years had carried the planets. Before him astronomers admitted only circular motion and motion compounded of circular motion. Copernicus, for instance, used five circles to describe the motion of Mars.

531

The ellipse was not welcomed; Galileo, to whom Kepler had sent a copy of his work, apparently paid no attention. In 1605 Kepler complained to a skeptical astronomer:

> You have disparaged my oval orbit . . . . If you are enraged because I cannot take away oval flight how much more you should be enraged by the motions assigned by the ancients, which I did take away . . . . You disdain my oval, a single cart of dung, while you endure a whole stable. (If indeed my oval is a cart of dung.)

But the Rudolphine astronomical tables, which Kepler based on his theories and published in 1627, proved to be more accurate than any other and the ellipse gradually gained acceptance. For instance, an English compiler of almanacs used the old tables in 1643, mixed the old with the Rudolphine in 1647, and relied completely on the Rudolphine in 1649.

The three laws stood as independent mysteries alongside a closely related question: If there are no crystal spheres, what propels the planets? Bullialdus, a French mathematician, suggested in 1645:

> That force with which the sun seizes or pulls the planets, a physical force which serves as hands for it, is sent out in straight lines into all the world's space . . . ; since it is physical it is decreased in greater space; . . . the ratio of this decrease is the same as that for light, namely as the reciprocal of the square of the distance.

In 1666 Hooke, more of an experimental scientist than a mathematician, wondered,

> . . . why the planets should move about the sun . . . being not included in any solid orbs . . . nor tied to it . . . by any visible strings . . . . All the celestial bodies . . . must have some other cause, besides the first impressed impulse, that must bend their motion into that curve . . . . I cannot imagine any other likely cause besides these two: The first may be from an unequal density of the medium . . . ; if we suppose that part of the medium, which is farthest from the centre, or sun, to be more dense outward, than that which is more near, it will follow, that the direct motion will be always deflected inwards, by the easier yielding of the inwards . . . .
>
> But the second cause of inflecting a direct motion into a curve may be from an attractive property of the body placed in the centre; whereby it continually endeavours to attract or draw it to itself. For if such a principle be supposed all the phenomena of the planets seem possible to be explained by the common principle of mechanic motions . . . . By this hypothesis, the phenomena of the comets as well as of the planets may be solved.

Hooke did not know that Newton, then 23, had already had some small success in this direction.

The straight line had replaced the circle as the natural path of motion. The problem was how to deal mathematically with "some other cause . . . that must bend their motion into that curve."

In 1674 Hooke, in an announcement to the Royal Society, went further:

> All celestial bodies have an attraction towards their own centers, whereby they attract not only their own parts but also other celestial bodies that are within the sphere of their

activity .... All bodies that are put into direct simple motion will so continue to move forward in a straight line till they are, by some other effectual powers, deflected and bent into a motion describing a circle, ellipse, or some other more compound curve .... These attractive powers are much more powerful in operating by how much the nearer the body wrought upon is to their own centers .... It is a notion which if fully prosecuted as it ought to be, will mightily assist the astronomer to reduce all the celestial motions to a certain rule ....

Trying to interest Newton in the question, Hooke wrote on November 24, 1679: "I shall take it as a great favor if ... you will let me know your thoughts of that of compounding the celestial motion of planets of a direct motion by the tangent and an attractive motion toward the central body." But four days later, Newton replied:

... my affection to philosophy [science] being worn out, so that I am almost as little concerned about it as one tradesman uses to be about another man's trade or a country-man about learning, I must acknowledge myself averse from spending that time in writing about it which I think I can spend otherwise more to my own content and the good of others ...

In this same letter Newton, while discussing an experiment concerning the earth's rotation, casually indicated that a stone would fall through the earth in a spiral path. In his reply of December 9, Hooke asserted that the path would be an ellipse. In a letter to Newton, January 17, 1680, Hooke returned to the problem of planetary motion:

... It now remains to know the properties of a curved line (not circular ...) made by a central attractive power which makes the velocities of descent from the tangent line or equal straight motion at all distances in a duplicate proportion to the distances recip-rocally taken. I doubt not that by your excellent method you will easily find out what that curve must be, and its properties, and suggest a physical reason of this proportion.

Hooke succeeded in drawing Newton back to science, as Newton himself admitted in his *Principia,* published in 1687: "I am beholden to him only for the diversion he gave me from my other studies to think on these things and for his dogmaticalness in writing as if he had found the motion in the ellipse, which inclined me to try it." It seems that Newton then obtained a proof—perhaps containing a mistake— that the motion (at least in space) would be elliptical. In 1684, at the request of the astronomer Halley, Newton provided a correct proof. With Halley's encouragement, Newton spent the next year and a half writing the *Principia.*

In the *Principia,* which develops the science of mechanics and applies it to celes-tial motions, Newton begins with two laws:

1. Every body continues in its state of rest, or of uniform motion in a straight line, unless it is compelled to change this state by forces impressed upon it.
2. The change of momentum is proportional to the motive force impressed; and is made in the direction of the straight line in which that force is impressed.

To state these in the language of vectors, let $\mathbf{V}$ be the velocity of the body, $\mathbf{F}$ the impressed force, and m the mass of the body. The first law asserts that $\mathbf{V}$ is constant if **F** is **0**. *Momentum* is defined as $m\,\mathbf{V}$; the second law asserts that

$$\mathbf{F} = \frac{d(m\,\mathbf{V})}{dt}$$

If m is constant, this reduces to

$$\mathbf{F} = m\,\mathbf{A}$$

where **A** is the acceleration vector.

From Kepler's laws Newton deduced his universal *law of gravity:* Any particle P exerts an attractive force on any other particle Q, and the magnitude of the force is proportional to the product of the masses of the particles and inversely proportional to the square of the distance between them. The direction of the force is from Q toward P.

1. Newton's laws and Kepler's laws.

In the *Principia,* Newton not only derived the law of gravity from Kepler's three laws, but in turn obtained Kepler's laws from the law of gravity. His proofs use geometry rather than calculus. (It is indeed possible that Newton did not employ the calculus in obtaining his results, even though he had invented the calculus some 20 years earlier.) We will use vectors to demonstrate the equivalence of Kepler's three laws and the law of gravity.

We first deduce Newton's law of gravity from Kepler's three assertions. Since the acceleration **A** of a given particle is proportional to the force **F** acting on it, it suffices to deal with **A**. Let us call the fixed particle "the sun" and the moving particle "the planet." We wish to prove on the basis of Kepler's laws that **A** is directed toward the sun and that the magnitude of **A** is inversely proportional to the square of the distance from the sun to the planet.

We introduce a polar coordinate system whose pole is at the sun. The planet is at the point (r,θ). Since we wish to show that **A** is directed toward the sun, let us obtain the components of **A** along the radius arm and perpendicular to it. (In Chap. 17 we found the components of **A** along a path and perpendicular to it.) Let **R** be the position vector of the planet. Let A_r be the component of **A** along **R**, and A_θ the component of **A** perpendicular to **R**. Let $\mathbf{U}_r$ be a unit vector in the direction of **R**, and $\mathbf{U}_\theta$ a unit vector perpendicular to $\mathbf{U}_r$ situated $\pi/2$ radians counterclockwise from $\mathbf{U}_r$. We sketch $\mathbf{A}$, A_r, A_θ, $\mathbf{R}$, $\mathbf{U}_r$, and $\mathbf{U}_\theta$:

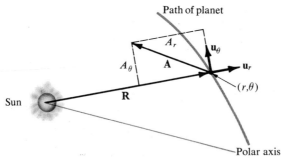

(We shall prove that $A_\theta = 0$ and that $A_r = -k/r^2$, for some fixed positive number k.)

In any case, we have

$$U_r = \overrightarrow{(\cos\theta, \sin\theta)} \qquad \text{and} \qquad U_\theta = \overrightarrow{\left(\cos\left(\theta + \frac{\pi}{2}\right), \sin\left(\theta + \frac{\pi}{2}\right)\right)} = \overrightarrow{(-\sin\theta, \cos\theta)}$$

Thus

(1) $$\frac{dU_r}{d\theta} = U_\theta \qquad \text{and} \qquad \frac{dU_\theta}{d\theta} = -U_r$$

and hence by the chain rule, Theorem 1(c), page 404,

(2) $$\frac{dU_r}{dt} = \frac{d\theta}{dt} U_\theta \qquad \text{and} \qquad \frac{dU_\theta}{dt} = -\frac{d\theta}{dt} U_r$$

Before we examine A we calculate V, the velocity vector of the planet. We begin by expressing R in terms of its components along U_r and U_θ; this expression is simply

(3) $$R = rU_r$$

By Theorem 1(a), page 404, and (1)

(4) $$V = \frac{dR}{dt} = r\frac{dU_r}{dt} + \frac{dr}{dt}U_r = r\frac{d\theta}{dt}U_\theta + \frac{dr}{dt}U_r$$

We have found the components of V along U_r and U_θ. For convenience let us write (4) in the dot notation ($\dot{x}$ denotes the derivative of x with respect to time, $\ddot{x}$ denotes the second derivative with respect to time, and so on):

$$V = r\dot{\theta}\,U_\theta + \dot{r}\,U_r$$

Now, $A = dV/dt$. Differentiating the equation $V = r\dot{\theta}\,U_\theta + \dot{r}\,U_r$ with respect to time t, we obtain

(5) $$A = (\ddot{r} - r\dot{\theta}^2)U_r + (r\ddot{\theta} + 2\dot{r}\dot{\theta})U_\theta$$

from which we immediately conclude that

(6) $$A_r = \ddot{r} - r\dot{\theta}^2 \qquad \text{and} \qquad A_\theta = r\ddot{\theta} + 2\dot{r}\dot{\theta}$$

[Though we may have guessed formula (4) for V, we may be surprised by the $2\dot{r}\dot{\theta}$ in formula (5) for A.] A simple differentiation verifies that

(7) $$A_\theta = \frac{1}{r}\frac{d(r^2\dot{\theta})}{dt}$$

a formula which will be much more useful than the formula for A_θ in (6).

Formulas (6) and (7) hold for any moving object. Now let us see what Kepler's laws imply about A_θ and A_r when the object is a planet.

The second law refers to the area swept out by the radius arm. As the polar angle of the planet changes from α to β, the area swept out by the radius is $\int_\alpha^\beta (r^2/2)\,d\theta$ (see page 183).

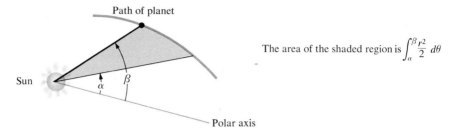

Path of planet

Sun

Polar axis

The area of the shaded region is $\int_{\alpha}^{\beta} \frac{r^2}{2}\, d\theta$

The rate of change of this area with respect to β is simply the integrand, $r^2/2$, evaluated at β (Theorem 3, page 146). Using θ instead of β, we may say that the rate of change of the area swept out by the radius arm with respect to θ is $r^2/2$, evaluated at θ. Thus the rate of change with respect to time of the shaded area in the diagram is, by the chain rule,

$$(8) \qquad\qquad \frac{r^2}{2}\dot\theta$$

Kepler's second law thus implies that $r^2\dot\theta$ is constant with respect to time. A glance at (7) thus shows that this would mean that $A_\theta = 0$. *Thus we see from Kepler's second law that the acceleration* $\mathbf{A}$ *lies along the line joining the sun to the planet.*

With the aid of (6) and Kepler's first two laws, we show that A_r is inversely proportional to r^2. Since $r^2\dot\theta$ is constant for each planet, we have $r^2\dot\theta = h$, or equivalently,

$$(9) \qquad\qquad \dot\theta = \frac{h}{r^2}$$

where h depends on the planet. Since the orbit is an ellipse with the sun at one focus, its equation takes the form (see Appendix A, Eq. (23), page 563).

$$r = \frac{pe}{1 + e\cos\theta}$$

It will simplify our computations to write the equation of the ellipse as

$$(10) \qquad\qquad \frac{1}{r} = \frac{1}{pe} + \frac{\cos\theta}{p}$$

Now we are ready to show that $A_r = \ddot r - r\dot\theta^2$ is negative and inversely proportional to the square of r. First of all, (9) already expresses $\dot\theta$ in terms of r. To express $\ddot r$ in terms of r, we proceed as follows. We have

$$(11) \qquad \dot r = \frac{dr}{dt} = \frac{dr}{d\theta}\dot\theta = \frac{dr}{d\theta}\frac{h}{r^2} = -h\frac{d(1/r)}{d\theta} = \frac{h\sin\theta}{p}$$

and

$$(12) \qquad \ddot r = \frac{d(\dot r)}{dt} = \frac{d(\dot r)}{d\theta}\dot\theta = \frac{h\cos\theta}{p}\frac{h}{r^2}$$

By (10), we have

$$(13) \qquad\qquad \frac{\cos\theta}{p} = \frac{1}{r} - \frac{1}{pe}$$

Combining (12) and (13), we arrive at

(14)
$$\ddot{r} = h\left(\frac{1}{r} - \frac{1}{pe}\right)\frac{h}{r^2} = \frac{h^2}{r^3} - \frac{h^2}{per^2}$$

Thus

(15)
$$A_r = \ddot{r} - r\dot{\theta}^2 = \left(\frac{h^2}{r^3} - \frac{h^2}{per^2}\right) - r\left(\frac{h}{r^2}\right)^2 = -\frac{h^2}{pe}\frac{1}{r^2}$$

From (15), together with $A_\theta = 0$, we conclude that the *acceleration of any given planet is directed toward the sun and has a magnitude inversely proportional to the square of the distance from the planet to the sun.*

All that remains is to show that the constant of proportionality h^2/pe appearing in (15) is the same for all planets. To establish this we use Kepler's third law, which we state as

(16)
$$\frac{T^2}{a^3} = c$$

where T is the time of one revolution, a is one-half the diameter of the elliptic orbit, and c is some fixed number independent of the planet.

Since $r^2\dot{\theta} = h$, we have $(\frac{1}{2})r^2\dot{\theta} = h/2$; thus $h/2$ is the rate at which area is swept out by the radius to the planet. We have, therefore,

$$\underbrace{T}_{\substack{\text{Time to}\\\text{orbit sun}}} \qquad \underbrace{\frac{h}{2}}_{\substack{\text{Rate at which}\\\text{area is swept}\\\text{out}}} = \underbrace{\pi a b}_{\text{Area of ellipse}}$$

and so

(17)
$$h = \frac{2\pi ab}{T}$$

where b is the semi-minor axis of the orbit. We indicate p, e, a, and b in a diagram and recall their relations, which are established in Appendix A, page 563:

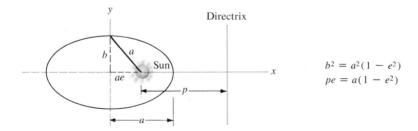

$$b^2 = a^2(1 - e^2)$$
$$pe = a(1 - e^2)$$

Using (17) and the relations $b^2 = a^2(1 - e^2)$ and $pe = a(1 - e^2)$, we obtain

(18)
$$\frac{h^2}{pe} = \left(\frac{2\pi ab}{T}\right)^2\frac{1}{pe} = \frac{4\pi^2 a^2 b^2}{T^2}\frac{1}{pe} = \frac{4\pi^2}{T^2}\frac{a^2 a^2(1 - e^2)}{a(1 - e^2)} = 4\pi^2\frac{a^3}{T^2}$$

From (15), (16), and (18) it follows that

(19) $$A_r = -\frac{4\pi^2 a^3}{T^2}\frac{1}{r^2} = -\frac{4\pi^2}{c}\frac{1}{r^2}$$

where c is the same for all planets. In other words, (19) assures us that A_r for any planet is of the form $-k/r^2$, where k is independent of the planet. Combining this with the equation $\mathbf{F} = m\mathbf{A}$, we arrive at Newton's law of gravity.

We have completed only half of the task. We next obtain Kepler's three laws from Newton's law of gravity and thus, as Hooke desired, "reduce all the celestial motions to a certain rule." Newton's law may be stated in terms of $\mathbf{A}$ as

$$A_\theta = 0 \qquad A_r = -\frac{k}{r^2}$$

where k is a constant independent of the planet. From $A_\theta = 0$ and (7), it follows that the rate at which the area is swept out is constant. This is Kepler's second law.

We next obtain Kepler's first law, which asserts that the path of a planet is an ellipse. We have

(20) $$A_r = \ddot{r} - r\dot{\theta}^2 = -\frac{k}{r^2}$$

and

(21) $$r^2\dot{\theta} = h$$

where h is a constant. From (20) and (21) we will obtain an equation linking r to θ by first expressing $\ddot{r}$ in (20) in terms of $dr/d\theta$ and $d^2r/d\theta^2$.

We have

(22) $$\dot{r} = \frac{dr}{dt} = \frac{dr}{d\theta}\frac{d\theta}{dt} = \frac{dr}{d\theta}\frac{h}{r^2}$$

If we let $u = 1/r$, then (22) takes the simpler form

(23) $$\dot{r} = -h\frac{du}{d\theta}$$

Then

(24) $$\ddot{r} = \frac{d\dot{r}}{dt} = \frac{d(-h\,du/d\theta)}{d\theta}\frac{d\theta}{dt} = -h\frac{d^2u}{d\theta^2}\frac{h}{r^2} = -h^2u^2\frac{d^2u}{d\theta^2}$$

Equation (20) becomes, in view of (21) and (24),

(25) $$-h^2u^2\frac{d^2u}{d\theta^2} - r\left(\frac{h}{r^2}\right)^2 = -\frac{k}{r^2}$$

Since $u = \dfrac{1}{r}$, (25) yields $\qquad -h^2u^2\dfrac{d^2u}{d\theta^2} - h^2u^3 = -ku^2$

Hence $$h^2\left(\frac{d^2u}{d\theta^2} + u\right) = k$$

or

(26) $$\frac{d^2u}{d\theta^2} + u = \frac{k}{h^2}$$

which we rewrite as

(27)
$$\frac{d^2[u - (k/h^2)]}{d\theta^2} + \left(u - \frac{k}{h^2}\right) = 0$$

Thus $u - k/h^2$ equals the negative of its second derivative.

The most general function having this property is $c_1 \cos \theta + c_2 \sin \theta$, where c_1 and c_2 are constants (see Example 3, page 340). With the aid of trigonometry such a function can be expressed as $c \cos (\theta - B)$ for some constants c and B. Thus we have

$$u - \frac{k}{h^2} = c \cos (\theta - B)$$

or
$$\frac{1}{r} = u = \frac{k}{h^2} + c \cos (\theta - B) = \frac{k + ch^2 \cos (\theta - B)}{h^2}$$

or
$$r = \frac{h^2}{k + ch^2 \cos (\theta - B)}$$

and finally

(28)
$$r = \frac{h^2/k}{1 + (ch^2/k) \cos (\theta - B)}$$

As shown in Appendix A, (28) describes an ellipse, parabola, or hyperbola having a focus at the pole of the polar coordinate system. *Since the planets have bounded paths, they must move in elliptical orbits with the sun at one focus.* This is Kepler's first law.

Finally we obtain Kepler's third law, which asserts that T^2/a^3 is constant. We saw that if a planet moves in an ellipse and if $A_\theta = 0$, then

(19)
$$A_r = -4\pi^2 \frac{a^3}{T^2} \frac{1}{r^2}$$

But we are now assuming that there is a number k independent of the planet, such that

(29)
$$A_r = \frac{-k}{r^2}$$

Comparison of (19) and (29) shows that a^3/T^2 is the same for all planets. This is Kepler's third law. *We have obtained the three laws of Kepler from Newton's law.*

2. The gravitational attraction of a homogeneous sphere. In our reasoning we have assumed that the sun and the planets are points; since their dimensions are small relative to the distance separating them, this assumption has not disturbed us. However, when we are concerned with objects that are near each other, we cannot replace them with point-masses without justifying such a bold step. Newton ran into this problem when he tried to show that the law of gravity applies even to the earth and objects on its surface. In a letter to Halley in 1686, Newton touched on this difficulty:

I am almost confident by circumstances that Sir Cristopher Wren knew the duplicate proportion when I gave him a visit (1676).... I never extended the duplicate proportion lower than to the superficies of the earth and before a certain demonstration I found the last year have suspected it did not reach accurately enough down so low; and therefore in the doctrine of projectiles never used it.

The result to which Newton was referring is that a homogeneous sphere attracts as if all its mass were concentrated at its center. We shall obtain this result, using the calculus.

Consider a sphere S whose mass is M and whose radius is s. Let a point-mass of mass m be located at a distance H from the center of the sphere. If we rotated the sphere about the line through the particle and the center of the sphere, we would simultaneously rotate the vector representing the force of attraction of the sphere. Since the sphere is homogeneous, this rotated vector would be the same as the original vector. Thus we may assume that the force of attraction of the sphere on the point-mass is directed toward the center of the sphere. (For a mathematical demonstration, see Exercise 13.)

If all the mass of the sphere were at its center, then the gravitational attraction exerted by the sphere on the particle would have a magnitude

$$\frac{G M m}{H^2}$$

where G is a universal constant. We show that this is the same as the attraction of the uniform sphere.

Let us introduce a spherical coordinate system, whose origin is at the center of the sphere. We may assume, without loss of generality, that the positive vertical axis passes through the particle. We shall let x denote the distance from a typical point P in the sphere to the point-mass, and let α be the angle from the vertical axis to a typical line through the point-mass.

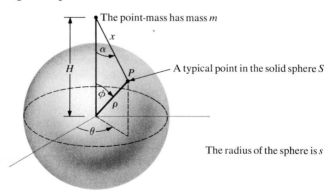

Consider the mass ΔM of that part of the sphere in a small region R of volume ΔV. Let P be a point in R. By the law of gravity, the magnitude of the attraction of the mass ΔM on the point-mass m is approximately

(30)
$$\frac{Gm\,\Delta M}{x^2}$$

Since the density of the sphere is $M/[(\tfrac{4}{3})\,\pi s^3]$, the mass ΔM is $M\,\Delta V/[(\tfrac{4}{3})\,\pi s^3]$. The vertical component of the force exerted by the mass ΔM is

(31)
$$-\frac{Gm\,\Delta M}{x^2}\cos\alpha = -\frac{GmM\cos\alpha}{(\tfrac{4}{3})\,\pi s^3 x^2}\,\Delta V$$

(The negative sign records that ΔM pulls downward on the point-mass.) Thus the magnitude of the total force exerted by the sphere on the point-mass is

(32)
$$\int_s \frac{GmM\cos\alpha}{(\tfrac{4}{3})\,\pi s^3 x^2}\,dV = \frac{GmM}{(\tfrac{4}{3})\,\pi s^3}\int_s \frac{\cos\alpha}{x^2}\,dV$$

We evaluate (32) by a repeated integral in spherical coordinates. We have

(33)
$$\int_s \frac{\cos\alpha}{x^2}\,dV = \int_0^s \left[\int_0^\pi \left(\int_0^{2\pi}\frac{\cos\alpha}{x^2}\,\rho^2\sin\phi\,d\theta\right)d\phi\right]d\rho$$

Since $(\rho^2\cos\alpha\sin\phi)/x^2$ is independent of θ, the inner definite integral in (33) has the value

$$\frac{2\pi\,\rho^2\cos\alpha\sin\phi}{x^2}$$

We next face

(34)
$$\int_0^\pi 2\pi\,\frac{\rho^2\cos\alpha\sin\phi}{x^2}\,d\phi$$

which is easier to compute if we use x, rather than ϕ, as the variable of integration.

Note in the diagram of the sphere S that as ϕ ranges from 0 to π, x ranges from $H-\rho$ to $H+\rho$. Also, by the law of cosines,

(35)
$$x^2 = \rho^2 + H^2 - 2\rho H\cos\phi$$

hence
$$2x\,dx = 2\rho H\sin\phi\,d\phi$$

and

(36)
$$\sin\phi\,d\phi = \frac{x\,dx}{\rho H}$$

To express $\cos\alpha$ in terms of x we use the relation

$$x\cos\alpha + \rho\cos\phi = H$$

from which we obtain

(37)
$$\cos\alpha = \frac{H-\rho\cos\phi}{x}$$

But, by (35),

(38)
$$\rho\cos\phi = \frac{\rho^2 + H^2 - x^2}{2H}$$

From (37) and (38) it follows that

(39)
$$\cos \alpha = \frac{H^2 + x^2 - \rho^2}{2Hx}.$$

Using (34), (36), and (39), we obtain

$$\int_0^\pi \frac{2\pi \rho^2 \cos \alpha \sin \phi}{x^2} \, d\phi = 2\pi\rho^2 \int_{H-\rho}^{H+\rho} \frac{H^2 + x^2 - \rho^2}{(2Hx)x^2} \frac{x \, dx}{\rho H}$$

which is simply

$$\frac{\pi\rho}{H^2} \int_{H-\rho}^{H+\rho} \left(\frac{H^2 - \rho^2}{x^2} + 1 \right) dx = \frac{\pi\rho}{H^2} (4\rho) = \frac{4\pi\rho^2}{H^2}$$

To complete the computation of the repeated integral in (33), we note that

$$\int_0^s \frac{4\pi\rho^2}{H^2} \, d\rho = \frac{4\pi}{H^2} \int_0^s \rho^2 \, d\rho = \frac{4\pi s^3}{3H^2}$$

Thus the attractive force (32) is

(40)
$$\left(\frac{GmM}{(\frac{4}{3}) \pi s^3} \right) \left(\frac{4\pi s^3}{3H^2} \right) = \frac{GmM}{H^2}$$

This result, GmM/H^2, is the force exerted on the point-mass by a mass M located at the center of the sphere. *A homogeneous sphere attracts as if all its mass were concentrated at its center.* This is what we wished to show.

Newton's contribution is the model for the application of mathematics; with one assumption he explained motion on earth and in the heavens. To be more precise, he explained everything except what gravity *is* and *why* it diminishes as the inverse square, mysteries that may always be with us. The mathematician builds a logical structure that simulates the phenomena of the world. He humbly accepts the existence of the natural phenomena and goes on from there; he does not wait until he has answers to the questions: What is it? Why does it behave as it does?

Newton realized that this way of thinking represented a break with tradition and in the *Principia* remarked:

. . . we do not know in what manner the ancients explained . . . how the planets came to be retained . . . into regular revolutions in curvilinear orbits. Probably it was to give some sort of satisfaction to this difficulty that solid orbs had been introduced.

The later philosophers pretend to account for it either by the action of certain vortices, as Kepler and Descartes; or by some other principle of impulse or attraction, as Borelli, Hooke, and others of our nation.

But our purpose is only to trace out the quantity and properties of this force from the phenomena, and to apply what we discover in some simple cases as principles, by which, in a mathematical way, we may estimate the effects thereof in more involved cases . . .

We said, *in a mathematical way*, to avoid all questions about the nature or quality of this force, which we would not be understood to determine by any hypothesis.

EXERCISES

1. (a) Explain how you might have guessed the two components of $\mathbf{V}$ in (4).

   (b) Explain how you might have guessed that the $\ddot{r}$, $-\dot{r}(\dot{\theta})^2$, and $r\ddot{\theta}$ are included in formula (5) for $\mathbf{A}$.

   (c) Obtain (5) from (4).

2. Prove that formula (7) for A_θ is valid.

3. Show that if $v = c_1 \cos \theta + c_2 \sin \theta$, then $d^2v/d\theta^2 = -v$.

4. (a) Show that if $c_1{}^2 + c_2{}^2 = 1$, then $c_1 \cos \theta + c_2 \sin \theta$ is identically equal to $\cos(\theta - B)$ for a suitable B.

   (b) Show that if c_1 and c_2 are any constants, then for a suitable B, $c_1 \cos \theta + c_2 \sin \theta = \sqrt{c_1{}^2 + c_2{}^2} \cos(\theta - B)$.

5. Without introducing $u = 1/r$, try to obtain a relation between r and θ, beginning with (20) and (21).

6. A space capsule orbits the earth in 90 minutes; the moon, 240,000 miles away, orbits in 28 days. Assuming that both orbits are circles, find the altitude of the capsule. (The earth's diameter is 7,930 miles.)   (Answer: 134 miles)

7. Which takes longer to orbit the earth, a satellite whose minimum altitude is 200 miles and maximum altitude 600 miles, or a satellite whose minimum altitude is 150 miles and maximum altitude 700 miles?

8. Fill in this table with the aid of Kepler's third law:

Satellite	Minimum height, miles	Maximum height, miles	Orbit time, minutes
Sputnik I	145	560	96
Vanguard	405	2,466	

(The earth's diameter is 7,930 miles.) Use a $\log_{10} x$ table for computations.

9. The density of the earth varies from three times that of water at the surface to 17 times that of water at the core, but depends only on the distance from the center. Nevertheless, it attracts as if all its mass were located at its center, as we sketch.

   (a) Let a sphere of radius s have a density $f(P)$ which, in spherical coordinates whose origin is at the center of the earth, depends only on ρ; say $f(P) = g(\rho)$. Show that the mass of the sphere is $4\pi \int_0^s \rho^2 g(\rho)\, d\rho$.

   (b) Show that such a sphere attracts as if all its mass were concentrated at its center.

10. Show that a homogeneous spherical shell bounded by $\rho = a$ and $\rho = b$ attracts a point-mass outside it as if all its mass were concentrated at the center of the shell.

11. Show that the shell in Exercise 10 exerts no force on a particle within it. (Hint: the only difference between this case and the one we presented in Sec. 2 lies in the limits of integration on x and on ρ.)

12. A particle is dropped into a tunnel dug straight through the earth, which we take to be homogeneous. Show on the basis of Exercise 11 that it is accelerated toward the center of the earth by a force which is directed toward the center and whose magnitude is *proportional to the distance* from the particle to the center. (This is similar to Hooke's law for a force exerted by a stretched spring.) Newton proved that a particle

subject to such a force moves in an ellipse whose center coincides with the origin of the force; this settled the question Hooke raised in his letter to Newton in 1679 (see also Exercise 17).

13. We used physical intuition to show that a sphere attracts an external particle toward its center. Prove this mathematically, expressing the horizontal components of the attractive force as definite integrals over S, and showing that their values are 0.

14. If we restrict our attention to "planets" moving in circular orbits with constant speed, the relation between Kepler's third law and the magnitude of the gravitational force is easier to see than it was in the general case we treated. As we saw on page 410 (and as Huyghens had announced in 1673 in his study of the pendulum), $|A_r| = v^2/r$. Assume that the gravitational force is proportional to $1/r^n$, and show that $n = 2$ if and only if Kepler's third law holds. Newton in 1665 or 1666, and Halley before 1684, had noticed this.

15. (a) Which of Kepler's laws is related to A_θ?
    (b) Which of Kepler's laws are needed to show that A_r is of the form $-k/r^2$?
    (c) Which of Kepler's laws shows that k in (b) is independent of the planet?

□ □ □

16. (a) Let k be a positive number. Show that the function $w = a_1 \cos \sqrt{kt} + a_2 \sin \sqrt{kt}$ satisfies the differential equation $\ddot{w} = -kw$.
    (b) Using the technique of Example 3, page 340, show that no other function satisfies the equation.

17. Assume that the gravitational force on a particle is proportional to the distance between the particle and a mass at $(0,0)$ in a two-dimensional rectangular coordinate system. (For instance, consider Exercise 12.) We have $\mathbf{A} = -k\mathbf{R}$, where $\mathbf{R}$ is the position vector of the particle and k is a positive constant. At time $t = 0$ a particle is on the x axis and is moving vertically.
    (a) Show that it travels in an ellipse whose center is at $(0,0)$.
    (b) Show that the time for one orbit is independent of the initial position and the speed. (Hint: Consider the rectangular components, A_x and A_y, of $\mathbf{A}$, and recall Exercise 16.)

18. At a certain instant a manned space capsule is traveling with a speed v_0 in a direction perpendicular to the radius arm extending from the capsule to the center of the earth. Let v_* be the speed it would have if it were in a circular orbit. Show that the capsule orbits in an ellipse if $v_* < v_0 < \sqrt{2}v_*$, in a parabola if $v_0 = \sqrt{2}v_*$, and in a hyperbola if $v_0 > \sqrt{2}v_*$. Suggestions: Place the pole of a polar coordinate system at the center of the earth, and its axis through the capsule. Thus B in Eq. (28) is 0 or π. Since $v_0 > v_*$, the earth occupies the nearer focus of the conic, and $B = 0$. Let the capsule initially have polar coordinates $(r_0,0)$.
    (a) Why is ch^2/k in Eq. (28) the eccentricity of the orbit?
    (b) Using (28), show that the eccentricity $e = (h^2/kr_0) - 1$.
    (c) Show that $h = r_0v_0$, and thus $e = (r_0v_0^2/k) - 1$.
    (d) Show that $(v_*)^2/r_0 = k/r_0^2$, and thus $e = (v_0/v_*)^2 - 1$.
    (e) From (d) deduce that for $v_* < v_0 < \sqrt{2}v_*$ the orbit is an ellipse, for $v_0 = \sqrt{2}v_*$ a parabola, and for $v_0 > \sqrt{2}v_*$ a hyperbola.
    (f) To deal with $v_0 < v_*$, determine why B must equal π. Show that in this case the eccentricity is $1 - (v_0/v_*)^2$, and that the orbit is an ellipse.
    (g) Draw the various orbits relative to the same axes.

Clearly a space maneuver, such as a rendezvous, involves unique problems. One capsule cannot "catch up" with another in the same orbit just by speeding up. When a capsule suddenly accelerates, it changes its orbit, as this exercise shows.

19. The acceleration at the earth's surface due to the earth's gravitational pull is 32 feet per second per second. Assume that the orbit of the moon around the earth is a circle of radius 240,000 miles. Determine how long it takes the moon to revolve once around the earth.

20. Assume that the path of a planet is along the spiral $r = ae^{k\theta}$. Show that in this case the gravitational pull of the sun is inversely proportional to r^3. (Begin with the equations $A_r = \ddot{r} - r\dot{\theta}^2$ and $r^2\dot{\theta} = h$.) This result is in the *Principia*, where Newton explores many hypothetical gravities whose magnitudes are not inversely proportional to the square of the distance (see also Exercise 21).

21. Let $r = f(\theta)$ be the polar equation of a curve in the plane such that the angle between the radius vector and the tangent line to the curve at the end of the radius is constant. Show that $f(\theta) = ae^{k\theta}$ for suitable constants a and k. (Hint: First show that the little memory device for polar coordinates, page 209, suggests that the tangent of the angle between the radius and the tangent line is $r/(dr/d\theta)$. (See Exercise 20.)

REFERENCES

1. Russell, J. L.: Kepler's Laws of Planetary Motion: 1609–1666, *Brit. J. Hist. Sci.*, **2**: 1–24 (1964). (This well-documented work describes in detail the gradual acceptance of Kepler's ideas in Europe.)

2. Newton, I.: "Mathematical Principles," University of California Press, Berkeley, Calif., 1947. (Even a casual reading of the Propositions will convey the immensity of Newton's contribution.)

3. "The Correspondence of Isaac Newton," H. W. Turnbull (ed.), Cambridge University Press, London, 1960. (See in particular pp. 297–313 of volume 2. This includes letters of Hooke to Newton.)

4. Koestler, A.: "The Watershed," Anchor Books, Doubleday, Garden City, N.Y., 1960. (This paperback presents a very readable personal and scientific biography of Kepler.)

5. Hall, A. R.: "The Scientific Revolution 1400–1800," McKay, New York, 1962. (See pp. 258–276 for the history of the idea of gravity from Kepler to Newton.)

6. Herivel, J. W.: "The Background of Newton's Principia," Oxford University Press, London, 1966. (This book is a study of the development of Newton's thinking on dynamics.)

APPENDIX A

Analytic geometry

IN this appendix we develop the analytic geometry used in the text. The results in the concluding portion (the conic sections in polar coordinates) are needed only in Chap. 26.

Analytic geometry in two dimensions. Analytic geometry deals algebraically with geometric ideas and problems. We introduce a number scale on a line, assuming a correspondence between points on the line and the real numbers.

 Point *P* is described by the number *x*

We select two such lines in the plane, perpendicular to each other, and each furnished with a number scale. Let us place the 0 of each line at the intersection of the two lines and make their number scales equal. The horizontal line is called the *x* axis; the vertical line is called the *y* axis. Their intersection is called the *origin.*

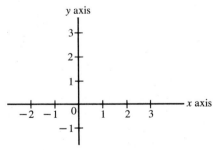

The basis of analytic geometry in the plane is the observation that each point P in the plane can be described, with the aid of the perpendicular lines introduced above, by two real numbers. Indeed the vertical line through a point *P* cuts the

547

x axis at a point corresponding to some number x, and the horizontal line through P cuts the y axis at a point corresponding to some number y. We call x the x *coordinate* or *abscissa* of P and y the y *coordinate* or *ordinate* of P. We write $P = (x,y)$; x and y are the *rectangular* coordinates of P.

Example 1. This figure shows the coordinates of a few points in the plane.

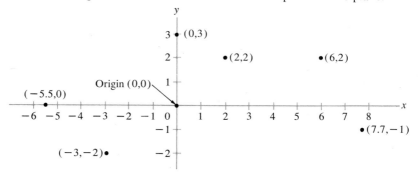

Observe that a point $(x,0)$ lies on the x axis, and a point $(0,y)$ lies on the y axis.

Having translated the fundamental notion "point" into the language of numbers, we shall have little trouble in describing such notions as "circle," "straight line," and "distance between two points" algebraically.

The distance formula. To find the distance d between $P_1 = (x_1,y_1)$ and $P_2 = (x_2,y_2)$ we make use of the Pythagorean theorem. We introduce a right triangle whose hypotenuse has the ends P_1 and P_2 and whose legs are parallel to the axes.

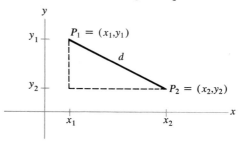

The horizontal leg of the triangle has length $x_1 - x_2$ or $-(x_1 - x_2)$, depending on whether $x_1 \geqslant x_2$ or $x_1 \leqslant x_2$. Similarly, the vertical leg has length $y_1 - y_2$ or $-(y_1 - y_2)$. In either case, the Pythagorean theorem implies that

$$d^2 = (x_1 - x_2)^2 + (y_1 - y_2)^2$$

Thus the distance between the points (x_1,y_1) and (x_2,y_2) is

(1) $$d = \sqrt{(x_1 - x_2)^2 + (y_1 - y_2)^2}$$

With the aid of the distance formula, we shall translate the geometric notion "circle" into an algebraic equation.

Example 2 (Circles). We describe algebraically the circle C whose radius is 3 and whose center is (1,2). When does the point $P = (x,y)$ lie on this circle C? When the distance from P to (1,2) is equal to the radius. That is, (x,y) is on C if and only if

$$\sqrt{(x-1)^2 + (y-2)^2} = 3$$

or equivalently, $\qquad\qquad (x-1)^2 + (y-2)^2 = 9$

Thus the algebraic analog of the circle whose center is (1,2) and whose radius is 3 is the equation $(x-1)^2 + (y-2)^2 = 9$, which may also be written as $x^2 + y^2 = 2x + 4y + 4$.

In a similar manner we may show that the circle whose radius is r and whose center is the origin has the equation $x^2 + y^2 = r^2$. In general, the circle with its center at (a,b) and with radius r has the equation $(x-a)^2 + (y-b)^2 = r^2$.

The circle of radius r and center (0,0) is called the *graph* of the equation $x^2 + y^2 = r^2$. More generally, the graph of an equation is the set of all points (x,y) whose coordinates satisfy the equation. For instance, the graph of the equation $x = 1$ consists of all points in the plane whose x coordinate is 1; in this case the graph is a straight line parallel to the y axis.

Line and slope. The algebraic treatment of (straight) lines is based on the notion of the "slope of a line." Let L be a line inclined at an angle θ (measured counterclockwise) from the positive x axis. If L is not parallel to the y axis, $\tan \theta$ is defined and is called the *slope* of L. Observe that parallel lines have equal slopes. A horizontal line has slope 0.

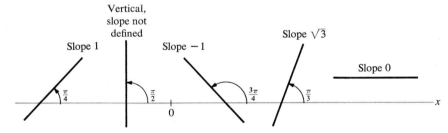

Example 3. We find the slope of the line through the points $(1,-1)$ and $(3,4)$. We introduce a right triangle whose legs are parallel to the axes and whose hypotenuse has the end points $(1,-1)$ and $(3,4)$. Then the angle of inclination of the line through $(1,-1)$ and $(3,4)$ is the angle θ in this diagram:

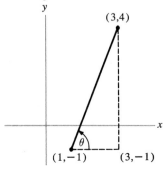

Now, tan θ = (opposite side)/(adjacent side) = $[4 - (-1)]/(3 - 1)$ = $\frac{5}{2}$. Hence the slope is $\frac{5}{2}$ = 2.5.

The argument used in Example 3 shows that *the slope of the line through the points (x_1,y_1) and (x_2,y_2) is*

$$(2) \qquad\qquad \frac{y_2 - y_1}{x_2 - x_1}$$

Example 4.   Are the points $(2,1)$, $(3,5)$, and $(4,8)$ colinear? In other words, is the line through $(2,1)$ and $(3,5)$ the same as the line through $(2,1)$ and $(4,8)$? To answer this question we compute the slopes of the two lines. The first line has slope $(5 - 1)/(3 - 2) = \frac{4}{1} = 4$. The second line has slope $(8 - 1)/(4 - 2) = \frac{7}{2} = 3.5$. Since the lines have different slopes, the three points are not colinear.

The argument used in Example 4 shows that *the three points (x_1,y_1), (x_2,y_2), and (x_3,y_3) are colinear if and only if*

$$(3) \qquad\qquad \frac{y_2 - y_1}{x_2 - x_1} = \frac{y_3 - y_1}{x_3 - x_1}$$

or equivalently,

$$\frac{y_2 - y_1}{x_2 - x_1} = \frac{y_3 - y_2}{x_3 - x_2}$$

Now that we have the algebraic criterion for colinearity, we are in a position to obtain the algebraic analog of the line through two given points.

When does the point (x,y) lie on the line through (x_1,y_1) and (x_2,y_2)? When (x_1,y_1), (x_2,y_2), and (x,y) are colinear, that is, when

$$(4) \qquad\qquad \frac{y - y_1}{x - x_1} = \frac{y_2 - y_1}{x_2 - x_1}$$

Thus (4) is the algebraic analog of a line. The next example illustrates its use.

Example 5.   We find the equation of the line through $(1,5)$ and $(2,4)$. In this case (x,y) is on the line if and only if

$$\frac{y - 5}{x - 1} = \frac{4 - 5}{2 - 1}$$

or equivalently,

$$\frac{y - 5}{x - 1} = \frac{-1}{1} = -1$$

A little algebra changes this to $y - 5 = (-1)(x - 1) = -x + 1$ and finally to $x + y - 6 = 0$.

Example 6.   We find the equation of the line of slope m that passes through $(0,b)$, a point on the y axis. When does (x,y) lie on this line? When the slope of the line through $(0,b)$ and (x,y) is m, that is, when

$$\frac{y - b}{x - 0} = m$$

or equivalently,

$$(5) \qquad\qquad y = mx + b$$

Note that if we are given the slope m and the y intercept b of a line, we may write its equation immediately in the form (5).

It can be shown that any line has an equation of the form $Ax + By + C = 0$, where A, B, and C are suitable numbers.

EXERCISES

1. (a) Graph the points (5,8) and $(-7,3)$.
   (b) Using your sketch, determine the distance between them.
   (c) Using the distance formula (1), find the distance between them.
                                                    [Answer: (c) 13]
2. (a) Find the equation of the circle of radius 5 whose center is $(1,-1)$.
   (b) Sketch the circle.
   (c) Does (4.5,2.5) lie on this circle? [Decide on the basis of your sketch and on the basis of (a).]
3. Sketch the circle whose equation is $x^2 + y^2 = 1$.
4. (a) Sketch the circle whose equation is $(x - 2)^2 + (y - 1)^2 = 16$.
   (b) Sketch the circle whose equation is $x^2 + y^2 = 6x + 8y + 61$. [Hint: For (b), use algebra to rewrite the equation in the form $(x - a)^2 + (y - b)^2 = r^2$.]
5. (a) Graph the three points (1,2), (5,3), and (18,6).
   (b) Do they seem to be colinear?
   (c) Using Eq. (3), determine whether they are colinear.
6. Prove that the equation of a straight line can be put into the form $Ax + By + C = 0$, where A, B, and C are numbers. (Hint: Consider vertical lines separately from other lines.)
7. (a) Find an equation of the line passing through (2,5) and having slope $-\frac{9}{2}$.
   (b) Sketch this line.
   (c) Does the point (4,2) lie on this line?
8. (a) Draw the graph of the equation $y = x$.
   (b) Draw the graph of $y = -x$.
9. (a) Find three points that satisfy the equation $2x - 3y + 5 = 0$.
   (b) Draw these points.
   (c) Do the points drawn in (b) seem to be colinear?
   (d) Prove that they are colinear, using Eq. (3).
10. What equation must x and y satisfy if the point (x,y) is to be on the line of slope m through the point (x_1,y_1)?
11. (a) Graph at least four points (x,y) such that $y = x^2$.
    (b) Sketch the set of all points (x,y) such that $y = x^2$.
12. Repeat Exercise 11, for $y = x^2 + 3$.
13. Repeat Exercise 11, for $y = 3x^2$.
14. Repeat Exercise 11, for $xy = 1$.

Analytic geometry in three dimensions. The analytic geometry of three-dimensional space is based on the selection of three mutually perpendicular lines. Two are x and y axes in the two-dimensional plane; the third is called the z axis.

They are usually arranged as in this diagram.

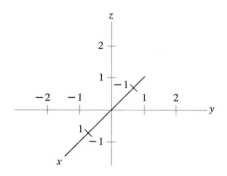

The plane of y and z is in the page, and the positive portion of the x axis is aimed upward from the plane of the page. Note that we have rotated the x and y axes $90°$ from their position described on page 547. A point P in space has three coordinates x, y, and z, determined as follows. Call the plane through the x and y axes the xy plane. Then point P in space is directly above (or below) a point (x,y) in the xy plane. The plane through P parallel to the xy plane cuts the z axis at a point whose coordinate is z. Then P is denoted (x,y,z). The set of points P in space whose coordinates satisfy a certain equation is (as in the plane) called the graph of the equation.

Example 7. We examine those points (x,y,z) such that $z = x + 2y + 1$. For instance, if $x = 0$ and $y = 0$, then $z = 0 + 2 \cdot 0 + 1 = 1$. Thus $(0,0,1)$ satisfies the equation $z = x + 2y + 1$. If $x = -2$ and $y = 1$, then $z = -2 + 2 \cdot (-1) + 1 = 1$. Hence $(-2,1,1)$ satisfies $z = x + 2y + 1$. Similarly $(0,1,3)$ satisfies $z = x + 2y + 1$. Let us graph these three points:

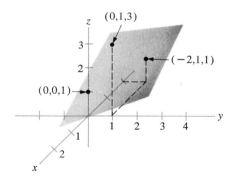

For every point (x,y) in the xy plane, there is a unique point (x,y,z) directly above (or below) it that satisfies the equation $z = x + 2y + 1$. It is shown in Chap. 16, page 388, that this set is a plane. (More generally, the graph of $Ax + By + Cz + D = 0$ is a plane.)

The distance d between $P_1 = (x_1,y_1,z_1)$ and $P_2 = (x_2,y_2,z_2)$ can be determined by applying the Pythagorean theorem twice. We consider the rectangular box whose edges are parallel to the x, y, and z axes and in which P_1 and P_2 are opposite vertices. In it we focus our attention on the right triangle whose vertices are P_1, P_2, and the point (x_2, y_2, z_1).

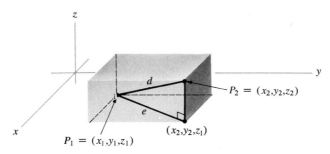

Letting e be the distance from P_1 to (x_2, y_2, z_1), we see that

$$d^2 = e^2 + (z_2 - z_1)^2$$

and, since the line joining P_1 and (x_2, y_2, z_1) lies in the xy plane,

$$e^2 = (x_2 - x_1)^2 + (y_2 - y_1)^2$$

Thus $\qquad\qquad d^2 = (x_2 - x_1)^2 + (y_2 - y_1)^2 + (z_2 - z_1)^2$

or

(6) $\qquad\qquad d = \sqrt{(x_2 - x_1)^2 + (y_2 - y_1)^2 + (z_2 - z_1)^2}$

a formula for the distance between points in space.

Example 8. What algebraic equation must x, y, and z satisfy if the point (x,y,z) is on the surface of the sphere of radius 3 whose center is $(0,0,0)$? Since the distance between the points (x,y,z) and $(0,0,0)$ is

$$\sqrt{(x - 0)^2 + (y - 0)^2 + (z - 0)^2} = \sqrt{x^2 + y^2 + z^2}$$

we must have $\qquad\qquad \sqrt{x^2 + y^2 + z^2} = 3$

or equivalently, $\qquad\qquad x^2 + y^2 + z^2 = 9$

Note the similarity of this example to Example 2.

EXERCISES

15. The equation $x + 2y + 3z = 6$ describes a plane.
    (a) Find at least three points on this plane.
    (b) Graph the three points.
    (c) With the aid of (b), graph the plane.
    (d) Where does the plane cut the x axis? The y axis? The z axis?
16. (a) Graph at least four points (x,y,z) such that $z = x^2 + y^2$.
    (b) Show that each plane parallel to the xy plane and above it intersects the graph of $z = x^2 + y^2$ in a circle.
    (c) Sketch the graph of $z = x^2 + y^2$.

17. Describe the graph in space of each of these equations: (*a*) $y = 3$; (*b*) $z = 2$; (*c*) $x = y$; (*d*) $x^2 + y^2 + z^2 = -1$; (*e*) $x^2 + y^2 + z^2 = 5$.
18. Describe the intersection of the graph of $z = xy$ with the planes (*a*) $y = 3$; (*b*) $x = 2$; (*c*) $z = 1$; (*d*) $z = 0$; (*e*) $x = y$.

Polar coordinates.   The rectangular coordinates x and y locate a point P in the plane as the intersection of a vertical line and a horizontal line. Polar coordinates locate a point P as the intersection of a circle and a ray. They are defined as follows.

Select a point in the plane and a ray emanating from this point. The point is called the *pole*, and the ray the *polar axis*. A point P in the plane lies on a unique circle whose center is the pole, and on a unique ray emanating from the pole. If the circle has radius r and the ray makes an angle θ with the polar axis (measured counterclockwise from the axis), then point P is denoted (r,θ).

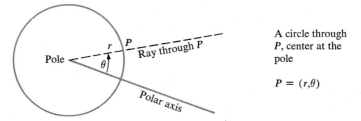

A circle through
P, center at the
pole

$P = (r,\theta)$

Example 9.   It is customary to have the polar axis coincide with the positive x axis, as in this diagram.

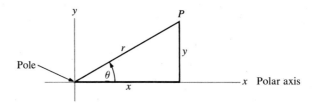

In that case, inspection of the diagram above shows that the following relationships exist between the rectangular and polar coordinates of the point $P = (x,y) = (r,\theta)$:

$$x = r \cos \theta \qquad y = r \sin \theta$$

and
$$r^2 = x^2 + y^2 \qquad \tan \theta = \frac{y}{x}$$

For instance, the point whose rectangular coordinates are $(1,1)$ has polar coordinates $(\sqrt{2},\pi/4)$, or $(\sqrt{2},(\pi/4) + 2\pi)$, or $(\sqrt{2},\pi/4 + 4\pi)$, and so on.

Just as we may graph the set of points (x,y), where x and y satisfy a certain equation, so may we graph the set of points (r,θ), where r and θ satisfy a certain equation. In so doing we may wish to consider negative values for r. How this is done is shown in the next example.

Example 10.   We graph the equation $r = 2\cos\theta$. To do so we make a table, choosing convenient values of θ.

θ	0	$\dfrac{4}{\pi}$	$\dfrac{\pi}{2}$	$\dfrac{\pi}{3}$	$\dfrac{3\pi}{4}$	π	$\dfrac{3\pi}{2}$	2π
$r = 2\cos\theta$	2	$\sqrt{2} = 1.4$	0	1	$-\sqrt{2} = -1.4$	-2	0	2

How shall we interpret, for example, the point for which $\theta = 3\pi/4$ and $r = -1.4$? When r is negative, it is customary to interpret (r,θ) as the point "directly opposite $(-r,\theta)$," that is, the point $(-r, \theta + \pi)$. Thus the point $(r,\theta) = (-1.4, 3\pi/4)$ is graphed as the point $(1.4, 3\pi/4 + \pi)$. We now sketch the eight points listed in the table:

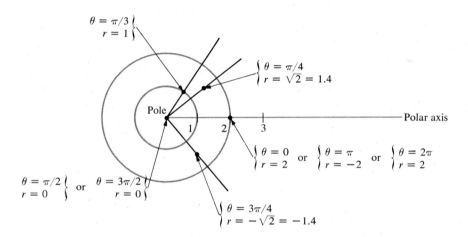

A little geometry and trigonometry show that the complete graph of $r = 2\cos\theta$ is a circle. To see this, recall that an angle inscribed in a semicircle is a right angle, and consider a typical point $P = (r,\theta)$, for $r > 0$, on the circle shown in this diagram.

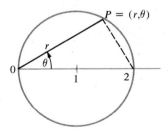

Since $\cos\theta = $ (adjacent side)/(hypotenuse) in the triangle, we have $\cos\theta = r/2$ or $r = 2\cos\theta$. This shows that the graph of $r = 2\cos\theta$ includes the indicated circle. It can be shown in a similar way that any point (r,θ) such that $r = 2\cos\theta$ lies on the circle.

EXERCISES

19. In Example 10 we used the fact that an angle inscribed in a semicircle is a right angle to show that the graph of $r = 2 \cos \theta$ is a circle. Another proof may be obtained by first finding the equation of the graph in rectangular coordinates.

    (a) Using the equations $x = r \cos \theta$ and $y = r \sin \theta$, show that the equation corresponding to $r = 2 \cos \theta$ is $x^2 + y^2 = 2x$. (Hint: First multiply both sides of $r = 2 \cos \theta$ by r.)

    (b) Show that the equation $x^2 + y^2 = 2x$ is equivalent to $(x - 1)^2 + y^2 = 1$, and explain why the graph of $(x - 1)^2 + y^2 = 1$ is a circle.

20. Graph the cardioid $r = 1 + \cos \theta$, using at least eight sample points.

21. Graph the curve $r = 3 + \cos \theta$.

22. Graph the spiral $r = \theta$ for $\theta \geqslant 0$.

23. Graph the circle $r = 4 \sin \theta$.

24. Using the equations $x = r \cos \theta$ and $y = r \sin \theta$, transform the following equations to polar coordinates: (a) $2xy = 1$; (b) $x + y = 1$; (c) $x^2 + y^2 = 2x + 4y$.

25. Using the equations $r = \sqrt{x^2 + y^2}$, $\theta = \tan^{-1}(y/x)$, and $r \cos \theta = x$, $r \sin \theta = y$, transform the following equations to rectangular coordinates: (a) $r = 4 \sin \theta$; (b) $r = e^{\theta}$; (c) $r^2 = \sin 2\theta$. [Hint: In (c) use the identity $\sin 2\theta = 2 \sin \theta \cos \theta$.]

26. (a) Show that the equations $(x^2 + y^2)^2 = 2(x^2 - y^2)$ and $r^2 = 2 \cos 2\theta$ describe the same curve.

    (b) Graph the curve, using the more convenient equation.

Conic sections in rectangular coordinates.   The circle is an example of a *conic section,* that is, the intersection of a plane and the surface of a right circular (double) cone. Depending on the relation between the plane and the (double) cone, the conic section may be an ellipse, a parabola, or a hyperbola. If the plane cuts off only a bounded curve, that curve is an *ellipse.* (Note that a circle is an ellipse.) If the plane is parallel to the edge of the cone, we obtain a *parabola.* If the plane meets both parts of the (double) cone and is not parallel to an edge, we obtain a *hyperbola.*

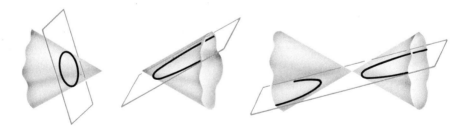

In order to deal with the conic sections quickly, we will employ a different (but equivalent) definition, which involves only the geometry of the plane.

DEFINITION: *Ellipse.*   Let F and F' be points in the plane and let a be a fixed positive number such that $2a$ is greater than the distance between F and F'. A point P in the plane is on the *ellipse* determined by F, F', and $2a$ if and only if the sum of the distances from P to F and from P to F' equals $2a$. Points F and F' are the *foci* of the ellipse.

To construct an ellipse place two tacks in a piece of paper, tie a string of length $2a$ to them, and trace out a curve with a pencil held against the string, keeping the string taut by means of the pencil point. The foci are at the tacks.

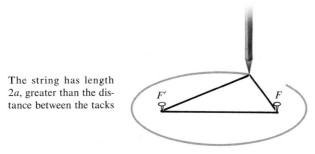

The string has length $2a$, greater than the distance between the tacks

(Note that when $F = F'$ we obtain a circle.)

We found that the equation of a circle is $x^2 + y^2 = r^2$; let us generalize this result by determining the equation of an ellipse. To make the equation as simple as possible, let us introduce the x and y axes in such a way that the x axis contains the foci and that the origin is midway between them. Thus we have $F = (c,0)$ and $F' = (-c,0)$, where $c \geqslant 0$ and $2c < 2a$, and thus $c < a$.

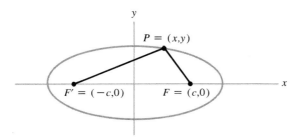

We now translate into algebra the assertion: The sum of the distances from $P = (x,y)$ to $F = (c,0)$ and from P to $F' = (-c,0)$ equals $2a$. Using the distance formula (1), we see that the distance from P to F is $\sqrt{(x - c)^2 + (y - 0)^2}$, and the distance from P to F' is $\sqrt{(x + c)^2 + (y - 0)^2}$. Thus (x,y) is on the ellipse if and only if

(7) $$\sqrt{(x - c)^2 + y^2} + \sqrt{(x + c)^2 + y^2} = 2a$$

Equation (7) is the algebraic condition that (x,y) must satisfy in order to lie on the ellipse. With a little algebra, we will now obtain from (7) an equivalent but much simpler equation.

Taking the left square root in (7) to the right, squaring, and canceling, we obtain

(8) $a^2 - cx = a\sqrt{(x - c)^2 + y^2}$

Squaring both sides of (8) and simplifying removes the radical and yields

(9) $(a^2 - c^2)x^2 + a^2y^2 = a^2(a^2 - c^2)$

or

(10) $\dfrac{x^2}{a^2} + \dfrac{y^2}{a^2 - c^2} = 1$

Since $a^2 - c^2 > 0$, there is a number b such that

(11) $b^2 = a^2 - c^2 \qquad b > 0$

and thus (10) takes the shorter form

(12) $\dfrac{x^2}{a^2} + \dfrac{y^2}{b^2} = 1$

which is equivalent to the cumbersome (7).

If we set $y = 0$ in (12), we obtain $x = a$ or $-a$; if we set $x = 0$ in (12), we obtain $y = b$ or $-b$. Thus the four "extreme" points of the ellipse have coordinates $(a,0)$, $(-a,0)$, $(0,b)$, and $(0,-b)$, as shown in the diagram below. Observe that the distance from F or F' to $(0,b)$ is a, "half the length of the string." The right triangle in the diagram below reminds us that $b^2 = a^2 - c^2$.

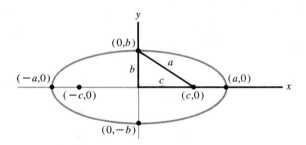

The definition of the hyperbola is similar to that of the ellipse.

DEFINITION: *Hyperbola.*   Let F and F' be points in the plane and let a be a fixed positive number such that $2a$ is less than the distance between F and F'. A point P in the plane is on the *hyperbola* determined by F, F', and $2a$, if and only if the difference between the distances from P to F and from P to F' equals $2a$ (or $-2a$). Points F and F' are the *foci* of the hyperbola.

A hyperbola consists of two separate curves. On one curve $\overline{PF'} - \overline{PF} = 2a$; on the other, $\overline{PF'} - \overline{PF} = -2a$. (For simplicity, we denote the distance between points P and Q as $\overline{PQ}$.) If we denote the distance $\overline{FF'}$ by $2c$, we have $2a < 2c$; hence $a < c$. Again let us place the axes in such a way that $F = (c,0)$ and $F' = (-c,0)$.

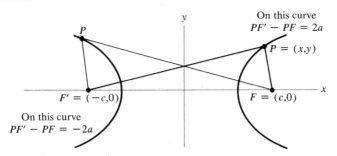

Let $P = (x,y)$ be a typical point on the hyperbola. Then x and y satisfy the equation

(13) $\sqrt{(x-c)^2 + y^2} - \sqrt{(x+c)^2 + y^2} = \pm 2a$

Some algebra similar to that we used in simplifying the equation of the ellipse transforms (13) into

(14) $\dfrac{x^2}{a^2} + \dfrac{y^2}{a^2 - c^2} = 1$

But now $a^2 - c^2$ is *negative* and can be expressed as $-b^2$ for some number $b > 0$. Hence the hyperbola has the equation

(15) $\dfrac{x^2}{a^2} - \dfrac{y^2}{b^2} = 1$

It should be remarked that there is no easy way to draw a hyperbola with the aid of string.

The definition of a parabola involves the distance to a point and the distance to a line.

DEFINITION: *Parabola.*   Let L be a line in the plane and let F be a point in the plane but not on the line. A point P in the plane is on the *parabola* determined by F and L if and only if the distance from P to F equals the distance from P to the line L. Point F is the *focus* of the parabola; line L is its *directrix.*

To obtain an algebraic equation for a parabola, let us denote the distance from point F to line L by c, and introduce axes in such a way that $F = (c/2,0)$ and L has the equation $x = -c/2$.

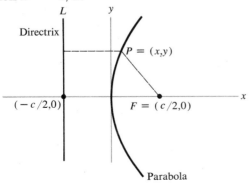

The two dotted lines have equal lengths

The distance from P to F is $\sqrt{(x - c/2)^2 + (y - 0)^2}$. Now, if $P = (x,y)$ is on the parabola, x is clearly not negative. The distance from P to the line L is therefore $x + (c/2)$. Thus the equation of the parabola is

(16)
$$\sqrt{\left(x - \frac{c}{2}\right)^2 + y^2} = x + \frac{c}{2}$$

Squaring and simplifying reduces (16) to

(17)
$$y^2 = 2cx \qquad c > 0$$

which is the equation of a parabola in "standard position."

If the center of an ellipse is not at the origin of our coordinate system, or if the line containing the foci is not parallel to the x axis or the y axis, the equation of the ellipse is not as simple as (12). However, it can be proved that any ellipse, hyperbola, or parabola, no matter where it lies relative to the axes, has an equation of the form

(18)
$$Ax^2 + Bxy + Cy^2 + Dx + Ey + F = 0$$

where A, B, C, D, E, and F are appropriate constants. Moreover, when $B^2 - 4AC$ is negative, (18) describes an ellipse; when $B^2 - 4AC$ is positive, (18) describes a hyperbola; and when $B^2 - 4AC = 0$, (18) describes a parabola. Thus the algebraic equivalent of a "conic section" is a "second-degree equation in x and y." This is an opportune moment to summarize the algebraic equivalents of the geometric ideas we have examined in this appendix.

Geometric concept	*Algebraic equivalent*
Point in the plane	An ordered pair of numbers, (x,y)
Distance between points P_1 and P_2 in the plane	$\sqrt{(x_2 - x_1)^2 + (y_2 - y_1)^2}$
Circle with center at $(0,0)$ and radius r	$x^2 + y^2 = r^2$
Colinear points P_1, P_2, P_3	$\dfrac{y_2 - y_1}{x_2 - x_1} = \dfrac{y_3 - y_1}{x_3 - x_1}$
Line	First-degree equation $Ax + By + C = 0$
Plane	First-degree equation $Ax + By + Cz + D = 0$
Conic section	Second-degree equation $\quad Ax^2 + Bxy + Cy^2 + Dx + Ey + F = 0$
Ellipse in standard position	$\dfrac{x^2}{a^2} + \dfrac{y^2}{b^2} = 1 \qquad a \geqslant b \qquad$ (foci on x axis)
Hyperbola in standard position	$\dfrac{x^2}{a^2} - \dfrac{y^2}{b^2} = 1 \qquad$ (foci on x axis)
Parabola in standard position	$y^2 = 2cx \qquad$ (c = distance from F to directrix)

EXERCISES

27. (a) Supply the missing steps in going from (7) to (12).
    (b) Why is $a \geqslant b$ in (12)?
    (c) When $a = b$, what kind of ellipse do we have?
28. Where would you place the tacks and what length of string would you use to draw the ellipse (a) $x^2/25 + y^2/9 = 1$; (b) $x^2/9 + y^2/25 = 1$?
29. How would you inscribe an elliptical garden in a rectangle whose dimensions are 8 feet by 10 feet?
30. A plane intersects the surface of a right circular cylinder in a curve. Prove that this curve is an ellipse, as defined in terms of foci and sum of distances. (Hint: Consider the two spheres inscribed in the cylinder and tangent to the plane, the spheres being on opposite sides of the plane. Let $2a$ denote the distance between the equators of the spheres perpendicular to the axis of the cylinder and let F and F' be the points at which they touch the plane.)
31. In the definition of the hyperbola we assumed that $2a$ is less than the distance between the foci. Show that if $2a$ were greater than the distance between the foci, the hyperbola would have no points.
32. Obtain Eq. (15).
33. (a) Using the definition of the hyperbola, show that the hyperbola having the foci $(\sqrt{2}, \sqrt{2})$ and $(-\sqrt{2}, -\sqrt{2})$ and $2a = 2\sqrt{2}$ has the equation $xy = 1$.
    (b) Graph $xy = 1$ and show the foci.
34. Obtain Eq. (17).
35. (a) Graph the parabola $y^2 = x$.
    (b) Show its focus and directrix.
36. (See Exercise 35.) (a) Graph the parabolas $y = x^2$, $y^2 = -x$, and $y = -x^2$.
    (b) Graph the hyperbola $x^2 - y^2 = 1$.
    (c) With the aid of (b), graph the hyperbola $y^2 - x^2 = 1$.
37. (See Exercise 30.) Show that the ellipse defined in terms of a cone satisfies the "sum-of-distances" definition of an ellipse. (Hint: Consider the two spheres inscribed in the cone and tangent to the plane of the ellipse.)

Conic sections in polar coordinates. For the study of the conic sections in terms of polar coordinates, it is convenient to use definitions that depend on the ratios of distances, rather than on their sums or differences. (Note that the definition of the parabola involves essentially the ratio of two distances being equal to 1.)

We shall illustrate this approach in the case of an ellipse. From (8) we obtain

$$a^2 - cx = a\overline{PF}$$

or equivalently,

(19)
$$\overline{PF} = a - \frac{c}{a}x$$

Let us denote the quotient c/a, which is less than 1, by e. We call e the *eccentricity* of the ellipse (when $e = 0$, the ellipse is a circle). Thus we obtain

(20)
$$\overline{PF} = a - ex = e\left(\frac{a}{e} - x\right)$$

an equation which is meaningful if the ellipse is not a circle. *But $(a/e) - x$ is the distance from P to the vertical line through $(a/e,0)$, which we will call line L.*

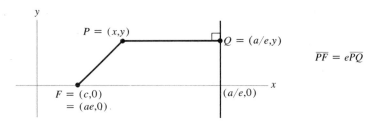

Letting $Q = (a/e,y)$, a point on the same horizontal line as P, we have

(21) $$\overline{PF} = e\overline{PQ}$$

In other words, *the ratio $\overline{PF}/\overline{PQ}$ has a constant value,* less than 1. Thus the ellipse, like the parabola, can be defined in terms of a point F and a line L. The hyperbola can be treated in a similar manner. The main difference is that the eccentricity of a hyperbola, again defined as c/a, is greater than 1. With this background, we now present an alternative approach to the conic sections in terms of the ratios of certain distances.

DEFINITION: *Conic section.*   Let L be a line in the plane, and let F be a point in the plane but not on the line. Let e be a positive number. A point P in the plane is on the conic section determined by F, L, and e if and only if

$$\frac{\text{Distance from } P \text{ to } F}{\text{Distance from } P \text{ to } L} = e$$

When $e = 1$, the conic section is a parabola; when $e < 1$, it is an ellipse; when $e > 1$, it is a hyperbola. The point F is called a *focus*; the line L is called the *directrix*.

To obtain the simplest description of the conic sections in polar coordinates, we place the pole at the focus F. Let the polar axis make an angle B with a line perpendicular to the directrix. The following diagram shows a typical point $P = (r,\theta)$ on the conic section, as well as the point Q, on the directrix, nearest P. We let the distance from F to the directrix be p.

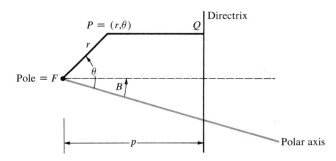

Then we have $\overline{PQ}/\overline{PF} = e$. But $\overline{PF} = r$ and $\overline{PQ} = p - r\cos(\theta - B)$. Thus

(22)
$$\frac{r}{p - r\cos(\theta - B)} = e$$

Solving (22) for r yields *the equation of a conic section in polar coordinates,*

(23)
$$r = \frac{ep}{1 + e\cos(\theta - B)}$$

Example 11. Consider the graph of the equation

$$r = \frac{8}{5 + 6\cos\theta}$$

This can be put in the form (23) by dividing numerator and denominator by 5:

$$r = \frac{8/5}{1 + 6/5\cos\theta} = \frac{(6/5)(8/6)}{1 + 6/5\cos\theta}$$

Hence the graph is a conic section for which $p = 8/6$ and $e = 6/5$. It is a hyperbola, since $e > 1$.

In the description of an ellipse in rectangular coordinates the numbers a (half the "constant distance") and b were used (see pages 556–558); in the description in polar coordinates we used p, the distance from the focus to the directrix, and the eccentricity e. There are two relations involving these four quantities which we need in Chap. 26. These relations are

$$b^2 = a^2(1 - e^2) \qquad \text{and} \qquad pe = a(1 - e^2)$$

We establish them as follows: From the definition of b, we have $b^2 = a^2 - c^2$, and e is defined as c/a. Then

$$b^2 = a^2 - c^2 = a^2 - (ae)^2 = a^2(1 - e^2)$$

and $\qquad pe = \left(\frac{a}{e} - c\right)e = \left(\frac{a}{e} - ae\right)e = a - ae^2 = a(1 - e^2)$

The *mean radius* from the focus F to the ellipse is also needed in Chap. 26. It is defined as the average of the smallest distance from F to the ellipse and the largest distance from F to the ellipse. This is the average of the distances from F to $(a,0)$ and $(-a,0)$. Since $F = (c,0)$, we have

$$\text{Mean radius} = \frac{(a - c) + (a + c)}{2} = a$$

EXERCISES

38. (*a*) Sketch the four points on the graph of $r = 10/(3 + 2\cos\theta)$ corresponding to $\theta = 0, \pi/2, \pi, 3\pi/2$.
    (*b*) Using (23), show that the curve in (*a*) is an ellipse.
39. Obtain (23) from (22).

40. (a) Find the eccentricity of these conics: $r = 5/(3 + 4\cos\theta)$; $r = 5/(4 + 3\cos\theta)$; $r = 5/(3 + 3\cos\theta)$; $r = 5/(3 - 4\cos\theta)$.
    (b) What type of conic is each?

41. Assume that a rectangular coordinate system is placed in such a way that an ellipse has the equation $x^2/a^2 + y^2/b^2 = 1$. Place a polar coordinate system so that the polar axis coincides with the positive x axis (the pole thus being at the center of the ellipse, *not at a focus*). Show that the polar equation of the ellipse is (the relatively complicated)

$$r^2 = \frac{a^2 b^2}{b^2 \cos^2\theta + a^2 \sin^2\theta}$$

    (Hint: Recall that $x = r\cos\theta$ and $y = r\sin\theta$.)

42. (a) Show that $r = 8/[1 - (1/2)\cos\theta]$ is the equation of an ellipse. [Hint: Set $B = \pi$ in Eq. (23).]
    (b) Graph the ellipse and its foci.
    (c) Find a, where $2a$ is the fixed sum of the distances from points on the ellipse to the foci.

[Answer: (c) $32/3$]

43. (a) Show that $r = 3\cos\theta + 4\sin\theta$ is the equation of a circle.
    (b) Show that $r = 1/(3\cos\theta + 4\sin\theta)$ is the equation of a line.
    (c) Show that $r = 1/(3\cos\theta + 4\sin\theta + 5)$ is the equation of a conic. [Hint: For (c) see Exercise 4, page 543.]

APPENDIX B

The real numbers

THIS appendix describes those properties of the real number system which are used in the text. While it is possible to construct the real numbers from the positive integers 1, 2, 3, 4, . . . , a description of the procedure would require a small book. We will assume that the set of real numbers exists and content ourselves with a summary of its important attributes.

The field axioms. Let S be the set of real numbers. On S are defined two operations, addition, denoted $+$, and multiplication, denoted $\cdot$, which satisfy the following axioms.

A1. For each a and b in S,
$a + b$ is in S.

A2. For each a and b in S,
$a + b = b + a$.

A3. For each a, b, and c in S,
$a + (b + c) = (a + b) + c$.

A4. There is an element in S,
denoted 0, such that
$0 + a = a$ for all a in S.

A5. For each a and b in S,
there is a unique element c
in S such that $a + c = b$.

M1. For each a and b in S,
$a \cdot b$ is in S.

M2. For each a and b in S,
$a \cdot b = b \cdot a$.

M3. For each a, b, and c in S,
$a \cdot (b \cdot c) = (a \cdot b) \cdot c$.

M4. There is an element in S,
denoted 1, such that
$1 \cdot a = a$ for all a in S.

M5. For each element a in S (other
than 0) and each element b in
S, there is a unique element c
in S such that $a \cdot c = b$.

D. For each a, b, and c in S,

$$a \cdot (b + c) = (a \cdot b) + (a \cdot c)$$

565

The first four axioms for addition and for multiplication are analogous. The second axiom (A2 or M2) is the commutative law; the third axiom is the associative law. The element c, whose existence is assumed by A5, is usually denoted $b - a$ and is called *the difference of a and b*. In particular, $0 - a$ is denoted $-a$ and is called *the additive inverse of a*. The element c, whose existence is assumed by M5, is usually denoted b/a and is called *the quotient of b by a*. In particular, $1/a$ is called *the reciprocal of a* or *the multiplicative inverse of a*. Every element has an additive inverse; every element except 0 has a multiplicative inverse. The distributive axiom, D, distinguishes addition from multiplication: We do *not* have a companion axiom relating $a + (b \cdot c)$ to $a + b$ and $a + c$.

The ordering axioms.   There is a relation between real numbers, denoted "$>$" and read as "greater than," that satisfies the following axioms.
O1. If a is not 0, then $a > 0$ or $-a > 0$, but not both.
O2. If $a > b$ and $b > c$, then $a > c$.
O3. If $a > b$ and $c > 0$, then $ca > cb$ and, for any c, $c + a > c + b$.
If $a > 0$, then a is called *positive*. If $-a > 0$, then a is called *negative*.

If we think of the real numbers as describing points on a number line, then "$a > b$" may be thought of as meaning "a is to the right of b"; "a is positive" as meaning "a is to the right of 0"; and "a is negative" as meaning "a is to the left of 0." In this figure $a > b$, a is positive, and b is negative.

In the figure $a > b$,
a is positive,
and b is negative

Axiom O3 tells us, for instance, that "multiplication by a positive number preserves an inequality." Multiplication by a negative number reverses it: $4 > 3$, but $(-5)(3) > (-5)(4)$. Analogous remarks hold for division by a positive or by a negative number.

The *absolute value* of a is a if a is positive, and $-a$ if a is negative. The absolute value of 0 is 0. If we think in terms of the number line, then the absolute value of a is the distance from a to 0. The absolute value of a is denoted $|a|$. Thus $|3| = 3 = |-3|$.

The symbol $a \geqslant b$ shall mean "$a > b$ or $a = b$." Thus $4 \geqslant 3$ and $3 \geqslant 3$. The symbol $a < b$ shall mean $b > a$. The symbol $a \leqslant b$ shall mean $b \geqslant a$. Thus $3 < 4$, $3 \leqslant 4$, $3 \leqslant 3$.

The absolute value has two important properties:

$$|ab| = |a||b| \qquad \text{and} \qquad |a + b| \leqslant |a| + |b|$$

For instance,

$$|(-3) \cdot 7| = |-3||7| \qquad \text{and} \qquad |(-3) + 7| \leqslant |-3| + |7|$$

as the reader may verify.

Rational and irrational numbers.   Within the real numbers we distinguish certain types of numbers: The *positive* integers, $1, 2, 3, \ldots$; the *integers* $\ldots, -3,$
$-2, -1, 0, 1, 2, 3, \ldots$; and the *rational numbers* a/b, where a and b are integers and $b \neq 0$. On the number line the rational numbers correspond to the points
obtainable by dividing the interval between integers into equal divisions. For instance, $7/5$ corresponds to the point between 1 and 2 shown in this diagram:

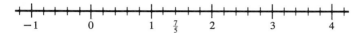

Note that any integer n is a rational number: we have $n = n/1$.

Not every real number is rational. The decimal representation of a rational number always *repeats:* from some point on, the digits repeat in blocks. For instance

$$^{23}\!/_{14} = 1.6428571428571428571 \ldots$$

Conversely, any *repeating* decimal represents a rational number. For instance, consider the number

$$x = 0.5313131 \ldots$$

We have $\hspace{3cm} 100x = 53.1313131 \ldots$

Subtraction of the former from the latter yields $100x - x = 52.6$, or $99x = 52.6$.
We obtain

$$x = \frac{52.6}{99} = \frac{526}{990}$$

Hence $0.53131 \ldots$ is expressible as the quotient of two integers and is a rational
number. The same type of argument may be applied to any repeating decimal.

A real number that is not rational is called *irrational.* Irrational numbers (as well
as rational numbers) are plentiful. Any nonrepeating decimal, such as

(1) $\hspace{3cm} 0.12122122212222 \ldots$

(in which the numeral 1 alternates with lengthening blocks of 2's) is irrational. The
ratio between the circumference and diameter of a circle is irrational (this is demonstrated in Exercise 30, page 301). So are $\sqrt{2}$, $\sqrt{3}$, $\sqrt{5}$, $\sqrt{6}$, and $\sqrt[3]{2}$.

Example 1.   How many irrational numbers are there between 0.12 and 0.13? One
such number is given above in (1). We may construct an infinite set of irrational numbers
between 0.12 and 0.13 by, let us say, changing one 1 or 2 in the decimal in (1) to a 3. Thus

$$0.12322122212222 \ldots$$
$$0.12132122212222 \ldots$$
$$0.12123122212222 \ldots$$

and so on are irrational numbers between 0.12 and 0.13. Thus there is an infinite set
of irrational numbers between 0.12 and 0.13. Similarly, by constructing *repeating* decimals that begin $0.12 \ldots$, we may show that between 0.12 and 0.13 there is an infinite
set of rational numbers.

The same reasoning shows that both the rational numbers and the irrational numbers are distributed abundantly on the number line: *between any two real numbers is an infinity of rational numbers and an infinity of irrational numbers.*

Example 2. The sum, difference, product, and quotient of two rational numbers are also rational numbers. For instance,

$$\frac{3}{4} + \frac{5}{7} = \frac{3 \cdot 7 + 5 \cdot 4}{28} = \frac{41}{28} \qquad \frac{3}{4} - \frac{5}{7} = \frac{3 \cdot 7 - 5 \cdot 4}{28} = \frac{1}{28}$$

$$\frac{3}{4} \cdot \frac{5}{7} = \frac{15}{28} \qquad \frac{3/4}{5/7} = \frac{3}{4} \cdot \frac{7}{5} = \frac{21}{20}$$

The set of rational numbers satisfies the field axioms and the order axioms. The set of irrational numbers satisfies the order axioms but not all the field axioms. For instance, the sum of two irrational numbers is not necessarily irrational: $(\sqrt{2}) + (-\sqrt{2}) = 0$.

EXERCISES

1. (*a*) If a and b are both negative, or else both positive, what is the relation between $|a + b|$, $|a|$, and $|b|$? Explain and illustrate by examples.
   (*b*) Prove that if $|a - b| < c$, then $|a| < |b| + c$. (Hint: Consider the cases a, b, $a - b$ positive or negative.)
2. Find the decimal expansion of the following rational numbers, and show the repeating block in each case. (*a*) ⁴⁄₁₃; (*b*) ³⁄₇; (*c*) ⁵⁄₈; (*d*) ²⁄₁₇.
3. Which of these numbers are rational? Which are irrational? (*a*) -8; (*b*) $5\sqrt{2}/2$; (*c*) π; (*d*) $-3/(-7)$; (*e*) $\sqrt{4}$; (*f*) 5.238. Explain.
4. Construct at least four irrational numbers and at least four rational numbers between 3.17 and 3.18.
5. Find integers m and n such that (*a*) $m/n = 6.2457457457 \ldots$; (*b*) $m/n = 20.3656565 \ldots$.
6. Let $S = \{0, 1, 2, 3, 4\}$, and let the operations $+$ and $\cdot$ be defined completely by these tables:

+	0	1	2	3	4
0	0	1	2	3	4
1	1	2	3	4	0
2	2	3	4	0	1
3	3	4	0	1	2
4	4	0	1	2	3

·	0	1	2	3	4
0	0	0	0	0	0
1	0	1	2	3	4
2	0	2	4	1	3
3	0	3	1	4	2
4	0	4	3	2	1

For instance, $2 + 4 = 1$ and $3 \cdot 4 = 2$. Verify that (a) $2 + 3 = 3 + 2$; (b) $(1 + 3) + 4 = 1 + (3 + 4)$; (c) $3 \cdot 4 = 4 \cdot 3$; (d) $(0 \cdot 3) \cdot 2 = (0 \cdot 2) \cdot 3$; (e) the equation $2 + x = 1$ has a solution in S; (f) the equation $2 \cdot x = 1$ has a solution in S; (g) $2 \cdot (3 + 4) = 2 \cdot 3 + 2 \cdot 4$. (h) Find $\frac{3}{4}$ and -2.

It can be shown that this structure satisfies the 11 axioms of a field.

Completeness of the real numbers. We now come to the property of the real numbers which is most important in the calculus. In order to state it precisely, we introduce two definitions.

DEFINITION: *Upper bound.* Let X be a set of real numbers. The number u is an *upper bound* for the set X if $u \geqslant x$ for all x in X.

For instance, if $X = \{1,2,3\}$, then $u = 17$, $u = 6.2$, and $u = 3$ are some of the upper bounds for X. The set $X = \{1,2,3,4, \ldots\}$ has no upper bound. The set $X = \{\frac{1}{2}, \frac{2}{3}, \frac{3}{4}, \frac{4}{5}, \frac{5}{6}, \ldots \}$ has $u = 1,000$, $u = 15$, and $u = 1$ as upper bounds. In fact any number $u \geqslant 1$ is an upper bound.

DEFINITION: *Least upper bound.* A number is the *least upper bound* of a set X if it is an upper bound of X and it is less than or equal to every upper bound of X.

For instance, the set $X = \{\frac{1}{2}, \frac{2}{3}, \frac{3}{4}, \frac{4}{5}, \ldots \}$ has the least upper bound 1. So has the set $Y = \{1, \frac{1}{2}, \frac{2}{3}, \frac{3}{4}, \frac{4}{5}, \ldots \}$.

We are now ready to state the most useful property of the real number system.

The Completeness Axiom. *Any set X of real numbers that has an upper bound has a least upper bound.*

The set of rational numbers, which satisfies the field axioms and the order axioms, does *not* satisfy the completeness axiom, as the next example illustrates.

Example 3. Let $X = \{1, 1.7, 1.73, 1.732, \ldots \}$, the set of successive (rational) decimal approximations to $\sqrt{3} = 1.732051 \ldots$. Since $2^2 > 3$, we see that 2 is larger than any number in X, hence X has an upper bound which is rational. But there is no smallest *rational* upper bound for X. Specifically, if r is rational and is an upper bound of X, then $r > \sqrt{3}$. Between $\sqrt{3}$ and r, select any rational number r^*. Then r^* is also an upper bound of X but is less than r.

The notions *lower bound* of X and *greatest lower bound* of X are defined in a similar manner. It can be shown that the completeness axiom implies that a set X of real numbers that has at least one lower bound has a greatest lower bound.

EXERCISES

7. Can a set of irrational numbers have a rational least upper bound? Explain.
8. (a) Show that $1/(1 \cdot 2) + 1/(2 \cdot 3) + 1/(3 \cdot 4) + \cdots + 1/(n) \cdot (n+1) = 1 - 1/(n+1)$.
   [Hint: Use the identity $1/i - 1/(i+1) = 1/(i)(i+1)$.]
   (b) Show that the set

$$X = \left\{ \frac{1}{1 \cdot 2}, \frac{1}{1 \cdot 2} + \frac{1}{2 \cdot 3}, \frac{1}{1 \cdot 2} + \frac{1}{2 \cdot 3} + \frac{1}{3 \cdot 4}, \cdots \right\}$$

has an upper bound.
   (c) What is the least upper bound of X?
   (d) Using (b) or (c), find an upper bound for the set

$$Y = \left\{ \frac{1}{2 \cdot 2}, \frac{1}{2 \cdot 2} + \frac{1}{3 \cdot 3}, \frac{1}{2 \cdot 2} + \frac{1}{3 \cdot 3} + \frac{1}{4 \cdot 4}, \cdots \right\}$$

   In Exercise 55, page 178, it is shown that the least upper bound of Y is $(\pi^2 - 6)/6$.
9. (a) What is the least upper bound of the set of real numbers x such that $x \leqslant 10$?
   (b) What is the least upper bound of the set of real numbers x such that $x < 10$?
10. (a) Define "lower bound" and "greatest lower bound" of a set X of real numbers.
    (b) Using the completeness axiom, prove that if a set X has a lower bound, then it has a greatest lower bound.

APPENDIX C

Functions

FUNCTIONS are basic not only to the calculus but throughout mathematics and its applications. In this appendix we define "function" and show some of the many forms in which this concept appears.

DEFINITIONS: *Function, value (image), range, and domain.* Let X and Y be sets (perhaps the same set). A function f is a rule or method for assigning a unique element y in the set Y to each element x in the set X. If y is that element assigned to x, then we say that y is *the value of f at x* (or the *image* of x) and write $y = f(x)$. The *domain* of f is X. The *range* of f is the set of values of f. We say that f is a function *from X to Y*.

The sets X and Y may consist of numbers, or points, or any elements whatsoever. We may think of a function as a vending machine. When an element x of the set X is inserted into the machine, an element y of the set Y falls out the chute. What falls out depends on x and is denoted $f(x)$; the machine itself is denoted f.

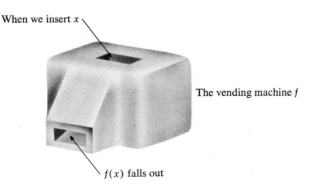

When we insert x

The vending machine f

$f(x)$ falls out

571

Example 1.   Let $X = \{1, 2, 3, \ldots\}$, the set of positive integers, and let Y be the set of real numbers. Let f be given by the formula $f(x) = (-1)^x$. We then have $f(1) = (-1)^1 = -1$, $f(2) = (-1)^2 = 1$, $f(3) = (-1)^3 = -1$. A table for f begins as follows:

x	1	2	3	4	5	$\ldots$
$f(x) = (-1)^x$	-1	1	-1	1	-1	$\ldots$

The range of f has just two elements, 1 and -1.

Example 2.   Let X and Y be the same as in Example 1. Let us define $f(x) = \cos(x\pi)$. For instance, $f(1) = \cos(1\pi) = \cos \pi = -1$, $f(2) = \cos(2\pi) = 1$, $f(3) = \cos(3\pi) = -1$. A table for this function begins as follows:

x	1	2	3	4	5	$\ldots$
$f(x) = \cos(x\pi)$	-1	1	-1	1	-1	$\ldots$

The tables in Examples 1 and 2 are identical. We regard the function defined in these two examples as the *same* function described in different words. We will consider two functions f and g identical if $f(x) = g(x)$ for all x in X. (In other words, the tables for f and g are the same.) Pursuing the vending-machine analogy, we say that two vending machines describe the same function if, when we put the same element x in each of them, the same elements $f(x)$ fall out of their chutes.

In fact, a function from X to Y is sometimes defined as a set S of ordered pairs (x,y), where x is in X and y is in Y, such that for each x^* in X there is exactly one element (x,y) in S that has $x = x^*$. A gazetteer of the United States is a function given in this manner; it consists of the ordered pairs (x,y), where y is the number of people in town x.

Example 3.   Let X be the set of towns in the United States. Let Y be the set of positive integers. Let $f(x)$ be the population of x in the 1960 census. For instance, $f(\text{New York}) = 7,781,984$; $f(\text{San Francisco}) = 740,316$; $f(\text{Chicago}) = 3,530,404$. This function is usually recorded in a table consisting of two vertical columns.

x	$f(x) = $ population of x
New York	7,781,984
San Francisco	740,316
Chicago	3,530,404
. . . .	. . . . . .

Example 4.   Let X and Y be the same as in Example 3. This time let $f(x)$ be the area of x in square miles, rounded to the nearest integer. For instance, $f(\text{New York}) = 299$, $f(\text{San Francisco}) = 45$, $f(\text{Chicago}) = 225$.

Most functions in the calculus have subsets of the real numbers as their domain and range. Such functions determine a subset of the plane, as the next example illustrates.

Example 5.   Let X and Y both be the set of all real numbers. Let $y = f(x) = x^3$. A table for f is infinite and includes these entries:

x	0	1	-1	2	-1.1	$\sqrt[3]{2}$	-2
$f(x) = x^3$	0	1	-1	8	-1.331	2	-8

Each column in this table may be interpreted as the rectangular coordinates of a point in the plane. For instance, the information $f(2) = 8$ can be recorded by drawing the point $(2,8)$. The complete table would correspond to a curve:

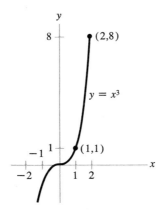

The curve or "graph" conveys at a glance the general behavior of the function x^3. (It is customary to abbreviate "the function f such that $f(x) = x^3$" to "the function x^3.") In this case, as x increases, $f(x)$ increases; as x becomes arbitrarily large, so does $f(x)$.

If, as in Example 5, the domain and the range of f consist of real numbers, we say that f is a *real function of a real variable.* The domain is said to contain the *independent variable,* and the range to contain the *dependent variable.*

Example 6.   Let X consist of the points P in the (rectangular) daily weather map printed in many newspapers. Let Y be the set of real numbers. Let $f(P) =$ air pressure at P, in millibars. Usually $f(P)$ is about 1,013 millibars. If $f(P)$ is near 1,030 millibars, we probably have fair weather at P. If $f(P)$ is around 1,000 millibars, we probably have foul weather at P.

EXERCISES

1. Let $X = \{1,2,3\}$ and $Y = \{a,b\}$.
   (a) How many functions are there whose domain is X and whose range is a subset of Y?
   (b) How many functions are there whose domain is Y and whose range is a subset of X? Explain in each case.   [Answer: (a) 8; (b) 9]
2. A function f is described by these directions: "Think of a number, add 2, multiply by 5, subtract 11." Find $f(0)$, $f(1)$, and $f(-4)$.

3. Let X be the set of people now alive, and let Y be the set of real numbers. Describe three functions f from X to Y.
4. Let $X = \{1,2,3\}$ and $Y = \{a,b\}$.
   (a) How many functions have domain X and range *all* of Y?
   (b) How many functions have domain Y and range *all* of X? Explain.

   [Answer: (a) 6; (b) 0]
5. Let X and Y be the set of real numbers. Show a few entries in the tables of each of the following functions and graph the subset of the plane which they determine: (a) $f(x) = 2x$; (b) $f(x) = x$; (c) $f(x) = x^2$; (d) $f(x) = x^2 + 5$; (e) $f(x) =$ largest integer not greater than x.

Inverse of a one-to-one correspondence.   We discuss next the notion of inverse function, used in Chap. 4 to obtain the derivative of $x^{1/n}$, e^x, $\sin^{-1} x$, and so on.

DEFINITION: *One-to-one function.*   Let X and Y be sets and f a function from X to Y. If $f(x_1) = f(x_2)$ implies $x_1 = x_2$ for all x_1 and x_2 in X, then f is a *one-to-one* function.

In other words, a one-to-one function assigns to distinct elements of X distinct elements of Y. The function of Examples 1 and 2 is not one-to-one, since $f(3) = f(5)$. The population function in Example 3 is not one-to-one since both Lynchburg, Kentucky, and Scottsburg, Indiana, had the same population in 1960, namely, 3,810. The function x^3 in Example 5 is one-to-one, since $x_1{}^3 = x_2{}^3$ implies that $x_1 = x_2$.

DEFINITION: *One-to-one correspondence.*   Let X and Y be sets. A one-to-one function from X to Y whose range is *all* of Y is a *one-to-one correspondence* between X and Y.

The function x^3 in Example 5 is a one-to-one correspondence. We may think of a one-to-one correspondence f as a function that pairs the elements of X with the elements of Y. For each element y in Y there is precisely one element x in X such that $f(x) = y$.

Example 7.   Let $X = \{1,2,3\}$ and $Y = \{a,b,c\}$. The function f defined by $f(1) = a$, $f(2) = b$, $f(3) = c$ is a one-to-one correspondence between X and Y. There are in fact 6 one-to-one correspondences between these two sets.

If X has three elements and Y has four elements, there are *no* one-to-one correspondences between X and Y.

DEFINITION: *Inverse function.*   Let X and Y be sets, and f a one-to-one correspondence between X and Y. The function that assigns to each element y in Y the unique element x in X such that $f(x) = y$ is the *inverse* of f. It is written f^{-1}.

Note that the domain of f^{-1} is Y, and the range of f^{-1} is all of X. Furthermore, f^{-1} is itself a one-to-one correspondence.

Example 8.   The inverse of the one-to-one correspondence x^3 (that is, $f(x) = x^3$) in Example 5 is easily computed. Let y be any real number and let x be the unique real number such that $y = x^3$. Then x is the cube root of y, and $f^{-1}(y) = \sqrt[3]{y}$. Thus we have $f(2) = 8$ and $f^{-1}(8) = 2$; $f(-3) = -27$ and $f^{-1}(-27) = -3$. The inverse of the "cube" function is the "cube root" function.

EXERCISES

6. Compute the inverse of the function constructed in Example 7.
7. (a) Show that the function $f(x) = 2x + 5$, where X and Y are the set of real numbers, is a one-to-one correspondence.
   (b) Find a formula for f^{-1}.   [Answer: (b) $(y - 5)/2$]
8. Let X and Y be the set of real numbers. Which of the following functions are one-to-one? Which have a range coinciding with Y? Which are one-to-one correspondences? (a) $f(x) = x^5$; (b) $f(x) = x - x^3$; (c) $f(x) = x^2$; (d) $f(x) = 10^x$; (e) $f(x) = x - 3$.
9. Let X and Y be the set of positive integers, and f a one-to-one correspondence between X and Y whose table includes these values:

x	1	2	3	4	. . .
$f(x)$	15	1	4	27	. . .

   List a few entires in the table for f^{-1}.
10. Find all 6 one-to-one correspondences between $X = \{1,2,3\}$ and $Y = \{a,b,c\}$.
11. (a) How many one-to-one functions are there from a set of four elements to a set of five elements?
    (b) How many one-to-one correspondences are there between two sets each of which has four elements?
12. Let X and Y be the set of real numbers, and f a function from X to Y. Complete these statements concerning the graph of f, that is, the set of points in the plane which are of the form $(x,f(x))$.
    (a) Each _____ line meets the graph of f exactly once.
    (b) If f is one-to-one, then each horizontal line meets the graph of f _____.
    (c) If f is a one-to-one correspondence, then each horizontal line meets the graph of f _____.
13. If f is a one-to-one correspondence, $f(3) = 7$, and $f(2) = 6$, what can we say about f^{-1}?
14. If f is a one-to-one correspondence, how do $(f^{-1})^{-1}$ and f compare? Explain.
15. Let X and Y be the set of real numbers other than 0. Let $f(x) = 1/x$.
    (a) Show that f is a one-to-one correspondence.
    (b) Compute $f(2)$ and $f^{-1}(2)$.
    (c) Show that $f = f^{-1}$.

Special types of functions. Certain types of functions have special names. For instance, when X is the set of all integers greater than 0, and Y is the set of real numbers, then any function f from X to Y is called a *sequence*. A sequence is usually indicated by listing its values in order: $f(1), f(2), f(3), \ldots$. Sometimes the "front end" of a sequence is cut off; that is, the domain of f consists of the integers greater than some fixed integer a. Such a function is also called a sequence. The function in Examples 1 and 2 is a sequence.

If the range of f has just one element, the function is called *constant*.

The next definition, describing certain sets of real numbers, will be needed in defining "curve" and "parameterization."

DEFINITION: *Closed interval, open interval.*   Let a and b be real numbers, $a < b$. The set of real numbers x, where $a \leqslant x \leqslant b$, is the *closed interval* from a to b; it is denoted $[a,b]$. If the numbers a and b are deleted from $[a,b]$, the *open interval* from a to b is obtained; it is denoted (a,b).

DEFINITION: *Curve, parameterization.*   A set in the plane or in three-dimensional space is a *curve* if it is the range of a continuous function f whose domain is a closed interval $[a,b]$. The function f is a *parameterization* of the curve.

("Continuous" is defined in Appendix F.)

It is convenient to think of x in the closed interval as denoting time, and $f(x)$ as the position of some moving object at the time x. Usually x is replaced by t, for time. Thus a curve may be considered as the set of points through which a moving particle passes.

Example 9.   Let $f(t) = (t,t^2)$ for t in $[0,1]$. The range of f is the parabolic curve from $(0,0)$ to $(1,1)$ sketched here:

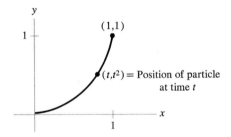

Another parameterization for the same curve is given by $f(t) = (t^3,t^6)$ for t in $[0,1]$. Generally a curve may be parameterized in many ways.

If the function f appearing in the definition of a curve is a one-to-one correspondence between the interval $[a,b]$ and the curve, then the curve is called an *arc*. The curve in Example 9 is an arc. While a curve may cross over itself, an arc does not.

If the function f appearing in the definition of a curve has the property that $f(a) = f(b)$, then the curve is called a *closed curve*. (A circle is a closed curve; an arc is never a closed curve.)

Sometimes the function f appearing in the definition of a curve has the property that $f(a) = f(b)$ and that if $f(x_1) = f(x_2)$, then x_1 is x_2, or else x_1 and x_2 coincide with *a* and *b*. In this case the curve is called a *simple closed curve* or *loop*. A circle is thus a loop. These sketches show the three special types of curves:

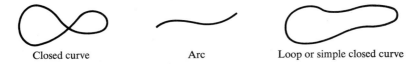

Closed curve   Arc   Loop or simple closed curve

Example 10. The circle of radius 1 and center $(0,0)$ is a simple closed curve, for it is the range of the function f given by $f(t) = (\cos 2\pi t, \sin 2\pi t)$, for t in $[0,1]$. Note that $f(0) = f(1) = (1,0)$, but otherwise f does not assign equal values to different values of t in $[0,1]$.

The next example is an instance of a *vector field,* a function that assigns vectors to points in the plane in a continuous manner.

Example 11. Let X be the weather map in rectangular coordinates referred to in Example 6. We consider the wind vector at each point P in X. In this case let Y be the set of vectors, and let $f(P)$ be the wind vector at P. The daily weather map indicates the wind vector at a few key stations.

EXERCISES

16. How many constant functions are there from $X = \{a,b,c,d,e\}$ to $Y = \{1,2,3,4\}$?
17. Give four examples of sequences.
18. Draw (*a*) a curve that is not closed; (*b*) a curve that is not closed and is not an arc; (*c*) a closed curve that is not a simple closed curve.
19. Give three *different* parameterizations, each of which shows that the line segment from $(0,0)$ to $(1,1)$ is an arc.

Composite function. We next introduce a notion which is useful in finding the derivative of such functions as $(x^2 + 1)^{10}$ and e^{x^2}.

DEFINITION: *Composition of functions.* Let X, Y, and Z be sets. Let f be a function from X to Y; let g be a function from Y to Z. The function h, from X to Z, given by

$$h(x) = g(f(x))$$

is the *composition* of f and g. It is denoted $g \circ f$ and called a *composite function.*

Example 12. Let X, Y, and Z be the set of real numbers. Let $f(x) = 1 + x^5$ and $g(x) = x^2$. Then

$$(g \circ f)(x) = g(f(x)) = g(1 + x^5) = (1 + x^5)^2$$

while

$$(f \circ g)(x) = f(g(x)) = f(x^2) = 1 + (x^2)^5$$

If we think of f and g as separate vending machines, then $g \circ f$ is the single machine we obtain by linking the two together in such a way that the output from the machine representing f falls automatically into the machine representing g.

Example 13. If f is a one-to-one correspondence, then $(f^{-1} \circ f)(x) = f^{-1}(f(x)) = x$ and $(f \circ f^{-1})(y) = f(f^{-1}(y)) = y$.

EXERCISES

20. (*a*) Show that if $f(x) = x^3$ and $g(x) = x^2$, then $f \circ g = g \circ f$.
    (*b*) Show that if $f(x) = x^3$ and $g(x) = 1 + x^2$, then $f \circ g \neq g \circ f$.
21. Let $X = Y$, and let f be a function from X to Y. If $f \circ f$ is a one-to-one correspondence, what can we say about f? Explain.
22. Let $f(x) = 1/(1 - x)$. Show that $[f \circ (f \circ f)](x) = x$.
23. Let X and Y be the set of people who have ever lived. Let $f(x)$ be the mother of x and $g(x)$ be the father of x.
    (*a*) What is $(f \circ f)(x)$?
    (*b*) What is $(f \circ g)(x)$?
    (*c*) What is $(g \circ f)(x)$?
    (*d*) If $f(x_1) = f(x_2)$ and $g(x_1) = g(x_2)$, then what are x_1 and x_2 called?
    (*e*) If $(f \circ f)(x_1) = (f \circ f)(x_2)$, but $f(x_1) \neq f(x_2)$, then what are x_1 and x_2 called?
24. Let $f(x) = [x + (4/x)]/2$.
    (*a*) Compute $f(1)$, $(f \circ f)(1)$, and $(f \circ f \circ f)(1)$.
    (*b*) What do you think happens as more f's are "composed"?
25. Let $X = Y = Z = \{1,2\}$.
    (*a*) How many functions h from X to Z are expressible as the composition of a function from X to Y and a function from Y to Z?
    (*b*) Can some function h in (*a*) be expressed as a composition of the type described in (*a*) in more than one way? Give illustrations.
26. Let X and Y be sets, f a function from X to Y, and g a function from Y to X. Assume that $(f \circ g)(y) = y$ for all y in Y and that $(g \circ f)(x) = x$ for all x in X. What can we conclude about f and g? Explain.
27. Inspect a table of the common logarithms of the trigonometric functions (to be found in most mathematical handbooks). Show that the table is the composition of other functions tabulated elsewhere in the handbook.

APPENDIX D

Summation notation

WHEN we deal with the sum of several terms of the same general form it is more convenient to make use of a summation notation than to write out each term explicitly.

Summation over i. The sum of the n numbers a_i, where $1 \leqslant i \leqslant n$, is denoted $\sum_{i=1}^{n} a_i$ and called *the sum of a_i as i goes from 1 to n.*

Example 1.

$$\sum_{i=1}^{3} i^2 = 1^2 + 2^2 + 3^2 = 14$$

$$\sum_{i=1}^{4} 1/i = \tfrac{1}{1} + \tfrac{1}{2} + \tfrac{1}{3} + \tfrac{1}{4} = \tfrac{25}{12} = 2.083$$

$$\sum_{i=1}^{3} 1^i = 1^1 + 1^2 + 1^3 = 1 + 1 + 1 = 3$$

The letter i stands for "index." Frequently j, k, or n is used. Thus

$$\sum_{j=1}^{3} j^2 = 1^2 + 2^2 + 3^2 = 14 = \sum_{k=1}^{3} k^2 = \sum_{n=1}^{3} n^2$$

Moreover we need not restrict ourselves to sums beginning at 1. For instance, we denote the sum $a_3 + a_4 + a_5 + a_6$ by $\sum_{i=3}^{6} a_i$.

Example 2.

$$\sum_{i=1}^{3} 10i = 10 \cdot 1 + 10 \cdot 2 + 10 \cdot 3 = 10(1 + 2 + 3) = 10 \sum_{i=1}^{3} i$$

Generally, a constant factor, c, can be "moved past the summation sign":

$$\sum_{i=1}^{n} ca_i = c \sum_{i=1}^{n} a_i$$

579

Consider $\sum\limits_{i=1}^{5} 1$. In this case we have $a_i = 1$ for each i from 1 through 5. Thus

$$\sum_{i=1}^{5} 1 = 1 + 1 + 1 + 1 + 1 = 5$$

More generally, if c is independent of i,

$$\sum_{i=1}^{n} c = cn$$

Example 3. Say that the numbers x_0, x_1, x_2, x_3 are given. Then $\sum\limits_{i=1}^{3} (x_i - x_{i-1}) = (x_1 - x_0) + (x_2 - x_1) + (x_3 - x_2)$, which after cancellation reduces to $x_3 - x_0$.

Example 4. Let $f(x) = x^2$, let $x_i = i/3$, and let $X_i = i/3 - 1/6$. Let us compute

$$\sum_{i=1}^{3} f(X_i)(x_i - x_{i-1})$$

an instance of a type of sum that is of great importance in the calculus. Since i runs from 1 through 3, the sum in question is

(1) $f(X_1)(x_1 - x_0) + f(X_2)(x_2 - x_1) + f(X_3)(x_3 - x_2)$

Now, $x_0 = 0/3 = 0$; $x_1 = 1/3$; $x_2 = 2/3$; $x_3 = 3/3$. Also, $X_1 = 1/3 - 1/6 = 1/6$; $X_2 = 3/6$; $X_3 = 5/6$. Since $f(x) = x^2$, the sum (1) equals

$(\tfrac{1}{6})^2(\tfrac{1}{3} - 0) + (\tfrac{3}{6})^2(\tfrac{2}{3} - \tfrac{1}{3}) + (\tfrac{5}{6})^2(\tfrac{3}{3} - \tfrac{2}{3}) = \tfrac{1}{36}(\tfrac{1}{3} + \tfrac{9}{3} + \tfrac{25}{3})$

$$= \tfrac{1}{108}(1 + 9 + 25) = \tfrac{35}{108} = 0.324$$

EXERCISES

1. Show that (*a*) $\sum\limits_{i=1}^{4} i = 10$; (*b*) $\sum\limits_{i=1}^{3} (1/i^2) = 49/36$.

2. Show that (*a*) $\sum\limits_{j=1}^{6} \sin 2\pi j = 0$; (*b*) $\sum\limits_{j=1}^{4} \cos 2\pi j = 4$; (*c*) $\sum\limits_{k=2}^{6} 1^k = 5$; (*d*) $\sum\limits_{n=3}^{7} 1 = 5$;

   (*e*) $\sum\limits_{k=1}^{5} (-1)^k = -1$.

3. Show that (*a*) $\sum\limits_{i=1}^{4} 5i^3 = 500$; (*b*) $\sum\limits_{i=3}^{4} 6/i = 7/2$.

4. (*a*) Compute $\sum\limits_{i=1}^{4} [(1/i) - 1/(i+1)]$.

   (*b*) Show that $\sum\limits_{i=1}^{n} [(1/i) - 1/(i+1)] = 1 - 1/(n+1)$.

   (*c*) Show that $\sum\limits_{i=1}^{n} 1/[(i)(i+1)] = 1 - 1/(n+1)$.

5. (a) Show that $1/2^i = 1/2^{i-1} - 1/2^i$.

   (b) Show that $\sum\limits_{i=1}^{n} 1/2^i = 1 - 1/2^n$.

6. (a) Show that $\sum\limits_{i=1}^{3} (a_i + b_i) = \sum\limits_{i=1}^{3} a_i + \sum\limits_{i=1}^{3} b_i$.

   (b) Generalize the result in (a).

Summation over several indices. The sum of the mn numbers $a_{i,j}$, for $1 \leqslant i \leqslant n$ and $1 \leqslant j \leqslant m$ is denoted $\sum\limits_{i=1, j=1}^{m,n} a_{i,j}$ and is called *the sum of $a_{i,j}$ as i goes from* 1 *to n and j goes from 1 to m*. (For convenience we will write $a_{i,j}$ as a_{ij}.) When $m = n$, we frequently write $\sum\limits_{i=1, j=1}^{m,n}$ as $\sum\limits_{i,j=1}^{n}$.

Example 5. Let us compute $\sum\limits_{i,j=1}^{3,3} i/j$. This sum consists of nine terms

$$\tfrac{1}{1} + \tfrac{1}{2} + \tfrac{1}{3} + \tfrac{2}{1} + \tfrac{2}{2} + \tfrac{2}{3} + \tfrac{3}{1} + \tfrac{3}{2} + \tfrac{3}{3}$$

which we may rewrite as

$$1(\tfrac{1}{1} + \tfrac{1}{2} + \tfrac{1}{3}) + 2(\tfrac{1}{1} + \tfrac{1}{2} + \tfrac{1}{3}) + 3(\tfrac{1}{1} + \tfrac{1}{2} + \tfrac{1}{3}) = (1 + 2 + 3)(\tfrac{1}{1} + \tfrac{1}{2} + \tfrac{1}{3}) = 6 \cdot \tfrac{11}{6} = 11$$

Example 6. $\sum\limits_{i,j=1}^{2} i^j = 1^1 + 1^2 + 2^1 + 2^2 = 8$

Let us compare $\sum\limits_{i=1}^{2} (\sum\limits_{j=1}^{3} a_{ij})$ and $\sum\limits_{j=1}^{3} (\sum\limits_{i=1}^{2} a_{ij})$. We have

$$\sum_{i=1}^{2} (\sum_{j=1}^{3} a_{ij}) = \sum_{i=1}^{2} (a_{i1} + a_{i2} + a_{i3}) = (a_{11} + a_{12} + a_{13}) + (a_{21} + a_{22} + a_{23})$$

On the other hand,

$$\sum_{j=1}^{3} (\sum_{i=1}^{2} a_{ij}) = \sum_{j=1}^{3} (a_{1j} + a_{2j}) = (a_{11} + a_{21}) + (a_{12} + a_{22}) + (a_{13} + a_{23})$$

In each case we end up with the sum of all a_{ij}, for $1 \leqslant i \leqslant 2$ and $1 \leqslant j \leqslant 3$. The sums are equal and have the value $\sum\limits_{i,j=1}^{2,3} a_{ij}$. More generally, we have

$$\sum_{i,j=1}^{n,m} a_{ij} = \sum_{i=1}^{n} (\sum_{j=1}^{m} a_{ij}) = \sum_{j=1}^{m} (\sum_{i=1}^{n} a_{ij})$$

Example 7. If $a_{ij} = b_i c_j$, then

$$\sum_{i,j=1}^{4} a_{ij} = \sum_{i=1}^{4} (\sum_{j=1}^{4} b_i c_j) = \sum_{i=1}^{4} (b_i \sum_{j=1}^{4} c_j) = (\sum_{j=1}^{4} c_j)(\sum_{i=1}^{4} b_i) = (\sum_{i=1}^{4} b_i)(\sum_{j=1}^{4} e_j)$$

Example 8.   Let $f(x,y) = x^2y$; $x_i = i/4$; $y_j = j/4$; and $P_{ij} = (x_i,y_j)$. We compute

(2)
$$\sum_{i,j=1}^{4} f(P_{ij})(x_i - x_{i-1})(y_j - y_{j-1})$$

an instance of a sum related to a definite integral over a region in the plane. Observe that $x_i - x_{i-1} = i/4 - (i-1)/4 = 1/4$ and $y_j - y_{j-1} = 1/4$. Also, $f(P_{ij}) = f(x_i,y_j) = x_i^2y_j = (i/4)^2(j/4) = i^2j/64$. Thus the sum is

$$\sum_{i,j=1}^{4} \frac{i^2j}{64}\frac{1}{4}\frac{1}{4} = \frac{1}{64}\frac{1}{16}\sum_{i,j=1}^{4} i^2j$$

By Example 7,

$$\sum_{i,j=1}^{4} i^2j = \sum_{i=1}^{4} i^2 \sum_{j=1}^{4} j = (1^2 + 2^2 + 3^2 + 4^2)(1 + 2 + 3 + 4) = (30)(10) = 300$$

Hence the original sum (2) equals $300/(64 \cdot 16) = 75/256 = 0.293$.

The symbol $\sum\limits_{i,j,k=1}^{n} a_{i,j,k}$ denotes the sum of the n^3 terms of the form $a_{i,j,k}$, where $1 \leqslant i \leqslant n, 1 \leqslant j \leqslant n$, and $1 \leqslant k \leqslant n$. (For convenience we will write $a_{i,j,k}$ as a_{ijk}.)

Example 9.

$$\sum_{i,j,k=1}^{2} (i^j + k) = (1^1 + 1) + (1^2 + 1) + (1^1 + 2) + (1^2 + 2) + (2^1 + 1) +$$
$$(2^2 + 1) + (2^1 + 2) + (2^2 + 2) = 28$$

EXERCISES

7. Show that (a) $\sum\limits_{i,j=1}^{3} i^j = 56$; (b) $\sum\limits_{i,j=1}^{3,4} 1 = 12$.

8. Show that (a) $\sum\limits_{i,j=1}^{3} (i + j) = 12$; (b) $\sum\limits_{i=2,j=1}^{4,2} (i - j) = 9$.

9. Show that (a) $\sum\limits_{i=1}^{3} ij = 6j$; (b) $\sum\limits_{i=1}^{3} i^2j^3 = 14j^3$; (c) $\sum\limits_{j=1}^{4} i^2j^3 = 100i^2$.

10. Let $f(x,y) = x^2y$, $x_i = i/6$, $y_j = j/6$, and $P_{ij} = (x_i,y_j)$. Show that

$$\sum_{i,j=1}^{6} f(P_{ij})(x_i - x_{i-1})(y_j - y_{j-1}) = 1,911/7,776 = 0.246$$

11. Show that (a) $\sum\limits_{i,j,k=1}^{2} i^{jk} = 30$; (b) $\sum\limits_{i,j,k=1}^{3} ijk = 216$.

12. Compare these sums: $\sum\limits_{i=1}^{3} \{ \sum\limits_{j=1}^{3} [\sum\limits_{k=1}^{3} (a_{ijk})]\}$, $\sum\limits_{j=1}^{3} (\sum\limits_{i,k=1}^{3} a_{ijk})$, and $\sum\limits_{i,j,k=1}^{3} a_{ijk}$.

13. How would you denote the sum of the numbers a_{ijk} for $2 \leqslant i \leqslant m$, $3 \leqslant j \leqslant n$, and $2 \leqslant k \leqslant p$?

APPENDIX E

Length, area, and volume

IN common usage the word *area* has two meanings. In "a densely populated area of the world," it refers to a geometric region on the earth. In "the area of New York City is 299 square miles," it refers to a number. It is even possible to speak of the "area of an area." The same double use is made of the word *volume*.

In mathematics, the terms *length, area,* and *volume, always refer to numbers.* To name geometric objects or regions, we use terms such as *plane set, surface,* and *solid.*

Throughout the text we assume that the curves we deal with have length, that the surfaces have area, and that the solids have volume. We use or calculate these numbers. In this appendix we will consider the questions: What is length? What is area? What is volume? Does every curve have a length? Does every plane set or surface have an area? Does every solid have a volume?

We consider first the *length of a line segment*. In the diagram the line segment P_1P_2 joins the point $P_1 = (x_1, y_1)$ to the point $P_2 = (x_2, y_2)$.

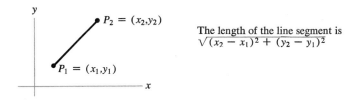

The length of the line segment is
$$\sqrt{(x_2 - x_1)^2 + (y_2 - y_1)^2}$$

On the basis of our experience with Euclidean geometry, in particular with the Pythagorean theorem, we *define* the length of P_1P_2 as $\sqrt{(x_2 - x_1)^2 + (y_2 - y_1)^2}$.

583

Next, consider a curve C. How shall we define its length? To do so, we consider any finite sequence of points P_i in order along C, and the sum s of the lengths of the straight-line segments $P_1P_2, P_2P_3, \ldots, P_{n-1}P_n$, which we sketch with dashed lines.

The sum s depends on the manner in which the points P_i are chosen. Let S be the set of all numbers s obtainable in this manner. If S has an upper bound, then we define the length of C as *the least upper bound of S*. (See Appendix B for the definition of "upper bound" and "least upper bound.") An example of a curve to which we cannot assign a length is found in Exercise 19, page 211.) We may say that a curve has a length if the approximating polygonal paths cannot be arbitrarily long.

Our approach to the concept of *area* of a plane set begins in a similar way. First *we define the area of a rectangle* as the product of its width and its length. We shall permit a rectangle to have a width or length 0.

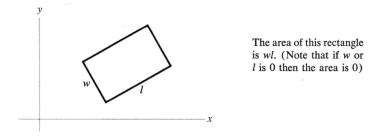

The area of this rectangle is *wl*. (Note that if *w* or *l* is 0 then the area is 0)

Now, let R be a plane set that lies totally within some rectangle, so that it does not stretch out indefinitely. Consider any finite set of rectangles $R_1, R_2, \ldots, R_n$ lying within R, such that each pair of rectangles, if they meet at all, merely touch or share part of a common border.

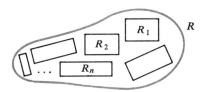

Let the sum of the areas of the rectangles R_i be s. Let S be the set of all numbers s obtainable in this manner. If S has an upper bound, let A^{inner} denote the least upper bound of S. We might be tempted to define the area of R as A^{inner}, but A^{inner} is only part of the story, as we now show.

Consider any finite set of rectangles $R_1^*, R_2^*, \ldots, R_n^*$, whose union contains R. (We use the asterisk * to distinguish this situation from the preceding one.)

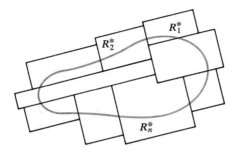

Denote the sum of the areas of the rectangles by s^*. Let S^* be the set of all numbers s^* obtainable in this manner. Clearly 0 is a lower bound for S^*. Let A^{outer} denote the greatest lower bound of S^*.

We now have two numbers, A^{inner} and A^{outer}, associated with R. It can be proved that $A^{\text{inner}} \leqslant A^{\text{outer}}$. (If R is complicated, A^{inner} can be less than A^{outer}. For instance, let R consist of those points in the plane of the form (x,y), where x is in $[0,1]$, y is in $[0,1]$, and both x and y are *rational*. We can think of R as a dust cloud scattered through the unit square:

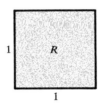

The only rectangles lying in R are points, hence the rectangles R_i have both w and l equal to 0. Thus $A^{\text{inner}} = 0$. On the other hand, if a finite set of rectangles contains R, it must contain the whole unit square. It can be proved from this that $A^{\text{outer}} = 1$.)

Most sets that appear in practice have $A^{\text{inner}} = A^{\text{outer}}$. We say that a set R for which $A^{\text{inner}} = A^{\text{outer}}$ is *measurable*, or *has an area*; its area is defined as A^{inner} or, if we prefer, A^{outer}.

The definition of the *volume* of a solid is similar to that of the *area* of a plane set. The basic difference is that one uses boxes instead of rectangles. For a set in space, we define V^{inner} and V^{outer}; it is always the case that $V^{\text{inner}} \leqslant V^{\text{outer}}$. When $V^{\text{inner}} = V^{\text{outer}}$ we say that the set *is measurable,* or has a *volume,* and its volume is V^{inner}.

The *area of a curved surface* is much more difficult to define than the length of a curve, the area of a flat surface, or the volume of a solid. The direct analog of the approach we used on curves fails. We approximated the curve by inscribed polygonal paths, each of which necessarily has a length less than or equal to that of the curve. If we approximate the area of a surface by inscribed polyhedral surfaces, we travel in dangerous waters, even in so simple an instance as the curved surface of a right circular cylinder.

The reason for this is simple. Consider three points A, B, and C on the curved surface of the cylinder. If A and B lie on a circle parallel to the base of the cylinder, and C is situated very near this circle and equally distant from A and B, then the plane of the (flat) triangle ABC is inclined steeply to the surface of the cylinder.

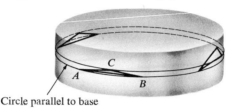

Circle parallel to base

(Note that if C were on the circle in question, the plane of ABC would be perpendicular to the axis of the cylinder.) Because of this, we can construct inscribed polyhedra having triangular faces whose total area far exceeds the surface area of the cylinder. (See R. P. Agnew, "Calculus," p. 447, McGraw-Hill, New York, 1962, for more details about this example.) Thus the area of a surface *cannot* be defined as the least upper bound of the areas of inscribed polyhedra.

There are various ways of defining surface area. In the special case in which the surface is obtained by rotating a curve around a line, we may define its area as a definite integral, $\int_a^b 2\pi y \sqrt{(dx/dt)^2 + (dy/dt)^2} \, dt$. (See pages 212–214 for details.)

A more general approach is the following: Let a plane be inclined at an angle γ to the xy plane. Let U be a set in the xy plane, and let V be the set directly above (or below) U on the inclined plane. (A line perpendicular to the inclined plane also makes an angle γ with a line perpendicular to the xy plane.)

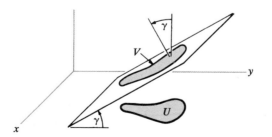

The area of U
is equal to
$(\cos \gamma)$ (area of V)

The area of U is simply $(\cos \gamma)$ (area of V). Thus the area of V is $(\sec \gamma)$ (area of U).

Now let S be the graph of the equation $F(x,y,z) = 0$ situated above (or below) the set R in the xy plane. Assume that each vertical line through R meets S in exactly one point, and that at each point of S a tangent plane is defined. (See page 395 for the definition of tangent plane.) For each point P in S let $\gamma(P)$ be the angle between the tangent plane at P and the xy plane. Let R_i be a "small" subset of R, let P_i be a point in R_i, and let V_i be the set of points on the tangent plane at P_i directly above (or below) R_i. Then we may expect that the area of V_i is a good approximation to the area of that part of S directly above (or below) R_i.

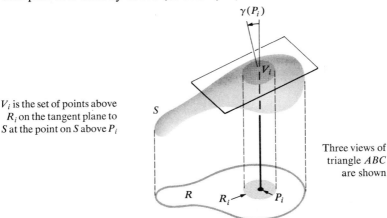

V_i is the set of points above R_i on the tangent plane to S at the point on S above P_i

Three views of triangle ABC are shown

For this reason we *define* the area of S as $\displaystyle\int_R \sec \gamma \, dA$, assuming, of course, that the definite integral exists. Another approach to the definition of surface area is described in Exercise 11.

When we say that "area is the definite integral of cross-sectional length" or that "volume is the definite integral of cross-sectional area," the reader should realize that we are quoting theorems which assume certain conditions on the plane set or the solid in question. The sets met in the usual applications of the calculus satisfy these conditions, and thus our intuitive arguments then lead to correct results.

EXERCISES

1. Let R be all the points in space of the form $(x,y,0)$, where x and y are rational numbers, and where $0 \leqslant x \leqslant 1$ and $0 \leqslant y \leqslant 1$.
   (a) Show that R does not have an area.
   (b) Show that R has a volume equal to 0.
2. Prove that if R and S are plane sets with areas, and R is a subset of S, then the area of R is not larger than the area of S. (Use the definition of area.)
3. Explain why the area of U is $(\cos \gamma)$ (area of V), where U, V, and γ are defined as on page 586. (Hint: Recall that area is the definite integral of cross-sectional length.)
4. Show that if the surface S has the equation $F(x,y,z)$, then

$$\sec \gamma = \sqrt{ F_x{}^2 + F_y{}^2 + F_z{}^2} / \left| F_z \right|$$

   (Hint: The gradient ∇F is perpendicular to S.)

5. Find the area of that portion of the parabolic cylinder $z = (\frac{1}{2})x^2$ between the three planes $y = 0$, $y = x$, and $x = 2$. (Hint: See Exercise 4, and use $F(x,y,z) = z - (\frac{1}{2})x^2$.)

[Answer: $(\frac{1}{3})(5\sqrt{5} - 1)$]

6. Find the area of the part of the spherical surface $x^2 + y^2 + z^2 = 1$ that lies within the vertical cylinder erected on the circle $r = \cos \theta$ and above the xy plane.

(Answer: $2\pi - 4$)

7. (a) Find the area of that part of the spherical surface $x^2 + y^2 + z^2 = a^2$ that lies above the horizontal disk of radius $R < a$ whose center is $(0,0,0)$, using a definite integral over the disk.

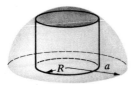

The radius of the hemisphere is a and the radius of the cylinder is R

(b) From the result in (a), obtain the surface area of a hemisphere.

[Answer: (a) $2\pi a(a - \sqrt{a^2 - R^2})$]

8. Let C be a curve in the xy plane whose equation is $y = f(x)$ for x in $[a,b]$. Let $\gamma(x,y)$ be the angle between a line perpendicular to the curve at (x,y) and the y axis. Show that the length of C is $\int_a^b \sec \gamma \, dx$. (Hint: Make use of the formula for arc length given on page 204.)

9. Review Exercise 20, page 138.

(a) Why would the expected (theoretical average) number of intersections of a needle of length 1 with parallel lines a distance 1 apart be $2/\pi$?

(b) Why would the expected number of intersections of a needle or any rigid piece of curved wire of length L with the lines in (a) be presumably $2L/\pi$?

(c) How could the relation in (b) be used to *define* arc length?

10. (See Exercise 9.) Let C be a curve bounding a convex set in the plane. Each time we rotate C in the plane by an angle θ, it will have a "projection" or "shadow" on the x axis. (This is the set of points x on the x axis such that the line through x and parallel to the y axis meets the rotated curve.) Let p be the average of the lengths of those shadows as a function of θ. Why would you expect the length of C to be equal to $2\pi p$, even if C is not a circle? (Hint: Consider Exercise 9.)

11. (See Exercise 10.) Let S be a surface bounding a convex set in space.

(a) Develop the analogs of Exercises 9 and 10 for S.

(b) Why would you expect the area of S to be four times its "average shadow" even if S were not a sphere? (Hint: Instead of the set of lines parallel to the y axis and passing through (n,o), where n is an integer, use the set of lines parallel to the z axis and passing through the points (m,n,o), where m and n are integers.)

APPENDIX F

Limits and continuous functions (proofs)

In this appendix we shall prove several assertions about limits which have been used repeatedly in the text. We shall also prove that any polynomial is continuous. A concluding, and independent, section presents a function that is continuous for all x in $[0,1]$ but differentiable nowhere.

Limits of functions of x.   We recall the definition of $\lim\limits_{x \to a} f(x)$. For our purposes the second definition on page 86, stated in terms of absolute value, is preferable. We say that

$$\lim_{x \to a} f(x) = A$$

if for any $\varepsilon > 0$ there is a number $\delta > 0$ (which may depend on ε) such that

$$|f(x) - A| < \varepsilon$$

whenever $|x - a| < \delta$ (except, perhaps, $x = a$). (If it happens that the domain of f does not contain an open interval that includes a, we insist only that the domain

589

of f contain points other than a in each open interval that includes a. We demand that $|f(x) - A| < \varepsilon$ for $|x - a| < \delta$, $x \neq a$, and x in the domain of f.)

THEOREM 1.   *If* $\lim_{x \to a} f(x) = A$ *and* $\lim_{x \to a} g(x) = B$, *then* $\lim_{x \to a} [f(x) + g(x)] = A + B$.

PROOF.   We must show that there exists, for any $\varepsilon > 0$ no matter how small, a number $\delta > 0$ such that

(1) $$|[f(x) + g(x)] - (A + B)| < \varepsilon$$

whenever $|x - a| < \delta$ for $x \neq a$.

Let us rewrite $[f(x) + g(x)] - (A + B)$ in the more suggestive form $[f(x) - A] + [g(x) - B]$, which is a sum of two quantities we assume are small when x is near a. Since the absolute value of the sum of two numbers is not larger than the sum of their absolute values, we have

$$|[f(x) - A] + [g(x) - B]| \leqslant |f(x) - A| + |g(x) - B|$$

Thus

(2) $$|[f(x) + g(x)] - (A + B)| \leqslant |f(x) - A| + |g(x) - B|$$

Since $\lim_{x \to a} f(x) = A$, we know that there is a positive number δ_1 such that $|f(x) - A| < \varepsilon/2$ when $|x - a| < \delta_1$, for $x \neq a$. (Why we pick $\varepsilon/2$ rather than ε will be clear in a moment.) Similarly there is a positive number δ_2 such that $|g(x) - B| < \varepsilon/2$ when $|x - a| < \delta_2$, for $x \neq a$.

Now let δ be the smaller of δ_1 and δ_2. For any x such that $|x - a| < \delta$ we have both

$$|x - a| < \delta_1 \quad \text{and} \quad |x - a| < \delta_2$$

and therefore, simultaneously,

(3) $$|f(x) - A| < \frac{\varepsilon}{2} \quad \text{and} \quad |g(x) - B| < \frac{\varepsilon}{2}$$

Combining (2) and (3), we conclude that when $|x - a| < \delta$, for $x \neq a$, we have $|[f(x) + g(x)] - (A + B)| < \varepsilon/2 + \varepsilon/2 = \varepsilon$. We have shown that for each $\varepsilon > 0$ there exists a suitable $\delta > 0$, depending, of course, on ε, f, and g. This ends the proof.

Theorem 1 is the basis of the proof of the next theorem.

THEOREM 2.   *The sum of two functions that are continuous at* a *is itself continuous at* a.

PROOF.   Let f and g be continuous at a. Let h be their sum; that is, $h(x) = f(x) + g(x)$. We wish to show that h is continuous at a.

In view of the definition of continuity, page 82, we must show that $h(a)$ is defined and that $\lim_{x \to a} h(x) = h(a)$.

Since f and g are defined at a, so is h, and $h(a) = f(a) + g(a)$. All that remains is to show that $\lim_{x \to a} [f(x) + g(x)] = f(a) + g(a)$. But Theorem 1 assures us that

$\lim\limits_{x \to a} [f(x) + g(x)] = \lim\limits_{x \to a} f(x) + \lim\limits_{x \to a} g(x)$. Since f and g are continuous at a, we have $\lim\limits_{x \to a} f(x) = f(a)$ and $\lim\limits_{x \to a} g(x) = g(a)$. This concludes the proof.

THEOREM 3. *If* $\lim\limits_{x \to a} f(x) = A$ *and* $\lim\limits_{x \to a} g(x) = B$, *then* $\lim\limits_{x \to a} f(x)g(x) = AB$.

Plan of proof. We know that $|f(x) - A|$ and $|g(x) - B|$ are small when x is near a. We wish to conclude that $|f(x)g(x) - AB|$ is small when x is near a. We shall make use of the algebraic identity

(4)
$$f(x)g(x) - AB = f(x)[g(x) - B] + B[f(x) - A]$$

From (4) and properties of the absolute value, we conclude that

(5)
$$|f(x)g(x) - AB| \leqslant |f(x)||g(x) - B| + |B||f(x) - A|$$

Now $|B|$ is fixed; and $|f(x) - A|$ and $|g(x) - B|$ are small where x is near a. The real problem is to control $|f(x)|$. Watch carefully how we deal with $|f(x)|$ in the proof.

PROOF. We consider only the case $B \neq 0$. Let $\varepsilon > 0$ be given. We wish to show that there is a number $\delta > 0$ such that $|f(x)g(x) - AB| < \varepsilon$ when $|x - a| < \delta$, for $x \neq a$. Observe that

(6)
$$|f(x)g(x) - AB| = |f(x)[g(x) - B] + B[f(x) - A]|$$
$$\leqslant |f(x)||g(x) - B| + |B||f(x) - A|$$

Since $\lim\limits_{x \to a} f(x) = A$, there is a number $\delta > 0$ such that $|f(x) - A| < \varepsilon/(2|B|)$ when $|x - a| < \delta_1$, for $x \neq a$. [Thus we have already seen to it that the second summand in (5) is less than $|B|\varepsilon/(2|B|) = \varepsilon/2$.]

For x such that $|x - a| < \delta_1$, we see that $|f(x)|$ does not become arbitrarily large, since $|f(x) - A| < \varepsilon/(2|B|)$. Indeed for such x we have $|f(x)| < |A| + \varepsilon/(2|B|)$. Calling $|A| + \varepsilon/(2|B|)$ simply C, we have $|f(x)| < C$ when $|x - a| < \delta_1$, for $x \neq a$. (This controls the size of $|f(x)|$.)

Since $\lim\limits_{x \to a} g(x) = B$, we know that there is a $\delta_2 > 0$ such that $|g(x) - B| < \varepsilon/(2C)$ when $|x - a| < \delta_2$, for $x \neq a$.

Now let δ be the smaller of δ_1 and δ_2. When $|x - a| < \delta$, we have both $|x - a| < \delta_1$ and $|x - a| < \delta_2$; hence $|f(x) - A| < \varepsilon/(2|B|)$, $|f(x)| < C$, and $|g(x) - B| < \varepsilon/(2C)$. Inspection of (6) then shows that for x such that $|x - a| < \delta$, and for $x \neq a$, we have

$$|f(x)g(x) - AB| \leqslant C\frac{\varepsilon}{2C} + |B|\frac{\varepsilon}{2|B|} = \frac{\varepsilon}{2} + \frac{\varepsilon}{2} = \varepsilon$$

The proof is completed. (The case $B = 0$ is less involved and is left to the reader.)

THEOREM 4. *The product of two functions that are continuous at a is itself continuous at a.*

The proof is like that of Theorem 2, but depends on Theorem 3 instead of Theorem 1.

THEOREM 5.   *The function f, such that $f(x) = x$, is continuous everywhere. So are the functions $x^2, x^3, x^4, \ldots$.*

PROOF.   Since $f(a) = a$, we must show that $|f(x) - a|$ is small whenever $|x - a|$ is sufficiently small. More precisely, for $\varepsilon > 0$ we wish to exhibit $\delta > 0$ such that $|f(x) - a| < \varepsilon$ whenever $|x - a| < \delta$. But $f(x) = x$; hence $|f(x) - a|$ is simply $|x - a|$. Thus when $|x - a| < \varepsilon$, it follows that $|f(x) - a| < \varepsilon$. In other words, $\delta = \varepsilon$ suffices. This shows that the function x is continuous.

Since the function x^2 may be considered the product of the function x and the function x, we conclude from Theorem 4 that x^2 is continuous. Similarly, x^3 is continuous, for $x^3 = x^2x$. In a similar manner, x^4 and x^5 can be shown to be continuous. Mathematical induction establishes the continuity of x^n for all positive integers n.

THEOREM 6.   *Any constant function is continuous everywhere.*

PROOF.   Let $f(x) = c$ for all x. For any $\varepsilon > 0$, choose $\delta = 1{,}776$. Now $|f(x) - f(a)| = |c - c| = 0 < \varepsilon$ for any x, and hence for x such that $|x - a| < 1{,}776$. Thus f is continuous at any number a.

THEOREM 7.   *Any polynomial is continuous everywhere.*

PROOF.   We illustrate the idea of the proof by showing that $6x^2 - 5x + 1$ is continuous everywhere.

By Theorem 6, the constant functions $f(x) = 6$, $f(x) = -5$, and $f(x) = 1$ are continuous everywhere. By Theorem 5, the functions x and x^2 are continuous everywhere.

By Theorem 4, the functions $6x^2$ and $(-5)x$ are continuous. By Theorem 2, the function $[6x^2 + (-5)x]$ is continuous. Again, by Theorem 2, the function $[6x^2 + (-5)x] + 1$ is continuous. Thus $6x^2 - 5x + 1$ is continuous. The same argument applies to any polynomial.

EXERCISES

1. Prove that the function $2x$ is continuous at the point $x = 3$, using only the definition of continuity.
2. Using the definition of continuity, prove that $3x + 8$ is continuous at the point $x = 2$.
3. Using the definition of continuity, prove that x^2 is continuous at the point $x = 3$.
4. Prove that if f is continuous at a and g is continuous at $f(a)$, then the composite function $g \circ f$ is continuous at a.
5. Prove that $1/x$ is continuous at any $a \neq 0$.
6. (a) Using Exercises 4 and 5, prove that $1/f(x)$ is continuous at any point a such that $f(a) \neq 0$.

(b) Using (a) and Theorem 4, deduce that the quotient of two continuous functions, $g(x)/f(x)$, is continuous at any a such that $f(a) \neq 0$.

(c) Prove that $(x^3 + 1)/(x^2 + 1)$ is continuous everywhere.

7. Prove Theorem 3 for the case $B = 0$.

8. (a) Find $\delta > 0$ such that $|\sqrt{x} - \sqrt{9}| < 0.04$ when $|x - 9| < \delta$.

(b) Prove that $\sqrt{x}$ is continuous at any $a \geqslant 0$. (Hint: Make use of the identity $\sqrt{b} - \sqrt{a} = (b - a)/(\sqrt{b} + \sqrt{a})$.

9. Find $\delta > 0$ such that (a) $|x^2 - 4| < 1$ when $|x - 2| < \delta$; (b) $|x^2 - 4| < 0.1$ when $|x - 2| < \delta$; (c) $|x^2 - 4| < 0.01$ when $|x - 2| < \delta$; (d) $|x^2 - 4| < t$ when $|x - 2| < \delta$; (e) $|x^2 - 4| < \varepsilon$ when $|x - 2| < \delta$. (Hint: Note that $|x^2 - 4| = |x - 2||x + 2|$, and be sure to control $|x + 2|$.)

10. Prove that the difference of two continuous functions is continuous, (a) using the definition of continuity, and (b) using theorems proved in this appendix.

Limits of functions of x and y and of sequences.   Theorems like Theorems 1 through 7 hold for continuous functions of two variables. The proofs are similar and depend on the following two definitions.

DEFINITION: $\lim\limits_{(x,y) \to (a,b)} f(x,y)$.   Let $P = (a,b)$ be a point in the plane such that every disk whose center is P contains a point in the domain of f, other than (a,b). Then $\lim\limits_{(x,y) \to (a,b)} f(x,y) = A$ if for any $\varepsilon > 0$ there is a number $\delta > 0$ such that

$$|f(x,y) - A| < \varepsilon$$

whenever the distance from (x,y) to (a,b) is less than δ, and (x,y) is in the domain of f, but different from (a,b).

DEFINITION: *Continuity of a function at (a,b).*   A function f of x and y is continuous at (a,b) if f is defined at (a,b) and $\lim\limits_{(x,y) \to (a,b)} f(x,y) = f(a,b)$.

The proofs that the sum and product of continuous functions defined on the plane are continuous are virtually the same as the proofs of Theorems 2 and 4. (We simply replace $|x - a|$ with $\sqrt{(x - a)^2 + (y - b)^2}$ in the various proofs.)

The analogs of Theorems 1 and 3 hold for sequences. We have, for instance, $\lim\limits_{n \to \infty} (a_n + b_n) = A + B$ if $\lim\limits_{n \to \infty} a_n = A$ and $\lim\limits_{n \to \infty} b_n = B$. The proofs are similar to those of Theorems 1 and 3 and will not be given here.

Instead we will prove a property of a special sequence that we have used several times (for instance, when finding the sum of a geometric series.)

THEOREM 8.   *Let r be a number such that $0 < r < 1$. Then* $\lim\limits_{n \to \infty} r^n = 0$.

PROOF.   Let $X = \{r, r^2, r^3, r^4, \ldots\}$. Since each element of X is positive, 0 is a lower bound of X. Thus X has a greatest lower bound, which we denote g. We shall show that $g = 0$; once we know that $g = 0$, it will be a brief matter to deduce that $\lim\limits_{n \to \infty} r^n = 0$.

Observe that since $g < r^n$ for each n, we have $g/r < r^{n-1}$ for each n. Thus g/r is a lower bound of X. Since g is the *greatest* lower bound of X, we must have $g/r \leqslant g$. Thus $g = 0$ or $1/r \leqslant 1$; since $r < 1$, the latter is impossible, so we conclude that $g = 0$.

We now prove that $\lim_{n \to \infty} r^n = 0$. Let $\varepsilon > 0$. Since 0 is the greatest lower bound of X, it follows that ε is *not* a lower bound of X. Thus there is an integer N such that $r^N < \varepsilon$. For $n > N$ it follows that $r^n < \varepsilon$, and therefore that $|r^n - 0| < \varepsilon$ when $n > N$. Thus $\lim_{n \to \infty} r^n = 0$, and the proof is completed.

A similar proof establishes the following theorem, which is used in the proof of the comparison test, page 324.

THEOREM 9.   *Let $a_1 < a_2 < a_3 < \ldots < a_n < \ldots$ be a sequence such that there is a number u greater than all a_n. Then $\lim_{n \to \infty} a_n$ exists and is no larger than u.*

EXERCISES

11. Prove that if $-1 < r < 1$, then $\lim_{n \to \infty} r^n = 0$.

12. Prove Theorem 9.

13. Prove that if $\lim_{n \to \infty} a_n = A$ and $\lim_{n \to \infty} b_n = B$, then (a) $\lim_{n \to \infty} (a_n + b_n) = A + B$, and (b) $\lim_{n \to \infty} a_n b_n = A \cdot B$.

14. Prove that $\lim_{n \to \infty} 1/n^2 = 0$.

A function continuous throughout [0,1] but differentiable nowhere.   None of the preceding results is contrary to our intuition. However, advanced mathematics holds many surprises. One such example, well worth patient and careful study, was discovered by Bolzano in 1834; it is a function that is continuous at all x in [0,1] but differentiable nowhere. It would be futile to try to graph such a function, since its misbehavior is microscopic. We shall define it by explicit directions. Our approach is different from Bolzano's and will make use of the base 2. We take a moment to describe this system of representing the positive numbers.

In base 10 we use the digits $0,1,2, \ldots, 9$ and represent integers by a sequence of such digits, each corresponding to a power of 10. For instance, 503 is short for $5 \cdot 10^2 + 0 \cdot 10^1 + 3$. We represent numbers between 0 and 1 similarly, but use the negative powers of 10, rather than the positive. Thus 0.503 is short for $5 \cdot 10^{-1} + 0 \cdot 10^{-2} + 3 \cdot 10^{-3}$. Sometimes a decimal representation is endless. For instance, $\frac{1}{3} = 0.33\overline{3}$, which is repeating, and $\sqrt{2} = 1.414 \ldots$, which is not repeating. (The bar over a group of digits indicates the repeating block.) Moreover, some numbers can have two different representations—one ending in 0's, the other in 9's. For instance, $2.1000\overline{0} = 2.0999\overline{9}$.

The representation of numbers in base 2 is similar, except that we use only the digits 0 and 1, and we use powers of 2 instead of powers of 10. Thus 1,101 (base 2) is short for $1 \cdot 2^3 + 1 \cdot 2^2 + 0 \cdot 2^1 + 1 = 13$ (base 10).

A number less than 1 has a representation in terms of the negative powers of 2 alone. For instance, 0.101 (base 2) is short for $1 \cdot 2^{-1} + 0 \cdot 2^{-2} + 1 \cdot 2^{-3} = \frac{1}{2} + \frac{1}{8} = \frac{5}{8}$. And the repeating expression $0.1010101\overline{0}$ (base 2) represents $\frac{1}{2} + \frac{1}{8} + \frac{1}{32} + \frac{1}{128} + \cdots$, an endless geometric progression whose first term is $\frac{1}{2}$ and whose ratio is $\frac{1}{4}$. Thus

$$0.1010101\overline{0} \text{ (base 2)} = \frac{1/2}{1 - 1/4} = \frac{2}{3}$$

A number that has a base-2 representation involving an endless string of 1's also has a base-2 representation involving an endless string of 0's (a "terminating" expression). For instance, the base-2 expressions $0.011\overline{1}$ and $0.100\overline{0}$ represent the same number, since $0.011\overline{1} = \frac{1}{4} + \frac{1}{8} + \frac{1}{16} + \cdots = \frac{1}{2} = 0.100\overline{0}$.

Now we are ready to define our function f for any x in [0,1]. The directions for computing $f(x)$ are simple:

1. We express x in base 10: $x = 0.a_1a_2a_3 \cdots$ (base 10). Each a_i is 0, 1, 2, . . . , or 9.
2. We express $f(x)$ in base 2: $f(x) = 0.b_1b_2b_3 \cdots$ (base 2). Each b_i is 0 or 1 and is determined from the a_i's by this procedure:
   (a) We have $b_1 = 0$ if a_1 is 0; $b_1 = 1$ if a_1 is 1, 2, 3, . . . , or 9.
   (b) Generally, given b_{i-1}, we have $b_i = b_{i-1}$ if $a_i = a_i$, and $b_i \neq b_{i-1}$ if $a_i \neq a_{i-1}$. (Note that since base 2 involves only the digits 0 and 1, this is an adequate description of b_i.)

As an illustration, let us compute $f(\frac{1}{2})$. Here $x = \frac{1}{2} = 0.500\overline{0}$. Since a_1 is not 0, we have $b_1 = 1$. Since $a_2 \neq a_1$, we have $b_2 \neq b_1$; thus $b_2 = 0$. Since $a_3 = a_2$, we have $b_3 = b_2$; thus $b_3 = 0$. Similarly $0 = b_4 = b_5 = \cdots$. Hence $f(\frac{1}{2}) = 0.1000$ (base 2). In short, $f(\frac{1}{2}) = \frac{1}{2}$.

There is, however, an important point that we must consider. What if we had used the representation $0.499\overline{9}$ for $\frac{1}{2}$? Would we still have $f(\frac{1}{2}) = \frac{1}{2}$? Let us see. Again $b_1 = 1$. Since $a_2 \neq a_1$, we have $b_2 = 0$. Since the a_i's are equal from a_2 on, the remaining b_i's are all 0. Thus we obtain $f(\frac{1}{2}) = 0.100\overline{0}$ (base 2), which is again $\frac{1}{2}$.

As another example, consider $f(\sqrt{2}/2) = f(0.707. . .)$. In this case $x = \sqrt{2}/2$ has a unique expression in base 10. Using the definition of f, we see that the representation of $f(\sqrt{2}/2)$ begins with 0.101 . . . (base 2).

Note that $f(0) = 0$ and $f(1) = f(0.99\overline{9}) = 0.11\overline{1}$ (base 2) $= 1$.

Now we indicate why f is continuous. As we have defined f, the first n b_i's are determined by the first n a_i's. Hence if two numbers, x and x', agree in their first n base-10 digits, $a_1, a_2, \ldots, a_n$, then $f(x)$ and $f(x')$ agree in their first n base-2 digits, $b_1, b_2, \ldots, b_n$, and it is not difficult to show that if $|x - x'| < 1/10^n$, then $|f(x) - f(x')| < \tfrac{1}{2}^{n-1}$. *Thus f is continuous.*

Now we show why f is *not differentiable* at any $x = 0.a_1 a_2 a_3 \cdots$ in [0,1]. For any positive integer n there is a number x_n such that the base-2 representation of $f(x_n)$ coincides with the base-2 representation of $f(x)$ except at the nth place, and the base 10 representation of x_n coincides with the base 10 representation of x in at least the first $n - 1$ places. We illustrate this by an example.

Say that $x = 0.7433625 \ldots$ and $n = 4$. Then we have $f(x) = 0.1011010 \ldots$. We will construct an x_4 such that $f(x_4) = 0.1010010 \ldots$ and the base-10 representation of x_4 is $0.743 c_4 c_5 c_6 \ldots$. How shall we define c_4? Observe that the third and fourth digits of $f(x_4)$ are unequal. Hence we must have $c_4 \neq c_3$, that is, $c_4 \neq 3$. We have nine choices for c_4; let us choose $c_4 = 2$. How shall we define c_5? Since the fourth and fifth digits of $f(x_4)$ are equal, we must have $c_4 = c_5$; hence $c_5 = 2$. In a similar manner we see that $c_6 \neq c_5$ and $c_7 \neq c_6$. We may choose $c_6 = 0$ and $c_7 = 8$, for the sake of variety. Thus one choice of x_4 has a representation beginning $0.7432208 \cdots$

The importance of the numbers $x_1, x_2, x_3, x_4, \ldots$ lies in these two facts: First, $f(x_n) - f(x) = \tfrac{1}{2}^n$ or $-\tfrac{1}{2}^n$, and second, x_n differs from x by at most $\tfrac{1}{10}^{n-1}$ (since the base-10 representations of x and x_n coincide in their first $n - 1$ places).

Now we show why f fails to have a derivative at any number x. Consider the quotient

$$\frac{f(x_n) - f(x)}{x_n - x}$$

Since $f(x_n) - f(x)$ is $\tfrac{1}{2}^n$ or $-\tfrac{1}{2}^n$, and since $x_n - x$ is between $\tfrac{1}{10}^{n-1}$ and $-(\tfrac{1}{10}^{n-1})$, we see that $\left| [f(x_n) - f(x)]/(x_n - x) \right|$ is at least

$$\frac{1/2^n}{1/10^{n-1}} = \frac{1}{2^n} \cdot 10^{n-1} = \frac{1}{10} \cdot \frac{10^n}{2^n} = \frac{1}{10} \cdot 5^n$$

a number that becomes arbitrarily large as n increases.

This implies that $\lim_{n \to \infty} [f(x_n) - f(x)]/(x_n - x)$ does not exist. In fact, there are arbitrarily steep chords of f, each with one end at $(x, f(x))$, that are as short as we please. Though f is continuous for all x in [0,1], it has a derivative nowhere.

EXERCISES

15. Show that $0.010\overline{1}$ (base 2) $= \tfrac{1}{3} = 0.33\overline{3}$ (base 10).

In Exercises 16 through 21, the f refers to the specific function constructed in this appendix.

16. Show that (a) $f(0) = 0$; (b) $f(\tfrac{1}{2}) = \tfrac{1}{2}$; (c) $f(\tfrac{2}{3}) = 1$; (d) $f(\tfrac{1}{4}) = \tfrac{2}{3}$; (e) $f(\tfrac{1}{20}) = \tfrac{1}{4}$.

17. (a) Show that if x is rational, then $f(x)$ is rational.
　　(b) If x is irrational, must $f(x)$ be irrational? Explain.

18. (*a*) If we had used the base 2 to represent both *x* and *f*(*x*), would the resulting function *f* have been continuous? Differentiable?
(*b*) If we had used the base 10 for both *x* and *f*(*x*), what trouble would arise?
(*c*) Could we have used the base 3 for *x*? Explain.

19. If $x = 0.74405622 \ldots$, show that (*a*) the base-2 representation of *f*(*x*) begins with $0.10010100 \ldots$; (*b*) one choice of x_1 begins with $0.61124766 \ldots$; (*c*) one choice of x_2 begins with $0.75453011 \ldots$; (*d*) one choice of x_3 begins with $0.74005622 \ldots$; (*e*) give three choices for x_4.

20. Show in detail that if $|y - x| < 1/1{,}000$ then $|f(y) - f(x)| < \frac{1}{4}$.

21. Show that if the decimal representation of *x* in [0,1] does not have an endless string of 0's (that is, does not terminate), or of 1's, or of 2's, . . . , or of 9's, then there is *y* as close as we please to *x* such that $f(y) = f(x)$.

APPENDIX G

Partial fractions

IN this appendix we present an algebraic result used in Chap. 7 for finding anti-derivatives of rational functions.

Partial-fraction representation of rational numbers. We begin with a few definitions. An integer D *divides* an integer A if there is an integer Q such that $A = DQ$. The integer D is a *divisor* of A. An integer A *greater than* 1 is *prime* if, whenever it is expressed as the product BC of integers B and C, at least one of B and C has absolute value 1. Thus 2, 3, 5, 7, 11, and 13 are primes, but 1, 4, 6, 8, 9, 10, and 12 are not primes.

Now, a little arithmetic will show that

(1)
$$\frac{19}{24} = \frac{0}{2} + \frac{1}{2^2} + \frac{-1}{2^3} + \frac{2}{3}$$

Note in (1) that the denominators are powers of prime numbers, that these prime powers divide the denominator in the left member of (1), and that the numerators in the right member of (1) have small absolute value. This illustrates the following theorem concerning rational numbers, that is, quotients of integers. (We shall not prove Theorem 1 or any of the theorems in this appendix.)

THEOREM 1: *Partial fractions for rational numbers.* Let a and b be integers such that $|a| < |b|$, and b is not 1 or -1. Then the rational number a/b can be represented as a sum of rational numbers of the form N/p^e, where p is prime, p^e divides b, and $|N| < p$.

The representation described in Theorem 1 is a *partial-fraction representation* of a/b; the summands N/p^e are the *partial fractions* in the representation.

598

Example 1. If $a = 19$ and $b = 24$, then the prime powers that divide b are 2, 2^2, 2^3 and 3. Equation (1) illustrates Theorem 1. Note that in each partial fraction on the right side of (1), the absolute value of the numerator is less than the prime appearing in its denominator.

Example 2. Since 37 is not less than 10, Theorem 1 makes no statement about $a/b = {}^{37}\!/_{10}$. In this case we may write ${}^{37}\!/_{10}$ as $3 + {}^{7}\!/_{10}$ and apply Theorem 1 to ${}^{7}\!/_{10}$. According to Theorem 1, there are integers N_1 and N_2 such that

$$\frac{7}{10} = \frac{N_1}{2} + \frac{N}{5} \quad \text{and} \quad |N_1| < 2 \qquad |N_2| < 5$$

A little experimentation shows that $N_1 = 1$ and $N_2 = 1$; therefore ${}^{37}\!/_{10} = 3 + \frac{1}{2} + \frac{1}{5}$.

We shall not present a method for finding the numerators, since we are interested mainly in the analog of Theorem 1 for rational functions.

EXERCISES

1. Verify that these representations satisfy the conditions of Theorem 1:
   (a) ${}^{18}\!/_{35} = {}^{4}\!/_{5} + {}^{-2}\!/_{7} = {}^{5}\!/_{7} + {}^{-1}\!/_{5}$; (b) ${}^{7}\!/_{27} = {}^{2}\!/_{9} + {}^{1}\!/_{27}$.
2. Find partial-fraction representations for (a) ${}^{1}\!/_{6}$; (b) ${}^{4}\!/_{15}$; (c) ${}^{11}\!/_{36}$; (d) ${}^{1}\!/_{15}$; (e) ${}^{7}\!/_{9}$; (f) ${}^{19}\!/_{27}$.
3. Prove that if a is an integer and $0 \leqslant a < 16$, then $a/16 = N_1/2 + N_2/4 + N_3/8 + N_4/16$, where each N_i is 0 or 1. Do not use Theorem 1. (Hint: Consider the base-2 representation of a.)

Partial-fraction representation of rational functions. An expression of the form $a_0 x^n + a_1 x^{n-1} + \cdots + a_n$, where the a_i's are real numbers, is a *polynomial*. If $a_0 \neq 0$, then n is the *degree* of the polynomial. A *rational function* is the quotient of two polynomials. An *irreducible* (or *prime*) *polynomial* is a polynomial of degree at least 1 that is not the product of polynomials of lower degree. The polynomial D *divides* the polynomial A if there is a polynomial Q such that $A = DQ$. The polynomial D is a *divisor* of A.

Example 3. The polynomial $1x^4 + 1$, which is usually written $x^4 + 1$, is a polynomial of degree four. It is *not* prime, since

$$x^4 + 1 = (x^2 + \sqrt{2}\,x + 1)(x^2 - \sqrt{2}x + 1)$$

as can be checked by multiplication.

Any first-degree polynomial $ax + b$ is prime. A second-degree polynomial $ax^2 + bx + c$ is prime if and only if $b^2 - 4ac < 0$. It can be proved that *no polynomial whose degree is larger than 2 is prime.*

Example 4. The polynomial $6x + 8$ is prime, since its degree is 1. The polynomial $x^2 + \sqrt{2}x + 1$ is prime, since $(\sqrt{2})^2 - 4(1)(1) = 2 - 4 < 0$. The polynomial $x^3 + 1$ is *not* prime, since its degree is greater than 2; indeed we have $x^3 + 1 = (x + 1)(x^2 - x + 1)$.

The following theorem is frequently helpful in finding first-degree divisors of a polynomial.

THEOREM 2: *Factor theorem.* Let c be a real number. The polynomial $x - c$ divides the polynomial f if and only if $f(c) = 0$.

Example 5. Let $f(x) = x^3 + 1$. Since $f(-1) = (-1)^3 + 1 = 0$, the factor theorem tells us that $x + 1$ divides $x^3 + 1$. (Compare with Example 4.) Similarly, since 2 is a root of the equation $4x^3 - 6x^2 - x - 6 = 0$, we know that $x - 2$ divides $4x^3 - 6x^2 - x - 6$.

Just as every integer greater than 1 is a prime number or the product of prime numbers, every polynomial of degree at least 1 is either a prime polynomial or the product of prime polynomials.

Example 6. We shall express $x^4 - 2x^3 + 2x^2 - 2x + 1$ as the product of prime polynomials. Since 1 is a root of the equation $x^4 - 2x^3 + 2x^2 - 2x + 1 = 0$, we know that $x - 1$ is a divisor of $x^4 - 2x^3 + 2x^2 - 2x + 1$. To determine the quotient, we carry out the division:

$$
\begin{array}{r}
x^3 - x^2 + x - 1 \\
x - 1 \overline{)\,x^4 - 2x^3 + 2x^2 - 2x + 1} \\
\underline{x^4 - x^3} \\
-x^3 + 2x^2 \\
\underline{-x^3 + x^2} \\
x^2 - 2x \\
\underline{x^2 - x} \\
-x + 1 \\
\underline{-x + 1} \\
0
\end{array}
$$

Hence $x^4 - 2x^3 + 2x^2 - 2x + 1 = (x - 1)(x^3 - x^2 + x - 1)$. But 1 is a root of $x^3 - x^2 + x - 1 = 0$; hence $x - 1$ is a divisor of $x^3 - x^2 + x - 1$. Long division shows that $x^3 - x^2 + x - 1 = (x - 1)(x^2 + 1)$. Since $x^2 + 1$ is prime, the representation of $x^4 - 2x^3 + 2x^2 - 2x + 1$ as the product of prime polynomials is

$$x^4 - 2x^3 + 2x^2 - 2x + 1 = (x - 1)(x - 1)(x^2 + 1).$$

The prime polynomials are analogs of prime numbers; the next theorem shows that degree is the analog of absolute value.

THEOREM 3: *Partial fractions for rational functions.* Let $A(x)$ and $B(x)$ be polynomials such that the degree of $A(x)$ is less than the degree of $B(x)$. Then the rational function $A(x)/B(x)$ can be represented as a sum of rational functions of the form $N(x)/[P(x)]^e$, where $P(x)$ is a prime polynomial, $[P(x)]^e$ divides $B(x)$, and the degree of $N(x)$ is less than the degree of $P(x)$ [or possibly all the coefficients of $N(x)$ are 0].

It should be pointed out that the representation in Theorem 3 is unique for given $P(x)$'s. (The representations for rational numbers in Theorem 1 is not necessarily unique; for instance, $^{13}\!\!/_{35} = \frac{4}{5} + -\frac{3}{7} = -\frac{1}{5} + \frac{4}{7}$.)

Example 7.
$$\frac{2}{1 - x^2} = \frac{1}{1 - x} + \frac{1}{1 + x}$$

$$\frac{x^2 + 4x - 10}{(x - 1)^3} = \frac{1}{x - 1} + \frac{6}{(x - 1)^2} - \frac{5}{(x - 1)^3}$$

$$\frac{1}{x^4 + 1} = \frac{(\sqrt{2}/4)x + 1/2}{x^2 + \sqrt{2}\,x + 1} + \frac{(-\sqrt{2}/4)x + 1/2}{x^2 - \sqrt{2}\,x + 1}$$

Since any prime polynomial has degree 1 or 2, Theorem 3 may be expressed as follows.

THEOREM 3 *(Rephrased): Partial fractions for rational functions.* Let $A(x)$ and $B(x)$ be polynomials such that the degree of $A(x)$ is less than the degree of $B(x)$. Then the rational function $A(x)/B(x)$ can be represented as the sum of rational functions of the form

$$\frac{k}{(ax + b)^e} \quad \text{and} \quad \frac{cx + d}{(ax^2 + bx + c)^f}$$

where $ax^2 + bx + c$ is prime, $(ax^2 + bx + c)^f$ and $(ax + b)^e$ divide $B(x)$, and k, c, and d are real numbers.

It must be kept in mind that if $(ax + b)^n$ divides $B(x)$, then so do $(ax + b)^{n-1}$, $(ax + b)^{n-2}, \ldots$, and $ax + b$.

Example 8. According to the rephrased Theorem 3, there are real numbers a and b such that

(2)
$$\frac{4x - 17}{x^2 - x - 6} = \frac{a}{x - 3} + \frac{b}{x + 2}$$

To find a and b, we multiply both sides of (2) by $x^2 - x - 6$, obtaining

$$4x - 17 = a(x + 2) + b(x - 3)$$

or

(3)
$$4x - 17 = (a + b)x + (2a - 3b)$$

Comparing the constant term and coefficients of x on both sides of (3), we have

$$4 = a + b \quad \text{and} \quad -17 = 2a - 3b$$

simultaneous equations for a and b. Solving these equations for a and b, we find that $a = -1$ and $b = 5$. Thus

$$\frac{4x - 17}{x^2 - x - 6} = \frac{-1}{x - 3} + \frac{5}{x + 2}$$

Example 9. Before we can begin to represent

$$\frac{6x^2 + 2x + 1}{x^3 - 3x + 2}$$

as a sum of partial fractions, we must express $f(x) = x^3 - 3x + 2$ as a product of prime polynomials. Since $f(1) = 0$, we know that $x - 1$ is a divisor of $x^3 - 3x + 2$. Long division shows that $x^3 - 3x + 2 = (x - 1)(x^2 + x - 2)$. But $x^2 + x - 2$ is *not* prime, for the quadratic formula shows that the equation $x^2 + x - 2 = 0$ has the roots 1 and -2. Thus

$x^2 + x - 2 = (x - 1)(x + 2)$, and $x^3 - 3x + 2 = (x - 1)^2(x + 2)$. According to Theorem 3, then,

$$\frac{6x^2 + 2x + 1}{x^3 - 3x + 2} = \frac{a}{x - 1} + \frac{b}{(x - 1)^2} + \frac{c}{x + 2}$$

for suitable real numbers a, b, and c. Multiplying both sides by $x^3 - 3x + 2$, we obtain

(4) $\qquad 6x^2 + 2x + 1 = a(x - 1)(x + 2) + b(x + 2) + c(x - 1)^2$

Rather than expand the right side of (4) and compare coefficients, as we did in Example 8, let us use a shortcut.

Since (4) holds for all x, it holds for $x = 1$, $x = -2$, and $x = 0$. (We choose 1 because it is a root of $x - 1 = 0$, and -2 because it is a root of $x + 2 = 0$; we choose 0 because it is easy to work with. We need three values to obtain three equations for the three unknowns a, b, c.) We find a, b, c as follows. Substitution of 1, -2, and 0 into (4) yields

$$9 = 3b \qquad \text{(from } x = 1)$$
$$21 = 9c \qquad \text{(from } x = -2)$$
$$1 = -2a + 2b + c \qquad \text{(from } x = 0)$$

We quickly obtain $b = 3$ and $c = \frac{7}{3}$. Last, we find a by means of the third of the above equations:

$$1 = -2a + 2 \cdot 3 + \frac{7}{3}$$

and $a = \frac{11}{3}$. Thus

$$\frac{6x^2 + 2x + 1}{x^3 - 3x + 2} = \frac{11/3}{x - 1} + \frac{3}{(x - 1)^2} + \frac{7/3}{x + 2}$$

Example 10.   Just as Theorem 1 says nothing about $\frac{37}{10}$ (see Example 2), Theorem 3 says nothing about the partial-fraction representation of $(3x^2 - 3x - 4)/(x^2 - 1)$, since the degree of the numerator is *not* less than the degree of the denominator. Just as in Example 2, we carry out a division,

$$
\begin{array}{r}
3 \\
x^2 - 1 \overline{\smash{)}3x^2 - 3x - 4} \\
3x^2 - 3 \\
\hline
-3x - 1
\end{array}
$$

which shows that $\qquad \dfrac{3x^2 - 3x - 4}{x^2 - 1} = 3 + \dfrac{-3x - 1}{x^2 - 1}$

Theorem 3 does hold for $(-3x - 1)/(x^2 - 1)$, and it is not difficult to show that

$$\frac{-3x - 1}{x^2 - 1} = \frac{1}{x - 1} + \frac{2}{x + 1}$$

Hence $\qquad \dfrac{3x^2 - 3x - 4}{x^2 - 1} = 3 + \dfrac{1}{x - 1} + \dfrac{2}{x + 1}$

EXERCISES

4. Factor into prime polynomials and check by multiplying: (a) $2x^3 + 7x^2 + 4x - 4$; (b) $x^2 - 3x + 10$; (c) $2x^2 + x - 7$. [Hint: For (a) use Theorem 2.]
5. Factor into prime polynomials and check: (a) $x^3 - 8$; (b) $x^3 - 4$.
6. (a) Verify that $x^4 + x^2 + 1 = (x^2 + x + 1)(x^2 - x + 1)$.
   (b) Express $(6x + 1)/(x^4 + x^2 + 1)$ in partial fractions.
7. Obtain the first two partial-fraction decompositions given in Example 7.
8. Solve for a and b in Example 8 by substituting two convenient values for x in the equation $4x - 17 = a(x + 2) + b(x - 3)$.
9. Find the partial-fraction decomposition of each of the following rational functions, and check your answers:

   (a) $\dfrac{2x^2 + 1}{(x - 2)^3}$;   (b) $\dfrac{x}{(x + 1)^2}$;   (c) $\dfrac{x^3 - 5x^2 + 9x + 1}{(x^2 + 1)(x - 3)^2}$

10. Express $1/(4x^3 - 6x^2 - x - 6)$ as a sum of partial fractions. (Hint: Use Theorem 2.)
11. How many constants would we have to determine in the partial-fraction decomposition of (a) $\dfrac{A(x)}{(x^2 - 3x + 2)^{10}}$;   (b) $\dfrac{A(x)}{(x^2 + 2x + 3)^{10}}$, where the degree of $A(x)$ is less than 20? Explain.
12. Express as a sum of partial fractions: (a) $x^2/(x^2 + 3x + 1)^2$; (b) $x/(x - 1)^2(x + 2)^2$.
13. Express as the sum of a polynomial and partial fractions (a) $(x^5 + 1)/(x^3 + 1)$; (b) $x^4/(x^2 + 1)^2$.
14. Let $ax^2 + bx + c$ be a polynomial of degree 2.
    (a) Prove that if $b^2 - 4ac \geqslant 0$, then the polynomial *is not* prime.
    (b) Prove that if $b^2 - 4ac < 0$, then the polynomial *is* prime.
15. (a) Using a graph, suggest why any polynomial of odd degree has at least one real root.
    (b) With the aid of (a), show that any polynomial whose degree is odd and greater than two *is not* prime.
16. Prove Theorem 3 for the special case $B(x) = x^{1,000}$.
17. Prove Theorem 2, the factor theorem.
18. Prove this frequently encountered special case of Theorem 3.

   THEOREM.   If c and d are two unequal numbers, then there exist numbers a and b such that

$$\frac{1}{(x + c)(x + d)} = \frac{a}{x + c} + \frac{b}{x + d}$$

Short tables of functions

The numerical tables presented here indicate the behavior of the important functions of the calculus. The tables of derivatives and antiderivatives emphasize only the most common cases. Extensive tables are to be found in any mathematical handbook. Such handbooks contain a wealth of information, including formulas from algebra (e.g., the binomial theorem), geometry, trigonometry, statistics, and actuarial work. In particular, R. S. Burington's classical "Handbook of Mathematical Tables and Formulas," 4th ed., McGraw-Hill, New York, 1964, has a specially clear format and organization.

In the following tables, entries are rounded off, generally to three decimal places.

x	0	0.1	0.2	0.3	0.4	0.5	1	2	3	4	5
e^x	1	1.105	1.221	1.350	1.492	1.649	2.718	7.389	20.09	54.60	148.41
e^{-x}	1	0.905	0.819	0.741	0.670	0.607	0.368	0.135	0.050	0.018	0.007
10^x	1	1.259	1.585	1.995	2.512	3.162	10	100	1000	10,000	100,000

x	0.01	0.1	1	2	3	4	5	6	7	8	9	10	100
$\ln x$	-4.606	-2.303	0	0.693	1.099	1.387	1.609	1.792	1.946	2.079	2.197	2.303	4.606
$\log_{10} x$	-2	-1	0	0.301	0.477	0.602	0.699	0.778	0.845	0.903	0.954	1	2

n	1	2	3	4	5	6	7	8	9	10
$\sqrt{n}$	1	1.414	1.732	2	2.236	2.449	2.646	2.828	3	3.162
$1/n$	1	0.500	0.333	0.250	0.200	0.167	0.143	0.125	0.111	0.100

x	0.01	0.1	0.2	0.3	0.4	0.5	$\pi/6 = 0.524$	0.6	0.7	$\pi/4 = 0.785$
$\sin x$	0.0099998	0.09983	0.199	0.296	0.389	0.479	$0.500 = \frac{1}{2}$	0.565	0.644	$0.707 = \sqrt{2}/2$
$\cos x$	0.99995	0.9950	0.980	0.955	0.921	0.878	$0.866 = \sqrt{3}/2$	0.825	0.765	$0.707 = \sqrt{2}/2$

$\sin x$ and $\cos x$—angles in radians

x	1	10	20	30	40	45
$\sin x$	0.017	0.0174	0.342	$0.500 = \frac{1}{2}$	0.643	$0.707 = \sqrt{2}/2$
$\cos x$	0.99985	0.985	0.940	$0.876 = \sqrt{3}/2$	0.766	$0.707 = \sqrt{2}/2$

$\sin x$ and $\cos x$—angles in degrees

Some important derivatives

$$D(x^a) = ax^{a-1} \qquad D(\sqrt{x}) = \frac{1}{2\sqrt{x}} \qquad D\left(\frac{1}{x}\right) = -\frac{1}{x^2}$$

$$D(\sqrt{1+x^2}) = \frac{x}{\sqrt{1+x^2}} \qquad D(\ln|x|) = \frac{1}{x} \qquad D(e^x) = e^x$$

$$D(\sin x) = \cos x \qquad \text{and} \qquad D(\cos x) = -\sin x \qquad \text{(angle in radians)}$$

Some important antiderivatives

$$\int x^a \, dx = \frac{x^{a+1}}{a+1} \qquad a \neq -1 \qquad \int \frac{1}{x^2} \, dx = -\frac{1}{x}$$

$$\int \frac{1}{x} \, dx = \ln|x| \qquad \int \frac{1}{\sqrt{1-x^2}} \, dx = \sin^{-1} x \qquad \int \frac{1}{1+x^2} \, dx = \tan^{-1} x$$

$$\int \sin x \, dx = -\cos x \qquad \text{and} \qquad \int \cos x \, dx = \sin x \qquad \text{(angle in radians)}$$

Index

607